About the Cover

The design shown on the cover of this book was created from a black and white photograph of a cooling grill of a computer. The original photograph was posterized; that is, all the gray tones were reduced either to black or to white. Negative and positive impressions of this posterization were then made and assigned different colors to attain the final result.

About the Title Page

The pattern, entitled *Samadhi,* shown on the next page is a moving-light design created by the swinging of a flashlight on a stick. The total exposure time for this photograph was about three seconds.

Algebra 2
and TRIGONOMETRY

Mary P. Dolciani

William Wooton

Edwin F. Beckenbach

Sidney Sharron

editorial adviser
Robert H. Sorgenfrey

HOUGHTON MIFFLIN COMPANY/BOSTON

ATLANTA   DALLAS   GENEVA, ILL.   HOPEWELL, N.J.   PALO ALTO

The Authors

Mary P. Dolciani, Associate Provost for Academic Services and Professor, Department of Mathematics, Hunter College of the City University of New York. Dr. Dolciani has been a director and teacher in numerous National Science Foundation and New York State Education Department institutes for mathematics teachers.

William Wooton, Mathematics Consultant, Vista, California, Unified School District. Mr. Wooton was formerly a professor of mathematics at Los Angeles Pierce College and has taught mathematics at both the junior and senior high school levels. He has also been a team member of the National Council of Teachers of Mathematics (NCTM) summer writing projects.

Edwin F. Beckenbach, Professor of Mathematics, University of California, Los Angeles. Dr. Beckenbach has been a team member and coordinator of the NCTM summer writing projects for elementary mathematics teachers. He is currently serving as Chairman of the Committee on Publications of the Mathematical Association of America.

Sidney Sharron, Mathematics Supervisor, Los Angeles City Schools. Mr. Sharron has taught at both junior college and high school levels and has conducted a number of workshops and institutes for teachers.

Editorial Adviser

Robert H. Sorgenfrey, Professor of Mathematics, University of California, Los Angeles. Dr. Sorgenfrey does research work in topology and has won the Distinguished Teaching Award at U.C.L.A. He has been a team member of the NCTM summer writing projects.

Printed in the United States of America

ISBN: 0–395–18086–4

contents

Symbols

A main concern of the world today is the preservation of our natural resources.

1 review of essentials

basic properties

After completing the first four sections, you will have reviewed:
1. Set notation.
2. Solving simple open sentences, given the replacement set.
3. Graphing sets of real numbers on a number line.
4. Applications of the basic properties of real numbers.

1-1 sets and symbols

Try this▶

REVIEW TEST 1

Replace each __?__ with one of the symbols =, ≠, ∈, ∉, ⊂, or ⊄ to make a true statement. There may be more than one correct answer.

1. France __?__ {the countries of Europe}
2. 7 __?__ {3, 5, 7, 9}
3. {Tuesday, Wednesday} __?__ {the days of the week}
4. 5 + 12 __?__ 20 − 3
5. {$\frac{1}{2}$} __?__ {0.25, 0.5, 0.75}
6. 8 __?__ {the numbers that differ from 5 by 2}
7. ∅ __?__ {0}
8. {the letters in the word ''horse''} __?__ {e, h, o, r, s}

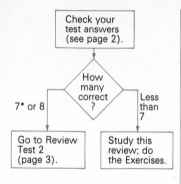

Check your test answers (see page 2).

How many correct?

7* or 8 — Go to Review Test 2 (page 3).

Less than 7 — Study this review; do the Exercises.

Can you read the statement

$$5 \in \{1, 3, 5, 7\}?$$

You can if you recall from earlier mathematics courses that the symbol "$\in$" is read "is a member of" or "is an element of" and that "$\{1, 3, 5, 7\}$" is read "the set whose members are 1, 3, 5, and 7." These and other familiar set symbols are reviewed in the following table.

Symbolism	How Read	Meaning
$\{\ \ \}$	"the set whose members are"	Denotes a collection or set.
$\in$	"is a member of" or "is an element of"	Is in the collection or set.
$A \subset B$	"A is a subset of B"	Every member of set A is also a member of set B. Of course, for every set A, $A \subset A$.
$\emptyset$	"the null set" or "the empty set"	The set which contains no elements. The empty set is considered a subset of every set.
$A = B$	"A is equal to B"	"A" and "B" denote the same set.
$/$	"is not"	Used in conjunction with $\in$, $=$, or $\subset$ to denote negation. $5 \notin A$ means "5 is not an element of A."

*You should always understand the reason for any incorrect answer before proceeding.

Answers to Review Test 1
1. $\in$ 2. $\in$ 3. $\subset$ (or $\neq$)   4. $=$ 5. $\subset$ (or $\neq$)   6. $\notin$
7. $\neq$ (or $\subset$)   8. $=$ (or $\subset$)

EXERCISES

Replace each __?__ with one of the symbols ∈, ⊂, =, or negations of these to make a true statement. There may be more than one correct answer.

A

1. 7 __?__ {2, 4, 6, 8}

2. {7} __?__ {2, 4, 6, 8}

3. ∅ __?__ {2, 4, 6, 8}

4. {2, 4} __?__ {2, 4, 6, 8}

5. g __?__ {the vowels in the English alphabet}

6. t __?__ {the letters in the word "hot"}

7. $\dfrac{7 + 3}{2}$ __?__ $\dfrac{8 - 3}{2}$

8. 8(6 − 1) __?__ {10, 20, 30, 40}

9. {7, 8} __?__ {1, 3, 5, 7, 9}

10. {2, 1, 3} __?__ {1, 2, 3}

1–2 *solving open sentences*

Try this➡

REVIEW TEST 2

State the solution set of each open sentence, using the replacement set {1, 2, 3, 4, 5}. If the solution set is ∅, so state.

1. $y + 3 = 6$

2. $y - 2 \neq 4$

3. $x + 7 = 0$

4. $2z = 6$

5. $3t = 6$

6. $u - 3 = 2$

7. $2t + 1 = 3$

8. $2v - 1 = 7$

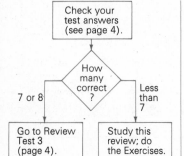

Check your test answers (see page 4).

How many correct ?

7 or 8 — Go to Review Test 3 (page 4).

Less than 7 — Study this review; do the Exercises.

Meaningful groups of symbols involving ∈, ⊂, and = are called sentences. Sentences, such as

$$5 + 4 = 9 \quad \text{and} \quad 3 \notin \{1, 2, 3\},$$

which can be classified as true or false are called statements. On the other hand, a sentence such as

$$x - 3 \neq 2$$

is neither true nor false unless you know the object referred to by the symbol "x." In this usage, x is called a variable. A variable is a symbol which may represent any one of the members of a specified set, called the replacement set or domain of the variable. The members of the domain are called the values of the variable. A variable with just one value is called a constant.

Sentences containing variables are called open sentences. The set that consists of the values of the variable for which an open sentence is true is called the solution set or truth set of the open sentence over the domain of the variable. Each member of the solution set is said to satisfy and to be a solution or root of the open sentence. To solve an open sentence over a given domain means to find its solution set over this domain.

EXAMPLE Solve $x - 3 \neq 2$, if $x \in \{3, 4, 5, 6\}$.

SOLUTION Replacing x in the given sentence with each of its values in turn, you have

$$3 - 3 \neq 2 \quad \text{True} \qquad 5 - 3 \neq 2 \quad \text{False}$$
$$4 - 3 \neq 2 \quad \text{True} \qquad 6 - 3 \neq 2 \quad \text{True}$$

$\therefore$ (read "therefore") the solution set is $\{3, 4, 6\}$. **Answer.**

NOW DO THESE ▶ EXERCISES

Specify the solution set of the given open sentence over $\{1, 2, 3, 4, 5\}$. If the set is ∅, so state.

A
1. $x - 7 = 0$
2. $y + 2 = 5$
3. $3z = 9$
4. $5t \neq 10$
5. $3z - 1 = 11$

6. $3z - 1 = 10$
7. $m = m + 1$
8. $u = u$
9. $2n - 4 = 0$
10. $x + x = 4$

Answers to Review Test 2
1. $\{3\}$ 2. $\{1, 2, 3, 4, 5\}$ 3. $\emptyset$ 4. $\{3\}$ 5. $\{2\}$ 6. $\{5\}$
7. $\{1\}$ 8. $\{4\}$

1-3 *sets of numbers*

Try this ▶ REVIEW TEST 3

Let $A = \{-18, 2.3, -6, -\sqrt{3}, 0, 2, 5, 3.1, 7\}$. Graph the subset of A that contains:

1. All the positive integers in A.
2. All the whole numbers in A.
3. All the odd integers in A.
4. All the positive even integers in A.

Graph each set. Select a suitable unit of measure.

5. $\{-1, 0, 1\}$
6. $\{-\frac{5}{2}, -\frac{3}{2}, \frac{3}{2}, \frac{5}{2}\}$
7. $\{2, 4, 8, 12\}$

8. $\{-16, -8, -4, -2\}$
9. $\{-20, 0, 20\}$
10. $\{-3.5, 2, 10\}$

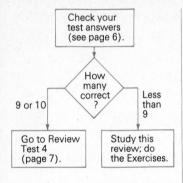

Check your
test answers
(see page 6).

How
many
correct
?

9 or 10 | Less
than
9

Go to Review
Test 4
(page 7).

Study this
review; do
the Exercises.

The diagram below pictures the graph of the set $\{-\frac{3}{2}, \frac{1}{2}, \sqrt{3}\}$ on a number line.

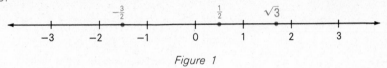

Figure 1

On a number line, the point paired with a number is called the graph of the number, while the number paired with a point is the coordinate of the point.

The set of all the positive numbers, the negative numbers, and zero is called the set $\Re$ of real numbers. A basic assumption is that for each real number there corresponds a point on the number line, and, conversely, for each point on the number line there corresponds a real number. Thus, there is a one-to-one correspondence between the members of $\Re$ and the points on a geometric line. Below are shown the graphs of several familiar subsets of $\Re$.

1. {the natural numbers} = {the positive integers} = $\{1, 2, 3, \ldots\}$

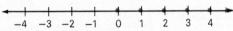

2. {the whole numbers} = $\{0, 1, 2, 3, \ldots\}$

3. {the integers} = $\{\ldots, -3, -2, -1, 0, 1, 2, 3, \ldots\}$

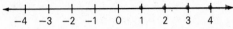

4. {the even integers} = $\{\ldots, -4, -2, 0, 2, 4, \ldots\}$

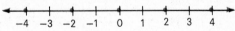

5. {the odd integers} = $\{\ldots, -3, -1, 1, 3, \ldots\}$

Notice that in the examples above each set is specified by an *incomplete roster*, or list. The three dots indicate that the pattern shown in the list continues in one or both directions without end. The heavy arrowhead on the accompanying diagram indicates that the graph of the set similarly continues without end.

NOW DO THESE ▶ EXERCISES

Graph each set. Select a suitable unit of measure.

A 1. $\{-3, -1, 1, 3\}$ 3. $\{-5, -3, -1, \frac{1}{3}\}$ 5. $\{-45, -25, 0\}$
   2. $\{-7, 2, 3.5, 4\}$ 4. $\{-\frac{4}{3}, -\frac{2}{3}, \frac{2}{3}, \frac{4}{3}\}$ 6. $\{5, 50, 100\}$

Let $B = \{-20.3, -16, -7, -4, -1.5, 0, 2, 3\frac{1}{3}, 5, 6\}$. Graph the subset of B that contains

7. All the positive integers in B.
8. All the whole numbers in B.
9. All the positive even integers in B.
10. All the negative odd integers in B.
11. All the numbers in B that are not integers.

Let $A = \{-8, -6, 0, 4, 6\}$ and $B = \{-6, -3, 0, 3, 6\}$. Graph each set.

B 12. {the integers in A and also in B}
13. {the integers in A or in B or in both sets}
14. {the integers in A but not in B}
15. {the even integers in A or in B or in both}
16. {the odd integers in A or in B or in both}

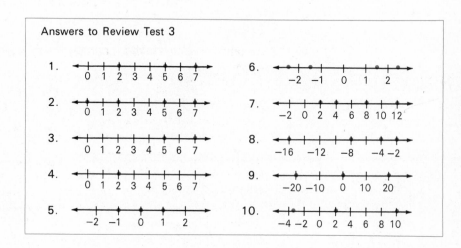

Answers to Review Test 3

Bourbaki

Bourbaki is the name not of a mathematician but of a group of European and American mathematicians, whose goal is "to present a view of the entire field of mathematical science as it exists." Since 1939, more than 30 volumes of Bourbaki's *Eléments de Mathématiques* have been published and there are more volumes to come. The composition of the Bourbaki group changes, with members retiring when they reach age 45 and being replaced by new ones. The *Eléments de Mathématiques* uses a formal axiomatic approach, attempting to integrate all of mathematics into a single framework.

1-4 *axioms for the real numbers*

Try this▶ REVIEW TEST 4

Each of the following statements is true by virtue of one or more of the axioms for the real numbers or by the substitution principle. In each case, name the axiom or axioms justifying the statement. Assume that the domain of each variable is $\mathcal{R}$.

1. $(-3)(5) = (5)(-3)$

2. $(7 + 2) + 3 = 7 + (2 + 3)$

3. $7 \cdot 1 = 7$

4. $4 + 0 = 0 + 4$

5. $x + (-x) = 0$

6. $3(z + 2) = 3z + 3 \cdot 2$

7. If $r + 3 = 7$, then $7 = r + 3$.

8. If $x = y$, then $x + (-2) = y + (-2)$.

9. If $t = z$ and $z = 3$, then $t = 3$.

10. $4 + 7 \in \mathcal{R}$

11. $2 \cdot \frac{3}{5} \in \mathcal{R}$

12. If $x \neq 0$, then $x \cdot \dfrac{1}{x} = 1$.

13. $8 + (-8) = 0$

14. If $p = 4$ and $p + t = 7$, then $4 + t = 7$.

State **(a)** the additive inverse, and **(b)** the multiplicative inverse (if it exists) of each number.

15. -6

16. $\frac{3}{4}$

17. $-\frac{2}{3}$

18. 2.1

19. 0.2

20. -2000

21. 0

22. $-(-1)$

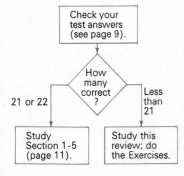

Check your test answers (see page 9).

How many correct?

21 or 22 → Study Section 1-5 (page 11).

Less than 21 → Study this review; do the Exercises.

There are two basic operations used in working with real numbers, *addition* and *multiplication*. Each of these operations is called a binary operation because it pairs any two real numbers with a third real number. The addition operation, $+$, pairs any two real numbers a and b with another real number, $a + b$, called the sum of the two real numbers. Multiplication assigns to any two real numbers a and b their product denoted by $a \times b$, $a \cdot b$, $a(b)$, $(a)(b)$, or simply ab. In the sum $a + b$, a and b are called addends; in the product ab, a and b are called factors.

The properties of these operations in $\mathcal{R}$ all stem from a few basic statements, called axioms or postulates, that are assumed to be true. These familiar assumptions are listed on page 8.

Notice that parentheses, ( ), are used in some of the axioms to indicate an order of operations. For example, $(a + b) + c$ represents the result of first adding a and b, and then adding c to the sum. In some cases, such as in the distributive law where $(ab) + (ac)$ occurs, the parentheses usually are omitted. Thus, $(ab) + (ac) = ab + ac$.

Axioms of Addition and Multiplication in $\Re$

Let a, b, and c denote real numbers (a, b, and $c \in \Re$).

1. $a + b$ is a unique real number.   **Closure Axiom for Addition**

2. $(a + b) + c = a + (b + c)$ **Associative Axiom for Addition**

3. $a + b = b + a$ **Commutative Axiom for Addition**

4. There exists an element $0 \in \Re$ such that for each $a \in \Re$,
$$0 + a = a \quad \text{and}$$
$$a + 0 = a.$$
Axiom of 0 (Identity Element for Addition)

5. There exists an element $-a \in \Re$ for each $a \in \Re$, such that
$$a + (-a) = 0 \quad \text{and}$$
$$(-a) + a = 0.$$
Axiom of Additive Inverses

6. ab is a unique real number.   **Closure Axiom for Multiplication**

7. $(ab)c = a(bc)$ **Associative Axiom for Multiplication**

8. $ab = ba$ **Commutative Axiom for Multiplication**

9. There exists an element $1 \in \Re$, $1 \neq 0$, such that for each $a \in \Re$,
$$a \cdot 1 = a \quad \text{and} \quad 1 \cdot a = a.$$
Axiom of 1 (Identity Element for Multiplication)

10. There exists an element $\frac{1}{a} \in \Re$ for each nonzero $a \in \Re$ such that
$$\frac{1}{a} \cdot a = 1 \text{ and } a \cdot \frac{1}{a} = 1.$$
Axiom of Multiplicative Inverses

11. $a(b + c) = (ab) + (ac)$ and $(b + c)a = (ba) + (ca)$ **Distributive Axiom**

The word "unique" used in two of the axioms means "one and only one," and has this implication:

Substitution Principle

Since $a + b$ and ab are unique, changing the numeral by which a number is named in an expression involving sums or products does not change the value of the expression.

For example, since $8 + 2 = 10$ and $10 - 3 = 7$, you know that

$$(8 + 2) - 3 = 10 - 3 = 7.$$

In $\mathcal{R}$, 0 and 1 are called the identity elements for addition and multiplication, respectively. $-a$ and $\frac{1}{a}$ are called the additive inverse and the multiplicative inverse (or reciprocal) of a, respectively. Note also that you should always read $-a$ as "the additive inverse of a" or "the negative of a." The expression "negative a" should not be used since $-a$ may represent either a negative number, a positive number, or zero.

The way you use the symbol $=$ in sentences is consistent with the following assumptions.

Axioms of Equality

Let a, b, and c be any elements of $\mathcal{R}$.

$a = a$	**Reflexive Property**
If $a = b$, then $b = a$.	**Symmetric Property**
If $a = b$ and $b = c$, then $a = c$.	**Transitive Property**

How do you add or multiply three or more real numbers? If a, b, c, d, ... are real numbers, we define $a + b + c$ to be $(a + b) + c$, abc to be $(ab)c$, $a + b + c + d$ to be $(a + b + c) + d$, and so on. Of course, because addition and multiplication are associative and commutative, you may add the addends in a sum, or multiply the factors in a product, of three or more numbers in any convenient groups of two and in any order, and still obtain the same result. For example,

$$8 + 9 + 17 + 11 = (8 + 17) + (9 + 11) = 25 + 20 = 45.$$

Answers to Review Test 4
1. Commutative axiom for multiplication   2. Associative axiom for addition   3. Axiom of 1   4. Commutative axiom for addition   5. Axiom of additive inverses   6. Distributive axiom   7. Symmetric property of equality   8. Substitution principle   9. Transitive property of equality
10. Closure axiom for addition   11. Closure axiom for multiplication
12. Axiom of multiplicative inverses   13. Axiom of additive inverses
14. Substitution principle   15. 6; $-\frac{1}{6}$ 16. $-\frac{3}{4}$; $\frac{4}{3}$ 17. $\frac{2}{3}$; $-\frac{3}{2}$
18. -2.1; $\frac{1}{2.1}$ 19. -0.2; 5   20. 2000; -0.0005 21. 0; none
22. -1; 1

NOW DO THESE ► EXERCISES

In Exercises 1–12 state the axiom that justifies the given statement. Assume that each variable denotes a real number.

A
1. $x + 5 \in \mathcal{R}$
2. $t + 0 = t$
3. $2 + (3 + y) = (2 + 3) + y$
4. $m \cdot t = t \cdot m$
5. $n + (-n) = 0$
6. If $r = t$, then $r + v = t + v$.
7. If $z = w$, then $rz = rw$.

8. If $x + 3 = y - 2$, then $y - 2 = x + 3$.
9. If $z = 7$, then $x + z = x + 7$.
10. $7 \cdot (x + 1) = (x + 1) \cdot 7$
11. $3(t - y) = 3t - 3y$
12. $6 + (x - 2) = (x - 2) + 6$

In Exercises 13–16 determine the value of the expression.

13. $23 + 8 + 17 + 32$
14. $31 + (-7) + 9 + 7$

15. $38 + 12 + 17 + (-50)$
16. $84 + 7 + 16 + 23 + (-100)$

In Exercises 17–25 give the solution set of each sentence over $\mathcal{R}$.

B
17. $z + 2 = 0$
18. $-4t = 1$
19. $-k = 18$

20. $-(-r) = 23$
21. $-6 + t = 0$
22. $3 + (-x) = 0$

23. $\frac{1}{3}y = 1$
24. $5(-r) = 1$
25. $-3 + (-z) = 0$

SELF-TEST 1

Section 1–1, page 1

1. Use set notation to represent the sentence "6 is not a member of the set whose members are 1, 2, and 3."

Section 1–2, page 3

Specify the solution set over $\{1, 2, 3, 4, 5\}$.

2. $3x - 2 = 7$
3. $2x - 12 = 0$

Section 1–3, page 4

4. Graph $\{-\frac{2}{3}, 0, \frac{4}{3}\}$.
5. Graph the subset of $A = \{-\frac{9}{2}, -3, -\frac{4}{2}, 0, \frac{2}{3}, 1, \frac{7}{3}\}$ that contains all the integers in A.

Section 1–4, page 7

State the axiom which justifies each statement.

6. $(-12) \cdot 7 \in \mathcal{R}$
7. If $t \in \mathcal{R}$ and $3t = 1$, then $t = \frac{1}{3}$.
8. $7 + (4 + 3) = (4 + 3) + 7$
9. If $z \in \mathcal{R}$, then $(z + 2)(z - 3) = z(z - 3) + 2(z - 3)$.
10. Solve over $\mathcal{R}$: $7(-z) = 1$

Check your answers with those printed at the back of the book. If you did not answer a question correctly, study the referenced section again.

properties of operations in $\mathcal{R}$

After completing the next four sections, you will have reviewed:
1. The meaning and methods of *direct proof*.
2. Important theorems giving properties of real numbers.
3. Applications of these theorems in simplifying expressions for sums, products, differences, and quotients.

BE SURE TO
STUDY THIS
SECTION
CAREFULLY

1–5 *theorems and proof: addition*

The basic properties of $\mathcal{R}$ stated in Section 1–4 imply other properties of $\mathcal{R}$. These implications are stated as theorems. A theorem consists of two parts, a hypothesis (or premise) and a conclusion. The hypothesis states what is assumed to be true, and the conclusion states something which logically follows from the assumptions. To give a direct proof of a theorem, you start with its hypothesis and by a logical chain of steps arrive at its conclusion. Here is an example of a direct proof.

Theorem. For all real numbers b and c,

$$(b + c) + (-c) = b.$$

PROOF

First note that the hypothesis is that b and c denote real numbers. Reasoning from this assumption, you have:

Statement	Reason
1. b and c are real numbers.	Hypothesis
2. $b + c$ is a real number.	Closure axiom for addition
3. $-c$ is a real number.	Axiom of additive inverses
4. $(b + c) + (-c)$ is a real number.	Closure axiom for addition
5. $(b + c) + (-c) = b + [c + (-c)]$	Associative axiom for addition
6. $c + (-c) = 0$	Axiom of additive inverses
7. $(b + c) + (-c) = b + 0$	Substitution principle
8. $b + 0 = b$	Axiom of 0
9. $(b + c) + (-c) = b$	Transitive property of equality (or substitution principle)

Observe that each step in the sequence in the foregoing proof is guaranteed either by hypothesis or by an axiom. Frequently, simple steps involving closure, substitution, and other basic properties of equality are omitted. For example, the foregoing proof might be replaced by the following:

Statement	Reason
1. b and c are real numbers.	Hypothesis
2. $-c$ is a real number.	Axiom of additive inverses
3. $(b + c) + (-c) = b + [c + (-c)]$	Associative axiom of addition
4. $\qquad\qquad = b + 0$	Axiom of additive inverses
5. $\qquad\qquad = b$	Axiom of 0
6. $(b + c) + (-c) = b$	Transitive property of equality

Theorems that have been proved can then be used to help prove other theorems.

Theorem. For all real numbers a, b, and c,

$$\text{if } a + c = b + c, \text{ then } a = b.$$

PROOF

Statement	Reason
1. a, b, and c are real numbers and $a + c = b + c$.	Hypothesis
2. $(a + c) + (-c) = (b + c) + (-c)$	Substitution principle
3. $\qquad\qquad\qquad = b$	Theorem proved above
4. $(a + c) + (-c) = b$	Transitive property of equality
5. $(a + c) + (-c) = a$	Theorem proved above with a in place of b
6. $a = b$	Substitution principle

From one theorem you can sometimes quickly deduce a closely related theorem, called a corollary. Because addition in $\Re$ is a commutative operation, you can easily prove the following corollary of the preceding theorem (see Exercise 27, page 15).

Corollary. For all real numbers a, b, and c,

$$\text{if } c + a = c + b, \text{ then } a = b.$$

The preceding theorem and its corollary can be restated in the following combined form.

> ## Cancellation Property of Addition
>
> For all real numbers a, b, and c, if
>
> $$a + c = b + c \quad \text{or} \quad c + a = c + b,$$
>
> then $a = b$.

The next theorem is useful in computing sums. Its proof uses the cancellation property of addition.

> ## Property of the Negative of a Sum
>
> For all real numbers a and b,
>
> $$-(a + b) = (-a) + (-b).$$
>
> That is, the negative of a sum of real numbers is the sum of the negatives of the numbers.

PROOF

Plan: Show that $(a + b) + [(-a) + (-b)] = 0$. Then use the axiom of additive inverses $((a + b) + [-(a + b)] = 0)$ and the cancellation law to obtain the desired result.

Statement	*Reason*
1. a and b are real numbers	Hypothesis
2. $(a + b) + [(-a) + (-b)]$ $= [a + (-a)] + [b + (-b)]$	Commutative and associative axioms of addition
3. $\qquad\qquad = 0 + 0$	Axiom of additive inverses
4. $\qquad\qquad = 0$	Axiom of 0
5. $(a + b) + [(-a) + (-b)] = 0$	Transitive property of equality
6. $(a + b) + [-(a + b)] = 0$	Axiom of additive inverses
7. $\therefore (a + b) + [-(a + b)]$ $= (a + b) + [(-a) + (-b)]$	Transitive property of equality
8. $-(a + b) = (-a) + (-b)$	Cancellation property of addition

The property of the negative of a sum can be used to simplify expressions for sums of real numbers, given that you can compute the sum of positive real numbers.

EXAMPLE 1   Simplify $(-12) + (-3)$.

SOLUTION $(-12) + (-3) = -(12 + 3) = -15$. Answer.

EXAMPLE 2   Simplify $12 + (-16)$.

SOLUTION
$$\begin{aligned}
12 + (-16) &= 12 + [-(12 + 4)] \\
&= 12 + [(-12) + (-4)] \\
&= [12 + (-12)] + (-4) \\
&= 0 + (-4) \\
&= -4. \quad \text{Answer.}
\end{aligned}$$

Sums of real numbers can be pictured by displacements along the number line. Notice that arrows (vectors) in the positive direction are used to represent positive numbers and arrows in the negative direction are used to represent negative numbers. The sum of two numbers can be pictured by attaching the initial end of the arrow representing the second addend to the terminal end of the arrow representing the first (Figures 2 and 3).

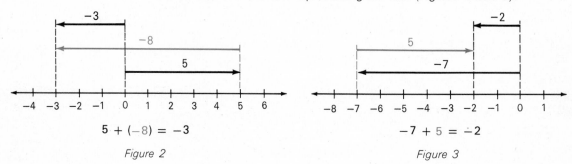

$5 + (-8) = -3$

Figure 2

$-7 + 5 = -2$

Figure 3

EXERCISES   In Exercises 1–8 replace the __?__ with a variable or a numeral so that a true statement results. Assume that each variable denotes a real number.

EXAMPLE $-(-t + 4) = $ __?__ $+ (-4)$

SOLUTION $-(-t + 4) = t + (-4)$. Answer.

A   1. If $n + 3 = 5 + 3$, then $n = $ __?__ .

2. $(-3 + 5) + 3 = $ __?__

3. $17 + (-3) = ($ __?__ $+ 3) + (-3)$

4. $-17 + 8 = [$ __?__ $+ (-8)] + 8$

5. $t + (2 + 5) = (2 + $ __?__ $) + t$

6. $-[7 + (-t)] = -7 + $ __?__

7. If $r + 7 = 7$, then $r = $ __?__ .

8. If $z + (-4) = 0$, then $z = $ __?__ .

Simplify each expression.

9. $38 + (-47)$

10. $-72 + (-65)$

11. $320 + (-245)$

12. $143 + (-172)$

13. $-28.6 + 41.7$

14. $-47.13 + (-17.72)$

15. $23 + (-7) + (-25) + 3$

16. $-28 + (-17) + 41 + (-10)$

17. $15 + [-(-3 + 7) + (-8)]$

18. $17 + (-6) + [-(3 + 8)]$

19. $-6 + (-3) + [8 + (-12)]$

20. $-5 + 17 + [-(6 + 5)]$

Find the sum of the numbers listed in each column.

21.	22.	23.	24.
23	-302	81.3	7.3
-57	151	-7.9	-18.6
8	-72	-15.3	-23.9
41	279	-60.7	47.2

State the axiom or theorem which justifies each step in the following proofs.

B 25. Prove: For all real numbers a and b, $-[(-a) + (-b)] = a + b$.

PROOF

1. a and b are real numbers.
2. $-a$ and $-b$ are real numbers.
3. $-[(-a) + (-b)] = -(-a) + [-(-b)]$
4. $-(-a) = a$ and $-(-b) = b$
5. $-[(-a) + (-b)] = a + b$

26. Prove: For all real numbers a and b, if $a = b$, then $-a = -b$.

PROOF

1. a and b are real numbers and $a = b$.
2. $-a$ and $-b$ are real numbers.
3. $a + (-a) = 0$ and $b + (-b) = 0$
4. $a + (-a) = b + (-b)$
5. $\qquad = a + (-b)$
6. $a + (-a) = a + (-b)$
7. $-a = -b$

Prove each theorem. Assume that each variable denotes a real number.

27. If $c + a = c + b$, then $a = b$.

28. If $b + a = a$, then $b = 0$. (Uniqueness of additive identity)

29. If $a + b = 0$, then $b = -a$. (Uniqueness of additive inverse)

30. $-(-a) = a$

31. If $a = b$ and $c = d$, then $a + c = b + d$.

32. If $a + c = b + d$ and $c = d$, then $a = b$.

33. If $x + 3 = 8$, then $x = 5$.

34. If $x + (-6) = -4$, then $x = 2$.

35. If $x + 7 = -5$, then $x = -12$.

C   **36.** If $x + b = a$, then $x = a + (-b)$.

      37. If $x = a + (-b)$, then $x + b = a$.

BE SURE TO STUDY THIS SECTION CAREFULLY

1–6   *properties of products*

Multiplication in $\mathcal{R}$ has properties similar to those of addition in $\mathcal{R}$. Compare the three theorems stated below with those for addition on pages 11–13. (See Exercises 23–26 on page 19 for proofs.)

Theorem. For all real numbers b and all nonzero real numbers c,

$$(bc)\,\frac{1}{c} = b.$$

Cancellation Property of Multiplication

For all real numbers a and b and all nonzero real numbers c, if

$$ac = bc \qquad \text{or} \qquad ca = cb,$$

then $a = b$.

Property of the Reciprocal of a Product

For all nonzero real numbers a and b,

$$\frac{1}{ab} = \frac{1}{a} \cdot \frac{1}{b}.$$

That is, the reciprocal of a product of nonzero real numbers is the product of the reciprocals of the numbers.

EXAMPLE   Simplify (a) $24 \cdot \frac{1}{3}$ and (b) $8 \cdot \frac{1}{24}$.

SOLUTION   a. $24 \cdot \frac{1}{3} = (8 \cdot 3) \cdot \left(\frac{1}{3}\right) = 8 \cdot \left(3 \cdot \frac{1}{3}\right) = 8 \cdot 1 = 8.$ **Answer.**

          b. $8 \cdot \dfrac{1}{24} = 8 \cdot \left(\dfrac{1}{8 \cdot 3}\right) = 8 \cdot \left(\dfrac{1}{8} \cdot \dfrac{1}{3}\right) = \left(8 \cdot \dfrac{1}{8}\right) \cdot \dfrac{1}{3} = 1 \cdot \dfrac{1}{3} = \dfrac{1}{3}.$

                                                              Answer.

Some real numbers, such as the identity element 1, have special properties with respect to multiplication. Two other such numbers are 0 and −1.

Multiplicative Property of Zero

For all real numbers a,

$$a \cdot 0 = 0 \qquad \text{and} \qquad 0 \cdot a = 0.$$

PROOF

1. a is a real number.	Hypothesis
2. $0 + 0 = 0$	Axiom of 0
3. $a \cdot (0 + 0) = a \cdot 0$	Substitution property
4. $a \cdot 0 + a \cdot 0 = a \cdot 0$	Distributive axiom
5. $a \cdot 0 = a \cdot 0 + 0$	Additive identity axiom
6. $a \cdot 0 + a \cdot 0 = a \cdot 0 + 0$	Transitive property of equality
7. $a \cdot 0 = 0$	Cancellation property of addition
8. $0 \cdot a = 0$	Commutative axiom of multiplication

The next theorem leads to the familiar ''rules'' for multiplying additive inverses.

Multiplicative Property of −1

For all real numbers a,

$$a(-1) = -a \qquad \text{and} \qquad (-1)a = -a.$$

PROOF

Plan: Show that $(-1)a$ satisfies $x + a = 0$; because $-a$ is the unique solution of this equation (see Exercise 29, page 15), the conclusion $(-1)a = -a$ will follow.

1. a is a real number.	Hypothesis
2. $a = 1 \cdot a$	Axiom of 1
3. $(-1)a + a = (-1)a + 1 \cdot a$	Substitution
4. $\qquad = (-1 + 1)a$	Distributive axiom
5. $\qquad = 0 \cdot a$	Axiom of additive inverses
6. $\qquad = 0$	Multiplicative property of 0
7. $(-1)a + a = 0$	Transitive property of equality

Thus, $(-1)a$ satisfies $x + a = 0$, and must, therefore, equal $-a$. Because multiplication in $\mathcal{R}$ is commutative, $a(-1) = (-1)a$, so that $a(-1) = -a$.

The following examples show how the foregoing theorem and the fact that $(-1)(-1) = -(-1) = 1$ (Exercise 30, page 15) enable you to simplify expressions for products involving negative numbers.

$$15 \cdot (-3) = 15 \cdot [3 \cdot (-1)] = (15 \cdot 3)(-1) = (45)(-1) = -45$$

$$(-8)(-7) = (-1 \cdot 8)(-1 \cdot 7) = [(-1)(-1)](8 \cdot 7) = 1 \cdot 56 = 56$$

$$(-2)(5) + 3(-1) = -1(2)(5) + (-3) = -1(10) + (-3)$$
$$= -10 + (-3) = -13$$

These examples suggest how to deduce the following corollary of the multiplicative property of -1. (See Exercises 30–32, page 19.)

Properties of Negatives in Products

For all real numbers a and b,

$$(-a)b = -ab, \qquad a(-b) = -ab, \qquad (-a)(-b) = ab.$$

Can you explain why the following statements are true?

A product of several nonzero real numbers of which an even number are negative is a positive number.

A product of several nonzero real numbers of which an odd number are negative is a negative number.

The fact that $(-1)(-1) = 1$ means that the reciprocal of -1 is -1; that is, $-1 = \dfrac{1}{-1}$. You can use this fact to show that for every nonzero real number a,

$$\frac{1}{-a} = -\frac{1}{a};$$

that is, *the reciprocal of the negative of a is the negative of the reciprocal of a.*

$$\frac{1}{-a} = \frac{1}{(-1)a} = \frac{1}{-1} \cdot \frac{1}{a} = -1 \cdot \frac{1}{a} = -\frac{1}{a}$$

Thus,

$$\frac{1}{-5} = -\frac{1}{5}, \quad \text{and} \quad \frac{1}{-7} = -\frac{1}{7}.$$

EXERCISES Simplify each expression.

A
1. $(-8)(-3)(5)$
2. $4(-7)(-11)$
3. $(-18)(-5)(-\frac{1}{10})$
4. $(-24)(-\frac{1}{8})(3)$
5. $6(-2) + (-3)(5)$
6. $-8(10) + (-3)(-20)$
7. $-12(\frac{1}{3} + \frac{1}{4})$
8. $16[\frac{1}{8} + (-\frac{1}{2})]$
9. $(-36)(-\frac{1}{12})(\frac{1}{2})$

10. $\frac{1}{5}(-100)(-\frac{1}{10})$
11. $15(-\frac{1}{3})(20)(-1)$
12. $27(\frac{2}{3})(-18)(0)$
13. $(1.2)(-3)(-5)(-1)$
14. $(-1.4)(-7)(-5)(-3)$
15. $(-8)\left(-\frac{1}{3}\right)\left(\frac{1}{-4}\right)(18)$
16. $144\left(-\frac{1}{6}\right)\left(\frac{1}{-2}\right)\left(\frac{1}{-3}\right)$

State whether the value of the given expression is positive, negative, or zero. Do not compute.

17. $(-72)(-3.1)(2)(7)$
18. $5(-7.2)(-18)(-0.2)$
19. $(-3)(5)(83)(117)$
20. $(-23)(-8)(-0.2)(-84)$
21. $(173)(-851)(0)(-273)$
22. $86(-\frac{1}{3})(-\frac{5}{7})(83)$

Prove each of the following theorems. Assume that each variable denotes a real number.

B
23. $bc\left(\dfrac{1}{c}\right) = b$ $\quad (c \neq 0)$

24. If $ac = bc$, then $a = b$ $\quad (c \neq 0)$.

25. If $ca = cb$, then $a = b$ $\quad (c \neq 0)$.

26. $\dfrac{1}{ab} = \dfrac{1}{a} \cdot \dfrac{1}{b}$ $\quad (a, b \neq 0)$

27. If $ab = a$ and $a \neq 0$, then $b = 1$. (Uniqueness of multiplicative identity)

28. If $ab = 1$, then $b = \dfrac{1}{a}$. (Uniqueness of multiplicative inverses)

29. $\dfrac{1}{\frac{1}{a}} = a$ $\quad (a \neq 0)$

30. $(-a)b = -ab$

31. $a(-b) = -ab$

32. $(-a)(-b) = ab$

33. If $a = b$, then $\dfrac{1}{a} = \dfrac{1}{b}$ $\ (a, b \neq 0)$.

34. $-a(b + c) = -ab + (-ac)$

C
35. If $xb = a$, then $x = a \cdot \dfrac{1}{b}$ $\ (b \neq 0)$.

36. If $x = a \cdot \dfrac{1}{b}$, then $bx = a$ $\ (b \neq 0)$.

1-7 *properties of differences*

Try this

REVIEW TEST 5

Simplify each expression.

1. $15 - 7$
2. $7 - 15$
3. $3 - (-5)$
4. $-3 - (-8)$

5. $3 + 18 - 15 - 2$
6. $18 + 21 - 47 + 0$
7. $3(8 - 17) + 2(5 - 6)$
8. $5(3 - 12) - 4(6 - 1)$

Test Items 9–20 give the steps in proofs of two theorems. Justify each step. Assume that each variable denotes a real number.

I. $a(b - c) = ab - ac$ II. $a - (-b) = a + b$

PROOF   PROOF

9. a, b, and c are real numbers.   16. a and b are real numbers.

10. $b - c = b + (-c)$ 17. $-b$ is a real number.

11. $a(b - c) = a[b + (-c)]$ 18. $a - (-b) = a + [-(-b)]$

12. $= ab + a(-c)$ 19. $-(-b) = b$

13. $= ab + (-ac)$ 20. $a - (-b) = a + b$

14. $= ab - ac$

15. $a(b - c) = ab - ac$

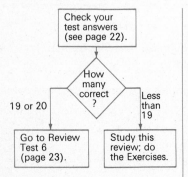

Check your test answers (see page 22).

How many correct ?

19 or 20 — Go to Review Test 6 (page 23).

Less than 19 — Study this review; do the Exercises.

Two other operations are defined in terms of the basic operations of addition and multiplication in $\mathcal{R}$. In this section, we shall consider the first of these. The difference between a and b, $a - b$, is defined as follows:

Relationship between Addition and Subtraction

For all real numbers a and b,

$$a - b = a + (-b).$$

You can interpret this to say "to subtract b from a, add the additive inverse of b to a." For example,

$$-3 - (-2) = -3 + 2 = -1,$$

and

$$8 - 11 = 8 + (-11) = -3.$$

Since

$$a - b + b = [a + (-b)] + b$$
$$= a + [(-b) + b]$$
$$= a + 0$$
$$= a,$$

you can see that $a - b$ is the number which when added to b produces a.

Since $a - b$ is the number that you add to b to obtain a, you can interpret $a - b$ on the number line as follows (see Figure 4):

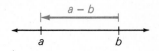

$a - b$ tells the number of units and the direction of the displacement *from* the graph of b *to* the graph of a.

Figure 4

Because $\mathcal{R}$ is closed under addition, it follows from the definition of a difference that $\mathcal{R}$ is also closed under subtraction. If you notice that $7 - 2 = 5$ whereas $2 - 7 = -5$, you can see that subtraction is not commutative in $\mathcal{R}$. The fact that $(3 - 2) - 1 = 1 - 1 = 0$ while $3 - (2 - 1) = 3 - (1) = 2$ demonstrates that subtraction is not associative in $\mathcal{R}$.

Knowing the relationship between addition and subtraction, you can prove several theorems about subtraction. For example, Test Items 9–15, page 20, outline a proof of the fact that *multiplication is distributive with respect to subtraction*. Thus, for each real number y,

$$7(y - 5) = 7 \cdot y - 7 \cdot 5 = 7y - 35.$$

NOW DO THESE ▶ EXERCISES

Simplify each expression.

A

1. $-3 - 6$
2. $8 - (-10)$
3. $182 - 275$
4. $386 - 293$
5. $-152 - 83$
6. $-41 - 81$
7. $-18 - (-28) + 2$

8. $26 - (-15) + 31$
9. $-7(15 - 23)$
10. $8(-17 - 5)$
11. $-3[6 - (2 - 3)] + 1$
12. $2[-6 - (3 + 5)] - 7$
13. $5[-3(2 + 1)] + 2(-5)$
14. $-[3 + 5(-6 - 3)] + 7(5 - 7)$

Show that the number represented by the red numeral satisfies the given equation.

15. $(x - 3)(x + 5) = 2x + 10$; 5
16. $(z - 3)(4 - z) = 14z - 2$; -2
17. $(3 - n)(n - 2) = -(n + 1)(n - 2) + 6n$; -4
18. $(t + 3)(2 - t) = (2t + 1)(t - 1) - 10t - 1$; 4

Justify each step in the proofs of the following theorems. Assume that each variable denotes a real number.

B 19. $-a + b = b - a$ 20. $-(a - b) = b - a$

PROOF

1. a and b are real numbers.
2. $-a$ is a real number.
3. $-a + b = b + (-a)$
4. $\qquad = b - a$
5. $-a + b = b - a$

PROOF

1. a and b are real numbers.
2. $a - b = a + (-b)$
3. $-(a - b) = -[a + (-b)]$
4. $\qquad = (-a) + [-(-b)]$
5. $\qquad = -a + b$
6. $\qquad = b - a$
   (See Exercise 19.)
7. $-(a - b) = b - a$

Prove each theorem. Assume that each variable denotes a real number.

21. $(a - b) + b = a$
22. $-a(b + c) = -ab - ac$
23. $-a(b - c) = ac - ab$
24. If $a - c = b - c$, then $a = b$.
25. If $c - a = c - b$, then $a = b$.
26. If $a = b$, then $a - c = b - c$.
27. If $a = b$, then $c - a = c - b$.
28. If $a = b$, then $-a = -b$.

C 29. If $x - b = a$, then $x = a + b$.
30. If $x = a + b$, then $x - b = a$.

Answers to Review Test 5
1. 8   2. -8 3. 8   4. 5   5. 4   6. -8 7. -29
8. -65 9. Hypothesis   10. Relationship between addition and subtraction   11. Substitution principle   12. Distributive axiom   13. Property of negatives in products   14. Relationship between addition and subtraction   15. Transitive property of equality   16. Hypothesis   17. Axiom of additive inverses   18. Relationship between addition and subtraction   19. Axiom of additive inverses   20. Substitution principle

1-8 properties of quotients

Try this▶

REVIEW TEST 6

Simplify each expression.

1. $-35 \div 7$

2. $(-18) \div (-9)$

3. $\dfrac{24}{-6}$

4. $\dfrac{-32}{-8}$

5. $5 \div (-\tfrac{1}{2}) \div 1$

6. $7 \div (-\tfrac{1}{3}) \cdot (-2)$

7. $18 - 6 \div 3 + 2 \cdot (-5)$

8. $-51 \div 3 - 15 \cdot (-2)$

Test Items 9–18 give the steps in proofs of two theorems. Justify each step. Assume that each variable denotes a real number.

I. $\dfrac{a + b}{c} = \dfrac{a}{c} + \dfrac{b}{c}$ $(c \neq 0)$

II. $\dfrac{-a}{b} = -\dfrac{a}{b}$

PROOF

9. a, b, and c are real numbers; $c \neq 0$.

10. $\dfrac{a + b}{c} = (a + b) \cdot \dfrac{1}{c}$

11. $\phantom{\dfrac{a+b}{c}} = a \cdot \dfrac{1}{c} + b \cdot \dfrac{1}{c}$

12. $\phantom{\dfrac{a+b}{c}} = \dfrac{a}{c} + \dfrac{b}{c}$

13. $\dfrac{a + b}{c} = \dfrac{a}{c} + \dfrac{b}{c}$

PROOF

14. a and b are real numbers; $b \neq 0$.

15. $\dfrac{-a}{b} = -a\left(\dfrac{1}{b}\right)$

16. $\phantom{\dfrac{-a}{b}} = -\left(a \cdot \dfrac{1}{b}\right)$

17. $\phantom{\dfrac{-a}{b}} = -\dfrac{a}{b}$

18. $\dfrac{-a}{b} = -\dfrac{a}{b}$

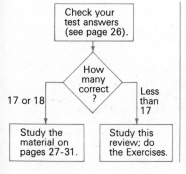

Check your test answers (see page 26).

How many correct?

17 or 18 → Study the material on pages 27-31.

Less than 17 → Study this review; do the Exercises.

Still another operation in $\mathcal{R}$ is defined in terms of multiplication. The quotient of a and b, $a \div b$ or $\dfrac{a}{b}$, $b \neq 0$, is defined as follows:

Relationship between Multiplication and Division

For all real numbers a and all nonzero real numbers b,

$$\dfrac{a}{b} = a \cdot \dfrac{1}{b}.$$

For example,

$$\frac{-24}{3} = (-24)\left(\frac{1}{3}\right) = (-8 \cdot 3)\frac{1}{3} = -8 \cdot \left(3 \cdot \frac{1}{3}\right) = -8 \cdot 1 = -8$$

and

$$20 \div \left(-\tfrac{1}{5}\right) = 20 \cdot (-5) = -100.$$

Since

$$(a \div b) \cdot b = \left(a \cdot \frac{1}{b}\right) \cdot b$$

$$= a \cdot \left(\frac{1}{b} \cdot b\right)$$

$$= a \cdot 1$$

$$= a,$$

you can see that $a \div b$ is the number which when multiplied by b produces a.

Notice that *division by 0 is not defined*. This is because:

1. If $a \neq 0$, $\frac{a}{0} = c$ would imply that $0 \cdot c = a$, but $0 \cdot c = 0$ for every real number c (page 17).

2. If $a = 0$, $\frac{a}{0} = c$ would not be unique, since $0 \cdot c = 0$ for every real number c.

Because $\mathcal{R}$ is closed under multiplication and $a \div b = a \cdot \frac{1}{b}$, the set $\mathcal{R}$ is closed with respect to division, excluding division by zero. Test Items 13 and 18 on page 23 and Exercises 19–25 on page 25 state several additional properties of division, among which are the facts that division is distributive over both addition and subtraction.

What is the value of an expression like $12 - 15 + 6 \cdot 8 \div 12$ that has no grouping symbols to show the order in which operations are to be performed? To assign a value to such an expression, you take the following steps, performing the operations within each grouping symbol, if any, beginning with the innermost grouping symbol and working out to the entire expression.

1. Perform multiplications and divisions in order from left to right.
2. Then perform additions and subtractions in order from left to right.

EXAMPLE 1 Simplify $12 - 15 + 6 \cdot 8 \div 12$.

SOLUTION
$$\begin{aligned}
12 - 15 + 6 \cdot 8 \div 12 &= 12 - 15 + 48 \div 12 \\
&= 12 - 15 + 4 \\
&= -3 + 4 \\
&= 1. \text{ Answer.}
\end{aligned}$$

EXAMPLE 2 $\frac{1}{5}[-6 + 2(18 - 5)]$

SOLUTION $\frac{1}{5}[-6 + 2(18 - 5)] = \frac{1}{5}[-6 + 2(13)]$
$$= \frac{1}{5}(-6 + 26)$$
$$= \frac{1}{5}(20)$$
$$= 4. \text{ Answer.}$$

NOW DO THESE ▶   **EXERCISES**

Simplify each expression.

A   1. $46 \div (-23)$

2. $(-136) \div 8$

3. $-105 \div (-21)$

4. $(-322) \div (-14)$

5. $90 + \frac{1}{2} \div (-\frac{1}{5})$

6. $-25 \cdot \frac{1}{2} \div \frac{5}{4}$

7. $21 \cdot (-6) \div (-\frac{1}{3})$

8. $24 \div (-\frac{1}{3}) \cdot (-\frac{1}{12})$

9. $15 + 8 \div 4 - 6$

10. $12 - 28 \div 4 + 3$

11. $[18 - 3(5 - 1)] \div [2(5 - 2)]$

12. $[-3 + 5(8 - 15)] \div [2(7 - 8)]$

13. $15 + 3[-7 + 2(6 - 8)] - 32$

14. $[23 - 7(2 - 5)] \div 2 + 3$

Show that the number represented by the red numeral satisfies the given equation.

15. $\dfrac{x - 3}{5} + 2 = x + \dfrac{x + 2}{-2};\ 8$

16. $3x - 7 + \dfrac{x + 2}{5} = 6x - 1;\ -2$

17. $2z(z - 3) + \dfrac{2}{z - 3} = -3z;\ 2$

18. $\left(\dfrac{z}{4} + 18\right)\left(\dfrac{8}{z} - 2\right) = 3z - 12;\ 4$

Prove each of the following theorems. Assume that each variable denotes a real number.

B   19. If $ax = b$, then $x = \dfrac{b}{a}$ $(a \ne 0)$.

20. If $x = \dfrac{b}{a}$, then $ax = b$ $(a \ne 0)$.

21. $\dfrac{a - b}{c} = \dfrac{a}{c} - \dfrac{b}{c}$ $(c \ne 0)$

22. $\dfrac{a}{a} = 1$ 23. $\dfrac{-a}{a} = -1$ 24. $\dfrac{a}{1} = a$ 25. $\dfrac{a}{-a} = -1$

SELF-TEST 2   Simplify each expression.

Section 1–5, page 11   **1.** $12 + (-18) + (-6)$

Section 1–6, page 16   **2.** $10(-3) + (-5)(-2)$

Section 1–7, page 20   **3.** $-8 - [3 + (-4 + 2)]$

Section 1–8, page 23   **4.** $-3[5 - 2(3 + 6)] \div (-13)$

5. $12 + 18 \div 6 + 8 \cdot (-3)$

Prove the following theorem.

6. $b \cdot \left(\dfrac{1}{ab} \right) = \dfrac{1}{a}$ $(a, b \neq 0)$

Check your answers with those printed at the back of the book. If you did not answer a question correctly, study the referenced section again.

Albert Einstein
1879–1955

Albert Einstein's career as a student had not been impressive, but while working as an examiner for a Swiss patent office he thought a great deal about a wide variety of unexplained experiments which had to do with light and motion. In 1905, Einstein attempted to account for these experiments in his Special Theory of Relativity. Today many observations are in complete accord with special relativity. Among the observations predicted by the special theory is the equivalence of mass and energy related by the equation $E = mc^2$, where c is the speed of light.

In 1916 Einstein included the effects of acceleration among various observers in what is called the General Theory of Relativity. Einstein's general laws predict results identical to Newton's when the velocities are not extremely great.

Einstein left Europe shortly before World War II for a lifetime appointment at the Institute for Advanced Study in Princeton, New Jersey.

Answers to Review Test 6
1. −5   **2.** 2   **3.** −4   **4.** 4   **5.** −10   **6.** 42   **7.** 6
8. 13   **9.** Hypothesis   **10.** Relationship between multiplication and division   **11.** Distributive axiom   **12.** Relationship between multiplication and division   **13.** Transitive property of equality   **14.** Hypothesis   **15.** Relationship between multiplication and division   **16.** Property of negatives in products   **17.** Relationship between multiplication and division   **18.** Transitive property of equality

careers *data processing*

The woman in the upper photo is analyzing computer print-out. Below, meteorologists use a computer to compile weather data. The computer has been programmed to plot a weather map.

Computers do a variety of jobs, from keeping track of a business firm's inventory and bills to guiding rockets. However, before a computer can do any job, it must be *programmed,* or given instructions. This is the task of a computer programmer. The first step in writing a program is to analyze the job so that a logical method of doing it can be found. The steps in the procedure are often represented by a *flow chart.* (See page 102 for style of flowcharts.) At this stage, the programmer must be sure that the computer being used is equipped to perform each step, and that the steps are arranged in logical order.

The programmer then translates the flow chart into a *program,* a list of instructions in a *language* which the computer is designed to "understand." There are many different programming languages, and the one used for a particular program depends upon the job and the computer to be used. Every programming language has a limited number of instructions, each telling the computer to perform a specific operation.

If you enjoy working puzzles and have the ability to think logically, you might like computer programming. In this book you will learn about a programming language called BASIC and you will have the opportunity to write some programs.

EXAMPLE   Follow the directions in the flow chart.

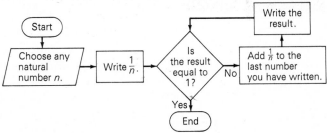

1. How many numbers have you written?
2. Which number is the least?
3. Choose some other values of *n* and compare your answers to Exercises 1 and 2.
4. Draw a similar flow chart which will produce the same numbers in reverse order.

Be sure that you understand the meaning of each of the following words, referenced by section, before starting Chapter 2.

Section 1–1
  set
  member (of a set)
  element (of a set)
  subset
  empty set
  null set

Section 1–2
  statement
  variable
  replacement set of a variable
  domain of a variable
  values of a variable
  open sentence
  solution set
  truth set
  solution of an open sentence
  root of an open sentence

Section 1–3
  number line
  graph of a number
  coordinate of a point
  real numbers

Section 1–4
  binary operation
  addends
  factors
  axiom (postulate)
  identity element for addition
  identity element for multiplication
  additive inverse
  multiplicative inverse
  reciprocal

Section 1–5
  theorem
  hypothesis
  conclusion
  direct proof
  corollary

Section 1–7
  difference

Section 1–8
  quotient

chapter summary

1. Some of the familiar set symbols include { } (indicates a set), ∈ (denotes a member of a set), ⊂ (indicates a subset), = (denotes the same set), and ∅ (the empty set).

2. A **variable** is a symbol which may represent any one of the members of a set called the **replacement set** of the variable. A sentence containing a variable is called an **open sentence**. You can convert an open sentence about numbers to a statement by replacing the variable with a numeral for one of the values of the variable. Values of a variable that convert a sentence to a true statement are **solutions** of the sentence.

3. **Axioms**, or **postulates**, are statements whose truth is assumed. These statements are used to prove **theorems**. The "if-clause" of a theorem is called the **hypothesis** of the theorem and the "then-clause" is called the **conclusion** of the theorem. By reasoning from the hypothesis to the conclusion, you can give a **direct proof** of a theorem.

4. The axioms for the set ℜ of real numbers determine the properties of the system of real numbers and are included in the tables on pages 29–30.

Some Properties of Real Numbers

For all $a, b, c \in \mathcal{R}$:

Sums	Products	Property
$a + b$ is a unique element of $\mathcal{R}$.	ab is a unique element of $\mathcal{R}$.	Closure
$a + b = b + a$	$ab = ba$	Commutative
$(a + b) + c = a + (b + c)$	$(ab)c = a(bc)$	Associative
$a + 0 = a$ and $0 + a = a$	$a \cdot 1 = a$ and $1 \cdot a = a$	Identity element (Axioms of 0 and 1)
$a + (-a) = 0$ and $(-a) + a = 0$	$a \cdot \dfrac{1}{a} = 1$ and $\dfrac{1}{a} \cdot a = 1$ for $a \neq 0$	Inverse element
$a(b + c) = ab + ac$ $(b + c)a = ba + ca$		Distributive (of multiplication with respect to addition)
If $a + c = b + c$, then $a = b$.	If $ac = bc$ $(c \neq 0)$, then $a = b$.	Cancellation
$-(a + b) = (-a) + (-b)$	$(-a)(b) = -ab$ $a(-b) = -ab$ $(-a)(-b) = ab$	Negative of a sum and negatives in products
	$\dfrac{1}{ab} = \dfrac{1}{a} \cdot \dfrac{1}{b} \begin{cases} a \neq 0 \\ b \neq 0 \end{cases}$	Reciprocal of a product
	$a \cdot 0 = 0$ and $0 \cdot a = 0$	Multiplicative property of 0
	$a(-1) = -a$ and $(-1)a = -a$	Multiplicative property of -1
$a - b = a + (-b)$		Relationship between addition and subtraction
	$\dfrac{a}{b} = a \cdot \dfrac{1}{b}$ $(b \neq 0)$	Relationship between multiplication and division

Equality Axioms	
$a = a$	Reflexive Property
If $a = b$, then $b = a$.	Symmetric Property
If $a = b$ and $b = c$, then $a = c$.	Transitive Property

chapter test   1–1   Replace each __?__ with one of the symbols, $=$, $\neq$, $\in$, $\notin$, $\subset$, or $\not\subset$ to make a true statement.

   1. {the first three whole numbers} __?__ {integers}

   2. 28 __?__ {multiples of 4}

1–2   **3.** Solve $2x - 3 = 7$ if $x \in \{1, 2, 3, 4, 5\}$.

1–3   **4.** Graph $\{-3, 0, 4\}$ on a number line.

1–4   State the axiom justifying each statement.

   5. $5 + (7 + 9) = (5 + 7) + 9$

   6. $6 \cdot (8 - 3) = (8 - 3) \cdot 6$

Simplify each expression.

1–5   **7.** $58 + (-117) + 63$ **8.** $-28 + (-38 + 50)$

1–6   **9.** $(-32)(-\frac{1}{16})(4)$ **10.** $-24(\frac{1}{3} + \frac{1}{8})$

1–7   **11.** $-21 - (-15) - 3$ **12.** $-3[5 - (6 - 2)]$

1–8   **13.** $-3 + 48 \div 16 \cdot 3$

   14. $[-4 + 2(6 - 1)] \div [5 + 2(10 - 11)]$

programmed chapter review

1–1   **1.** Ø is called the __?__ __?__ and is the set which contains __?__   null (or empty) set
   __?__ .   no elements

1–2   **2.** A symbol which may represent any one of the members of a
   specified set is called a __?__ .   variable

   3. Sentences containing variables are called __?__ sentences.   open

   4. The solution set of $3x + 1 \neq 7$ over $\{1, 2, 3, 4\}$ is __?__ . $\{1, 3, 4\}$

1–3   5. The set $\{1, 2, 3, \ldots\}$ is called the set of __?__ __?__ .   natural numbers
                                                                            (or positive integers)

       6. On a number line, the point paired with a number is called
          the __?__ of the number, and the number is called the __?__   graph; coordinate
          of the point.

       7. The number line

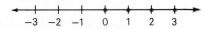

          pictures the graph of the set of __?__ numbers.   whole

       8. The subset of $A = \{-\frac{3}{5}, -\frac{1}{2}, 0, 3, \frac{7}{2}, \frac{27}{4}\}$ that contains all
          the integers in A is __?__ . $\{0, 3\}$

1–4   9. The symbol "$-a$" represents the __?__ __?__ of a.   additive inverse

      10. The number 0 is called the __?__ element for __?__ in the set   identity; addition
          of real numbers.

      11. The multiplicative inverse of -3 is __?__ . $-\frac{1}{3}$

      12. The fact that $3 \cdot (-7) = -7 \cdot (3)$ is justified by the __?__ axiom   commutative
          for __?__ .   multiplication

1–5   13. The part of a theorem which states the assumptions is called
          the __?__ of the theorem.   hypothesis (or premise)

      14. A theorem that can quickly be deduced from another theorem
          is called a __?__ .   corollary

      15. For all real numbers a, b, and c, if $a + c = b + c$, then
          $a = $ __?__ . b

      16. For all real numbers a and b, $-(a + b) = $ __?__ $+$ __?__ . $-a$; $-b$

1–6   17. For all nonzero real numbers a and b, $\dfrac{1}{ab} = $ __?__ . $\dfrac{1}{a} \cdot \dfrac{1}{b}$

      18. For all real numbers a, $a \cdot 0 = 0 \cdot a = $ __?__ . 0

      19. In simple form, $(-3)(8)(-2)(-1) = $ __?__ . -48

      20. In simple form, $(-1)(3)(8)(-\frac{1}{3}) = $ __?__ . 8

1–7   21. For all real numbers a and b, $a - b = $ __?__ $+$ __?__ . a; $(-b)$

      22. In simple form, $-213 + 183 = $ __?__ . -30

      23. In simple form, $2(3 - 12) - 2(3 - 6) = $ __?__ . -12

1–8   24. For all real numbers a and b, if $b \neq 0$, then $\dfrac{a}{b} = $ __?__ $\cdot$ __?__ . a; $\dfrac{1}{b}$

      25. In simple form, $-124 \div (-62) = $ __?__ . 2

      26. In simple form, $5 + 16 \div 4 \cdot 2 = $ __?__ . 13

These are not models for a new apartment complex, but stacks of computer information recording discs. The "records" are made of thin aluminum and are coated with magnetic recording material. Large amounts of data can be stored on these discs for processing in computer systems.

2 review of essentials

solving and applying equations

After completing the next three sections, you will have reviewed:
1. Simplifying expressions for sums and differences of polynomials.
2. Solving first-degree equations in one variable.
3. Applying linear equations to solve word problems.

2–1 sums and differences of polynomials

Try this REVIEW TEST 7

State the coefficients and the degree of each polynomial.

1. $2x^2 - 3x + 5$
2. $x^2y - 3xy - 2x$
3. $2r^2s^2 - 3rs^2 + r^2s + 1$
4. $-4t^4 + 3t^2 + 4t - 3$

Simplify each expression.

5. $3t^2 + 4t - t^2 - 4t$
6. $4x + 7x^2 - 2x - 6x^2$
7. $3y + 2(y + 1)$
8. $4x^2 - (4x^2 - 3x + 2)$
9. $(z^2 - 3z + 5) - (2z^2 - 3z + 2)$
10. $(4r^3 - 3r + 7) + (2r^2 - 2r + 1)$

11. $(5x^2 - 3x + 2) - (3x^2 + 5x - 1) + (2x^2 - 3)$
12. $(8t^3 - 3t^2 + 4t) + (3t^2 - 2t + 1) - (4t^3 + 2t^2 - 3)$
13. $(3r + 2) - [r + (2 - r) + 1]$
14. $[2z^2 - (4 - z)] + [z^2 - (2 + z)]$

15. What polynomial must be added to $4x^3 - 3x^2 + 2x - 1$ to obtain $4x^2 - 3x + 3$?

16. What polynomial must be subtracted from $3t^3 - 2t^2 + t + 2$ to obtain the constant 1?

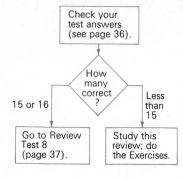

Check your test answers (see page 36).

How many correct?

15 or 16 → Go to Review Test 8 (page 37).

Less than 15 → Study this review; do the Exercises.

A monomial in the variable x is an expression of the form

$$ax^n,$$

where $a \in \mathfrak{R}$, and n denotes a positive integer. The number denoted by a is called the coefficient (or numerical coefficient) of the monomial.

The symbol

$$x^n$$

represents a power of x, where x is called the base and n the exponent. In general, the nth power of x denotes the product of n factors, each equal to x. For example:

$$x^1 = x$$
$$x^2 = x \cdot x \text{ (also read ''x-squared'' or ''the square of x'')}$$
$$x^3 = x \cdot x \cdot x \text{ (also read ''x-cubed'' or ''the cube of x'')}$$
$$x^4 = x \cdot x \cdot x \cdot x \text{ (also read ''x-fourth'' or ''x to the fourth'')}$$

In the monomial ax^n, if $a \neq 0$, you call n the degree of the monomial. Thus, for the monomial $-x^4$, the coefficient is -1 and the degree is 4. Monomials such as -3, 5, and 0 are called constant monomials, and, with the exception of the zero monomial, 0, are assigned *degree zero*. The zero monomial has *no degree*.

A monomial such as

$$4x^2y^3,$$

which contains more than one variable, is assigned as degree the sum of the exponents of the variables. Thus, the degree of $4x^2y^3$ is $2 + 3$, or 5, while its coefficient is 4.

· An expression such as

$$5x^3 + 0x^2 + (-2x) + (-5),$$

which consists of a string of monomials connected by plus (+) signs, is called a polynomial. The monomials in the expression are called the terms of the polynomial and the coefficients of the terms are called the coefficients of the polynomial. Thus, the terms of the foregoing polynomial are $5x^3$, $0x^2$, $-2x$, and -5, while the coefficients are 5, 0, -2, and -5. Another way to write the polynomial is

$$5x^3 - 2x - 5,$$

where the term with 0 coefficient is omitted and the connecting + signs are taken as understood.

Two monomials are said to be like or similar if they are exactly the same or if they differ only in numerical coefficients. Thus,

$$5x^5, \qquad -3x^5, \qquad \text{and} \qquad x^5$$

are *like* monomials, while

$$5x^2, \qquad 5x^4, \qquad \text{and} \qquad 5x^5y$$

are *unlike*. A polynomial is said to be in simple form when no two of its terms are like terms. For example,

$$2x^3 - 5x + 7$$

is in simple form, whereas

$$2x^3 - 3x - 2x + 7$$

is not. The terms of a simplified polynomial are usually written in order of decreasing degree from left to right.

The degree of a polynomial in simple form is defined to be the degree of its nonzero term of highest degree. Thus, the polynomial $2x^3 - 5x + 7$ is of degree 3. A polynomial of degree 2 that contains a single variable is called a quadratic polynomial.

Given any two polynomials such as

$$4x^2 - 3x \quad \text{and} \quad x^2 + 2x - 1,$$

you call the expression

$$(4x^2 - 3x) + (x^2 + 2x - 1)$$

the sum of the polynomials, and the expression

$$(4x^2 - 3x) - (x^2 + 2x - 1)$$

their difference. To replace the sum or difference by polynomials in simple form, you use the following rules.

Rules for Adding and Subtracting Polynomials

1. To **add** polynomials, add the coefficients of similar terms in the polynomials.
2. To **subtract** one polynomial from another, subtract the coefficient of each term in the one polynomial from the coefficient of the similar term in the other polynomial.

Using these rules, you find

$$(4x^2 - 3x) + (x^2 + 2x - 1) = (4 + 1)x^2 + (-3 + 2)x + (0 + (-1))$$
$$= 5x^2 + (-1)x + (-1)$$
$$= 5x^2 - x - 1$$

and

$$(4x^2 - 3x) - (x^2 + 2x - 1) = (4 - 1)x^2 + (-3 - 2)x + (0 - (-1))$$
$$= 3x^2 + (-5)x + (1)$$
$$= 3x^2 - 5x + 1.$$

Because it can be proved, by using properties of the real numbers, that the equation

$$(4x^2 - 3x) + (x^2 + 2x - 1) = 5x^2 - x - 1$$

is a true statement for *every* numerical replacement of the variable, the two *members* of the equation (the expressions related by the = symbol) are called equivalent expressions. Whenever you replace a given polynomial by an equivalent polynomial in simple form, you say that you have simplified the given polynomial.

Answers to Review Test 7
1. $2, -3, 5$; degree 2   2. $1, -3, -2$; degree 3   3. $2, -3, 1, 1$, degree 4   4. $-4, 3, 4, -3$; degree 4   5. $2t^2$ 6. $x^2 + 2x$
7. $5y + 2$ 8. $3x - 2$ 9. $-z^2 + 3$ 10. $4r^3 + 2r^2 - 5r + 8$
11. $4x^2 - 8x$ 12. $4t^3 - 2t^2 + 2t + 4$ 13. $3r - 1$
14. $3z^2 - 6$ 15. $-4x^3 + 7x^2 - 5x + 4$ 16. $3t^3 - 2t^2 + t - 3$

NOW DO THESE ▶ **EXERCISES**

In Exercises 1–6 add the given polynomials.

A 1. $2z^3 - 3z^2 + 2z + 5$
$\underline{\quad z^3 + \ z^2 - 2z + 3}$

4. $x^5 - \ x^4 - 2x^3$
$\underline{\qquad\quad 4x^4 + 3x^3 - 2x + 1}$

2. $t^4 - 3t^3 + 2t^2 \qquad - 4$
$\underline{\qquad 2t^3 + 3t^2 + 2t + 1}$

5. $4p^2q - 3pq^2 + 4pq - 5$
$\underline{-p^2q - \ pq^2 - \ pq + 5}$

3. $5n^5 - 3n^3 \qquad + 2n - 1$
$\underline{2n^5 + \ n^3 - 3n^2 \qquad + 2}$

6. $x^2y^2 - 3x^2y + 2xy^2 - 3xy + 2$
$\underline{2x^2y^2 - 3x^2y + 2xy^2 - 3xy + 1}$

7–12. In Exercises 1–6 subtract the second polynomial from the first.

Simplify each expression.

13. $(3y + 5) - (-y + 8)$
14. $(3 + 2b) - (5 - 3b)$
15. $(2x - y) - (x + y) - (x - 2y)$
16. $(4r + s) - (2r - 3s) - (2r + 3s)$
17. $(n^2 + 8n - 2) + (3n^2 - 2n - 1)$
18. $(2t^2 - 2t + 4) - (t^2 - t - 4)$
19. $(n^3 - 3n^2 + 2) + (n^3 + 5n - 3) - (2n^3 + 2n^2 - 2n + 1)$
20. $(r^2 - 3r + 5) - (r^3 + 2r^2 - 3r + 1) - (-r^3 + 2r + 3)$

21. $(2z^4 - 3z^2 + 2) - (z^4 + 3z^3 - 2) + (-z^4 + 2z^3 - 3z^2 + z)$

22. $(3x^4 + 2x^3 - 3x) + (5x^3 - 2x^2 + x) - (x^4 + 5x^3 + 4x - 2)$

23. $(3x^2 - 2xy + 4y^2) - (x^2 - 2xy + y^2) + (-x^2 + 3xy + 2y^2)$

24. $(4a^2 - 3ab + b^2) + (a^2 + 3ab - b^2) - (4a^2 - ab + 3b^2)$

25. $(x^3 - 2x^2 + 3x + 4) - (x^3 - 4x^2 + 2x - 1) + (x^2 - 3)$

26. $(r^4 - 7r^3 - 2r^2 + r - 1) + (-3r^4 + 5r^3 - r^2 - r - 1)$

B 27. $[t^2 - (2t + 1)] - [2t^2 - (t - 3)]$

28. $3a - (2b - a) - \{b - [2a - (b - 2a)] + 3b\}$

29. $3[5s - 2(t + 1)] + 3[2t - (1 + s)]$

30. $-2[3x + 3(y - x)] - 4[-2y + 2(x - 3)]$

31. What polynomial must be added to $4z^5 - 3z^2 + 2z$ to obtain the zero polynomial?

32. From what polynomial must $5a^3 - 3a^2 + 2a$ be subtracted to obtain $a^3 - 1$?

2–2 *transforming equations*

REVIEW TEST 8

Solve each of the following equations over $\mathcal{R}$.

1. $2r - 3 = 11$

2. $3(t + 2) = 12$

3. $\dfrac{-5y}{3} = 15$

4. $4(x - 3) + x = 5$

5. $-4r + 3 = r + 2$

6. $2p + 3(2p + 5) = p + 1$

7. $\dfrac{3h}{7} - \dfrac{4h}{7} = -2$

8. $\frac{1}{2}(2x + 1) + \frac{3}{2}(2 - x) = 5$

Solve each equation for the symbol shown in red.

9. $4az = a + 2az$

10. $2(a - x) = -3(2a + x)$

11. $\dfrac{a}{b} = \dfrac{c}{d}$

12. $S = \dfrac{a}{1 - r}$

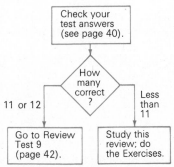

Check your test answers (see page 40).

How many correct ?

11 or 12

Less than 11

Go to Review Test 9 (page 42).

Study this review; do the Exercises.

The equations

$$3x - 2(x + 3) = 2x - 8 \qquad \text{and} \qquad x = 2$$

have the same solution set over $\mathcal{R}$, namely, $\{2\}$. Equations that have the same solution set over a given set are called equivalent equations over that set.

To solve an equation, either you identify the root by inspection or else you perform a sequence of transformations on the equation until you arrive at an equivalent equation whose solution is evident by inspection. The properties of real numbers guarantee that the following transformations of a given equation always produce an equivalent equation.

Transformations That Produce an Equivalent Equation

1. Substituting for either member of the given equation an expression equivalent to it.
2. Adding to or subtracting from each member of the given equation the same polynomial in any variable(s) appearing in the equation.
3. Multiplying or dividing each member by the same nonzero number.

EXAMPLE 1

Solve $6z - 3(z + 1) = z + 1$ over $\mathfrak{R}$.

SOLUTION

1. Copy the equation.

$$6z - 3(z + 1) = z + 1$$

2. Use the distributive axiom to help simplify the left member.

$$6z - 3z - 3 = z + 1$$
$$3z - 3 = z + 1$$

3. Subtract z from each member.

$$3z - 3 - z = z + 1 - z$$
$$2z - 3 = 1$$

4. Add 3 to each member.

$$2z - 3 + 3 = 1 + 3$$
$$2z = 4$$

5. Divide each member by 2 (or multiply each member by $\frac{1}{2}$).

$$\frac{2z}{2} = \frac{4}{2}$$
$$z = 2$$

Because errors may occur in transforming equations, you should always check each solution in the original equation.

$$6z - 3(z + 1) = z + 1$$
$$6(2) - 3(2 + 1) \overset{?}{=} 2 + 1$$
$$12 - 3(3) \overset{?}{=} 3$$
$$12 - 9 \overset{?}{=} 3$$
$$3 = 3 \checkmark$$

$\therefore$ the solution set is $\{2\}$. **Answer.**

Note that, in the foregoing example, the replacement set of the variable was specified as $\mathcal{R}$. From here on, in this book, *unless otherwise stated, all open sentences are to be solved over $\mathcal{R}$.*

The "operational" properties of equality upon which the transformations used to solve equations are based are contained in the following theorem (see Exercises 43–46 on page 40).

For all real numbers a, b, and c, if $a = b$, then:	
$a + c = b + c$, $c + a = c + b$	**Additive Property**
$ac = bc$, $ca = cb$	**Multiplicative Property**
$a - c = b - c$	**Subtraction Property**
$\dfrac{a}{c} = \dfrac{b}{c}$, provided $c \neq 0$	**Division Property**

NOW DO THESE ▶

EXERCISES

State the transformation used to produce the second equation from the first and the third from the second.

A

1. $4 - 7u = 18$; $-7u = 14$; $u = -2$

2. $6a - 8 = a + 4$; $5a - 8 = 4$; $5a = 12$

3. $\dfrac{z}{4} - 6 = 3$; $\dfrac{z}{4} = 9$; $z = 36$

4. $\dfrac{t}{-3} + 5 = -3$; $\dfrac{t}{-3} = -8$; $t = 24$

5. $-2(4 - z) + 3 = 8$; $-8 + 2z + 3 = 8$; $2z - 5 = 8$

6. $5m + 3 = 4m - 2$; $m + 3 = -2$; $m = -5$

7. $6r - 7 = 5r + 3$; $r - 7 = 3$; $r = 10$

8. $2t + 8 = 5t - 3$; $8 = 3t - 3$; $11 = 3t$

Solve each of the following equations.

9. $3x - 9 = 27$

10. $2z + 15 = 7$

11. $3k + (6 - k) = 8$

12. $4r - (3 + 2r) = 17$

13. $3t + 5 = t - 7$

14. $x - (8 - x) = 4$

15. $3a - (3 + a) = 0$

16. $\frac{3}{5}k = -9$

17. $\dfrac{2z}{3} = 8$

18. $\dfrac{3n}{4} = 6$

19. $6n - 2(2n + 5) = 6(5 + n)$

20. $3(7 - 2x) = 30 - 7(x + 1)$

21. $-3[t - (2t + 3) - 2t] = -9$

22. $-2[z - (z - 1)] = -3(z + 1)$

23. $\dfrac{y}{5} - \dfrac{3y}{5} = -2$

24. $\dfrac{7r}{3} + \dfrac{2r}{3} = 18$

25. $\dfrac{1}{3}(n - 5) - \dfrac{2}{3}(4 - 2n) = -6$

26. $\dfrac{1}{5}(2t + 3) + \dfrac{3}{5}(8 - 3t) = -3$

Solve each equation for the variable shown in red. That is, find an equivalent equation in which the symbol shown in red is alone in the left member.

B

27. $3ar - b = c$

28. $7bt + c = b$

29. $3an - 4a = an$

30. $4z - 3(z - b) = 8b$

31. $v = k + gt$

32. $p = 2l + 2w$

33. $E = IR$

34. $I = PRT$

35. $S = 3\pi d + 5\pi D$

36. $A = 2\pi rh + 2\pi r^2$

37. $\dfrac{a}{b} = \dfrac{c}{d}$

38. $l = a + (n - 1)d$

Solve each equation for the variable shown in red. Use the resulting equation to find the value of that variable for the given values of the other variables.

39. $xy - 2yz = 3z$; y: 2; z: 12

40. $mn + 4np = 3p$; n: 6; p: 12

41. $t(p + q) + 2t(p - q) = 6q + p$; p: 6; q: 3

42. $m(r - s) - 2m(r + s) = m - 2r$; r: -5; s: 2

Prove each of the following theorems.

C

43. For all real numbers a, b, and c, if $a = b$, then $a + c = b + c$.

44. For all real numbers a, b, and c, if $a = b$, then $a - c = b - c$.

45. For all real numbers a, b, and c, if $a = b$, then $ac = bc$.

46. For all real numbers a and b, and nonzero real numbers c, if $a = b$, then $\dfrac{a}{c} = \dfrac{b}{c}$.

47. For all real numbers b and c, and nonzero real numbers a, if $ax + b = c$, then $x = \dfrac{c - b}{a}$.

Answers to Review Test 8

1. $\{7\}$ 2. $\{2\}$ 3. $\{-9\}$ 4. $\{\tfrac{17}{5}\}$ 5. $\{\tfrac{1}{5}\}$ 6. $\{-2\}$

7. $\{14\}$ 8. $\{-3\}$ 9. $z = \tfrac{1}{2}$ 10. $x = -8a$ 11. $d = \dfrac{bc}{a}$

12. $r = 1 - \dfrac{a}{S}$

careers

electronics

Electronic components are a vital part of many of the machines used today, including computers, radio and TV equipment, quality control equipment for industry, satellites, and telephone equipment. Electronics engineers must often solve equations about circuits. One important equation in electronics is **Ohm's Law**,

$$V = IR,$$

where V, measured in volts, is the difference in potential energy between two points when a current I, measured in amperes, flows through a resistor, or wire, of resistance R. The unit used to measure resistance is the ohm (Ω).

If two or more resistors are connected one after the other, ⌇⌇⌇, they are said to be *in series*. If two or more resistors are connected like this ⌇⌇⌇, they are said to be *in parallel*. In a series circuit, the total resistance is simply the sum of the individual resistances. However, in a parallel circuit the sum of the reciprocals of the individual resistances is the reciprocal of the total resistance.

EXAMPLE   In the circuit diagram below, resistors **A** and **B** are connected in parallel, and resistor **C** is connected to the circuit in series. A current of 42 amperes is flowing through the circuit. To find the combined resistance R of **A** and **B**, we know that $\frac{1}{R} = \frac{1}{3} + \frac{1}{6} = \frac{1}{2}$. Therefore $R = 2$ ohms.

We can now determine the potential difference across each resistor by applying Ohm's Law. Since the potential difference across each resistor connected in parallel is the same, we have $V = 42 \cdot 2 = 84$ volts for each of the resistors **A** and **B**. For resistor **C**, $V = 42 \cdot 5 = 210$ volts.

These are photographs of the intricate electronic circuits used in computer hardware. A circuit layout is shown above, and in the picture below you can see how the circuit is constructed.

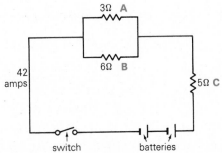

2-3 *applying equations*

Try this

REVIEW TEST 9

Solve each of the following problems.

1. Find two integers which differ by 17 and whose sum is 3.

2. One number is 2 greater than a second number. The greater added to four times the lesser gives 17. Find the numbers.

3. Find the measure of two complementary angles such that one of the angles measures 6° less than twice the measure of the other.

4. The sum of the ages of Mr. Charles and his son is 60 years. Four years from now, Mr. Charles will be three times as old as his son. How old is each now?

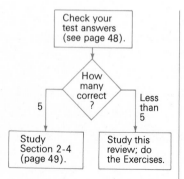

5. The first-class air fare from Central City to Kingsville is $80, while the tourist fare is $64. If the total receipts from a flight carrying 43 passengers were $2880, how many first-class and how many tourist passengers were on the flight?

Algebraic expressions and sentences can be used as descriptions or models for many real-life situations. Such models can be used to help solve practical problems.

EXAMPLE 1

In the Central City Water Reclamation Center, one purifier can process twice as much sewage per minute as a second purifier, and a third purifier can process 50 more liters per minute than the first purifier. If the three units working together can purify 1100 liters per minute, how many liters per minute can each purifier process?

SOLUTION

1. Read the problem carefully and decide what numbers are asked for. The problem asks for the number of liters of sewage each of three machines can purify per minute.

2. Choose a variable to represent one of the numbers asked for or described in the problem. Let x represent the number of liters per minute the second machine can process. Then $2x$ represents the capacity per minute of the first machine, and $2x + 50$ represents the capacity per minute of the third machine.

3. Write an open sentence showing the relationship(s) given in the problem.

Capacity of machine 1	added to	capacity of machine 2	added to	capacity of machine 3	is	total capacity of plant.
$2x$	$+$	x	$+$	$2x + 50$	$=$	1100

4. Solve the open sentence. Knowing the solution of the open sentence, you can determine the numbers asked for in the problem.

$$2x + x + 2x + 50 = 1100$$
$$5x + 50 = 1100$$
$$5x = 1050$$
$$x = 210$$

∴ the only solution of the sentence is 210. This means that:

The second machine can process 210 liters per minute.
The first machine can process 420 liters per minute.
The third machine can process 470 liters per minute.

5. Check your results with the requirements stated in the problem.

Capacity of first machine = twice second machine

$$420 \stackrel{?}{=} 2(210)$$
$$420 = 420 \checkmark$$

Capacity of third machine = 50 more than first machine

$$470 \stackrel{?}{=} 50 + 420$$
$$470 = 470 \checkmark$$

Total capacity = sum of the capacities of all three machines

$$420 + 210 + 470 \stackrel{?}{=} 1100$$
$$1100 = 1100 \checkmark$$

∴ the three machines can process 420, 210, and 470 liters per minute, respectively. **Answer.**

The five steps taken to solve the preceding problem form a useful plan in solving any problem. Notice how they are used in the solutions of Examples 2 and 3 on pages 45 and 46.

In solving problems about geometric figures, sketches picturing the facts of the problem may help you to see relationships. You may wish to review some familiar facts about geometry shown in the table which follows.

Facts from Geometry–Plane Figures

1. Complementary angles A and B

   $m\angle A + m\angle B = 90°$

   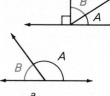

   Supplementary angles A and B

   $m\angle A + m\angle B = 180°$

2. Square with side of length a

   Perimeter: $P = 4a$

      Area: $A = a^2$

   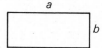

3. Rectangle with length a and width b

   Perimeter: $P = 2a + 2b$

      Area: $A = ab$

   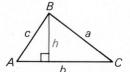

4. Triangle ABC with sides of length a, b, and c, with base b and altitude h

   Perimeter: $P = a + b + c$

      Area: $A = \frac{1}{2}bh$

   Sum of angles: $m\angle A + m\angle B + m\angle C = 180°$

   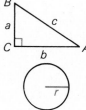

   A. isosceles triangle:

      two congruent sides
      two congruent (base) angles

   B. Equilateral triangle:

      three congruent sides
      three congruent angles (measuring 60° each)

   C. Right triangle with hypotenuse c:

      $a^2 + b^2 = c^2$ (Pythagorean Theorem)

5. Circle with radius r or diameter $d = 2r$

   Perimeter (circumference): $C = 2\pi r$ or $C = \pi d$

   Area: $A = \pi r^2$ or $A = \frac{1}{4}\pi d^2$

   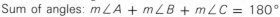

6. Trapezoid with legs of length a and c, bases of length b_1 and b_2, and altitude h

   Perimeter: $P = a + b_1 + b_2 + c$

   Area: $A = \frac{1}{2}h(b_1 + b_2)$

Facts from Geometry–Space Figures

1. Rectangular prism with length a, width b, and height c

   Surface area: $2(ab + ac + bc)$
   Volume: $V = abc$

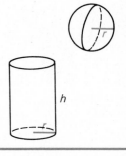

2. Sphere with radius r or diameter $d = 2r$
   Surface area: $A = 4\pi r^2$ or $A = \pi d^2$
   Volume: $V = \frac{4}{3}\pi r^3$ or $V = \frac{1}{6}\pi d^3$

3. Right circular cylinder with height h,
   radius of base r, and area of base B

   Lateral area: $L = 2\pi rh$
   Total surface area: $S = 2\pi rh + 2\pi r^2$
   Volume: $V = \pi r^2 h$ or $V = Bh$

EXAMPLE 2

The length of each of the congruent sides of an isosceles triangle is 3 cm greater than twice the length of the base. If the perimeter of the triangle is 91 cm, find the length of each side of the triangle.

SOLUTION

1. The problem asks for the length of each side of the triangle.
2. Let $x = $ the length of the base. (Note that the symbol $=$ is used here to mean "represent.") Then you can express the length of each of the congruent sides by $2x + 3$.
3. $\underbrace{\text{Perimeter of triangle}}_{x + 2(2x + 3)} \quad \underset{=}{\text{is}} \quad \underbrace{91 \text{ centimeters.}}_{91}$

4.
$$x + 2(2x + 3) = 91$$
$$x + 4x + 6 = 91$$
$$5x + 6 = 91$$
$$5x = 85$$
$$x = 17$$

   The lengths of the other sides of the triangle then are $2(17) + 3 = 37$ cm.

5. Is the perimeter 91 cm? $17 + 2(37) \overset{?}{=} 91$
$$17 + 74 \overset{?}{=} 91$$
$$91 = 91 \checkmark$$

$\therefore$ the lengths of the sides of the triangle are 17 cm, 37 cm, and 37 cm.
Answer.

Formulas from the social and physical sciences also are often useful in solving practical problems.

EXAMPLE 3

Eleven hours after the fishing boat *Mary, Jane* leaves harbor on a southerly course, a helicopter leaves the same harbor to pick up an injured crewman on the boat. The helicopter flies at a rate 108 knots (nautical miles per hour) greater than the rate of the boat. If the boat reverses direction at the time the helicopter leaves the harbor and if the helicopter arrives at the ship in 1 hour, find the rate of the boat and the rate of the helicopter.

SOLUTION

1. The problem asks for the rate of the boat and the rate of the helicopter.
2. Let r = the rate of the boat. Then $108 + r$ = the rate of the helicopter. Using the relationship distance = rate $\times$ time, or

$$d = rt,$$

you have the following facts about the situation.

	r	t	d
Boat	r	$11 - 1 = 10$	$10r$
Helicopter	$r + 108$	1	$r + 108$

3. Distance of boat from   is   distance of helicopter
          harbor   from harbor.

$$10r \qquad = \qquad r + 108$$

4-5. Completing the solution and checking the results is left for you.

You will find that the rate of the boat is 12 knots and that of the helicopter is 120 knots. **Answer.**

NOW DO THESE ▶ **PROBLEMS**

Solve each of the following problems.

A   1. If one integer is 24 greater than another and the sum of the integers is 110, what are the integers?
    2. One number is three less than another. The sum of four times the lesser number and twice the greater is 42. Find the numbers.
    3. The Brooks Feed Store has two trucks. The gasoline tank of one truck holds 16 liters more than that of the other. If it takes 576 liters of gasoline to fill the tanks of both trucks 3 times, find the capacity of each gasoline tank.

4. A mathematics textbook that contains 368 pages has 28 more pages of exercises than it has pages of explanatory material. How many pages of each kind are in the book?

5. Find three consecutive integers whose sum is 153.

6. Find three consecutive integers such that the sum of the first and third is 146.

7. Find two consecutive even integers such that the difference between 7 times the lesser and 6 times the greater is 0.

8. Find three consecutive odd integers such that the sum of the first and third is 9 less than three times the second.

9. The vertex angle of an isosceles triangle measures 20° more than the sum of its other two (congruent) angles. Find the measure of each angle in the triangle.

10. Find the measures of two complementary angles such that one of the angles measures 8° less than three times the measure of the other.

11. The length of a rectangle is 1 meter less than five times its width. Find its length and width if the perimeter is 34 meters.

12. Each of the congruent sides of an isosceles triangle is 4 cm longer than twice the length of the base. If the perimeter of the triangle is 43 cm, find the length of each side.

13. Each side of a long-playing record contains 5 songs of equal length. If there is a 15-second interval between the songs on each side, and if it takes 52 minutes to play both sides (not counting the turnover), how many minutes long is each song?

14. The Elm City Construction Company uses two trucks to carry 112 tonnes of building material to a building site. If one truck has a capacity 4 tonnes greater than the other, and if the smaller truck makes 5 trips and the larger truck makes 7 trips, what is the capacity of each truck?

B **15.** The fishing boat *Queenie* travels at 20 knots (nautical miles per hour). A missing crewman leaves shore in a motorboat when the *Queenie* is 5 nautical miles out of the harbor. If the motorboat travels at 30 knots, how long will it take the crewman to overtake the *Queenie?*

16. Midcontinent Airlines Flights 211 and 115 both depart from the Central City airport at noon and fly in directly opposite directions. If Flight 211 averages 440 kilometers (km) per hour over the ground while Flight 115 averages 560 km per hour, at what time will they be 2500 km apart?

17. The Monarch Company has a retirement plan with monthly benefits computed according to the formula

$$B = \frac{9}{20} w \left(1 + \frac{n}{50} \right),$$

where w is the average monthly salary of the employee and n the number of years the employee has been with the company. How many years must a person be employed if her average salary is \$920 per month and her monthly benefits are to be \$621?

18. If C is the total finance charge made on a loan requiring N monthly payments of M dollars per month to repay the loan, then the true interest rate r on the loan is given approximately by

$$r = \frac{24C}{MN(N + 1)}.$$

What should the finance charge be on a loan requiring 24 monthly payments of $50 each if the true interest rate is to be approximated by 12% (0.12)?

19. The sum of the ages of Carlos and his father is 54 years. Three years from now, Carlos will be one-half as old as his father. How old is each now?

20. Four years ago, Myra was three times as old as her daughter. Six years from now, she will be twice as old as the girl. How old are Myra and her daughter now?

SELF-TEST 1

Simplify each expression. Assume that each variable denotes a real number.

Section 2–1, page 33

1. $(t - s + 2) + (3t + 2s - 2)$

2. $3(r - 4) - 2(r + 3)$

3. $(5x^2 - 3x + 7) + (2x^2 - 3x) - (x + 7)$

4. $(3 + 2y - y^2) - (5 - y^2) + (y^2 - 3y + 1)$

Solve over $\mathcal{R}$.

Section 2–2, page 37

5. $4z - 2(3 - z) = 2(z + 3) - 8$

6. $3 - 2(r + 5) = 4r - 1$

7. Solve for x: $ax - b = 2ax + c$, $a \neq 0$

Section 2–3, page 42

8. Find two integers such that their sum is 19, and for which twice the lesser differs from 3 times the greater by 17.

9. Find the measures of two complementary angles for which three times the greater measure exceeds twice the lesser measure by 55°.

10. If Jack can increase his average cycling speed by 2 km per hour, he will be able to cover the same distance on his bicycle in 3 hours as he does now in 4 hours. What is his average cycling speed now?

Check your answers with those printed at the back of the book. If you did not answer a question correctly, study the referenced section again.

order in the set of real numbers

After completing the next four sections, you will have reviewed:
1. Solving linear inequalities.
2. Applying linear inequalities to practical problems.
3. Simple indirect proofs.
4. Solving inequalities involving absolute value.

BE SURE TO
STUDY THIS
SECTION
CAREFULLY

2-4 *properties of order*

The symbol $<$ is read "is less than." It is used to show the relative order of two real numbers. You say that

$$3 < 5 \text{ (read ''3 is less than 5''),}$$

because there is a positive number, 2, such that $3 + 2 = 5$. The statement $3 < 5$ can be written equivalently as $5 > 3$ (read "5 is greater than 3"). In general, we have the following definition:

If a and b are real numbers, then

$$a < b \qquad \text{(or } b > a\text{)}$$

if and only if there is a positive real number c such that

$$a + c = b.$$

Note the phrase "if and only if," which condenses two statements into one. In this case it means:

If there is a positive real number c such that $a + c = b$, then $a < b$;

and

If $a < b$, then there is a positive real number c such that $a + c = b$.

These statements are called converses of each other, as are any two "If . . . , then . . ." statements each of which can be obtained from the other by interchanging hypothesis and conclusion.

We make the following assumption about order in the set of real numbers.

Comparison Axiom

If a and b are real numbers, then one and only one of the following statements is true:

$$a > b, \qquad a = b, \qquad a < b.$$

The set of *positive real numbers* is denoted by the symbol $\mathcal{R}_+$. One further assumption we make is that the sum of two positive real numbers is a positive real number and the product of two positive real numbers is a positive real number.

Closure Axiom for $\mathcal{R}_+$

If a and $b \in \mathcal{R}_+$, then

$$a + b \in \mathcal{R}_+ \qquad \text{and} \qquad ab \in \mathcal{R}_+;$$

that is, $\mathcal{R}_+$ is closed under addition and multiplication.

Using the definition of "less than," and the closure axiom for $\mathcal{R}_+$, we can prove the following three theorems about order in $\mathcal{R}$.

Transitive Property of Order

If a, b, and c are real numbers, and if $a < b$ and $b < c$, then $a < c$.

PROOF

1. a, b, and c are real numbers, $a < b$, and $b < c$.	Hypothesis
2. There are positive real numbers e and f such that $a + e = b$ and $b + f = c$.	Definition of $<$
3. $a + e + f = c$	Substitution principle
4. $e + f$ is positive.	Closure axiom for $\mathcal{R}_+$
5. $a < c$	Definition of $<$

Additive Property of Order

If a, b, and c are real numbers, and if $a < b$, then $a + c < b + c$.

PROOF

1. a, b, and c are real numbers, and $a < b$.	Hypothesis
2. There is a positive real number d such that $a + d = b$.	Definition of $<$
3. $(a + d) + c = b + c$	Additive property of equality
4. $a + (d + c) = b + c$	Associative axiom of addition
5. $a + (c + d) = b + c$	Commutative axiom of addition
6. $(a + c) + d = b + c$	Associative axiom of addition
7. $a + c < b + c$	Definition of $<$

Multiplicative Property of Order

Let a, b, and $c \in \mathfrak{R}$.

I. If $a < b$ and c is positive, then $ac < bc$.

II. If $a < b$ and c is negative, then $ac > bc$.

The proofs of the two parts of this theorem are left for you. (Exercises 27 and 28, page 52.) Of course, the foregoing theorems are also true with $<$ replaced by $>$, and $>$ by $<$, throughout.

Graphically, given two different real numbers, the graph of the lesser lies to the *left* of the graph of the greater on a number line with positive direction to the right. Thus, if $x \in \mathfrak{R}$, the graph of the solution set of $x < 2$ appears as in Figure 1. Note that the endpoint is depicted by an open circle which indicates that the graph of that point is not in the set.

Figure 1
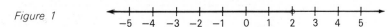

The additive and multiplicative properties of order imply that the following transformations on inequalities will produce equivalent inequalities over $\mathfrak{R}$, that is, inequalities having the same solution set over $\mathfrak{R}$.

Transformations That Produce an Equivalent Inequality

1. Substituting for either member of the inequality an expression equivalent to that member.

2. Adding to or subtracting from each member of the inequality the same polynomial in any variable(s) appearing in the inequality.

3. Multiplying or dividing each member by the same *positive* number.

4. Multiplying or dividing each member by the same *negative* number and reversing the direction of the inequality symbol.

EXAMPLE Solve $3x + 2 < 5x - 6$ over $\mathfrak{R}$ and graph the solution set.

SOLUTION

$$3x + 2 < 5x - 6$$
$$3x + 2 - 2 < 5x - 6 - 2 \qquad \text{Transformation 2}$$
$$3x < 5x - 8 \qquad \text{Transformation 1}$$
$$3x - 5x < 5x - 8 - 5x \qquad \text{Transformation 2}$$
$$-2x < -8 \qquad \text{Transformation 1}$$
$$\frac{-2x}{-2} > \frac{-8}{-2} \qquad \text{Transformation 4}$$
$$x > 4 \qquad \text{Transformation 1}$$

$\therefore$ the solution set is
$\{x: x > 4\}$. **Answer.**

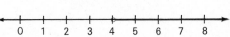

In Exercises 1–8 give the transformation used to produce the second sentence from the first, and the third from the second.

A

1. $2z - 5 > 4$; $2z > 9$; $z > \frac{9}{2}$
2. $5n + 3 < 2n - 1$; $3n + 3 < -1$; $3n < -4$
3. $7 - 2t < t - 5$; $7 < 3t - 5$; $12 < 3t$
4. $12z + 8 > 10z - 5$; $2z + 8 > -5$; $2z > -13$
5. $8 - 4r < 16$; $-4r < 8$; $r > -2$
6. $5 - \frac{y}{3} > -6$; $-\frac{y}{3} > -11$; $y < 33$
7. $3(t + 4) < 7$; $3t + 12 < 7$; $3t < -5$
8. $3z - 2 + z > z - 4$; $4z - 2 > z - 4$; $3z - 2 > -4$

Solve each inequality over $\mathcal{R}$ and graph its solution set.

9. $z - 7 < 8$
10. $b + 2 > -5$
11. $3x + 1 < 10$
12. $7 - 2z < 11$
13. $\frac{x}{12} - 2 < -3$
14. $\frac{v}{4} + 7 < 15$

15. $3d - 5 > 5d + 11$
16. $2(3y + 4) - 2y > 2y + 8$
17. $\frac{1}{2}(4 - z) < -1$
18. $\frac{1}{6}(6 - 3x) > -2$
19. $-2\left(3 + \frac{z}{4}\right) > 1$
20. $-3\left(5 + \frac{z}{6}\right) < -1$

B

21. $2[3 - (t + 2)] < 3(2 - t)$
22. $2x[x - (4 - x)] < 4x^2 - 2x + 1$
23. $3(2 - a) + a(2 + a) < -3 + a + a^2$
24. $-2(a + 3) - a(a + 4) > 2 - 3a - a^2$

C

25. Prove: For all real numbers a, if $a > 0$, then $-a < 0$.
26. Prove: For all real numbers a, if $a < 0$, then $-a > 0$.
27. Prove: For all real numbers a and b, if $a < b$ and $c > 0$, then $ac < bc$.
28. Prove: For all real numbers a and b, if $a < b$ and $c < 0$, then $ac > bc$.
29. Prove: For all real numbers a and b, $a < b$ if and only if $a - b < 0$.
30. Show by an example that if $a > b$, it need not be true that $a^2 > b^2$.
31. Let a, b, c, and d denote real numbers. Prove that if $a > b$ and $c > d$, then $a + c > b + d$.
    (*Hint:* Show that $a + c > b + c$, $b + c > b + d$.)
32. Let a, b, c, and d denote real numbers. Prove that if $a > b > 0$ and $c > d > 0$, then $ac > bd$. (*Hint:* Show that $ac > bc$ and that $bc > bd$.)

2-5 compound sentences

Try this ▸

REVIEW TEST 10

Solve each sentence over $\mathcal{R}$ and graph its solution set.

1. $3y - 4 \geq 14$

2. $7 - 5t \leq 32$

3. $2a + 8 \leq 3a - 4$

4. $7 + 5b \geq b - 1$

5. $0 \leq 5(n + 2) \leq 10$

6. $4 \leq 3n - 2 < 10$

7. $k(1 - 2k) + 1 \geq 2[k(2 - k) - 1]$

8. $d(2 - d) - 8 \leq -(d^2 + d + 5)$

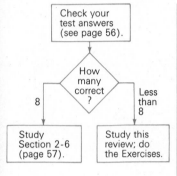

Check your test answers (see page 56).

How many correct?

8 → Study Section 2-6 (page 57).

Less than 8 → Study this review; do the Exercises.

Is it true that "$3 < 5$ or $3 = 5$"? The answer is "yes" because $3 < 5$. Of course, $3 = 5$ is *not* true, but the compound sentence "$3 < 5$ or $3 = 5$" is true because one part of it is true. A sentence such as

$$3 < 5 \qquad \text{or} \qquad 3 = 5$$

which is formed by joining two sentences with the word or is called a disjunction of sentences. For a disjunction to be true, *at least one* of the joined sentences must be true. Disjunctions such as "$3 < 5$ or $3 = 5$" are ordinarily written

$$3 \leq 5 \qquad (\text{or } 5 \geq 3)$$

(read "3 is less than or equal to 5" and "5 is greater than or equal to 3," respectively).

The graph of the solution set of the open sentence

$$x \leq 2$$

over $\mathcal{R}$ is shown in Figure 2, where the heavy dot at the right endpoint of the graph indicates that that point *is* in the set.

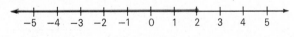

Figure 2

A compound sentence such as

$$2 < 3 \qquad \text{and} \qquad 3 < 5$$

which is formed by joining two sentences by the word "and" is called a conjunction of sentences, and is true if and only if *both* sentences are true. For example, the foregoing conjunction is true, while the conjunction

$$2 < 3 \qquad \text{and} \qquad 5 < 3$$

is false, because $5 < 3$ is false.

Conjunctions of the form "$a < b$ and $b < c$" are ordinarily written

$$a < b < c$$

(read "a is less than b and b is less than c").

Conjunctions and disjunctions frequently are combined in compound sentences. For example,

$$3 \leq x \leq 7$$

represents "3 is less than or equal to x, and x is less than or equal to 7." This sentence is true provided *both* disjunctions are true. Its graph over $\mathcal{R}$ appears in Figure 3, where both endpoints are shown as solid dots to denote that the endpoints are in the set.

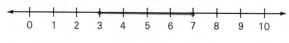

0   1   2   3   4   5   6   7   8   9   10

Figure 3

The transitive, additive, and multiplicative properties of order given on pages 50 and 51 also hold with $<$ replaced by $\leq$ and $>$ by $\geq$. Similarly, the transformations shown on page 51 will produce equivalent sentences when used in sentences containing $\leq$ or $\geq$.

EXAMPLE 1   Solve $3 - (x + 2) \leq 4 + x$ over $\mathcal{R}$ and graph its solution set.

SOLUTION
$$3 - (x + 2) \leq 4 + x$$
$$3 - x - 2 \leq 4 + x$$
$$-x + 1 \leq 4 + x$$
$$-2x + 1 \leq 4$$
$$-2x \leq 3$$
$$x \geq -\tfrac{3}{2}$$

$\therefore$ the solution set is $\{x\colon x \geq -\tfrac{3}{2}\}$ whose graph is shown. **Answer.**

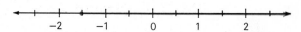

−2   −1   0   1   2

As illustrated by Figure 3 and the graph in the foregoing example, the solution set of a *conjunction* is the *intersection* of the solution sets of the simple sentences in the conjunction, while the solution set of a *disjunction* is the *union* of the solution sets of the simple sentences involved. Thus,

$$\{x\colon 3 \leq x \leq 7\} = \{x\colon 3 \leq x\} \cap \{x\colon x \leq 7\},$$

and

$$\{x\colon x \geq -\tfrac{3}{2}\} = \{x\colon x > -\tfrac{3}{2}\} \cup \{x\colon x = -\tfrac{3}{2}\}.$$

When negation symbols are used with the symbols $<$ and $>$, the results are equivalent to compound sentences:

$$a \not< b \text{ is equivalent to } a \geq b,$$
$$a \not> b \text{ is equivalent to } a \leq b.$$

Similarly, some negated compound sentences are equivalent to simple sentences. Thus,

$$a \nleq b \text{ is equivalent to } a > b,$$
$$a \ngeq b \text{ is equivalent to } a < b.$$

NOW DO THESE ▶

EXERCISES

Solve each sentence over $\mathcal{R}$ and graph its solution set.

A
1. $z - 4 \leq 8$
2. $t + 3 \geq 6$
3. $9 < x + 2 < 12$
4. $15 < n - 3 < 20$
5. $-4 \leq 2t - 6 \leq 2$
6. $-5 \leq 3n - 2 \leq 1$
7. $2(t - 3) \geq t + 1$
8. $4(z + 5) \geq 3z - 6$

9. $\frac{z}{5} - 1 \geq 7$
10. $2 - \frac{k}{3} \leq -2$
11. $0 < 3(k + 2) \leq 7$
12. $-6 \leq 2(v - 3) < 0$
13. $2r \leq 3(2r - 7)$
14. $3n + 5 \geq 5(n - 2) + 1$

B
15. $2[z - 2(3 + z)] \leq 2z + 4$
16. $3[k + 3(2 - k)] \geq k + 4$
17. $x[x - 2(3 - x)] \leq 3x^2 - 4$
18. $2y[y + 3(2 - y)] \geq y(10 - 4y) + 1$
19. $z(z + 1) < z^2 - 2z < z^2 + z + 2$
20. $t(t - 2) > t^2 - 3t \geq t^2 - 2t - 5$

C
21. $3b + 2(b - 1) \not< b + 4$ (Hint: First rewrite as a disjunction.)
22. $2s - 3(s + 5) \not> s - 2$

PROBLEMS

A

1. A certain positive integer exceeds two times a lesser positive integer by 5. The sum of the integers is at most 23. Find the greatest such integers.

2. Mr. Colvin's speed on a round trip is 5 km per hour faster going than it is returning. What is the least distance he could travel on the round trip if his trip going took at least 3 hours and returning at least $3\frac{1}{2}$ hours?

3. Celsius and Fahrenheit temperatures are related by $9C = 5F - 160$. Within what range is the temperature in Fahrenheit degrees if the Celsius temperature is between $-20°$ and $10°$?

B

4. A rectangular picture is to be mounted on a 120-cm-by-150-cm rectangular sheet of cardboard, leaving an equal margin at the top, bottom, and sides of the picture. If the overall perimeter of the cardboard must be at least $1\frac{1}{2}$ times the perimeter of the picture, what is the minimum width of the margins?

5. A northbound airplane takes off from an airport at the same time as a southbound airplane. If the northbound plane flies at least 440 km per hour and the southbound plane at least 520 km per hour, what is the latest possible time they can be 2400 km apart?

6. An oil well begins to pump 70 barrels of oil per day into a tank. After 3 days, the tank develops a leak. Following a total of seven days pumping, the tank is found to contain at least 410 barrels of oil. What is the greatest number of barrels per day the tank could be leaking?

7. Gwen on a bicycle trip averages 15 kilometers per hour. One hour after she leaves, her father sets out in a car with a sweater she forgot. What is the least speed the father can average if he is to overtake Gwen in no more than 15 minutes?

8. One of two full auditoriums at a conference holds 500 persons more than the other. If 200 persons leave each auditorium, there will remain at least twice as many persons in the larger one as in the smaller one. What is the greatest possible seating capacity of the smaller auditorium?

9. If the entertainment portion of a TV program must last at least 2 minutes longer than three times the duration of the commercial portion, what is the greatest amount of time that can be devoted to commercials in a one-hour program?

10. Ms. O'Connor awards a B grade to students whose test-score average is at least 80% and not greater than 89%. If Marie's grades on her first four tests were 98%, 76%, 86%, and 92%, what is the least score she can make on a fifth test to have a B average?

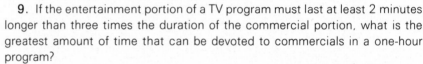

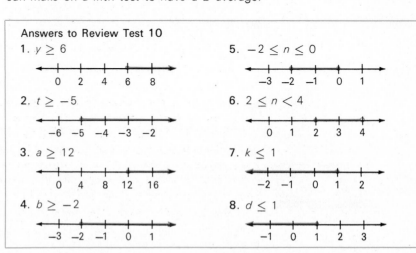

Answers to Review Test 10

1. $y \geq 6$

2. $t \geq -5$

3. $a \geq 12$

4. $b \geq -2$

5. $-2 \leq n \leq 0$

6. $2 \leq n < 4$

7. $k \leq 1$

8. $d \leq 1$

2–6 *additional properties of order*

The results of Exercises 25 and 26, page 52, can be stated in the following theorem about the order of opposites and 0.

Theorem. For all real numbers a,

$$\text{if } a > 0, \text{ then } -a < 0;$$

$$\text{if } a < 0, \text{ then } -a > 0.$$

Another useful inequality can be stated thus:

Theorem. If a is a nonzero real number, then $a^2 > 0$.

The proof is simple. If $a > 0$, then $a \cdot a > a \cdot 0$, from which $a^2 > 0$. On the other hand, if $a < 0$, then $-a > 0$, and $(-a)(-a) > (-a)(0)$, or $a^2 > 0$.

A corollary of the foregoing theorem is that $1 > 0$, because for $a = 1$, $1^2 > 0$ and $1^2 = 1$. Accordingly, by the first theorem in this section, $-1 < 0$.

We can use the fact that $1 > 0$ to prove the following property of reciprocals.

Theorem. For all nonzero real numbers a,

$$\text{if } a > 0, \text{ then } \frac{1}{a} > 0;$$

$$\text{if } a < 0, \text{ then } \frac{1}{a} < 0.$$

To prove this theorem, we shall use a method of reasoning called an indirect proof. In an indirect proof, you begin by assuming that the conclusion of a theorem is false, even though the hypothesis is accepted as true. You then show that a sequence of logically correct steps leads you to contradict an accepted fact, such as the hypothesis, an axiom, or a previously proved theorem. Because the assumption that the conclusion of the theorem is false leads to a contradiction, you know that the conclusion cannot be false, and thus that the theorem must be true.

As an example of an indirect proof, let us prove the first part of the theorem stated above.

PROOF

Suppose that a is a real number such that $a > 0$. To show that $\frac{1}{a} > 0$, we shall show that assuming $\frac{1}{a}$ is *not* greater than 0 (in symbols, $\frac{1}{a} \not> 0$) leads to a contradiction.

If $\frac{1}{a} \not> 0$, then by the comparison axiom of inequality there are two cases to consider: **(1)** $\frac{1}{a} = 0$, and **(2)** $\frac{1}{a} < 0$.

Case 1: Assume that $\frac{1}{a} = 0$.

1. $\frac{1}{a} \cdot a = 0 \cdot a$ Multiplicative property of equality

2. $\frac{1}{a} \cdot a = 0$ Multiplicative property of 0

3. $1 = 0$ Axiom of multiplicative inverses

Case 2: Assume that $\frac{1}{a} < 0$.

1. $\frac{1}{a} < 0$ and $a > 0$ Hypothesis

2. $\frac{1}{a} \cdot a < 0 \cdot a$ Multiplicative property of inequality

3. $\frac{1}{a} \cdot a < 0$ Multiplicative property of 0

4. $1 < 0$ Axiom of multiplicative inverses

In each case, the last step contains a statement that contradicts the fact that $1 > 0$, which was deduced on page 57. Therefore, the assumption that $\frac{1}{a} \not> 0$ leads to contradictions and must be incorrect. Hence, $\frac{1}{a} > 0$.

The proof of the second part of the theorem is left as an exercise for you (Exercise 19, page 59).

To Write an Indirect Proof of a Theorem

1. Assume that the conclusion of the theorem is false.
2. Reason from this assumption until you obtain a statement contradicting the hypothesis, an axiom, or a previously proved theorem.
3. Point out that the assumption must be incorrect, so that the conclusion of the theorem must be true.

In Exercises 1–8 state the assumption with which you would begin an indirect proof. Assume that each variable denotes a real number.

EXAMPLE 1   If $r^2 > 0$, then $r \neq 0$.

SOLUTION   Assume that $r = 0$. **Answer.**

A
1. If $2x - 1 = 3$, then $x \neq 1$.
2. If $r \neq s$, then $2r \neq 2s$.
3. If $a \neq b$, $a \neq 0$, and $b \neq 0$, then $\frac{1}{a} \neq \frac{1}{b}$.
4. If $a + c \neq b + c$, then $a \neq b$.

5. If $a \neq b$, then $-a \neq -b$.
6. If $n - 3 \neq m - 3$, then $n \neq m$.
7. If $\frac{1}{a} \neq \frac{1}{b}$, then $a \neq b$.
8. If $\frac{1}{a} < 0$, then $a < 0$.

9–16. Prove each of the assertions in Exercises 1–8 above using an indirect proof.

EXAMPLE 2   If $r^2 > 0$, then $r \neq 0$.

SOLUTION   Assume $r = 0$. Then $r \cdot r = 0 \cdot r$ or $r^2 = 0$. But, by hypothesis, $r^2 > 0$, and by the comparison axiom not both $r^2 > 0$ and $r^2 = 0$ can be true.

$\therefore$ the assumption that $r = 0$ must be false, and $r \neq 0$. **Answer.**

In Exercises 17–25 prove the given theorem. Use either a direct or indirect proof, whichever you believe is simplest. Assume that each variable denotes a real number.

B
17. If $a \neq 2$, then $2a - 4 \neq 0$.
18. If $b \neq 4$, then $\frac{b}{2} \neq 2$.
19. If $a < 0$, then $\frac{1}{a} < 0$.

20. If $a > 1$, then $\frac{1}{a} < 1$.
21. If $a > 0$ and $\frac{1}{a} < 1$, then $a > 1$.

C
22. If $0 < a < b$, then $\frac{1}{a} > \frac{1}{b}$.
23. If $a > 0$, $b > 0$, and $\frac{1}{a} < \frac{1}{b}$, then $a > b$.
24. If $a > 0$, $b > 0$, and $a^2 > b^2$, then $a > b$.
25. If $a > b > 0$, then $a^2 > b^2$.

2-7   *absolute value and order*

Try this

REVIEW TEST 11

Simplify each expression.

1. $-|-2|$

2. $|2 - 5|$

3. $|-2| - |2|$

4. $|3 - 2| + 2|1 - 1|$

5. $-|2 - 5|^2 - |-3|$

6. $\dfrac{2|3 - 1| - 5|7 - 2|}{|-7|}$

Solve each sentence over ℛ and graph its solution set.

7. $|t| > 4$

8. $|x - 3| = 5$

9. $|y + 3| \leq 1$

10. $|2x - 5| \geq 3$

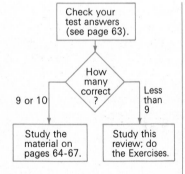

Check your test answers (see page 63).

How many correct ?

9 or 10 — Study the material on pages 64-67.

Less than 9 — Study this review; do the Exercises.

It is sometimes convenient to work with the nonnegative (0 or positive) one of the pair a and $-a$. We refer to this number as the **absolute value** of a and denote it by $|a|$. For example, $|-3|$ is the positive one of the pair 3 and -3, so $|-3| = 3$. Similarly, $|7| = 7$, $|-8| = 8$, and $|0| = 0$. Formally, we make the definition:

If a is a real number, then

$$|a| = \begin{cases} a, \text{ if } a \geq 0, \\ -a, \text{ if } a < 0. \end{cases}$$

EXAMPLE 1

Solve $|x - 3| = 4$ over ℛ.

SOLUTION

By definition, you have the disjunction

$$\begin{array}{lcl} (x - 3) = 4 & \text{or} & -(x - 3) = 4, \\ x - 3 = 4 & \text{or} & x - 3 = -4, \\ x = 7 & \text{or} & x = -1. \end{array}$$

∴ the solution set is $\{-1, 7\}$.   **Answer.**

Graphically, an expression of the form $|a - b|$ or $|b - a|$ represents the distance (nondirected) between the graph of a and the graph of b, as shown in Figure 4. In particular, $|a|$ or $|-a|$ represents the distance between the origin and the graph of a or $-a$ (Figure 5).

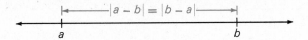

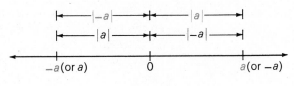

Figure 4

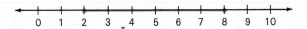

Figure 5

EXAMPLE 2

Solve $|x - 5| \leq 3$ over $\mathfrak{R}$ and graph its solution set.

SOLUTION

By inspection, $|x - 5|$ represents the distance between the graph of 5 and the graph of x. The sentence asserts that this distance is 3 or less. Since 2 and 8 are 3 units from 5, you see at once that $|x - 5| \leq 3$ is equivalent to $2 \leq x \leq 8$. Thus, by inspection, the solution set is $\{x: 2 \leq x \leq 8\}$, whose graph is as shown.

More formally,

$$|x - 5| \leq 3$$

is equivalent to the compound sentence

$$
\begin{array}{lcl}
(x - 5) \leq 3 & \text{and} & -(x - 5) \leq 3, \\
x - 5 \leq 3 & \text{and} & x - 5 \geq -3, \\
x \leq 8 & \text{and} & x \geq 2.
\end{array}
$$

Thus the solution set can be represented as

$$\{x: x \leq 8\} \cap \{x: x \geq 2\}$$

or

$$\{x: 2 \leq x \leq 8\},$$

whose graph is shown above. **Answer.**

Note from the foregoing example that sentences of the form $|x - a| \leq b$ are equivalent to conjunctions. On the other hand, sentences of the form $|x - a| \geq b$ are equivalent to disjunctions.

EXAMPLE 3

Solve $|z + 3| \geq 5$ over $\mathcal{R}$ and graph its solution set.

SOLUTION

Write $|z + 3| \geq 5$ as $|z - (-3)| \geq 5$. Then, by inspection, the distance between the graph of z and the graph of -3 must be 5 or greater. Since -8 and 2 are each 5 units from -3, the solution set must be

$$\{z: z \leq -8\} \cup \{z: z \geq 2\},$$

whose graph is shown below.

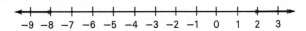

More formally,

$$|z + 3| \geq 5$$

is equivalent to

$$
\begin{array}{lll}
(z + 3) \geq 5 & \text{or} & -(z + 3) \geq 5, \\
z + 3 \geq 5 & \text{or} & z + 3 \leq -5, \\
z \geq 2 & \text{or} & z \leq -8.
\end{array}
$$

Thus, again, the solution set is

$$\{z: z \leq -8\} \cup \{z: z \geq 2\},$$

whose graph is shown above. **Answer.**

NOW DO THESE ➡ **EXERCISES**

Simplify each expression.

A
1. $|-3 - 2|$
2. $|7 - 12|$
3. $-|-6|$
4. $-|3 - 2|$
5. $|3| - |-3|$
6. $|-5| + |5|$
7. $|4 - 7| - 2|-3| + 4$
8. $|7 - 1| - 5|3 - 1| - 2$

9. $\dfrac{|6 - 12| + |-8 + 1|}{|-3|}$

10. $\dfrac{-|7 + 4| + |2 - 10|}{|-5|}$

11. $|6 - 7|^2 - 2|6 - 7| + 3$

12. $|-8 + 3|^2 + 3|0 - 3| - 1$

13. $\dfrac{|3(-5 + 2)| - |2(1 - 3)|}{-|13|} - 1$

14. $\dfrac{3|6 - 12| - 5|1 + 3|}{-|-2|} - 1$

Solve each open sentence over $\mathfrak{R}$ and graph its solution set.

15. $|x| = 2$

16. $|y| = 5$

17. $|t - 1| = 6$

18. $|r + 3| = 1$

B   19. $|8 - 2r| = 6$

20. $|9 + 3t| = 6$

21. $3|2 - x| \geq 12$

22. $-2|3 + r| \leq -6$

23. $\left|\dfrac{2x + 1}{3}\right| < 4$

24. $\left|\dfrac{3t - 2}{4}\right| \leq 5$

25. $\frac{1}{5}|4 - 2a| > 4$

26. $\frac{2}{3}|10 - 5b| < 10$

C   27. $1 < |x| < 5$

28. $2 < |y| < 3$

29. $4 \leq |x - 1| < 5$

30. $3 \leq |2 - x| \leq 4$

Answers to Review Test 11

1. -2 2. 3 3. 0 4. 1 5. -12 6. -3

7. $\{t: t > 4 \text{ or } t < -4\}$

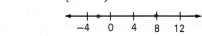
$\quad -4 \quad -2 \quad 0 \quad 2 \quad 4$

8. $\{-2, 8\}$

$\quad -4 \quad 0 \quad 4 \quad 8 \quad 12$

9. $\{y: -4 \leq y \leq -2\}$

$\quad -4 \quad -3 \quad -2 \quad -1 \quad 0$

10. $\{x: x \leq 1 \text{ or } x \geq 4\}$

$\quad 0 \quad 1 \quad 2 \quad 3 \quad 4$

Sonya Kovalevsky
1850–1891

Sonya Kovalevsky was the foremost woman mathematician of her time, and a lifelong pupil of the famous mathematician Karl Weierstrass.

Although a century ago women were seldom admitted to universities, Mme. Kovalevsky did secure her doctorate in absentia from the University of Göttingen. In 1884 she became a professor at the more liberal University of Stockholm.

She received the Burdin Prize of the French Academy of Sciences for a paper on the rotations of a solid body around a fixed point. The judges considered this paper so outstanding that they raised the prize from 3000 to 5000 francs.

Solve each open sentence over ℜ and graph its solution set.

Section 2–4, page 49   **1.** $x - 7 < 3$ **2.** $-1(r + 2) > (3r - 6)$

Section 2–5, page 53   **3.** $3z - 7 \leq 11$ **4.** $-3 \leq 2k + 1 < 5$

5. Find the least integer whose average with 12 is at least 15.

Section 2–6, page 57   **6.** Use an indirect proof to prove that if $n \neq 3$, then $2n + 1 \neq 7$.

Section 2–7, page 60   Solve each open sentence over ℜ and graph its solution set.

7. $|x - 3| \leq 8$ **8.** $|2t + 1| \geq 7$

Check your answers with those printed at the back of the book. If you did not answer a question correctly, study the referenced section again.

vocabulary   Be sure that you understand the meaning of each of the following words, referenced by section, before starting Chapter 3.

Section 2–1
  monomial
  (numerical) coefficient of a
    monomial
  power
  base
  exponent
  degree of a monomial
  polynomial
  coefficients of a polynomial
  like monomials
  similar monomials
  simple form of a polynomial
  degree of a polynomial
  equivalent expressions

Section 2–2
  equivalent equations
  transformations

Section 2–3
  model
  complementary angles
  supplementary angles
  isosceles triangle

Section 2–4
  is less than
  is greater than
  converse
  equivalent inequalities

Section 2–5
  compound sentence
  disjunction
  conjunction
  intersection of sets
  union of sets

Section 2–6
  indirect proof

Section 2–7
  absolute value

chapter summary

1. One polynomial is added to or subtracted from another by adding or subtracting coefficients of like terms. The result of this procedure is a simpler polynomial **equivalent** to the original sum or difference.

2. Transformations that produce an equivalent equation are:
   1. Substituting for either member of the given equation an expression equivalent to it.
   2. Adding to or subtracting from each member of the given equation the same polynomial in any variable(s) appearing in the equation.
   3. Multiplying or dividing each member by the same *nonzero* number.

3. To solve an applied problem stated in words:
   1. Read it carefully and decide what numbers are asked for.
   2. Choose a variable to represent each number asked for or described in the problem.
   3. Write an open sentence showing the relationship given in the problem.
   4. Solve the open sentence.
   5. Check the results with the requirements stated in the problem.

4. The real numbers are **ordered**. Some properties of order are the following. If $a, b, c \in \mathcal{R}$, then:
   1. One and only one of the following statements is true:
      $a < b, a = b, a > b$ Comparison axiom
   2. If $a < b$ and $b < c$, then $a < c$.
      If $a > b$ and $b > c$, then $a > c$.   Transitive property
   3. If $a < b$, then $a + c < b + c$.
      If $a > b$, then $a + c > b + c$.   Additive property
   4. If $a < b$ and $c > 0$, then $ac < bc$.
      If $a > b$ and $c > 0$, then $ac > bc$.
      If $a < b$ and $c < 0$, then $ac > bc$.
      If $a > b$ and $c < 0$, then $ac < bc$.   Multiplicative property

5. Compound sentences involving the word ''or'' are **disjunctions**, and are true whenever at least one of the simple sentences involved is true.

6. Compound sentences involving the word ''and'' are **conjunctions**, and are true whenever both of the simple sentences involved are true.

7. To write an **indirect proof**, you start with the assumption that the conclusion of a theorem is false and reason from this to a contradiction of the hypothesis, an axiom, or a previously proved theorem.

8. The **absolute value** of a real number a is defined by

$$|a| = \begin{cases} a, \text{ if } a \geq 0, \\ -a, \text{ if } a < 0. \end{cases}$$

Simplify each expression.

2-1 **1.** $(5r^2s^2 - 2rs + 3) + (r^2s^2 - 5rs) - (2r^2s^2 + 3)$

2. $(3x^3 - 2x^2 + 5x - 3) - (-2x^3 - x^2 + 3x + 2)$

Solve over $\mathcal{R}$.

2-2 **3.** $3t - 2(5t + 1) = 2t + 1$

4. $\dfrac{z}{7} + \dfrac{5z}{7} = 12$

2-3 **5.** One of two complementary angles measures $12°$ less than twice the other. Find the degree measures of the angles.

Solve over $\mathcal{R}$ and graph the solution set.

2-4 **6.** $2 - (y + 1) < 3 + y$

7. $4(\tfrac{1}{2} - z) + 7 > -3$

2-5 **8.** $5(a + 3) + 4 \leq a - 1$

9. Mr. Adams weighs 20 kilograms more than his son and together they weigh at least 116 kilograms. What is Mr. Adams' least possible weight?

2-6 **10.** Use an indirect proof to prove that if a is a real number and $a \neq -2$, then $3a - 2 \neq -8$.

2-7 **11.** Evaluate $\dfrac{|8 - 10| - 2|3 + 1|}{|6 - 4|}$.

12. Solve $|2x - 3| \leq 7$ over $\mathcal{R}$ and graph the solution set.

programmed chapter review

2-1 **1.** The degree of $x^2y - 3xy^2 + x^2y^2$ is __?__ .   4

2. In the polynomial $-2x^2 + 3x - 1$, the __?__ of x^2 is -2.   coefficient

3. In simple form, $(2y^2 - 3y) - (y^2 + 2) + (3y - 1) = $ __?__ . $y^2 - 3$

2-2 **4.** Equations having the same solution set over a given set are said to be __?__ equations over that set.   equivalent

5. The solution set of $6z + 5 - 7z = 2(5 - z) + 3$ is __?__ . $\{8\}$

6. After solving $ax - 3 = 2ax + b$ for x, you have $x = $ __?__ . $\dfrac{-b - 3}{a}$

2–3	7. To solve the problem ''Find two integers whose difference is 3 and for which three times the lesser is 6 more than twice the greater,'' you would use the equation __?__ .	$3(x - 3) = 2x + 6$ (or $3y = 2(y + 3) + 6$)
	8. The integers discussed in Exercise 7 are __?__ and __?__ .	12; 15
	9. By increasing the average speed of her car by 10 km per hour, Mrs. Evans can travel as far in 5 hours as she could at her original speed in 6 hours. Her original speed was __?__ km per hour.	50
2–4	10. For all real numbers a and b, $a < b$ if and only if there is a positive number c such that __?__ .	$a + c = b$
	11. For all real numbers a, b, and c, if $a < b$, then $a + c$ __?__ $b + c$.	$<$
	12. For all real numbers a and b, if c is a negative real number and if $a < b$, then $\dfrac{a}{c}$ __?__ $\dfrac{b}{c}$.	$>$
	13. Of two real numbers, the graph of the greater lies to the __?__ of the graph of the lesser on a horizontal number line with positive direction to the right.	right
2–5	14. Compound sentences involving the word ''or'' are called __?__ , and such a sentence is true provided __?__ of the simple sentences involved is (are) true.	disjunctions either
	15. The sentence ''$x - 2 \leq 4$'' is equivalent to the disjunction __?__ or __?__ .	$x - 2 < 4$ $x - 2 = 4$
	16. The sentence $3 < y < 5$ is equivalent to the conjunction __?__ and __?__ .	$y > 3$ $y < 5$
2–6	17. If a is a nonzero real number, then $a^2 > $ __?__ .	0
	18. If b is a positive real number, then $\dfrac{1}{b}$ is a __?__ real number.	positive
	19. In making an indirect proof, you begin by assuming that the __?__ of a theorem is false.	conclusion
	20. To use an indirect proof to establish that if $a \neq 2$, then $2a - 1 \neq 3$, you would begin by assuming that __?__ .	$2a - 1 = 3$
2–7	21. The absolute value of a is equal to the __?__ one of the pair a and $-a$.	nonnegative
	22. The sentence ''$|t + 1| = 7$'' is equivalent to the disjunction __?__ or __?__ .	$t + 1 = 7$ $-(t + 1) = 7$
	23. The sentence ''$|r - 2| < 5$'' is equivalent to a(n) __?__ of sentences, while ''$|r - 2| > 5$'' is equivalent to a(n) __?__ of sentences.	conjunction disjunction
	24. The solution set of $|r - 2| < 5$ is equal to $\{r$: __?__ $\}$.	$-3 < r < 7$

REVIEW OF ESSENTIALS **67**

. . . a view of the interior of Ottawa Station, a new railroad terminal. The skills and ideas of architects, engineers, and builders produced an attractive and functional structure.

linear functions and relations

specifying functions and relations

Objectives

After completing the next two sections, you should be able to:
1. Determine the range corresponding to the domain of a function whose rule is given.
2. Picture a function or relation by means of a mapping diagram and also by means of a graph.

3-1 *functions*

When you count to ten by 2's, you are really pairing the integers 1, 2, 3, 4, 5 with their doubles: 2, 4, 6, 8, 10. Such a set of *ordered pairs*,

$$\{(1, 2), (2, 4), (3, 6), (4, 8), (5, 10)\},$$

in which each *first component* is paired with exactly one *second component* according to a given rule, is called a function. The set of first components is called the domain, and the set of second components the range, of the function. Here the domain is $\{1, 2, 3, 4, 5\}$ and the range is $\{2, 4, 6, 8, 10\}$. If we let x represent an element of the domain and y of the range, the rule for pairing in this case is $y = 2x$.

Some letters commonly used to name a function are f, g, h, F, G, and H. Thus, you might designate the "counting-by-2's" function as follows:

$$f = \{(x, y): y = 2x\},$$

read "f is the set of ordered pairs, x, y, such that y is two times x." You might also use arrow notation:

$$f: x \rightarrow 2x,$$

read "the function f that assigns to x the value $2x$." Of course, in specifying a function you must also identify its domain.

The symbol $f(x)$, read "f of x," is often used instead of y to indicate the second component of the ordered pair in f whose first component is x. Thus you can write for f, above:

$$f = \{(x, f(x)): f(x) = 2x\}.$$

Then to denote "the value of f when $x = 3$," for example, you write $f(3)$. Here, $f(3) = 2 \times 3$, or 6.

Often a function is described simply by giving the rule, or formula, for obtaining the second component, $f(x)$. *The domain, unless otherwise specified, will be assumed to be the set of all real numbers x for which the rule produces one, and only one, real value for $f(x)$.*

EXAMPLE 1   If $f(x) = 2x + 1$, find **(a)** $f(3)$ and **(b)** $f(-7)$.

SOLUTION   a. $f(3) = 2 \cdot 3 + 1 = 7$. **Answer.**
b. $f(-7) = 2 \cdot (-7) + 1 = -13$. **Answer.**

EXAMPLE 2   State the domain and range of the function $f: x \rightarrow \dfrac{1}{x^2}$.

SOLUTION   The domain is the set of all real numbers except 0 because the rule $\dfrac{1}{x^2}$ produces a real value for each real value of x except 0. The range is the set of positive real numbers, since $\dfrac{1}{x^2} > 0$ for all real values of x (except 0). **Answer.**

EXAMPLE 3   If $f: x \rightarrow 5x + 3$ and $g: x \rightarrow x^2$, find $g(f(2))$ and $f(g(2))$.

SOLUTION   First, to find $f(x)$ when $x = 2$, we have $f(2) = 5 \cdot 2 + 3 = 13$. Then, $g(f(2)) = g(13)$. Since $g(x) = x^2$, $g(13) = 13^2 = 169$.
Similarly, $g(2) = 2^2 = 4$, and $f(g(2)) = f(4) = 5 \cdot 4 + 3 = 23$.
$\therefore g(f(2)) = 169$ and $f(g(2)) = 23$. **Answer.**

ORAL EXERCISES   1. Are (2, 4) and (4, 2) the same ordered pair of numbers? Why or why not?

2. Are (2, 4) and (2, 2 + 2) the same ordered pair of numbers? Why or why not?

State the domain and the range of each function, and give a rule for the pairing, such as $y = 2x$.

3. $\{(1, 1), (2, 2), (3, 3)\}$ 5. $\{(-3, -2), (0, 1), (2, 3), (7, 8)\}$
4. $\{(2, 6), (3, 9), (4, 12)\}$ 6. $\{(2, -1), (-2, -5), (3, 0)\}$

7. $\{(-2, -1), (-1, -\frac{1}{2}), (0, 0), (1, \frac{1}{2}), (2, 1)\}$
8. $\{(1, 1), (2, 3), (50, 99), (-1, -3)\}$

State $f(-2)$ for each of the following functions.

  9. $f: x \rightarrow -x$ 11. $f: x \rightarrow -2x - 8$ 13. $f: x \rightarrow -x + 4$

10. $f: x \rightarrow x - 3$ 12. $f: x \rightarrow \frac{1}{2}x + 6$ 14. $f: x \rightarrow \dfrac{3x + 8}{4}$

For the given rule, find the missing component of each ordered pair.

15. $y = \frac{1}{2}x$; $(3, \underline{\ ?\ })$, $(\underline{\ ?\ }, 4)$, $(-\frac{8}{7}, \underline{\ ?\ })$

16. $y = 3x - 2$; $(2, \underline{\ ?\ })$, $(\underline{\ ?\ }, 4)$, $(\frac{2}{3}, \underline{\ ?\ })$, $(\underline{\ ?\ }, 10)$

State the domain and range of each function f whose rule is given.

17. $f(x) = x^2$ 18. $f(x) = \dfrac{1}{x}$ 19. $f(x) = \dfrac{1}{x - 1}$ 20. $f(x) = 2x^3$

WRITTEN EXERCISES If $g: x \rightarrow -5x^2 + 3x - 2$, find each of the following.

A 1. $g(0)$ 3. $g(-1)$ 5. $\frac{1}{2}g(4)$ 7. $-\frac{3}{49}g(\frac{1}{2})$

  2. $g(1)$ 4. $g(3)$ 6. $g(-5)$ 8. $g(a)$

For each of the following functions, give a rule for the pairing.

  9. $\{(1, 3), (3, 9), (7, 21)\}$
10. $\{(-3, -4), (1, 0), (5, 4)\}$
11. $\{(6, 3), (10, 5), (-4, -2)\}$
12. $\{(-3, 1), (0, 0), (3, -1), (9, -3)\}$
13. $\{(2, 5), (0, 1), (5, 11), (-2, -3)\}$
14. $\{(2, \frac{4}{3}), (-3, -2), (0, 0), (6, 4)\}$

B 15. $\{(-2, -8), (1, 1), (\frac{1}{2}, \frac{1}{8}), (3, 27)\}$
16. $\{(2, \frac{1}{2}), (1, 1), (-3, -\frac{1}{3})\}$
17. $\{(1, 0), (2, 3), (3, 8), (-3, 8), (-1, 0)\}$
18. $\{(-1, 1), (-3, \frac{1}{9}), (2, \frac{1}{4}), (\frac{1}{2}, 4)\}$

If $f(x) = 3x - 2$ and $g(x) = x^2 + 1$, find each of the following.

19. $g(f(2))$ 21. $g(f(-\frac{3}{2}))$ 23. $f(g(a))$

20. $g(f(\frac{1}{3}))$ 22. $f(g(-1))$ 24. $f\left(g\left(\dfrac{1}{a}\right)\right)$

C 25. If f is a function such that $f(x + 3) = f(x) + f(3)$ for all $x \in \mathcal{R}$, show that **(a)** $f(0) = 0$, and hence **(b)** $f(-3) = -f(3)$.
26. If f is a function such that $f(3x) = f(3) + f(x)$ for all $x \in \mathcal{R}$, show that **(a)** $f(3) = 0$ and **(b)** $f(1) = 0$.
27. If $f(x) = x^2 - 1$, find $f(3 + h) - f(3)$.
28. If $f(x) = x^3$, find $f(2 + h) - f(2)$.

3-2   picturing functions and relations

In mathematics a relation is defined as *any* set of ordered pairs. The set of all the first coordinates is called the domain and the set of all the second coordinates the range.

Every function is a relation, but not every relation is a function. For example, compare these relations:

$$R = \{(x, y): y^2 = x\}$$
$$F = \{(x, y): y = x^2\}$$

In the relation R, when $x = 4$ you obtain two different pairs with the same first component, $(4, 2)$ and $(4, -2)$. In fact, each positive value, a, of x is paired with two values for y, namely, $\sqrt{a}$ and $-\sqrt{a}$. Hence, the relation R is *not* a function, since it does not pass the test, "with each x, only one y." In F the situation is reversed; each positive value of y is paired with two different values of x, for example: $(4, 16)$ and $(-4, 16)$. Nevertheless, F is a function because each x-value is associated with exactly one y-value.

The rule for the pairing in a relation can be thought of as "mapping" the domain onto the range.

EXAMPLE 1   **Tell whether or not each mapping diagram pictures a function, and give your reasons.**

a.

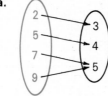

b.

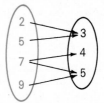

SOLUTION   a. The mapping represents a function because each element in the domain is mapped onto just one element in the range. **Answer.**
b. The mapping does not represent a function because the element 7 in the domain is mapped onto two different elements, 4 and 5, in the range. **Answer.**

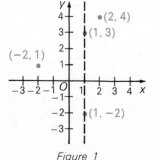

Figure 1

Another way to picture a relation depends on the fact that a plane rectangular (or Cartesian) coordinate system establishes a one-to-one correspondence between the set of points in the plane and the set of ordered pairs of real numbers. The horizontal x-axis serves to locate values in the domain, while the vertical y-axis locates the corresponding values in the range.

The four red dots in Figure 1 represent the graph of the four ordered pairs in the relation $\{(-2, 1), (1, -2), (1, 3), (2, 4)\}$. The graph shows that this relation is not a function, because there are two points in it that have the same abscissa, or x-coordinate, paired with different ordinates, or y-coordinates: (1, −2) and (1, 3). This fact suggests a simple test to determine whether or not a graph represents a function:

If you can draw a vertical line that intersects a graph in more than one point, then the graph does not represent a function.

EXAMPLE 2 Draw the graph of the function f: $x \rightarrow |x| - 2$, with domain $\{-3, -2, -1, 0, 1, 2, 3\}$.

SOLUTION First make a table of values for x and y. Then graph these ordered pairs.

x	$y = \lvert x \rvert - 2$
-3	1
-2	0
-1	-1
0	-2
1	-1
2	0
3	1

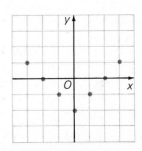

ORAL EXERCISES In Exercises 1–4 tell whether or not the given relation is a function.

1. $\{(-2, 6), (-3, 5), (-2, 4)\}$
2. $\{(1, 5), (2, 5), (3, 4), (4, 3)\}$
3. $\{(-3, 7), (-4, 7), (3, 7), (4, -4), (-4, 4)\}$
4. $\{(-2, 1), (-1, 1), (0, 1), (-1, 0)\}$

5. How can you determine at a glance whether or not a given mapping diagram pictures a function?
6. How can you decide whether or not a given graph is that of a function?

In Exercises 7–10 state the ordered pairs in the relation pictured by the mapping diagram or graph.

7. 8. 9. 10.

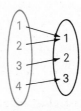
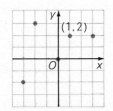
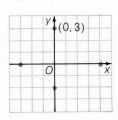

In Exercises 11–20 tell whether or not the relation pictured by the mapping diagram or graph is a function.

11–14. The relations pictured in Exercises 7–10.

15.

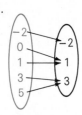

17.

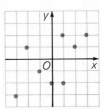

19.

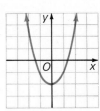

16.

18.

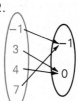

20.

WRITTEN EXERCISES   In Exercises 1–4 write the set of ordered pairs in the relation pictured by the mapping diagram, and tell whether or not the relation is a function.

A   **1.**

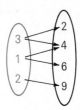

2.

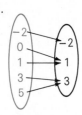

3.

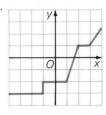

4.

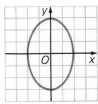

In Exercises 5–10 draw a mapping diagram for the given relation and determine whether or not the relation is a function.

5. $\{(2, 1), (3, 2), (0, 4)\}$ **8.** $\{(-4, 3), (2, 2), (-4, 1), (3, 1)\}$

6. $\{(1, 2), (2, 3), (4, 0)\}$ **9.** $\{(-3, 1), (0, 5), (2, -2), (5, 5)\}$

7. $\{(0, 0), (1, 1), (1, 2)\}$ **10.** $\{(1, -2), (2, -2), (3, -2), (4, -2)\}$

11–16. Graph the relations in Exercises 5–10. If the relation is not a function, draw a vertical line that intersects the graph in two points.

Graph each relation over the domain $\{-2, -1, 0, 1, 2, 3\}$, and tell whether or not the relation is a function.

17. $\{(x, y): y = x + 2\}$ **19.** $\{(x, y): |y| = |2x|\}$

18. $\{(x, y): y = -x\}$ **20.** $\{(x, y): 2|y| = 4 - |x|\}$

B **21.** $\{(x, y): y = x^2 - 3\}$

23. $\{(x, y): |y| = \dfrac{|x|}{|x| + 1}\}$

22. $\{(x, y): y = 2x^2 - 3x - 5\}$

24. $\{(x, y): |y| = 2|x - 1|\}$

Graph each relation when the domain is the subset of the integers $\{-3, -2, -1, 0, 1, 2, 3\}$ for which there are real values for y.

C **25.** $\{(x, y): |y| < x + 1\}$

28. $\{(x, y): |x + y| < 2\}$

26. $\{(x, y): |y| \leq x\}$

29. $\{(x, y): x^2 + y^2 \leq 8\}$

27. $\{(x, y): |y| \leq |x|\}$

30. $\{(x, y): x^2 + y^2 \leq 9\}$

SELF-TEST 1 Give the meaning of each of the following.

1. relation

3. abscissa

2. function

4. ordinate

Objective 1, page 69 For $f: x \rightarrow -x + 2$ and $g: x \rightarrow x^2$, find:

5. $f(3)$ **6.** $g(-2)$ **7.** $g(f(0))$ **8.** $f(g(0))$

Objective 2, page 69 Let $r = \{(0, 2), (-2, 1), (3, -1), (-2, 2)\}$.

9. Picture r by means of a mapping diagram.

10. Picture r by means of a graph.

Check your answers with those printed at the back of the book.

Norbert Wiener
1894–1964

Norbert Wiener was one of America's outstanding mathematicians and scientists. Interrelationships among the various branches of thought had become very complicated, and Wiener's creation of a new subject, called Cybernetics, deals with these matters. Specifically, cybernetics is the theoretical study of control processes in electronics and mechanical and biological systems, especially the mathematical analysis of the flow of information in such systems.

Wiener already showed great promise at an early age. He completed his undergraduate studies at 14, and obtained his doctorate at 18 from Harvard University. His thesis was in mathematical logic. At 25 he joined the faculty of Massachusetts Institute of Technology where he remained until his death in 1964.

graphs of linear equations and inequalities

Objectives

After completing the next two sections, you should be able to:
1. Graph a linear equation.
2. Use the graph of the associated linear equation to graph a linear inequality.

3–3   *the graph of a linear equation*

A *solution* of the open sentence

$$3x + y = 6$$

is any ordered pair (x, y) of real numbers that satisfies the equation. The *solution set* of the equation consists of all its solutions, that is, all ordered pairs in the relation

$$L = \{(x, y): 3x + y = 6, x, y \in \mathcal{R}\}.$$

By transforming $3x + y = 6$ into the equivalent equation

$$y = 6 - 3x$$

and assigning values to x, you can then easily obtain solutions (members of L), such as the following, which are graphed in red in Figure 2:

$$(-1, 9), (0, 6), (2, 0), (3, -3)$$

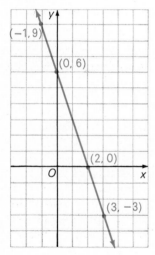

Figure 2

While it is not possible to graph the infinite set of pairs in L, the straight line on which all four of these points appear to lie suggests a pattern for the graph of the solution set of the equation $3x + y = 6$. The graph is a line that consists of *all* the points, and *only* those points, that represent the members of L. We call this line the *graph* of L. In general:

> The graph of an equation of the form $Ax + By = C$, where A, B, $C \in \mathcal{R}$ and A and B are not both zero, is a straight line. Conversely, every straight line in the plane is the graph of a *linear equation in two variables*, that is, an equation of the form $Ax + By = C$, where A and B are not both zero.

When graphing a linear equation, you need graph only two solutions in order to determine its unique line. It is safer, however, to plot a third point just as a check.

EXAMPLE 1   **Graph $5x - 3y = 9$.**

SOLUTION   First transform the equation into an equivalent one that expresses y in terms of x.

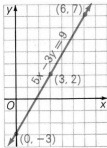

$$5x - 3y = 9$$
$$-3y = 9 - 5x$$
$$y = -3 + \tfrac{5}{3}x$$

It is usually simpler to graph the equation if you assign values to x that will make the solution (x, y) a pair of integers. Thus the values 0, 3, and 6 in this example yield the solutions $(0, -3)$ $(3, 2)$, and $(6, 7)$. Graph the points and the line through them. **Answer.**

In the relation

$$\{(x, y): Ax + By = C\},$$

if neither A nor B is zero, then each value of x is paired with exactly one value of y and hence the relation is a function. If $A = 0$, it is still a function, as you can see from the following example.

EXAMPLE 2   **Graph $Ax + By = C$ when $A = 0$, $B = 2$, $C = -4$. Explain why the graph represents a function.**

SOLUTION   The equation to be graphed is

$$0 \cdot x + 2y = -4,$$

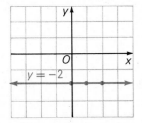

or $$y = -2.$$

The solution set consists of all ordered pairs (x, y) where x is any real number and y is always -2; for example, $(0, -2)$, $(1, -2)$, $(2, -2)$. Graph the line through these points. Since no vertical line intersects the horizontal-line graph representing $y = -2$ in more than one point, this graph represents a function. **Answer.**

If $B = 0$ and $A \neq 0$, then the graph of the solution set will be a *vertical* line. Such a relation, of the form $\{(x, y): Ax + 0 \cdot y = C\}$, is not a function.

EXAMPLE 3   **Graph $x = \tfrac{3}{2}$.**

SOLUTION   The solution set consists of all ordered pairs (x, y) such that $x = \tfrac{3}{2}$ and y is any real number; for example, $(\tfrac{3}{2}, -1)$, $(\tfrac{3}{2}, 0)$ and $(\tfrac{3}{2}, 1)$. Graph the points and the line through them. **Answer.**

Tell whether or not the given equation is that of a straight line.

1. $17x + y = -2$

2. $5y = -3 + 2x$

3. $y = \frac{2}{3}$

4. $x^2 - y = 4$

5. $x = -5$

6. $2x^2 + y^2 = 1$

7. $-4x + yx = 7$

8. $y = \sqrt{x}$

State which points with the given coordinates lie on the graph of the given equation.

9. $4x - y = 6$; $(0, -6)$, $(2, 2)$

10. $x + 2y = 7$; $(1, 3)$, $(-3, 0)$

11. $3x - 2y + 5 = 0$; $(2, 1)$, $(0, \frac{5}{2})$

12. $4y - \frac{1}{2}x = 2$; $(2, 1)$, $(4, 1)$

For each equation give the coordinates, $(x, 0)$ and $(0, y)$, of the points, if any, where the graph intersects each axis.

13. $x + y = 11$

14. $2x + 3y = 4$

15. $5x - 2y = 10$

16. $y = -4$

State a value for __?__ that makes the ordered pair a solution of the given equation.

17. $(5, \underline{\ ?\ })$; $2x + 3y = 31$

18. $(\underline{\ ?\ }, 0)$; $4x - 7y = 8$

19. $(0, \underline{\ ?\ })$; $x - y = 0$

20. $(a, \underline{\ ?\ })$; $-2x + y = 3$

21. $(7, \underline{\ ?\ })$; $x = 7$

22. $(5, \underline{\ ?\ })$; $y = 3$

23. Explain why the graph of $y = 5$ is the graph of a function.

24. Explain why the graph of $x = -1$ is not the graph of a function.

In Exercises 1–16 graph the equation.

A 1–8. The equations in Oral Exercises 9–16 above.

9. $\frac{1}{2}x - \frac{3}{4}y = 6$

10. $0.3x + 0.6y = 0.12$

11. $3x - \frac{y}{4} + 6 = 0$

12. $7(x - 4) + 14(y - 2) = 0$

B 13. $y = |x|$

14. $|x| = 4$

15. $y = \frac{1}{x}$

16. $y = |x| - x$

In Exercises 17–20 determine k in each equation so that the given ordered pair will be a solution.

17. $2x + ky = 10$; $(2, -2)$

18. $3y = kx - 2$; $(4, 2)$

19. $\frac{3}{2}x - \frac{1}{3}y + 2k = 0$; $(0, 0)$

20. $(k - 1)x + ky = 3$; $(4, -1)$

In Exercises 21–24 graph the pair of equations in the same coordinate plane and give the coordinates of the point where they seem to intersect. Then check whether or not these coordinates satisfy both equations.

21. $x + y = 1$, $x - y = 1$

22. $x + 2y = 3$, $x + 3y = 4$

23. $x - 2y = 6$, $3x + y = 4$

24. $2x - y = -1$, $3x + 2y = 9$

3-4 the graph of a linear inequality

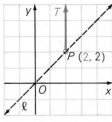

Figure 3

The *half-line* $\overrightarrow{PT}$ shown in red in Figure 3 is the graph of the relation

$$R = \{(x, y): y > x\}$$

when the value of x is 2. You can see that every point on $\overrightarrow{PT}$ has 2 as its abscissa, and a real number greater than 2 for its ordinate. Note that the point P lies on the dashed line ℓ, the graph of $y = x$, but not on $\overrightarrow{PT}$.

The pink-shaded region in Figure 4 consists of the totality of half-lines in the plane, such as $\overrightarrow{PT}$ of Figure 3, with "initial" points on the graph of $y = x$ and extending vertically upward from it. This region, called an open half-plane ("open" means the boundary is not included) is the graph of the given *linear relation* $\{(x, y): y > x\}$. It is also the graph of the *linear inequality*

$$y > x.$$

Thus every point located *above* $y = x$, and no other point in the plane, has coordinates that satisfy the inequality $y > x$.

By similar reasoning you can see that the gray-shaded, open half-plane below ℓ in Figure 4 is the graph of $y < x$.

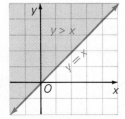

Figure 5

In Figure 5 the shaded, closed half-plane ("closed" means the boundary line is included) is the graph of the inequality

$$y \geq x.$$

The graph consists of all those points, but no others, with coordinates that satisfy either $y > x$ or $y = x$.

The fact that the boundary line, $y = x$, is shown solid rather than dashed indicates that the half-plane is closed rather than open.

EXAMPLE 1   Graph the relation $\{(x, y): 2x - y < 4\}$.

SOLUTION   1. Transforming to express y in terms of x, we have:

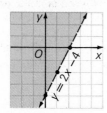

$$2x - y < 4$$
$$-y < 4 - 2x$$
$$y > 2x - 4$$

2. Draw the dashed-line graph of $y = 2x - 4$. Three solutions are $(0, -4)$, $(2, 0)$, and $(1, -2)$.

3. The graph is shown by the shaded open half-plane above the dashed line.
   Answer.

In general, the graph of a *linear inequality in two variables*, such as $Ax + By < C$, is either an open or closed half-plane (open for the signs $<$ and $>$, and closed for the signs $\leq$ and $\geq$). Its boundary is the graph of the *associated linear equation*, $Ax + By = C$.

Graph the given linear relation.

EXAMPLE 2   **a.** $\{(x, y): 2x < -5\}$ **b.** $\{(x, y): y \geq 3\}$

SOLUTION   a. The boundary line is the graph of $2x = -5$, or $x = -2\frac{1}{2}$. The shaded, open half-plane is the graph of $\{(x, y): 2x < -5\}$. **An-swer.**

b. The boundary line is the graph of $y = 3$. The shaded, closed half-plane is the graph of $\{(x, y): y \geq 3\}$. **Answer.**

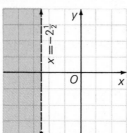   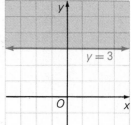

ORAL EXERCISES   In Exercises 1–10 tell whether the graph of the given inequality is an open or closed half-plane, and state the equation of the boundary line in the form $y = ax + b$ or $x = c$.

EXAMPLE $2y - x < 4$

SOLUTION   The graph is an open half-plane; $y = \frac{1}{2}x + 2$.

1. $y > 2$ 3. $x + y > 3$ 5. $2y + x < 6$
2. $y \leq x$ 4. $-4x + 2y \leq 0$ 6. $x \leq -1$

7. $x \geq y$

8. $2x - y \leq 2$

9. $8y - 16x > 32$

10. $3x + 1 \leq y$

In Exercises 11–16 tell whether or not the point with the given coordinates is in the graph of the given inequality.

11. $y + x \geq 0$; $(1, 2)$

12. $-2x + y \leq 4$; $(-2, 0)$

13. $3y > 2x - 1$; $(3, 1)$

14. $-y - 2x < 1$; $(-1, 3)$

15. $-3 > y$; $(4, -4)$

16. $2 \leq -x$; $(-2, 17)$

17. Is $\{(x, y): y > x\}$ a function? Why or why not?

18. Which of the relations $\{(x, y): y \geq 5\}$, $\{(x, y): y = 5\}$, $\{(x, y): x = 5\}$ is a function?

WRITTEN EXERCISES

Graph each inequality as a shaded region on a coordinate plane.

A

1. $y \leq x$

2. $y - x > 2$

3. $2x + y < 3$

4. $x < y$

5. $y + 1 > 2x$

6. $-8x + 2y \geq 0$

7. $-3y \geq 12x$

8. $x + 2 < 2y$

9. $x \geq -2y$

10. $4 \geq x - y$

11. $2y \leq 3$

12. $3x + 6y - 14 \geq -2$

13. $\frac{1}{3} - y < x + \frac{5}{6}$

14. $0.50 - x < -0.25y$

15. $\frac{1}{2} < 3x + 2y$

16. $x > -2$

B

In Exercises 17 and 18 graph both inequalities on the same plane, and shade the region containing all the points with coordinates that satisfy *both* inequalities.

17. $y \leq 3$ and $y \geq -1$

18. $y \leq x + 2$ and $x > -1$

SELF-TEST 2

Give the meaning of each of the following.

1. solution of an open sentence

2. solution set of an open sentence

3. linear equation in two variables

4. open half-plane

5. closed half-plane

Objective 1, page 76 Graph each linear equation in the coordinate plane.

6. $2x + y = 5$

7. $y = -4$

8. $x = 0$

Objective 2, page 76 Graph each linear inequality in the coordinate plane.

9. $x + 3y \geq 6$

10. $-2x + y < 1$

Check your answers with those printed at the back of the book.

lines and their equations

Objectives

After completing the next two sections, you should be able to:
1. Find the slope of the line through two given points.
2. Find an equation of the line through two given points.
3. Find an equation of a line when its slope and the coordinates of one of its points are given.
4. Find an equation of a line when its slope and y-intercept are given.

3–5 *the slope of a line*

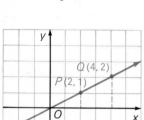

rise = 50 m

run = 100 m

Figure 6

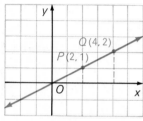

Q(4, 2)

P(2, 1)

O

x

y

Figure 7

Figure 6 shows a hill that is rising steadily at a rate of 50 meters of vertical "rise" for each 100 meters of horizontal "run." The steepness, or *grade*, of such an incline is defined to be the ratio of rise to run, in this case, $\frac{50}{100}$ or 50%.

This hill can be represented mathematically by the line $y = \frac{1}{2}x$, shown in Figure 7. By observing the coordinates of P and Q, you can readily confirm that this line rises at a rate of 1 vertical unit for each 2 horizontal units. Hence its steepness, or slope, is

$$\frac{\text{rise}}{\text{run}} = \frac{1}{2}.$$

In general, as in Figure 8, you can use *subscript notation* to name any two points $P(x_1, y_1)$ (read "x sub one, y sub one") and $Q(x_2, y_2)$, on a nonvertical line and form this ratio:

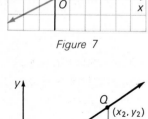

Q

(x_2, y_2)

rise = $y_2 - y_1$

P

(x_1, y_1) run = $x_2 - x_1$

O

x

y

Figure 8

$$m = \frac{\text{rise}}{\text{run}} = \frac{\text{ordinate of } Q - \text{ordinate of } P}{\text{abscissa of } Q - \text{abscissa of } P} = \frac{y_2 - y_1}{x_2 - x_1}$$

The proof of the theorem on page 83 shows that this ratio does not depend upon the particular points chosen to be P and Q; therefore, it may be taken as the definition of slope.

Thus in Figure 7, using the points P and Q, or O and P, you have

$$m = \frac{2 - 1}{4 - 2} = \frac{1}{2}, \quad \text{or} \quad m = \frac{1 - 0}{2 - 0} = \frac{1}{2}.$$

EXAMPLE 1   Find the slope of each line and graph both lines on the same plane.

a. $y = \frac{1}{2}x - 3$ **b.** $-3x + 6y = 2$

SOLUTION   Find two pairs of coordinates for each line, and then use the slope formula.

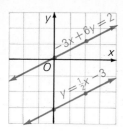

a. $(0, -3)$ and $(2, -2)$ satisfy $y = \frac{1}{2}x - 3$.

$$\therefore m = \frac{-2 - (-3)}{2 - 0} = \frac{1}{2}. \quad \text{Answer.}$$

b. Using $(0, \frac{1}{3})$ and $(2, \frac{4}{3})$ you get

$$m = \frac{\frac{4}{3} - \frac{1}{3}}{2 - 0} = \frac{1}{2}. \quad \text{Answer.}$$

The graph is shown at the left.

Notice that if you transform Equation **b** in Example 1 to the form $y = \frac{1}{2}x + \frac{1}{3}$ and then compare the equations of the lines in Figure 7 and Example 1,

$$y = \frac{1}{2}x,$$
$$y = \frac{1}{2}x - 3,$$
$$y = \frac{1}{2}x + \frac{1}{3},$$

you see that *the coefficient of x is equal to the slope* in each case. This illustrates the following theorem.

Theorem. For all A, B, and $C \in \mathcal{R}$ and $B \neq 0$, the slope m of the line $Ax + By = C$ is $-\dfrac{A}{B}$.

PROOF

Since $B \neq 0$, the equation $Ax + By = C$ is equivalent to $y = -\dfrac{A}{B}x + \dfrac{C}{B}$.

Let $P(x_1, y_1)$ and $Q(x_2, y_2)$ be any two points on the graph of the equation. Since the coordinates of both P and Q must satisfy this equation, we can write the following:

$$y_2 = -\frac{A}{B}x_2 + \frac{C}{B} \tag{1}$$

$$y_1 = -\frac{A}{B}x_1 + \frac{C}{B} \tag{2}$$

Subtracting (2) from (1), we obtain

$$y_2 - y_1 = -\frac{A}{B}(x_2 - x_1) \tag{3}$$

Notice from (3) that $x_2 - x_1 \neq 0$, since otherwise we would have $x_2 - x_1 = 0$, $y_2 - y_1 = 0$, and P and Q would be the same point. Therefore, dividing (3) by $x_2 - x_1$, we get

$$\frac{y_2 - y_1}{x_2 - x_1} = m = -\frac{A}{B}.$$

EXAMPLE 2 Find the slope m of $2x + 3y = 5$ and graph the line.

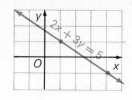

SOLUTION From the theorem above,

$$m = -\frac{A}{B} = -\frac{2}{3}.\quad \text{Answer.}$$

Two pairs of coordinates that satisfy the given equation are $(1, 1)$ and $(4, -1)$. The graph is shown above. The line graphed in Example 2 has a *negative slope*. In general, a line with *negative* slope *falls*, while one with *positive* slope *rises*, from left to right on the coordinate plane.

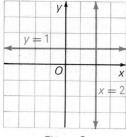

Figure 9

The slope of a horizontal line, such as $y = 1$ in Figure 9, is 0, because the numerator in the slope formula, $m = \dfrac{y_2 - y_1}{x_2 - x_1}$, is 0 for any two points on the line.

On a vertical line, such as $x = 2$ in Figure 9, every point has the same x-coordinate. Hence the denominator $x_2 - x_1$ in the formula for m would always be 0 and, accordingly, *slope is not defined for a vertical line.*

ORAL EXERCISES Find the slope of the line determined by the two given points.

1. $(-1, -3)$ and $(0, 0)$
2. $(0, 0)$ and $(-1, -3)$
3. $(1, 1)$ and $(3, 3)$
4. $(-2, -4)$ and $(2, 4)$
5. $(5, -1)$ and $(6, 8\frac{1}{2})$
6. $(-11\frac{1}{3}, 0)$ and $(\frac{1}{4}, 0)$

7. Judging from Exercises 1 and 2, what can you conclude about the order in which you use two given points to determine the slope of a line from the slope formula?

8. What can you say about the line in Exercise 6?

In Exercises 9–16 give the slope, if any, for the line and tell whether the line rises or falls from left to right.

9. $y = 2x + 3$
10. $2y = -3x$
11. $4x + 5y = 7$
12. $2x = 3y - 6$
13. $2x = 5$
14. $3 - y = 6$
15. $\frac{x}{4} + 1 = 8$
16. $2x + 5 = -y$

In Exercises 17–20 state the value of a for which the line through points P and Q has the given slope m.

17. $P(2, 3)$, $Q(3, a)$; $m = 0$
18. $P(2, 3)$, $Q(3, a)$; $m = 2$
19. $P(5, a)$, $Q(6, 1)$; $m = -3$
20. $P(a, 4)$, $Q(3, 5)$; $m = \frac{1}{2}$

In Exercises 21–24 let ℓ_1 and ℓ_2 have slopes m_1 and m_2, respectively. Tell whether $m_1 > m_2$, $m_1 = m_2$, or $m_1 < m_2$ in each case.

21.
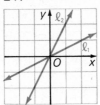

22.

23.
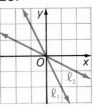

24.

WRITTEN EXERCISES

Graph the line through the given points and determine its approximate slope by inspecting the graph. Check your results using the slope formula.

A

1. $(1, 3)$ and $(2, 5)$

2. $(4, -1)$ and $(-1, 4)$

3. $(1, 2)$ and $(-5, 2)$

4. $(-2, 3)$ and $(4, -3)$

5. $(-1, -1)$ and $(2, 3)$

6. $(\frac{1}{3}, -\frac{5}{3})$ and $(\frac{4}{3}, 2)$

7. $(-\frac{3}{2}, -2)$ and $(4, -\frac{1}{2})$

8. $(2, -\frac{1}{2})$ and $(2, 5)$

Find the slope, $-\dfrac{A}{B}$, and graph the line by using the two points where it intersects the axes. Check that these points satisfy the slope formula.

9. $2x - 4y = 3$

10. $-3y + 2x = 7$

11. $4y = -8x - 6$

12. $6x = 4 - 2y$

13. $-5x - y = -5$

14. $\dfrac{x}{2} = -4y + 2$

For the line through the given point P and with given slope m, use m and the coordinates of P to determine the coordinates of a second point Q on the line. Then draw the line through P and Q.

EXAMPLE

$P(2, 1)$; $m = \frac{2}{3}$

SOLUTION

Since the slope is $\frac{2}{3}$, you can let the ordinate of Q be 2 more than the ordinate of P, and the abscissa be 3 more than the abscissa of P as shown in the diagram at the left. $\therefore Q(2 + 3, 1 + 2)$, or $Q(5, 3)$. **Answer.**

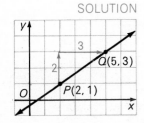

15. $P(0, 1)$; $m = \frac{1}{2}$

16. $P(-2, 3)$; $m = -\frac{2}{3}$

17. $P(1, -3)$; $m = \frac{3}{2}$

18. $P(\frac{5}{2}, 1)$; $m = 0$

19. $P(-2, -1)$; m is undefined

20. $P(-\frac{5}{4}, \frac{1}{4})$; $m = -\frac{3}{5}$

Determine the value of b that makes the given pairs of coordinates satisfy the given value for the slope m.

B

21. $(3, b)$ and $(4, -b)$; $m = \frac{1}{3}$

22. $(4, 1)$ and $\left(5, \dfrac{1}{b}\right)$; $m = 2$

23. $(2, |b|)$ and $(1, b)$; $m = 1$

24. $(|b|, 4)$ and $(b, 3)$; $m = 1$

3-6 *finding an equation of a line*

Since two points determine a unique line, you can use the slope formula,

$$m = \frac{y_2 - y_1}{x_2 - x_1},$$

to determine an equation of a line through two given points, P and Q, with coordinates (x_1, y_1) and (x_2, y_2) if $x_2 \neq x_1$.

EXAMPLE 1   **Find an equation of the line containing $P(3, -2)$ and $Q(4, 1)$.**

SOLUTION   The general equation of a nonvertical line, $Ax + By = C$, can be written equivalently in the form

$$y = -\frac{A}{B}x + \frac{C}{B}.$$

Since $-\frac{A}{B} = m$, we can simplify this to

$$y = mx + b,$$

where b is the constant term, $\frac{C}{B}$. First, we can calculate m from the slope formula,

$$m = \frac{1 - (-2)}{4 - 3} = 3.$$

Then we can substitute the coordinates of *either* P or Q in the equation $y = mx + b$ to find b. In this case, substituting $(3, -2)$ in $y = 3x + b$ yields

$$-2 = 3 \cdot 3 + b,$$
$$-11 = b.$$

Now we can use our known values for m and b to write an equation of the desired line: $y = 3x - 11$.

CHECK   Do $(3, -2)$ and $(4, 1)$ both satisfy $y = 3x - 11$?

$$-2 = 9 - 11. \checkmark$$

and

$$1 = 12 - 11. \checkmark$$

$\therefore$ an equation of the line is $y = 3x - 11$. **Answer.**

From Example 1 you can see that a line ℓ is uniquely determined by its slope m and the coordinates of just one point $P(x_1, y_1)$ on ℓ. That is, any point Q other than P lies on ℓ if and only if the coordinates of Q together with those of P satisfy the slope formula for the given value of m.

Theorem. Given a line ℓ with slope m and a point $P(x_1, y_1)$ on ℓ. Then for P and any other point $Q(x, y)$:

1. If Q is on ℓ, then $\dfrac{y - y_1}{x - x_1} = m$.

2. If $\dfrac{y - y_1}{x - x_1} = m$, then Q is on ℓ.

If the equation for slope m in the theorem is rewritten as

$$y - y_1 = m(x - x_1),$$

we then have the point-slope form of an equation of a line.

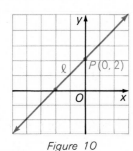

If the given point $P(x_1, y_1)$ of the line ℓ lies on the y-axis as in Figure 10, so that P is the point where ℓ intersects the y-axis, then $x_1 = 0$ and the ordinate y_1 of P is called the y-intercept of ℓ. (In Figure 10 the y-intercept of ℓ is 2.) Using the point-slope form of ℓ, we have

$$y - y_1 = m(x - 0)$$
$$y = mx + y_1.$$

Thus an equation of a line with slope m and y-intercept b is

$$y = mx + b.$$

Figure 10

This equation is called the slope-intercept form of an equation of a line.

The abscissa of the point in which a line ℓ intersects the x-axis is called the x-intercept of the line. The x-intercept of the line in Figure 10 is -2.

EXAMPLE 2   **Find an equation of the line whose y-intercept is 3 and whose x-intercept is 1.**

SOLUTION   To find m we use the axis-intersection points $(0, 3)$ and $(1, 0)$:

$$m = \frac{0 - 3}{1 - 0} = -3$$

Then, using the slope-intercept form, we have

$$y = -3x + 3. \quad \textbf{Answer.}$$

ORAL EXERCISES   1. Why do we speak of "*an* equation of a line" rather than "*the* equation of a line"?
2. How would you find an equation of a line, given its slope and its x-intercept?

State an equation of the line passing through the given point and having the given slope.

3. $(3, 1)$; $m = 2$

4. $(4, -2)$; $m = -3$

5. $(1, \frac{1}{2})$; $m = 4$

6. $(-2, -7)$; $m = \frac{1}{3}$

7. $(0, -\frac{3}{5})$; $m = -\frac{5}{3}$

8. $(0, b)$; $m = a$

State an equation of the line with the given slope m and y-intercept b.

9. $m = -2$; $b = 3$

10. $m = 0$; $b = -1$

11. $m = 3$; $b = 0$

12. $m = 1$; $b = 2$

13. $m = -1$; $b = -2$

14. $m = 0$; $b = 0$

State the slope and y-intercept of the given line.

15. $2x + 3y = 8$

16. $-3x + 5y - 6 = 0$

17. $y - 4x = 2$

18. $5x = y - 10$

19. $\frac{1}{2}x = -y$

20. $\frac{5}{3} = 2y + 5x$

State the coordinates of the point of intersection of the two given lines.

21. $y = 2x$ and $y = 4x$

22. $y = 1$ and $x = 1$

WRITTEN EXERCISES Write an equation in the form $Ax + By = C$ of the line passing through the point P with the given slope m.

A

1. $P(1, 3)$; $m = 2$

2. $P(2, -1)$; $m = -3$

3. $P(-5, 4)$; $m = \frac{4}{5}$

4. $P(1, 0)$; $m = -\frac{3}{2}$

5. $P(0, 0)$; $m = 6$

6. $P(6, -3)$; $m = 0$

7. $P(0, \frac{2}{3})$; $m = 0$

8. $P(4, 0)$; $m = 0$

9. $P(2, 8)$; m undefined

10. $P(a, b)$; m undefined

Write an equation in the form $Ax + By = C$ of the line containing the two given points.

11. $(3, 1)$; $(0, 2)$

12. $(-1, 5)$; $(0, 4)$

13. $(-2, -5)$; $(0, 0)$

14. $(-1, 3)$; $(2, 3)$

15. $(2, -6)$; $(7, 4)$

16. $(\frac{1}{3}, -2)$; $(\frac{1}{3}, -8)$

17. $(\frac{1}{4}, -\frac{3}{8})$; $(\frac{3}{2}, \frac{1}{8})$

18. $(0.5, 2.1)$; $(\frac{1}{2}, -\frac{1}{4})$

Write an equation of the line having slope m and y-intercept b.

19. $m = 3$; $b = -2$

20. $m = -1$; $b = 4$

21. $m = -2$; $b = 0$

22. $m = 5$; $b = 0$

23. $m = 0$; $b = 3$

24. $m = 0$; $b = -2$

Determine an equation of the line satisfying the given conditions.

B 25. Through the point $(7, 2)$ and having the same slope as the line through $(2, 4)$ and $(3, -1)$.

26. Through the point $(-1, 3)$ and having the same slope as the line through $(-1, -2)$ and $(-3, 4)$.

27. Through the point $(5, -4)$ and having the same slope as the graph of $y = 2x + 3$.

28. Through the point $(2, 1)$ and having the same slope as the graph of $y = -3x + 4$.

29. Through the point $(-2, 3)$ and having the same slope as the graph of $2x - 3y = 4$.

30. Through the origin and having the same slope as the graph of $3x + 4y = 2$.

31. With y-intercept 7 and having the same slope as the line through $(0, 0)$ and $(1, 2)$.

32. With y-intercept 0 and having the same slope as the line through $(-1, -3)$ and $(-4, -5)$.

33. With y-intercept -2 and having the same slope as the graph of $4x - 2y = 7$.

34. With y-intercept 3 and having the same slope as the graph of $x - y + 1 = 0$.

35. With slope 2 and x-intercept 3.

36. With slope -1 and x-intercept -4.

37. With x-intercept 2 and y-intercept -3.

38. With x-intercept -1 and y-intercept 4.

C 39. Determine a so that the graph of $2x + ay = 4$ has the same slope as the line through $(0, 1)$ and $(2, -3)$.

40. Determine k so that the graph of $3x + ky = 5$ has the same slope as the graph of $2x - y = -2$.

41. Show that the opposite sides of the quadrilateral with consecutive vertices $(2, 5)$, $(1, 3)$, $(-2, 6)$, and $(-1, 8)$ have the same slope.

42. Show that the line having x-intercept a $(a \neq 0)$ and y-intercept b $(b \neq 0)$ has an equation of the form (called the **intercept form**)

$$\frac{x}{a} + \frac{y}{b} = 1.$$

43. Show that the line passing through the points (x_1, y_1) and (x_2, y_2), with $x_1 \neq x_2$, has an equation of the form (called the **two-point form**)

$$y - y_1 = \frac{y_2 - y_1}{x_2 - x_1} (x - x_1).$$

Give the meaning of each of the following.

1. rise
2. run
3. slope

4. y-intercept
5. x-intercept

Objective 1, page 82   6. Find the slope of the line through the points $P(1, -3)$ and $Q(3, 5)$.

Objective 2, page 82   7. Find an equation of the line through the points $P(-3, 0)$ and $Q(0, 4)$.
                             8. Find an equation of the line through the points $P(2, 5)$ and $Q(4, -1)$.

Objective 3, page 82   9. Find an equation of the line having slope -2 and passing through the point $(-6, 2)$.

Objective 4, page 82   10. Find an equation of the line having slope 3 and y-intercept -4.

Check your answers with those printed at the back of the book.

applications of linear relations

Objective | After completing the next section, you should be able to:
1. Solve problems involving direct variation.

3–7   *direct variation*

A function f in which the rule for pairing is given by a linear equation of the form

$$y = mx + b \qquad (m, b \in \mathcal{R})$$

is called a linear function:

$$f: x \rightarrow mx + b$$

Generally, the domain of a linear function is taken to be $\mathcal{R}$, and its graph is a nonvertical line.

EXAMPLE 1   **a.** Find a rule for specifying a linear function G if $G(5) = 1$ and $m = \frac{1}{10}$.

           b. Does $(2, \frac{7}{10})$ belong to G?

SOLUTION   **a.** Since $m = \frac{1}{10}$ and $(5, 1)$ is a pair in G, we can substitute these in $G(x) = mx + b$:

$$1 = \tfrac{1}{10} \cdot 5 + b, \qquad \text{or} \qquad b = 1 - \tfrac{1}{2} = \tfrac{1}{2}.$$

Hence the rule is $G: x \rightarrow \frac{1}{10}x + \frac{1}{2}$. **Answer.**

       b. The pair $(2, \frac{7}{10})$ belongs to G because $\frac{7}{10} = \frac{1}{10} \cdot 2 + \frac{5}{10}$. **Answer.**

If $m = 0$, then $y = b$ for all $x \in \mathcal{R}$. In that case f is called a constant function, and its graph is the horizontal line through $(0, b)$.

If $b = 0$ and $m \neq 0$, we have $y = mx$. Then the function f is called a direct variation, and we say that y varies directly as x, or y is directly proportional to x, and that m is the constant of variation or the constant of proportionality. When the domain of a direct variation f is $\mathcal{R}$, the ordered pair $(0, 0)$ is always in f, and hence the graph of f is a line passing through the origin and having slope m ($m \neq 0$).

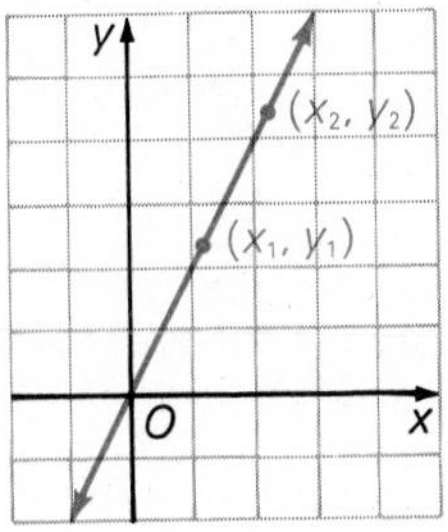

Figure 11 shows the graph of the direct variation specified by

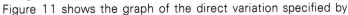

$$y = 2x \qquad (x \in \mathcal{R}).$$

For any two points (x_1, y_1) and (x_2, y_2) on the graph of this function, we have

$$y_1 = 2x_1 \qquad \text{and} \qquad y_2 = 2x_2.$$

If $x_1, x_2 \neq 0$, you can transform these equations to

$$\frac{y_1}{x_1} = 2, \qquad \frac{y_2}{x_2} = 2, \qquad \text{and therefore} \qquad \frac{y_1}{x_1} = \frac{y_2}{x_2}.$$

Figure 11

In general:

> If a linear function f is a direct variation, then for any two ordered pairs (x_1, y_1) and (x_2, y_2) in f, with $x_1, x_2 \neq 0$,
>
> $$\frac{y_1}{x_1} = \frac{y_2}{x_2}.$$

Such an equality of ratios, sometimes written as

$$y_1 : x_1 = y_2 : x_2,$$

is called a proportion. The terms y_1 and x_2 are called the extremes, and x_1 and y_2 the means, of the proportion. Since

$$\frac{y_1}{x_1} = \frac{y_2}{x_2}$$

can be transformed to the equivalent equation

$$y_1 x_2 = x_1 y_2,$$

you can see that:

> In any proportion the product of the means equals the product of the extremes.

EXAMPLE 2   If a 3-ounce jar of instant coffee costs 51 cents, is an 8-ounce jar costing
$1.40 a better value?

SOLUTION   Find what 8 ounces would cost at the rate given for 3 ounces, and then
compare that figure with $1.40:

$$\frac{3}{0.51} = \frac{8}{x}$$

$$3x = 4.08$$

$$x = 1.36, \quad \text{or} \quad \$1.36 \text{ for 8 ounces.}$$

Since $1.40 > 1.36$, the 8-ounce jar is *not* a better value! **Answer.**

ORAL EXERCISES   State whether or not the given function is linear, and if so, whether or not
it is a direct variation.

1. $f: x \rightarrow x - 3$

2. $f: x \rightarrow \frac{5}{3}x + 2$

3. $f: x \rightarrow x^3$

4. $f: x \rightarrow \dfrac{1}{x}$

5. $\{(x, g(x)): g(x) = \frac{1}{2}x\}$

6. $\{(x, y): y = 14\}$

7. $\{(x, G(x)): G(x) = -2x\}$

8. $\left\{(x, h(x)): h(x) = \dfrac{x + 1}{x}\right\}$

State an equation of the form $y = kx$ and then state a proportion for the
direct variation described in words.

EXAMPLE   The perimeter P of a square varies directly as the length s of a side.

SOLUTION $P = ks; \dfrac{P_1}{s_1} = \dfrac{P_2}{s_2}$. **Answer.**

9. The circumference C of a circle varies directly as its radius r.

10. The perimeter P of an equilateral triangle is directly proportional to the
length s of a side.

11. The amount of nitrous oxides n being emitted into the Los Angeles air
basin at any given time varies directly with the number c of cars on the
freeways at the time.

12. The cost C of a wooden floor varies directly with the number f of square
feet of floor space to be covered.

13. The amount of sales tax T on a retail item is 5% of the cost c of the
item.

For each set of ordered pairs examine the ratio $\dfrac{y}{x}$ and tell whether or not
the pairs are in a direct variation.

14. $\{(1, 1), (-2, -2), (3, 3)\}$

15. $\{(2, 3), (3, 5), (4, 7)\}$

16. $\{(-2, -6), (0, 0), (-3, -9)\}$

17. $\{(-\frac{2}{3}, \frac{4}{3}), (4, -8), (-2, 4)\}$

Determine a rule for pairing in a linear function f if:

A

1. $f(0) = 3$ and $f(1) = 2$
2. $f(0) = -2$ and $f(-4) = 0$
3. $f(1) = 1$ and $f(-2) = 7$
4. $f(3) = 4$ and $f(-3) = 2$

5. $f(-3) = 2$ and $f(1) = 2$
6. $f(5) = 0$ and $f(6) = 0$
7. $f(2) = 3$ and $f(3) = 4$
8. $f(2) = -3$ and $f(3) = -4$

Determine whether or not the given pairs are in a direct variation. If so, give the slope of the graph of the variation.

9. $\{(-2, -4), (-1, -2), (3, 6)\}$
10. $\{(1, 5), (2, 8), (\frac{1}{2}, 2)\}$
11. $\{(2, 3), (3, 4), (4, 5)\}$
12. $\{(-\frac{1}{2}, -1), (\frac{1}{4}, \frac{1}{2}), (\frac{5}{3}, \frac{10}{3})\}$

13. $\{(-\frac{7}{16}, 3), (0, 3), (\frac{8}{9}, 3)\}$
14. $\{(4, 2), (4, -2)\}$
15. $\{(0, 0), (\frac{7}{5}, 0), (-\frac{2}{3}, 0)\}$
16. $\{(a, \frac{1}{2}a), (4a, 2a), (3a, \frac{3}{2}a)\}$

Solve each proportion for a.

17. $a:2 = 3:4$
18. $a:5 = 4:2$
19. $3:a = 1:2$
20. $5:a = 3:7$

21. $3:5 = a:6$
22. $5:3 = a:6$
23. $4:9 = 5:a$
24. $3:6 = 7:a$

25. If y varies directly as x and y is 10 when x is 5, find x when y is 15.
26. If y varies directly as x and y is 36 when x is 45, find y when $x = 100$.
27. If the circumference C of a circle varies directly with the radius r, and C is π when r is $\frac{1}{2}$, find C when r is 4.
28. If $E = k(\frac{1}{2}x)$, and E is 18 when x is 4, find E when $x = -\frac{1}{3}$.

B

29. If $y = k(x + 2)$, and y is 4 when x is -3, find x when y is 5.
30. If g is a linear function such that $g(x) = k(2x + 1)$, and $(2, 5)$ is in g, is $(4, 7)$ in g?
31. If f is a linear function with $-\frac{1}{2}$ as the slope of its graph and 0 as its x-intercept, is f a direct variation? Tell why or why not.
32. If b varies directly as $\frac{3}{2}a$, and b is 35 when a is 5, find b when a is 7.

For the proportion $\dfrac{y_1}{x_1} = \dfrac{y_2}{x_2}$ (x_1, y_1, x_2, $y_2 \neq 0$), prove each of the following properties.

33. $\dfrac{x_1}{y_1} = \dfrac{x_2}{y_2}$

34. $\dfrac{y_1}{y_2} = \dfrac{x_1}{x_2}$

35. If $x_1 \neq x_2$, then $\dfrac{y_1 - y_2}{x_1 - x_2} = \dfrac{y_2}{x_2}$. (Hint: Let $y_1 = mx_1$ and $y_2 = mx_2$.)

36. If $g = \{(x, g(x)): g(x) = kx, x \in \mathcal{R}\}$, prove that $g(a + c) = g(a) + g(c)$ for all $a, c \in \mathcal{R}$.

PROBLEMS

A   **1.** If a student scores 26 on a mathematics-aptitude test on a scale from 0 to 36, what is his score on a scale from 0 to 100?

2. If the student in Problem 1 had scored 30 on the scale from 0 to 36, what would his score have been on a scale from 0 to 100?

3. If hydrogen and oxygen combine at a rate of 1 part of hydrogen to 16 parts of oxygen by weight to form hydrogen peroxide (H_2O_2), how many grams of each element are there in 204 grams of H_2O_2?

4. If a cubic centimeter (cm^3) of water becomes frozen, the volume of ice will be 9% greater than the original volume of water. How much water must be frozen to form 763 cm^3 of ice?

5. If property in Los Angeles is assessed at 25% of its market value, and the owner of a house assessed at $12,000 has to pay a property tax of $960, what would be the property tax on a house that sells for $32,000 if the tax is proportional to the assessed value?

6. A weight of 25 grams stretches a spring 9.5 centimeters. If the distance that the spring is stretched is directly proportional to the attached weight, what weight will stretch the spring 5.7 centimeters?

7. Ms. Whitacre owns 360 shares of stock in the Teledata Company and receives $708 per year in dividends. How much does Mr. Crane receive for an annual dividend if he owns 600 shares in the same company?

8. The average number of red cells in a cubic millimeter of a woman's blood is 4,500,000. In order to perform a test on a sample of Ms. Thornton's blood, a laboratory technician dilutes 1 part of blood with 299 parts of a salt solution. How many red blood cells would the technician expect to find in 0.5 cubic millimeters of the diluted solution?

In Problems 9 and 10, assume that if light and sound are sent at the same instant from the same source, then the distance of an observer from the source is directly proportional to the time elapsing from the moment the observer sees the light to the moment he hears the sound.

B   **9.** During a thunderstorm, Susan heard the sound of thunder associated with a bolt of lightning $4\frac{1}{2}$ seconds after she saw the lightning flash. Linda heard the thunder $7\frac{1}{3}$ seconds after she saw the lightning flash. If Susan was 900 meters from the lightning bolt, how far from it was Linda?

10. At a rocket launching, a tracker was located on a direct line between the launch pad and an observer. The observer saw the first flame of the rocket on the pad $10\frac{1}{2}$ seconds before he heard the sound associated with the combustion. The tracker heard the sound of the combustion $4\frac{1}{2}$ seconds before the observer did, and saw the flames 3 seconds before the observer did. If the tracker was 1.8 kilometers from the launching pad, how far from the pad was the observer?

careers *architecture*

Almost every modern building is planned and designed by an architect. In designing a structure, an architect must make sure that, in addition to meeting his client's requirements, it will be safe and attractive. The architect first makes preliminary drawings of the floor plan and the exterior and interior details of the building. He then meets with his client, and together they decide on a final design for the structure. This final design is used to prepare working drawings. Consulting engineers usually prepare detailed drawings of the plumbing, electrical connections, and heating and cooling systems. The architect then acts as his client's adviser and representative in dealing with the building contractor. He periodically visits the construction site to make sure that the design and specifications are being followed. Thus, the architect is involved in many stages of creating a structure, from the first sketches to the completed building.

Architects usually construct models of their designs for new buildings.

This architect is completing the specifications on a scale drawing.

EXAMPLE An architect is designing a house which will be 10 meters long and 8 meters wide. A scale drawing of the floor plan is 30 cm by 24 cm. In the drawing, find the dimensions representing a 4.2 m $\times$ 5.5 m living room.

SOLUTION 1 m = 100 cm, so 10 m = 1000 cm. Using the proportion

$$\frac{\text{actual size}}{\text{drawing size}} = \frac{1000}{30},$$

we have

$$\frac{420}{w} = \frac{1000}{30} \quad \text{and} \quad \frac{550}{l} = \frac{1000}{30}.$$

Solving:

$$w = \frac{420 \cdot 30}{1000} = 12.6 \text{ cm}$$

$$l = \frac{550 \cdot 30}{1000} = 16.5 \text{ cm}$$

Can you find the dimensions that represent the other rooms in the drawing?

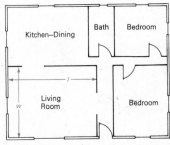

Give the meaning of each of the following.

1. linear function
2. direct variation
3. constant of proportionality

4. proportion
5. extremes
6. means

Objective 1, page 90   7. If y varies directly as x, and $y = 3$ when $x = 8$, find y when $x = 18$.

8. If your earnings vary directly as the number of hours you work, and you earn $7 for working 2 hours, how much would you earn in $3\frac{1}{2}$ hours?

Check your answers with those printed at the back of the book.

chapter summary

1. A **function** is a set of *ordered pairs* in which each **first component** is paired with exactly one **second component** according to a given rule. The set of first components is called the **domain** of the function, and the set of second components is called the **range**.

2. A **relation** is any set of ordered pairs. Every function is a relation, but not every relation is a function.

3. A function or relation can be pictured by means of a mapping diagram and also by means of a graph in a **coordinate plane**.

4. A **solution** of an open sentence in two variables is any ordered pair for which the sentence is true. The **solution set** of the sentence is the set of all its solutions.

5. A **linear equation in two variables** is an equation of the form $Ax + By = C$, where A, B, $C \in \mathfrak{R}$ and A and B are not both zero. The graph of a linear equation is a straight line.

6. The graph of a **linear inequality** is an **open** or **closed half-plane**. The boundary of the half-plane is the graph of the associated linear equation.

7. The **slope** of a nonvertical line is the ratio of **rise** to **run**. A line with *negative* slope *falls* from left to right, while one with *positive* slope *rises* from left to right. A horizontal line has *zero* slope, while a vertical line has *no* slope.

8. A **linear function** is a function in which the rule for pairing is given by a linear equation of the form $y = mx + b$, with m, $b \in \mathfrak{R}$. If $b = 0$, then the linear function is a **direct variation**.

9. An equality of ratios is called a **proportion**; the product of the **means** equals the product of the **extremes**.

chapter test   3-1   If $f(x) = \dfrac{x}{2x + 1}$, find each of the following.

1. $f(3)$ **2.** $f(-1)$ **3.** $f(0)$ **4.** $f(a)$

3-2   Draw a mapping diagram for the given relation and determine whether or not the relation is a function.

5. $\{(2, 2), (2, 3), (3, 1)\}$ **6.** $\{(2, 3), (3, 4), (4, 2)\}$

7. Graph the relation in Problem 5.

8. Graph the relation in Problem 6.

3-3   Graph the given equation for $-2 \leq x \leq 2$.

9. $x + 2y = 2$ **10.** $x - 2y = 3$

3-4   Graph the given inequality as a shaded region on a coordinate plane.

11. $2x + y < 4$ **12.** $3x - y \leq 2$

3-5   Find the slope of the line through the given points.

13. $(0, 2)$ and $(-3, 5)$ **14.** $(2, 1)$ and $(3, -4)$

Graph the line with the given equation.

15. $3x - 2y = 5$ **16.** $4x + 2y = 3$

3-6   Write an equation of the line passing through the point P and having slope m.

17. $P(-2, 3)$; $m = 1.5$ **18.** $P(4, -1)$; $m = 2$

19. Write an equation of the line passing through $(-1, -2)$ and $(3, -5)$.

20. Write an equation of the line with y-intercept -2 and slope -3.

3-7   **21.** Find y if $(2, 3)$ and $(5, y)$ are in a direct variation.

22. The area of a triangle with a given base is directly proportional to its altitude. If the area is 5 when the altitude is 2, find the area when the altitude is 5.

programmed chapter review

3-1   **1.** A set of ordered pairs in which each first component is paired with exactly one second component according to a given rule is called a __?__ .

2. The set of first components in a function is called its __?__ , and the set of second components its __?__ .

3. If $f(x) = 2x - 3$, then $f(1) = $ __?__ and $f(0) = $ __?__ .

function
domain
range
-1; -3

3–2	**4.** Any set of ordered pairs is called a __?__ .	relation
	5. A function or relation can be pictured by means of a __?__ __?__ or by means of a __?__ .	mapping diagram graph
3–3	**6.** The set of all solutions of a given open sentence is called its __?__ __?__ .	solution set
	7. The graph of a linear equation in two variables is a __?__ __?__ .	straight line
	8. The graph of $x = c$ is a __?__ line.	vertical
3–4	**9.** The graph of a linear inequality in two variables is a __?__-__?__ .	half-plane
	10. A(n) __?__ half-plane contains its boundary line.	closed
3–5	**11.** The slope of a line is the ratio of __?__ to __?__ .	rise; run
	12. The slope of a horizontal line is __?__ .	0
	13. A line with __?__ slope falls from left to right.	negative
3–6	**14.** An equation of the form $y = mx + b$ is called the __?__-__?__ form of the equation of a line.	slope-intercept
	15. An equation of the line with slope 5 and y-intercept 2 is __?__ .	$y = 5x + 2$
3–7	**16.** A function f in which the rule for pairing is given by a linear equation of the form $y = mx + b$ $(m, b \in \Re)$ is called a __?__ function.	linear
	17. If $m \neq 0, b = 0$, then a linear function is called a __?__ __?__ .	direct variation
	18. In the direct variation $y = mx$, __?__ is called the constant of proportionality.	m
	19. In any proportion, the product of the __?__ is equal to the product of the __?__ .	means extremes

OPTIONAL TOPIC *special functions and relations*

A function or relation may be specified by different formulas over different subsets of its domain.

For example, if a single person pays no federal income tax on a "taxable income" of less than $750, and 14% of $(x - 750)$ for "taxable income" x between $750 and $1250, then the income-tax function f is given by the rule

$$f(x) = \begin{cases} 0 & \text{if } 0 \leq x \leq 750; \\ \frac{14}{100}(x - 750) & \text{if } 750 < x \leq 1250. \end{cases}$$

The graph of this function is shown in Figure 12 for $0 \leq x \leq 1250$.

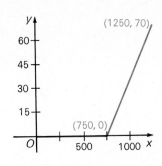

Figure 12

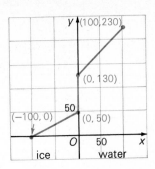

Figure 13

Perhaps you know that at sea level water freezes at 0°C (Celsius) and boils at 100°C, and that approximately one calorie (cal) of heat is required to raise the temperature of one gram (g) of water 1°. But do you know that it takes about 0.5 cal of heat to raise the temperature of one gram of ice 1° and about 80 cal to melt one gram of ice? The relation graphed in Figure 13 gives the approximate quantity y of heat required to increase the temperature of one gram of water (initially ice) at sea level from $-100°C$ to any temperature x up to 100°C.

EXAMPLE **Use the relation pictured in Figure 13 to determine the approximate quantity of heat required to convert 5 grams of ice at $-50°C$ to water at 65°C.**

SOLUTION In Figure 13 the ordinate of the graph at $x = -50$ is 25, and at $x = 65$, it is $130 + 65$, or 195. The difference $195 - 25$, or 170, is the approximate number of cal needed for 1 g. Therefore, for 5 g you need

$$5 \times 170, \text{ or } 850 \text{ cal. } \textbf{Answer.}$$

Sometimes you can combine in a single open sentence the rules specifying a function or a relation. Figure 14 shows the graph of the function f whose values are given by the rules:

$$f(x) = \begin{cases} x - 1 & \text{if} \quad x \geq 1; \\ 1 - x & \text{if} \quad x < 1. \end{cases}$$

But $|x - 1| = x - 1$ if $x \geq 1$, and if $x < 1$, $|x - 1| = -(x - 1) = 1 - x$; so you can indicate the values of f more compactly as follows:

$$f(x) = |x - 1| \quad \text{or} \quad f: x \rightarrow |x - 1|.$$

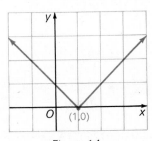

Figure 14

EXERCISES Find the total income tax paid by John and Rafe if their respective earnings were as given. Use the function whose graph is shown in Figure 12.

1. $600 and $700

2. $1000 and $900

3. $950 and $1250

4. $1150 and $700

5. $1200 and $1200

6. $1150 and $1250

Find the number of cal of heat that are required to increase the temperature of the given amount of water (or ice) at sea level by the given amount.

7. 5 g; from 0°C (ice) to 0°C (water)

8. 10 g; from 0°C (ice) to 30°C

9. 50 g; from −8°C to 15°C

10. 100 g; from −30°C to 40°C

11. 7 g; from −10°C to 0°C (ice)

12. 8 g; from −20°C to 0°C (water)

Graph each of the following functions.

13. $f: x \rightarrow \begin{cases} 0 \text{ if } x < 0 \\ 1 \text{ if } x \geq 0 \end{cases}$

14. $g: x \rightarrow \begin{cases} 3 \text{ if } x \leq 0 \\ 1 \text{ if } x > 0 \end{cases}$

15. $h: x \rightarrow \begin{cases} -x \quad \text{ if } x \leq 0 \\ x + 1 \text{ if } x > 0 \end{cases}$

16. $G: x \rightarrow \begin{cases} x \quad\quad \text{ if } x < 1 \\ 2x - 1 \text{ if } x \geq 1 \end{cases}$

17. Graph the function s defined by: $s(x) = \begin{cases} 1 \text{ if } x > 0 \\ 0 \text{ if } x = 0 \\ -1 \text{ if } x < 0 \end{cases}$

18. Use your graph from Exercise 17 to find the value of (a) $s(5)$, (b) $s(0)$, (c) $s(1.5)$, and (d) $s(s(2))$.

19. Graph the function G which maps each real number x into the greatest integer that is less than or equal to x. (This function is denoted by

$$G: x \rightarrow [x] \quad \text{ or } \quad G(x) = [x].)$$

20. Use your graph from Exercise 19 to find the value of (a) $[5]$, (b) $[0]$, (c) $[-1.1]$, and (d) $[[-0.2]]$.

21. Graph the postage function A which maps each real number x, $0 < x \leq 8$, into a counting number. Assume that postage is 10 cents for each ounce or fraction thereof up to and including 8 ounces.

22. Graph the function B specified by $B(x) = -10[-x]$, $0 < x \leq 8$.

23. If 1140 cal of heat are applied to 100 g of ice at sea level and at an initial temperature of −10°C, how much of the ice will be melted?

24. Repeat Exercise 23 for 500 cal applied to 40 g at an initial temperature of −5°C.

In Exercises 25 and 26 use the fact that at sea level it takes about 540 cal of heat to convert one gram of water at 100°C into steam at the same temperature, and that it takes about 0.5 cal of heat to raise the temperature of one gram of steam 1°.

25. Graph the relation giving the approximate quantity of heat required to increase the temperature of one g of water (initially ice) at sea level from −50°C to any temperature up to 150°C (steam).

26. Repeat Exercise 25 for an initial temperature of −200°C and a final temperature of 200°C.

programming in BASIC

These optional sections are for use by students who have access to a computer that will accept the language BASIC. Pages 101–109 contain a four-part review of the fundamentals of BASIC using material from Chapter 3. Additional work with BASIC will appear at intervals throughout the text.

Part I

You can use a computer to find values of functions and relations.

First, you must translate the algebraic expressions into the BASIC language by using:

+ for addition	* for multiplication
− for subtraction	/ for division
↑ for exponentiation	

The usual order of operations is:

first, ↑
then *, / in order from left to right
then +, − in order from left to right

You may use parentheses whenever necessary to indicate a different order of operations. Thus:

$2x^2 - 3x - 5$ would be written as $2 * X \uparrow 2 - 3 * X - 5$

but

$$\frac{a + b}{a - b}$$ would be written as $(A+B)/(A-B)$

The expression $A+B/A-B$ would mean: $a + \dfrac{b}{a} - b$

To find the value of

$$2x^2 - 3x - 5$$

for a single value of the *variable x*, you may use this *program:*

```
10  LET X=−2
20  PRINT 2*X↑2−3*X−5    (See next page.)
30  END
```

Notice that every line in a program must be numbered, and every program must end with an END statement.

The LET statement in line 10 assigns the value on the right-hand side of the equals sign to the variable named on the left.

If you communicate with your computer by means of a terminal, type in the program on page 101, pressing the RETURN key after each line, and then type the *command* RUN (a command has no line number) followed by RETURN. ·

The PRINT statement in line 20 causes the computer to compute the value and then print it:

$$9$$

But to use the computer effectively, you want it to find several values in succession. To do this, you use a loop. Here is an example where the domain is $\{-2, -1, 0, 1, 2\}$:

```
10   LET X=−2
20   PRINT  2*X↑2−3*X−5
30   LET X=X+1
40   IF X>2 THEN 60
50   GOTO 20
60   END
```

(loop brackets lines 20–50)

This program can be represented by the following flow chart (notice the shapes of the boxes):

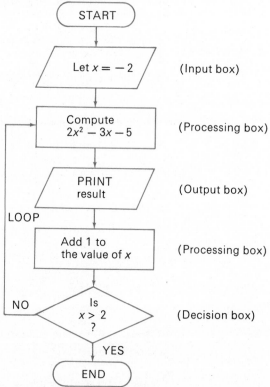

START

Let $x = -2$ (Input box)

Compute $2x^2 - 3x - 5$ (Processing box)

PRINT result   (Output box)

LOOP

Add 1 to the value of x (Processing box)

NO   Is $x > 2$?   (Decision box)

YES

END

The statement LET X = X + 1 in line 30 means that the computer takes the current value of X, adds 1 to it, and assigns this new value to X.

This program uses the following kinds of statement in addition to the LET, PRINT, and END statements:

IF...THEN... statement   This is a "conditional transfer" statement. If the condition is true, then the execution is transferred to the line specified. Otherwise, the computer goes on to the next line in the program.

GOTO statement   This is an "unconditional transfer." The execution is always transferred to the line specified.

If you run this program, you will see that only the values of the function are printed. You can make the computer print out the ordered pairs of the function

$$x \rightarrow 2x^2 - 3x - 5$$

in neatly labeled columns. The headings are made by using quotation marks and commas in a PRINT statement. Thus, add:

```
5   PRINT "X        ---->","2X↑2−3X−5"
```

and change:

```
20   PRINT X,2*X↑2−3*X−5
```

To get a listing of the program as it now stands, type the *command* LIST. You will see that the computer has inserted line 5 and changed line 20. In BASIC every line is given a number so that such changes can be made easily. Now run this revised program. In general:

Quotation marks in PRINT statements   The computer will copy and print out all the symbols and spaces that are typed within quotation marks. (If you need quotation marks within these, you must use the single ones, '.)

Commas in PRINT statements   The commas in lines 5 and 20 cause the computer to move the second item in the line over 15 spaces from the left margin. (In general, commas may be used to arrange print-outs in 5 columns across the page.)

Notice that whenever a numerical value is printed, space is left for a sign, but only the negative sign is printed.

BASIC has several built-in functions available, one of which is the absolute value function. $|x|$ is written as ABS(X) in BASIC. To print out some ordered pairs of the function

$$x \rightarrow |x|,$$

change:

```
5   PRINT "X        ---->","ABS(X)"

20   PRINT X, ABS(X)
```

Then run the program and observe the results.

In these exercises use the domain $\{-3, -2, -1, 0, 1, 2, 3\}$. Write programs to find the values of these functions for the given domain.

1. $x \rightarrow x^2 + x$

2. $x \rightarrow x^2 - 1$

3. $x \rightarrow |x| - 1$

4. $x \rightarrow 3 + 2|x|$

Part II

When you want to erase the entire program that you have been using, type the *command* SCR (for scratch) and press RETURN. This clears your working space for a new program.

To find ordered pairs to use in plotting a graph of an equation, you can transform the equation into an equivalent one that expresses y in terms of x and then use a computer program similar to that given on page 102. There is, however, a special shortcut for writing the kind of loop used in that program. Compare the following program with the earlier one:

```
 5   PRINT "X        ---->","2X↑2−3X−5"
10   FOR X=−2 TO 2
20   PRINT X, 2*X↑2−3*X−5
30   NEXT X
40   END
```

(lines 10–30 bracketed as: loop)

The FOR statement (line 10) and the NEXT statement (line 30) begin and end the loop, and the same variable must be used in both, in this case, the variable X.

When one loop is used inside another loop, they are called *nested loops*. We shall use nested loops in the next program. We shall give an interesting method of testing selected pairs of values of x and y within a given region to determine which pairs, if any, are solutions of a given open sentence. Run the following program, which finds some solutions of

$$x + y = 4.$$

```
 5   PRINT "SOME SOLUTIONS OF X+Y=4
10   FOR Y=4 TO −4 STEP −1
20   FOR X=−4 TO 4
30   IF X+Y=4 THEN 60
40   PRINT "        ";   (Leave 8 spaces.)
50   GOTO 70
60   PRINT "(";X;",";Y;")";   (Leave a single space.)
70   NEXT X
80   NEXT Y
90   END
```

(brackets labeled: Y loop, X loop)

This program uses several more features of the BASIC language:

STEP −1   This produces a countdown, in this program from 4 to −4. In a FOR statement, if no STEP value is given, the STEP value is assumed to be 1. The STEP value may be any BASIC expression.

Semicolons   These cause the items to be printed close together, although
in PRINT   space is always allowed for the sign of a numerical value.
statements

Placing a comma or a semicolon at the end of a PRINT statement holds the terminal carriage on the same line.

This program tests all pairs of integral values of x and y where

$$x \in \{-4, -3, -2, -1, 0, 1, 2, 3, 4\}$$

and

$$y \in \{-4, -3, -2, -1, 0, 1, 2, 3, 4\}.$$

The loops work like this:

Y = 4, while X = −4, −3, −2, −1, 0, 1, 2, 3, 4
Y = 3, while X = −4, −3, −2, −1, 0, 1, 2, 3, 4
and so on.

The number of values of x has been chosen so that the ordered pairs can be printed in 9 columns across the page. The number of values of y may be increased or decreased as desired, provided

$$-9 \leq y \leq 9.$$

(The spacing of this particular program allows for only single-digit integers.)

Each column in the print-out occupies 8 spaces, and 9 columns of 8 spaces fill the 72 spaces that are available in the terminal print-out. Notice that if (X,Y) is *not* a solution, the computer "prints" 8 spaces in the column.

In order to make it easy to transfer these values to a graph, we have started Y at the top with a positive value and X at the left with a negative value.

Make the following changes and run the program again:

5   PRINT "SOME SOLUTIONS OF X+Y<4"
30 IF X+Y<4 THEN 60

Change the inequality to X+Y <= 4 and run the program again.

In BASIC, the possible inequality symbols are:

< is less than	<= is less than or equal to
> is greater than	>= is greater than or equal to
<> is not equal to	

1. Marion wanted a program that would give three integral ordered pairs that are solutions of

$$Ax + By = C,$$

A, B, C integers, with x having the value 0 and two positive values. Work through the program shown below by hand and see if it does what is wanted. What value must B not have?

```
 1  LET A=5
 2  LET B=−3
 3  LET C=9
 5  PRINT "X","Y"
10  FOR X=0 TO 2*ABS(B) STEP ABS(B)
20  PRINT X, C/B−(A/B)*X
30  NEXT X
40  END
```

2. Write a program that will give the squares of the integers 0, 1, . . . , 10.

3. Write a program that will give the products of a given number and the integers 0, 1, . . . , 10.

Part III

If you want to evaluate a formula while working at a computer terminal, it is useful to INPUT the given values. Try this program:

```
10  PRINT "WHAT IS THE RADIUS OF THE CIRCLE";
20  INPUT R
30  PRINT "THE AREA IS";3.14159*R*R;"."
40  END
```

The INPUT statement (line 20) causes the computer to print a question mark and then wait for you to type in a number (an integer or a decimal). (The semicolon at the end of line 10 makes the computer print the question mark on the same line.) You type in the number and press RETURN. The computer then continues the program.

You can keep running the program, inputting a different value each time.

If you know ahead of time what values you want to use, you can put in a READ statement and a DATA statement as in the following program:

```
10  READ R
20  PRINT "THE AREA OF A CIRCLE WITH RADIUS";R;
30  PRINT "IS";3.14159*R*R;"."
40  PRINT                    (This "prints" a blank line here.)
50  GOTO 10
60  DATA 2,4,6,8,10,6.75
70  END
```

Run this program. The computer will "read" the first value in the DATA statement (line 60), do lines 20 and 30, skip a line (line 40 produces a line feed), READ the second value, and so on, until it has used all the values in line 60. It will then print that it is OUT OF DATA and stop.

We shall now write a program to find the slope of a line by using the formula on page 82.

So far we have used only single letters as variables. However, the BASIC language also allows us to use a single letter followed by a single digit:

$$A0, A1, \ldots A9, \ldots, Z1, \ldots Z9$$

Therefore we may translate the expression for the slope of a line

$$\frac{y_2 - y_1}{x_2 - x_1}$$

into BASIC as:

$$(Y2-Y1)/(X2-X1)$$

BASIC allows you to INPUT several values at a time. Since the computer will print only one question mark, it is useful to precede the INPUT statement with a PRINT statement reminding you of what values to type in. You must type them in exactly the order you have indicated in your program, separated by commas. Study and run this program:

```
10   PRINT "INPUT X1,Y1,X2,Y2"
20   INPUT X1,Y1,X2,Y2
30   IF X1=X2 THEN 60
40   PRINT "SLOPE =";(Y2-Y1)/(X2-X1)
50   STOP
60   PRINT "NO SLOPE"
70   END
```

There can be only one END statement in a program, and so a STOP statement is used in line 50.

EXERCISES

1. Draw a flow chart for the program for finding the slope of a line when two points on it are given.

2. Write a program that will find the x-intercept and the y-intercept of a line with equation of the form $Ax + By = C$ when you input values of A, B, and C.

3. Transform the two-point form given in Exercise 43, page 89, to the form:

$$Ax + By = C$$

Then write a program that will print an equation of a line through two points when you input their coordinates.

Part IV

Another built-in function that BASIC has is the greatest integer function, which is written INT(X). This gives the greatest integer less than or equal to X. Try this program to see how it works.

```
10   PRINT "X","INT(X)"
20   FOR X=1 TO 3 STEP .25
30   PRINT X,INT(X)
40   NEXT X
50   END
```

We have seen how commas and semicolons work in PRINT statements. By using TAB(X) in a print statement, you can print any symbol in a specified space. Try this program:

```
10   FOR X=0 TO 5
20   PRINT TAB(X);"*"
30   NEXT X
40   END
```

For example, TAB(5);"*" prints * in the 6th space, counting from the left margin. Change line 20 to

```
20   PRINT TAB(X); X
```

and run the program. Since these are numerical values, space is allowed for a sign.

If the values of X are not integral, TAB works like INT. Try this program:

```
10   FOR X=1 TO 3 STEP .25
20   PRINT TAB(X);"*"
30   NEXT X
40   END
```

TAB can be used in plotting graphs. On the facing page is a program that will print out rough sketches of portions of graphs of some equations of the form:

$$Ax + By = C, A \neq 0, B \neq 0.$$

In order to make a nearly square grid, it is necessary to use two horizontal spaces to represent the unit that one line feed represents.

If the absolute value of the x-intercept is greater than 8, the program prints the value of the x-intercept and TOO WIDE and stops.

There is no built-in stop in the program if the y-intercept is very large. However, the program prints out its value as well as the slope, and if these values seem unsuitable for a computer sketch, the operator can stop the program by pressing and releasing the BREAK key.

Study and run the following program for $x + y = 4$; that is, input 1,1,4. Compare this graph with the print-out of ordered pairs obtained on page 104.

```
10    PRINT "WHAT VALUES DO YOU WANT FOR A(<>0), B(<>0), C";
15    INPUT A,B,C
20    PRINT
25    LET X1=C/A
30    LET Y1=C/B
35    PRINT A;"X +";B;"Y =";C,"SLOPE =";-A/B,"Y-INTERCEPT =";Y1
40    PRINT
45    LET E=INT(ABS(X1))+5
50    IF E>13 THEN 170
55    LET D=INT(ABS(Y1))+5
60    LET M=2*E
65    LET N=2*M
70    PRINT TAB(M);"Y"
75    FOR Y=D TO -D STEP -1
80    LET X=(C-B*Y)/A
85    LET X2=2*X+M
90    IF X2>M THEN 145
95    IF X2=M THEN 130
100   IF X2<0 THEN 160
105   IF Y=0 THEN 120
110   PRINT TAB(X2);"*";TAB(M);"!";TAB(N+3);"(";X;",";Y;")"
115   GOTO 160
120   PRINT "+-+-+-+";TAB(X2);"*";TAB(N-6);"+-+-+-+X";
121   PRINT TAB(N+3);"(";X;",";Y;")"
125   GOTO 160
130   IF Y=0 THEN 120
135   PRINT TAB(X2);"*";TAB(N+3);"(";X;",";Y;")"
140   GOTO 160
145   IF X2>N THEN 160
150   IF Y=0 THEN 120
155   PRINT TAB(M);"!";TAB(X2);"*";TAB(N+3);"(";X;",";Y;")"
160   NEXT Y
165   STOP
170   PRINT "X-INTERCEPT =";X1;"    TOO WIDE"
175   END
```

EXERCISES

1. Run the above program using as input 1,1,-4; -1,1,4; 1,-1,4. Then try 2,-1,4; 2,1,9; 1,1,9.

2. Run each of these programs by hand, and describe what each one does.

```
10   LET A=.6666              10   LET A=9876
20   PRINT INT(100*A+.5)/100  20   PRINT INT(A/100+.5)*100
30   END                      30   END
```

3. Write a program that will print a multiplication table from 1 × 1 to 10 × 10. Use TAB to space the columns across the page.

Organizing and interpreting large amounts of data, analyzing problems, and applying mathematical principles have become vital skills in the business world. Computers and calculating machines are useful tools in marketing, production, management, and other areas of business operations.

110

solving systems of linear equations or inequalities

systems of equations in two variables

Objectives

After completing the next four sections, you should be able to:
1. Identify the solution set of a system of linear equations in two variables from the graphs of the equations.
2. Solve a system of two linear equations in two variables by the linear-combination method.
3. Use determinants to solve a system of two linear equations in two variables.
4. Solve problems by translating stated relationships into a system of equations.

4–1 graphing a system of equations in the plane

Figures 1, 2, and 3 on page 112 show the three possible configurations when two linear equations are graphed on the same plane. The lines representing a given pair of equations must do just one of the following:

A. Intersect in exactly *one* point (Figure 1).
B. Coincide, and thus have *every* point in common (Figure 2).
C. Parallel one another, and thus have *no* point in common (Figure 3).

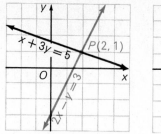 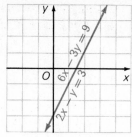 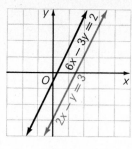

| Figure 1 | Figure 2 | Figure 3 |

The **system of linear equations** graphed in Figure 1 can be regarded as a conjunction of the two open sentences

$$2x - y = 3 \quad \text{and} \quad x + 3y = 5 \quad (x, y \in \mathcal{R})$$

The **solution set** of a system of linear equations in two variables consists of all the ordered pairs of real numbers that satisfy *every* equation of the system. Thus the intersection point P in Figure 1 is the graph of the single solution of the system:

$$2x - y = 3$$
$$x + 3y = 5$$

The coordinates of P appear to be (2, 1). To verify that these coordinates actually satisfy both equations of the system, we have:

$$\begin{array}{ccc} 2 \cdot 2 - 1 = 3 & & 3 = 3 \checkmark \\ 2 + 3 \cdot 1 = 5 & \text{or} & 5 = 5 \checkmark \end{array}$$

Therefore, the solution set of the system is {(2, 1)}.

In Figure 2 the graph of the solution set of the system

$$2x - y = 3$$
$$6x - 3y = 9$$

consists of the infinite set of points comprising the single line that represents either one of the equations. Thus, the solution set is $\{(x, y): 2x - y = 3\}$.

In Figure 3 the two parallel lines representing the system

$$2x - y = 3$$
$$6x - 3y = 2$$

have no points in common. Hence, the solution set of the system is the empty set $\emptyset$. We describe such a system as **inconsistent**.

A system of equations that has at least one solution is called **consistent**.

EXAMPLE 1 Graph the following system of linear equations, and then determine whether or not it is consistent.

$$2x - y = 4$$
$$x - y = 1$$
$$x - 3y = -3$$

SOLUTION Find the x- and y-intercept for each line. Then draw the three lines through their pairs of intercepts (diagram at left), and check to see if their apparent common point $(3, 2)$ satisfies all three equations.

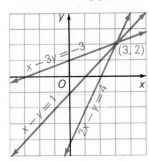

$2x - y = 4$	$x - y = 1$	$x - 3y = -3$
$2 \cdot 3 - 2 = 4$	$3 - 2 = 1$	$3 - 3 \cdot 2 = -3$
$4 = 4 \checkmark$	$1 = 1 \checkmark$	$-3 = -3 \checkmark$

Hence, $(3, 2)$ is a solution, and the system of equations is therefore consistent. **Answer.**

Observe from Figures 1, 2, and 3 that the number of solutions for a system of two linear equations is related to the slopes of their graphs. The following theorem summarizes the facts (see Exercises 37–41, pages 119–120).

Theorem. A system of two linear equations in two variables has:

(1) exactly *one solution* if the two graphs have *different slopes,* or if just one of them has no slope;

(2) an *infinite set of solutions* if both graphs have the *same slope and the same y-intercept,* or both have no slope and the same *x*-intercept;

(3) *no solution* if both graphs have the *same slope but different y-intercepts,* or else no slope and different *x*-intercepts.

EXAMPLE 2 Tell how many solutions each system has.

a. $4x - 3y = 2$
   $\frac{1}{3}x - \frac{1}{4}y = 1$

b. $2x + y = 3$
   $x - 3y = 6$

c. $\quad 2y = -6$
   $4y - 1 = -13$

SOLUTION a. Both graphs have the same slope, $\frac{4}{3}$, but different y-intercepts: $-\frac{2}{3}$ and -4. Hence the system has *no solution.*

b. The two graphs have slope -2 and $\frac{1}{3}$. Hence the system has exactly one solution.

c. Both graphs have slope $m = 0$ and y-intercept -3. Therefore the system has an infinite number of solutions.

In Exercises 1–9 the diagram shows the graphs of the equations in the given system. State what appears to be the solution set of the system.

1. $x + 2y = 4$
   $3x - y = 5$

2. $2x - y = 2$
   $x - y = 2$

3. $\frac{1}{2}x + \frac{1}{3}y = 1$
   $3x + 2y = 6$

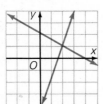
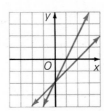
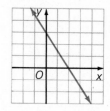

4. $4x - 10y = 20$
   $-2x + 5y = -5$

5. $3x + 4y = -5$
   $x - y = 3$
   $2x + y = 0$

6. $x = 2$
       $y = -1$
   $x - 2y = 2$

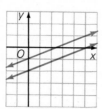
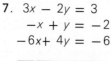

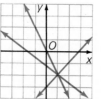
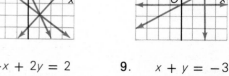
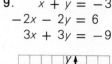

7. $3x - 2y = 3$
   $-x + y = -2$
   $-6x + 4y = -6$

8. $-x + 2y = 2$
   $2x - 4y = 4$
   $x - 2y = 3$

9. $x + y = -3$
   $-2x - 2y = 6$
   $3x + 3y = -9$

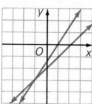
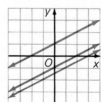
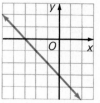

10–18. For the linear systems in Exercises 1–9 explain how you would verify that the solution sets are what the graphs make them appear to be.

In Exercises 1–16 (a) graph the given system of equations, (b) determine the apparent solution set of the system, and (c) verify that the apparent solution set actually is the solution set.

A   1. $x + y = 2$
       $x - y = 0$

2. $x + 2y = 2$
   $x - y = -1$

3. $-x + 3y = 5$
   $2x + y = 4$

4. $x - 2y = 4$
   $2x - y = 5$

5. $x = 4$
   $x - 2y = 2$

6. $3x + y = 6$
   $y = 3$

7. $4x - 5y = 2$
   $-\frac{4}{3}x + \frac{5}{3}y = -\frac{2}{3}$

8. $-x + 3y = 2$
   $2x - 6y = -4$

9. $y - 2x = 1$
   $2x - y = 1$

10. $y - 4x = 2$
    $4x - y = 2$

B 11. $2x - y = -4$
    $x + 2y = 3$
    $x - 3y = -7$

12. $x - 2y = 4$
    $3x + y = -2$
    $x + 3y = -6$

13. $x + y = 0$
    $x - y = 0$
    $3x + y = 3$

14. $-2x - 4y = -4$
    $x - y = 1$
    $x + 2y = 2$

15. $-x - 2y = 4$
    $2x + 4y = -8$
    $x + 2y = -4$

16. $4x + 6y = 12$
    $-2x - 3y = 3$
    $-4x - 6y = 6$

In Exercises 17–20 **(a)** use the theorem stated on page 113 to show that the given system has exactly one solution, and **(b)** graph the system.

17. $x - 3y = 1$
    $5x - 14y = 3$

18. $4x + y = 4$
    $10x + 3y = 10$

19. $7x - y = 4$
    $8x - y = 4$

20. $7x + 3y = 6$
    $5x + 2y = 6$

4–2 *solving a system of equations*

Your aim in solving a system of two linear equations in two variables is the same as that in solving a linear equation in one variable. That is, you want to *transform the system into an equivalent one,* in this case of the form

$$x = a$$
$$y = b,$$

which gives the solution explicitly.

Consider the system:

$$2x + 3y = 4 \quad (1)$$
$$x - 2y = 6 \quad (2)$$

Using the properties of equality, you can *multiply* both members of Equation (1) by the same nonzero number, say, 2, and likewise multiply Equation (2) by 3 and thereby obtain the *equivalent system:*

$$4x + 6y = 8 \qquad 2 \times (1) = (1')$$
$$3x - 6y = 18 \qquad 3 \times (2) = (2')$$

Equations (1) and (1') above are equivalent, and so are (2) and (2'). The *sum* of Equations (1') and (2'),

$$7x = 26, \qquad ((1') + (2'))$$

obtained by adding the left members and right members of both equations, is called a *linear combination* of the two equations (1) and (2). Note that one of the variables was eliminated in forming Equation ((1') + (2')), enabling us to solve directly for the other one.

In general, when you multiply both members of an equation by the same nonzero constant, and add the resulting expressions to the corresponding members of another equation, you obtain a linear combination of the two equations.

Transformations That Produce an Equivalent System of Linear Equations

1. Replace any equation of the system with an equivalent equation.
2. Replace any equation of the system with a linear combination of that equation and another one of the given equations.
3. Substitute for one variable in any equation either **(a)** its actual value, or **(b)** an equivalent expression for that variable obtained from another equation in the system.

EXAMPLE   Solve the system: $x + 3y = 6$ (1)
$$2x - y = 5 \quad (2)$$

SOLUTION 1   *Linear-combination method*

1. By inspection you can see that the variable y can be eliminated from the system as follows: Replace Equation (2) with $3 \times$ Equation (2). (Transformation 1). Replace (2') with the linear combination (1) + (2'). (Transformation 2).

$$x + 3y = 6 \quad (1)$$
$$6x - 3y = 15 \quad (2')$$

$$x + 3y = 6 \quad (1)$$
$$7x = 21 \quad (2'')$$

2. Replace (2'') with an equation of the form $x = a$. (Transformation 1). We have now reduced the original system to:

$$x + 3y = 6 \quad (1)$$
$$x = 3 \quad (2''')$$

$$x + 3y = 6$$
$$x = 3$$

3. Now we can solve for y by substituting the value 3 for x in Equation (1). (Transformation 3).

$$3 + 3y = 6 \quad (1')$$
$$x = 3 \quad (2''')$$

4. Replace Equation (1') with an equation of the form $y = b$. The system has now been transformed to an equivalent one that states the solution explicitly.

$$y = 1$$
$$x = 3$$

5. Check by substituting $x = 3$ and $y = 1$ in both Equations (1) and (2).

$$x + 3y = 6 \quad (1) \qquad\qquad 2x - y = 5 \quad (2)$$
$$3 + 3(1) = 6 \checkmark \qquad\qquad 2(3) - 1 = 5 \checkmark$$

$\therefore$ the solution set is $\{(3, 1)\}$. **Answer.**

Note: You could equally well have eliminated x instead of y in Step 1 by multiplying Equation (1) by -2 and adding the resulting equation to Equation (2). Also, in Step 3 you could have solved for y by substituting 3 for x in Equation (2) instead of in Equation (1).

SOLUTION 2   *Substitution method*

1. Replace Equation (1) with an expression for x in terms of y. (Transformation 1).

$$x = 6 - 3y \quad (1')$$
$$2x - y = 5 \quad (2)$$

2. Substitute in Equation (2) the expression for x in Equation (1'), and solve for y. (Transformation 3).

$$2(6 - 3y) - y = 5 \quad (2')$$
$$-7y = -7 \quad (2'')$$
$$y = 1 \quad (2''')$$

3. Solve for x in Equation (1') by substituting the value for y in Equation (2'''). (Transformation 3).

$$x = 6 - 3 \cdot 1 = 3 \quad (1'')$$

4. The original system has been transformed to the equivalent one that gives the solution directly.

$$y = 1$$
$$x = 3$$

5. Check the answer as in Step 5 of Solution 1.

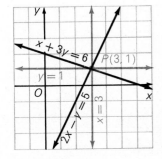

Figure 4

Figure 4 shows that the original system was finally transformed into a system of equations whose graphs are a pair of lines parallel to the two axes and having the same point of intersection (that is, the same solution) as the graphs of the original system. In general, the graph of an equation formed from a given pair of equations by using one or more of the transformations listed on page 116 is a line through the point of intersection of the graphs of the given pair if these lines intersect. (If the graphs of the given pair of equations are parallel lines, the graph of the new equation is parallel to them; if they are coincident, the new line is also coincident with them.)

State the value by which you would multiply both members of the second equation before adding equations to obtain a linear combination in which the coefficient of the variable printed in red will be 0.

1. $4x + 3y = -2$
   $5x - y = 7$

2. $6x - 5y = 8$
   $-x + 2y = 1$

3. $8x + 5y = 5$
   $2x - 4y = 3$

4. $4x + 9y = 5$
   $-2x + 3y = 5$

5. $7x - 6y = 0$
   $3x - 2y = -1$

6. $-x + 3y = 2$
   $-x - 4y = -4$

State how to form a linear combination of the two equations to obtain an equation in which the coefficient of the variable printed in red is 0.

7. $3x + 3y = 2$
   $5x - 2y = 1$

8. $7x + 3y = -1$
   $2x - 9y = 3$

9. $2x + y = 1$
   $5x + 2y = 4$

10. $3x + 4y = 2$
    $4x + 9y = 3$

11. $-3x + 3y = 4$
    $-5x + 6y = 3$

12. $\frac{2}{3}x - \frac{1}{5}y = -\frac{2}{15}$
    $x - \frac{1}{7}y = 2$

Transform the given equation into an equivalent equation expressing the variable printed in red in terms of the other variable.

13. $x - y = 4$

14. $4x + y = 6$

15. $6p - 3q = 3$

16. $2m - 6n = 2$

17. $5r + 2s - 3 = 0$

18. $3t - 4u - 5 = 0$

19. $3x + 2y = x - y + 4$

20. $2x - y = 5x - 3y + 1$

State how to transform each system into the equivalent system shown in red at the right.

21. $2x + 3y = 8$ $2x + 3y = 8$
    $x - 3y = -5$ $3x = 3$

22. $x + 3y = 4$ $x + 3y = 4$
    $x - y = 6$ $4y = -2$

23. $2x + 8y = 4$ $x = 2 - 4y$
    $x - 3y = 5$ $2 - 4y - 3y = 5$

24. $4x - y = 2$ $y = 4x - 2$
    $x + 3y = 4$ $x + 12x - 6 = 4$

A **1-12.** Solve the systems of equations in Oral Exercises 1–12 by the linear-combination method.

13-24. Solve the systems of equations in Oral Exercises 1–12 by the substitution method.

In Exercises 25–28 find the solution set of the given system.

B 25. $2x + 5y = 6$
$-x + 2y = -3$
$4x - y = 12$

27. $4x - y = 12$
$2x + y = 9$
$x + 2y = 7$

26. $8x - y = 2$
$3x + 2y = -4$
$x - 3y = 6$

28. $x + 6y = 1$
$-x + 2y = 3$
$2x + y = -3$

Although the systems in Exercises 29–32 are not systems of linear equations in x and y, they can be solved by the methods of this section. First solve for $\dfrac{1}{x}$ and $\dfrac{1}{y}$; then determine the values of x and y.

29. $\dfrac{1}{x} - \dfrac{1}{y} = 3$

$\dfrac{2}{x} + \dfrac{3}{y} = -4$

31. $\dfrac{3}{x} - \dfrac{4}{y} = -1$

$-\dfrac{1}{x} + \dfrac{2}{y} = 3$

30. $\dfrac{2}{x} + \dfrac{5}{y} = 1$

$\dfrac{1}{x} + \dfrac{2}{y} = 1$

32. $\dfrac{1}{x} + \dfrac{2}{y} = 0$

$-\dfrac{2}{x} + \dfrac{3}{y} = 14$

Determine A and B so that the graph of the given equation will contain the points whose coordinates are given.

C 33. $Ax + By = 7$; $(2, 1)$ and $(5, -1)$

34. $Ax + By = -2$; $(1, 2)$ and $(4, 6)$

35. $Ax - y = B$; $(3, -2)$ and $(4, 1)$

36. $2x + Ay = B$; $(5, 1)$ and $(2, 3)$

37. Prove that for all real numbers m_1, m_2, b_1, and b_2 such that $m_1 \neq m_2$, the following systems of equations are equivalent.

$$y = m_1x + b_1 \qquad \text{and} \qquad x = \dfrac{b_1 - b_2}{m_2 - m_1}$$
$$y = m_2x + b_2 \qquad\qquad\qquad y = \dfrac{m_2b_1 - m_1b_2}{m_2 - m_1}$$

38. Prove that for all real numbers m, b_1, and b_2, the solution set of each of the systems

$$y = mx + b_1 \qquad \text{and} \qquad x = b_1$$
$$y = mx + b_2 \qquad\qquad\qquad x = b_2$$

is an infinite set or the empty set according as $b_1 = b_2$ or $b_1 \neq b_2$.

39. Prove that for all real numbers m, b_1, and b_2, the solution set of the system

$$y = mx + b_1$$
$$x = b_2$$

   is $\{(b_2, mb_2 + b_1)\}$.

40. Use the results of Exercises 37–39 to prove the theorem stated on page 113.

41. Use the results of Exercises 37–39 to prove that two lines are parallel if and only if each line has no slope and different x-intercepts or both lines have the same slope and different y-intercepts.

4–3   *determinants*

You can find general formulas for the solution of a system of two linear equations in two variables by solving the general system

$$a_1x + b_1y = c_1 \qquad (1)$$
$$a_2x + b_2y = c_2 \qquad (2)$$

where a_1, b_1, c_1, a_2, b_2, and $c_2 \in \mathcal{R}$. Multiplying Equation (1) by b_2 and Equation (2) by $-b_1$, you get:

$$a_1b_2x + b_1b_2y = c_1b_2$$
$$-a_2b_1x - b_1b_2y = -c_2b_1.$$

Adding these equations gives

$$(a_1b_2 - a_2b_1)x = c_1b_2 - c_2b_1.$$

Similarly, multiplying Equation (1) by $-a_2$ and Equation (2) by a_1, and adding, you get

$$(a_1b_2 - a_2b_1)y = a_1c_2 - a_2c_1.$$

Therefore, if $a_1b_2 - a_2b_1 \neq 0$, you have

$$x = \frac{c_1b_2 - c_2b_1}{a_1b_2 - a_2b_1} \quad \text{and} \quad y = \frac{a_1c_2 - a_2c_1}{a_1b_2 - a_2b_1}. \qquad (3)$$

You can check that the values for x and y given by the formulas (3) do in fact satisfy Equations (1) and (2).

EXAMPLE 1   Use the formulas (3) to solve the system.

$$x - 2y = 5$$
$$3x + 4y = -5$$

SOLUTION   You have

$$a_1 = 1, \ b_1 = -2, \ c_1 = 5$$

and

$$a_2 = 3, \ b_2 = 4, \ c_2 = -5.$$

Substituting in the formulas (3), you get:

$$x = \frac{5 \cdot 4 - (-5)(-2)}{1 \cdot 4 - 3(-2)} \qquad\qquad y = \frac{1(-5) - 3 \cdot 5}{1 \cdot 4 - 3(-2)}$$

$$= \frac{20 - 10}{4 + 6} = \frac{10}{10} = 1 \qquad\qquad = \frac{-5 - 15}{4 + 6} = \frac{-20}{10} = -2$$

Checking that $(1, \ -2)$ is a solution is left to you.

$\therefore$ the solution set is $\{(1, \ -2)\}$. **Answer.**

There is a convenient way to denote the numerators and the denominator in the equations (3) for x and y.

For any $a_1, \ b_1, \ a_2, \ b_2 \in \mathfrak{R}$, the **determinant** $D = \begin{vmatrix} a_1 & b_1 \\ a_2 & b_2 \end{vmatrix}$ has the value $a_1b_2 - a_2b_1$.

Notice that the square array of numerals, set off with vertical bars (not absolute-value signs!), is just another numeral for "$a_1b_2 - a_2b_1$." The numerals $a_1, \ b_1, \ a_2, \ b_2$ in the array are called the entries (or elements) of the determinant.

Here is a convenient way to remember how to evaluate the determinant:

$$\begin{vmatrix} a_1 & b_1 \\ a_2 & b_2 \end{vmatrix} = a_1b_2 - a_2b_1$$

You simply take the difference of products as indicated.

From Equations (3) and the definition of D, you can see that, for $D \neq 0$,

$$x = \frac{D_x}{D} \qquad \text{and} \qquad y = \frac{D_y}{D} \qquad\qquad (4)$$

where $D = \begin{vmatrix} a_1 & b_1 \\ a_2 & b_2 \end{vmatrix}$, $D_x = \begin{vmatrix} c_1 & b_1 \\ c_2 & b_2 \end{vmatrix}$, and $D_y = \begin{vmatrix} a_1 & c_1 \\ a_2 & c_2 \end{vmatrix}$

Notice that the entries $a_1, \ b_1, \ a_2, \ b_2$ of D are just the coefficients of x and y in Equations (1) and (2); D is called the determinant of coefficients. To obtain the entries for D_x, you replace the x-coefficients $a_1, \ a_2$ in D with the constants $c_1, \ c_2$. Similarly, to obtain the entries for D_y, you replace the y-coefficients $b_1, \ b_2$ in D with the constants $c_1, \ c_2$.

The solution of a linear system in determinant form (4) is called Cramer's Rule. If $D = 0$, then either the system is inconsistent or the system has an infinite solution set.

EXAMPLE 2   Use Cramer's Rule to solve the system:

$$2x + y = 6$$
$$3x - 4y = 9$$

SOLUTION   By inspection, you have

$$D = \begin{vmatrix} 2 & 1 \\ 3 & -4 \end{vmatrix} = -8 - 3 = -11.$$

Then

$$x = \frac{D_x}{D} = \frac{\begin{vmatrix} 6 & 1 \\ 9 & -4 \end{vmatrix}}{-11} = \frac{-24 - 9}{-11} = \frac{-33}{-11} = 3,$$

and

$$y = \frac{D_y}{D} = \frac{\begin{vmatrix} 2 & 6 \\ 3 & 9 \end{vmatrix}}{-11} = \frac{18 - 18}{-11} = \frac{0}{-11} = 0.$$

You can check that $(3, 0)$ is a solution.

$\therefore$ the solution set is $\{(3, 0)\}$.   Answer.

ORAL EXERCISES   State the value of the given determinant.

1. $\begin{vmatrix} a & b \\ c & d \end{vmatrix}$

2. $\begin{vmatrix} p & q \\ r & s \end{vmatrix}$

3. $\begin{vmatrix} 2 & m \\ 3 & n \end{vmatrix}$

4. $\begin{vmatrix} 4 & x \\ -5 & y \end{vmatrix}$

5. $\begin{vmatrix} 2 & 5 \\ 0 & 3 \end{vmatrix}$

6. $\begin{vmatrix} 1 & 2 \\ 5 & 0 \end{vmatrix}$

7. $\begin{vmatrix} 2 & 3 \\ 4 & 6 \end{vmatrix}$

8. $\begin{vmatrix} 4 & 8 \\ -1 & 2 \end{vmatrix}$

9. $\begin{vmatrix} a & b \\ -\dfrac{1}{b} & \dfrac{1}{a} \end{vmatrix}$

10. $\begin{vmatrix} x & y \\ \dfrac{2}{y} & \dfrac{1}{x} \end{vmatrix}$

11. $\begin{vmatrix} a & b \\ 3a & 3b \end{vmatrix}$

12. $\begin{vmatrix} p & q \\ kp & kq \end{vmatrix}$

For the system of equations

$$2x - 3y = 4$$
$$5x + 6y = 7$$

name the number you would substitute for the given letter in

$$x = \frac{D_x}{D} = \frac{\begin{vmatrix} e & f \\ g & h \end{vmatrix}}{\begin{vmatrix} a & b \\ c & d \end{vmatrix}}, \quad \text{and} \quad y = \frac{D_y}{D} = \frac{\begin{vmatrix} i & j \\ k & l \end{vmatrix}}{\begin{vmatrix} a & b \\ c & d \end{vmatrix}}.$$

13. a	15. c	17. e	19. g	21. i	23. k
14. b	16. d	18. f	20. h	22. j	24. l

WRITTEN EXERCISES Use the formulas (3) on page 120 to find the solution set of the given system.

A 1. $3x - y = 3$
       $x + 2y = 8$

2. $x + 4y = 6$
    $2x - 3y = 1$

3. $x + y = 1$
    $2x + 3y = 6$

4. $2x + y = 3$
    $3x - 2y = 8$

5. $2x + 3y = 3$
    $6x - 5y = 9$

6. $3x - 8y = 6$
    $5x + 4y = -3$

Evaluate the given determinant.

7. $\begin{vmatrix} 1 & 2 \\ 3 & 4 \end{vmatrix}$

8. $\begin{vmatrix} 4 & 6 \\ 2 & 5 \end{vmatrix}$

9. $\begin{vmatrix} 3 & 0 \\ 2 & -6 \end{vmatrix}$

10. $\begin{vmatrix} 7 & -2 \\ 1 & 0 \end{vmatrix}$

Solve each equation for a.

11. $\begin{vmatrix} 3 & 2 \\ 1 & a \end{vmatrix} = 4$

12. $\begin{vmatrix} a & 5 \\ 2 & 7 \end{vmatrix} = 4$

13. $\begin{vmatrix} a & 4 \\ a & 3 \end{vmatrix} = 2$

14. $\begin{vmatrix} 2 & -1 \\ a & a \end{vmatrix} = 9$

15. $\begin{vmatrix} a & -2 \\ 3 & a \end{vmatrix} = 7$

16. $\begin{vmatrix} 4 & a \\ a & 6 \end{vmatrix} = -1$

Use Cramer's Rule to solve the given system.

B 17. $4x - 5y = 2$
       $3x + y = -4$

18. $x - 4y = 7$
     $2x + 5y = 4$

19. $x + 2y = 0$
    $x - 3y = 1$

20. $5x - 2y = 3$
    $7x + 4y = 8$

21. $3x + 2y = 4$
    $-x + y = 1$

22. $5x - 3y = -7$
    $2x + y = 8$

programming
in BASIC

EXERCISE

Write a computer program that uses the formulas on page 120 to solve a system of two equations in two variables. Be sure to include a special print-out if A1*B2−A2*B1 is 0.

4–4 *using two variables to solve problems*

The following examples illustrate how you can sometimes solve practical problems by translating the given relationships into a system of equations.

EXAMPLE 1 Jack has $10.00 to spend for entertainment. He found that he can spend all the money for two LP records and a ticket for himself to the basketball game, or he can buy one of the records and two tickets to the game for himself and a friend and have $2.75 left for refreshments. What is the price of a basketball ticket, and how much does an LP record cost?

SOLUTION   1. The problem asks for the price of a basketball ticket and for the price of an LP record.

2. Let the price of a ticket be x cents and the price of a record be y cents.

3.
$$
\underbrace{\text{The price of one ticket}}_{x} \quad \underbrace{\text{added to}}_{+} \quad \underbrace{\text{the price of two records}}_{2y} \quad \underset{\downarrow}{\text{is}} \quad \underbrace{\$10.00}_{1000} \text{ (1000 cents).}
$$

$$
x + 2y = 1000
$$

$$
\underbrace{\text{The price of two tickets}}_{2x} \quad \underbrace{\text{added to}}_{+} \quad \underbrace{\text{the price of one record}}_{y} \quad \underset{\downarrow}{\text{is}} \quad \underbrace{\$10.00 \text{ less } \$2.75}_{725} \text{ (\$7.25).}
$$

$$
2x + y = 725
$$

4. Solve the system: $x + 2y = 1000$
$$2x + y = 725$$

Showing that the solution of this system is (150, 425) and checking this result in the words of the problem (Step 5) is left to you.

∴ a basketball ticket costs $1.50 and an LP record costs $4.25.
Answer.

To solve motion problems about airplanes, as in Example 2, you must know the meanings of the following phrases:

tail wind: a wind blowing in the same direction as the one in which the airplane is heading.

head wind: a wind blowing in the direction opposite to the one in which the airplane is heading.

wind speed: the speed of the wind.

airspeed: the speed of the airplane in still air.

groundspeed: the speed of the airplane relative to the ground.

With a tail wind, an airplane's groundspeed is the sum of its airspeed and the wind speed. With a head wind, the groundspeed is the difference between the airspeed and the wind speed.

EXAMPLE 2   With a given head wind, a certain jet aircraft can travel 4800 kilometers
in 6 hours. But flying in the opposite direction with the same wind blowing,
the plane can fly that distance in one hour less. Find the plane's airspeed
and the wind speed.

SOLUTION   1. The problem asks for the speed of the aircraft in still air and for the speed
of the wind.

2. Let x = the speed of the aircraft in kilometers per hour (km/h);
y = the wind speed in kilometers per hour.
The facts of the problem are listed below in the chart. (Recall the use
of the relationship $d = rt$ on page 46.)

	Ground Speed (km/h) r	Time (hr) t	Distance (km) $rt = d$
With a head wind	$x - y$	6	$6(x - y)$
With a tail wind	$x + y$	5	$5(x + y)$

3. Distance with a head wind   is   4800 kilometers.
$$6(x - y) \quad = \quad 4800$$

Distance with a tail wind   is   4800 kilometers.
$$5(x + y) \quad = \quad 4800$$

4. Solve the system:

$$\begin{array}{ll} 6(x - y) = 4800 & \quad x - y = 800 \\ 5(x + y) = 4800 & \quad x + y = 960 \end{array}$$

or

Completing Step 4 and checking your results (Step 5) are left to you.
You should find that the plane's airspeed is 880 km/h and that the wind
speed is 80 km/h. **Answer.**

ORAL EXERCISES   In Exercises 1–8 let x represent the number of dollars that Arnie has and
y represent the number of dollars that Bernie has. In each case, translate
the stated relationship into an equation in x and y.

1. Arnie and Bernie together have eight dollars.
2. Bernie has two dollars more than Arnie.
3. If Arnie had twice as much money as he has, he would have a dollar
more than Bernie has.
4. If Arnie and Bernie each had two dollars less, Bernie would have three
times as much as Arnie.

5. If Arnie and Bernie each had three dollars more, Arnie would have $\frac{3}{4}$ as much money as Bernie.

6. If Arnie had five times as much money as he has, he would have three times as much money as Bernie has.

7. If Arnie gave Bernie a dollar, Bernie would have three times as much money as Arnie.

8. If Bernie gave Arnie a dollar, Arnie and Bernie would each have the same amount of money.

In Exercises 9–14 the airspeed of the airplane is 400 kilometers per hour.

9. What is the plane's groundspeed on a windless day?

10. What is the plane's groundspeed if there is a head wind of 100 km/h?

11. What is the plane's groundspeed if there is a tail wind of 150 km/h?

12. How long would it take the plane to make a 1000 km flight on a windless day?

13. How long would it take the plane to make the flight against a head wind of 150 km/h?

14. How long would it take the plane to make the flight with a tail wind of 100 km/h?

In Exercises 15–20 let x represent the rate of a boat in still water and y represent the rate of the current, both in kilometers per hour.

15. What is the rate of the boat when it is traveling downstream?

16. What is the rate of the boat when traveling upstream?

17. Translate into an equation in x and y: The boat can travel downstream 23 kilometers in two hours.

18. Translate into an equation in x and y: The boat can travel upstream 17 kilometers in two hours.

19. If $y > x$ and you wanted to travel upstream, why would you prefer to walk?

20. If $y = x$, would you still prefer to walk if you wanted to travel upstream?

PROBLEMS

A

1. Use the relationships stated in Oral Exercises 7 and 8 to find how much money Arnie and Bernie each had.

2. Use the information given in Oral Exercises 15–18 to find the rate of the boat and the rate of the current.

3. One number is 7 more than another number. The sum of the numbers is 63. What are the numbers?

4. Two more than twice one number is 3 times another number. If 3 times the first number is 1 less than the second, what are the numbers?

5. Three times one number is $\frac{2}{3}$ of a second number. The first number is 10 more than twice the second number. Find the numbers.

6. The difference $x - y$ of two numbers is half their sum, and 3 times the difference is 3 more than x. Find the numbers.

7. The degree measure of one of two complementary angles is 30 less than twice that of the other. What are the degree measures of the angles?

8. The degree measure of one of two supplementary angles is 6 more than one-half that of the other. What are the degree measures of the angles?

9. A collection of dimes and quarters has a total value of five dollars and contains 29 coins. How many of each kind of coin are there in the collection?

10. Tickets for a benefit performance of a new movie sold at $5.50 for the orchestra section and $3.25 for the balcony. If the receipts from the sale of 1800 tickets totaled $7110, how many tickets were sold at each price?

11. A glass manufacturer makes two grades of glass which differ in silica content. If she has 2400 kilograms of silica with which to make one batch of each type, and she uses 510 more kilograms of silica for one type than for the other, how many kilograms of silica are used for each type?

12. In five years a boy will be two-thirds as old as his uncle. Three years ago he was half as old as the uncle is now. How old are the boy and his uncle?

13. With an 80 km/h head wind, a plane can fly a certain distance in four hours. Flying in the opposite direction with the same wind blowing, it can fly that distance in one hour less. What is the plane's airspeed?

14. Traveling downstream, a boat can go 18 km in 2 hours. Going upstream, it makes only $\frac{2}{3}$ this distance in twice the time. What is the rate of the boat in still water, and what is the rate of the current?

B   **15.** Find values of A and B so that the line whose equation is $Ax + By = 6$ will contain the points whose coordinates are $(6, 8)$ and $(15, -4)$.

16. Find values for a and b so that the set of ordered pairs

$$\{(x, y): y = ax^2 + b\}$$

will contain $(2, 3)$ and $(-3, 13)$.

17. If $\{(x, y): y = mx + b\}$ contains $(1, 7)$ and $(-1, 1)$, find m and b.

18. If $\{(x, y): y = mx + b\}$ contains $(-4, -1)$ and $(2, -4)$, find m and b.

19. Two temperature scales are established, one, the R scale where water under fixed conditions freezes at $5°$ and boils at $405°$, and the other, the C scale where water freezes at $0°$ and boils at $100°$. If the R and C scales are linearly related, find an expression for any temperature R in terms of a temperature C.

20. The final velocity of a uniformly accelerated particle is linearly related to the elapsed time by the equation $v = v_0 + at$, where a and v_0 are constants. If $v = 15$ when $t = 10$, and $v = 35$ when $t = 25$, find values for v_0 and a.

In Problems 21–24, the original number is a positive integer whose decimal numeral contains two digits. In each problem, find this integer.

21. The sum of the numbers named by the digits is 8. When the digits are interchanged, the resulting numeral names a new number which exceeds the original number by 18.

22. The sum of the numbers named by the digits is 10. The original number is 2 less than three times the number represented when the order of the digits is reversed.

23. The number named by the units digit is 1 more than twice the number named by the tens digit. The number represented when the order of the digits is reversed is 7 less than 8 times the sum of the numbers named by the digits.

24. The number named by the tens digit is 5 more than the number named by the units digit. If the digits are interchanged and the number represented by the resulting numeral is added to the original number, the sum is 143.

25. A river steamer travels 48 km downstream in the same time that it travels 32 km upstream. The steamer's engines drive in still water at a rate which is 16 km/h greater than the rate of the current. Find the rate of the current.

26. Jean finds that in still water her outboard can drive her boat 3 times as fast as the rate of the current in Pony River. A 16 km trip up the river and back requires 4 hours. Find the rate of the current.

C   **27.** Two railroad workers are together in a 1.2 km mountain tunnel. One walks east and the other west in order to be out of the tunnel before the Bad Creek Express comes through at 60 km/h. Each man reaches his respective end of the tunnel in 6 minutes. If the man walking east reaches the east entrance just before the train enters, and the train passes the other man 0.24 km beyond the west end of the tunnel, at what rate did each man walk?

28. Two kilometers upstream from his starting point, a rower passed a log floating with the current. After rowing upstream for one more hour, he rowed back and reached his starting point just as the log arrived. How fast was the current flowing?

Objective 1, page 111 **5.** Graph the system of linear equations

$$5x + 2y = 8$$
$$x - y = 3$$

and determine whether or not it is consistent.

6. Determine how many solutions each system has.

a. $x - 2y = 3$ **b.** $2x - 3y = 1$ **c.** $x - 3y = 2$
   $x - 3y = 3$ $-2x + 3y = 1$ $-2x + 6y = -4$

Handwritten annotations:
$+ + u = 10$
$10 + 1u + 2 = 3(10u + +)$
$10T + u = 30u + 3T + ^-2$
$7D + + ^-29u = ^-2.$

Objective 2, page 111 **7.** Solve by the linear-combination method.

$$2x - 3y = 6$$
$$2x - y = 10$$

8. Solve by the substitution method.

$$3x - 2y = -3$$
$$5x + y = 8$$

Objective 3, page 111 **9.** Use determinants to solve the system.

$$3x + 4y = -7$$
$$4x + 5y = -10$$

Objective 4, page 111 **10.** Jack has $30 with which to buy some new clothes. He can spend all the money on two pairs of double-knit slacks and two shirts, or he can buy one pair of the slacks and five shirts and have $5 left to buy neckties. What is the price of one pair of slacks? of one shirt?

Check your answers with those printed at the back of the book.

Charles Babbage
1792–1871

Charles Babbage shortly after 1810 sought to revive mathematical research in England. As a result, a group of young Cambridge mathematicians, of which Babbage was one of the leaders, founded the Analytical Society. After more than half a century of waning interest in mathematics in England, the stage was set for renewed interest in mathematics for the latter part of the nineteenth century.

   Babbage did not produce any outstanding new results in mathematics. However, he may be called a forefather of our modern computers. In 1833 Babbage conceived a "difference engine." In fact, it was a digital computer which would have been able to perform arithmetic operations and even store data using gears, wheels and levers. His "engine" unfortunately was never completed.

systems of inequalities in two variables

Objectives | After completing the next two sections, you should be able to:
1. Graph the solution set of a system of linear inequalities in two variables.
2. Solve linear-programming problems in two variables.

4-5 graphing a system of linear inequalities

How would you describe the graph of the solution set of the following system of linear inequalities?

$$x + y < 9$$
$$y \geq 2x$$

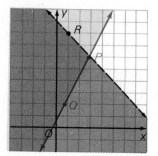

Figure 5

In Figure 5, gray shading is used to show (part of) the open half-plane that consists of the points lying below the line with equation $x + y = 9$. This is the graph of the inequality

$$x + y < 9$$

(recall Section 3–4). Red shading in Figure 5 shows the closed half-plane that is the graph of

$$y \geq 2x.$$

The region in Figure 5 where the two colors overlap is the *intersection* of the two half-planes; it consists of the points whose coordinates satisfy *both* inequalities in the given system. Thus, this region is the graph of the solution set of the given system. Note that the region includes the part of its boundary indicated by a solid half-line (the half-line from P through Q), but does not include the part shown by a dashed half-line (the half-line from P through R). P itself is not in the region.

In general:

> To show the graph of the solution set of a system of inequalities, you take these steps:
> 1. Graph each inequality in the system.
> 2. Show by heavier shading the region that consists of those points that belong to all of the graphs drawn in Step 1.

EXAMPLE Graph the solution set of the system:

$$0 \leq x \leq 7$$
$$x + 2y \geq 4$$

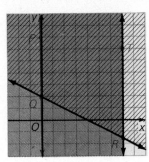

SOLUTION The given system is equivalent to the following system of *three* inequalities, hose graphs are shown in the diagram at the left as indicated:

$$0 \leq x \text{ (red shading)}$$

$$x \leq 7 \text{ (gray shading)}$$

$$x + 2y \geq 4 \text{ (diagonal hatching)}$$

The region common to all graphs is the graph of the system; it is the region between the rays $\overset{\circ}{QP}$ and $\overset{\circ}{RT}$ and above the segment $\overline{QR}$, *including all boundary points.* **Answer.**

ORAL EXERCISES The lines whose equations are $y = 2x$, $y = x + 3$, and $y = 1$ separate the plane into seven regions numbered as shown at the left. In Exercises 1–10 name the region or regions that form the graph of the solution set of the given system, and identify the part(s), if any, of the boundary that belongs to the graph.

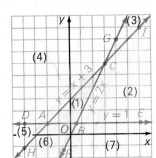

1. $y > x + 3$
   $y < 2x$

2. $y > x + 3$
   $y < 1$

3. $y < 2x$
   $y \leq 1$

4. $y > 1$
   $y \geq 2x$

5. $y \leq x + 3$
   $y \geq 2x$
   $y \geq 1$

6. $y > x + 3$
   $y > 2x$
   $y > 1$

7. $y \leq x + 3$
   $y \geq 1$

8. $y < x + 3$
   $y > 2x$

9. $y \leq x + 3$
   $y \leq 2x$
   $y \leq 1$

10. $y \leq x + 3$
    $y \leq 1$
    $y \geq 2x$

WRITTEN EXERCISES In a coordinate plane, graph the solution set of each system.

A

1. $x \geq 0$
   $y \geq 0$

2. $y \geq x$
   $y \leq -x$

3. $y \leq x$
   $x \geq 0$

4. $y \geq 0$
   $x \leq 0$

5. $y \geq x$
   $y \leq x + 1$

6. $y \geq 2x$
   $y \leq 2x + 3$

7. $y < 2x$
   $y > 2x - 1$

8. $y < x$
   $y > x - 1$

9. $x + 2y \leq 4$
   $x - y \geq 2$

10. $2x - y \geq 2$
    $x - 2y \leq 2$

11. $2x - 3y > 6$
    $3x + 2y < 6$

12. $x - 5y < 10$
    $5y + 2x > 10$

13. $1 \leq x \leq 4$

14. $3 \leq x \leq 5$

15. $x + 1 < y < x + 3$

16. $x - 1 < y < x$

17. $5 < x + y < 6$

18. $-1 < x - y < 1$

19. $0 < x < y$

20. $1 < y < 2x$

B 21. $|y| \leq 2$ and $y \geq x$

22. $|x| \leq 3$ and $y \leq x + 2$

23. $|x + 2y| \leq 2$

24. $|2x - 3y| \leq 6$

25. $y > 2x$
    $1 < x < 2$

26. $y < 3x$
    $2 < y < 3$

27. $2 < x + y \leq 4$
    $1 \leq x - y < 3$

28. $-2 \leq x + y \leq 2$
    $-3 < x - y < 3$

29. $x \geq 2$
    $x + 2y \geq 4$
    $2x + y \geq 6$

30. $y \geq 2$
    $2x + 3y \geq 6$
    $x - y \leq 0$

C 31. $0 \leq x \leq 3$
       $|2x + 3y| \leq 3$

32. $|x + 2y| < 6$
    $|x| < 3$

33. $|x + y| \leq 4$
    $|x - y| \leq 4$

34. $|x + y| > 2$
    $|x - y| > 2$

4-6 *linear programming*

The following situation illustrates a type of problem in economics that involves a system of inequalities in its solution:

An assembler of dune buggies carries two models: the Zoom Buggie and the Dune Dee. The company has equipment to assemble as many as 60 Zoom Buggies and as many as 45 Dune Dees per month. It takes 150 man-hours to assemble a Zoom Buggie and 200 man-hours to assemble a Dune Dee, and the company has up to 12,000 man-hours available for dune-buggy assembly each month. If the profit gained on each Zoom Buggie is $120 and on each Dune Dee is $180, find the number of each model the firm should assemble to gain the maximum (greatest) profit each month.

To solve this problem, let x represent the number of Zoom Buggies and y the number of Dune Dees that are assembled each month. Then

$$120x = \text{the monthly profit on Zoom Buggies,}$$
$$180y = \text{the monthly profit on Dune Dees, and}$$
$$120x + 180y = \text{the monthly profit on the two models together.}$$

The value of x and y must satisfy the following system of inequalities, called constraints:

$\left. \begin{array}{l} x \geq 0 \\ y \geq 0 \end{array} \right\}$ (The firm must assemble a nonnegative number of each model.)

$x \leq 60$ (At most 60 Zoom Buggies can be assembled each month.)

$y \leq 45$ (At most 45 Dune Dees can be assembled each month.)

$150x + 200y \leq 12000$ (Up to 12,000 man-hours are available for assembly each month.)

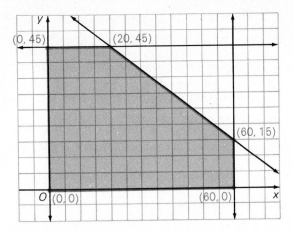

Figure 6

The shaded portion of Figure 6 is the solution set of the foregoing system of constraints. Notice that the graph of this solution set is the intersection of a finite number of closed half-planes (actually, five closed half-planes). The graph is called the feasibility region, and the points of the graph where the lines that form the boundary intersect are called corner points of the feasibility region. We can then find the maximum value of $120x + 180y$ over the feasibility region by using the following theorem that we accept without proof.

Theorem. If a and b are any real numbers, and if the linear expression $ax + by$ has a maximum (greatest) value over a feasibility region which is the intersection of a finite number of closed half-planes and which has corner points, then the maximum occurs for the coordinates of some corner point.

Similarly, if $ax + by$ has a minimum (least) value over the region, then the minimum occurs for the coordinates of some corner point.

Therefore, to maximize or minimize $120x + 180y$ (find its greatest or least value), we evaluate it at the five corner points, whose coordinates are found by solving simultaneously the equations of the boundary lines determining those points:

Corner Point	$120x + 180y$
(0, 0)	$120 \cdot 0 + 180 \cdot 0 = 0$
(60, 0)	$120 \cdot 60 + 180 \cdot 0 = 7200$
(60, 15)	$120 \cdot 60 + 180 \cdot 15 = 9900$
(20, 45)	$120 \cdot 20 + 180 \cdot 45 = 10,500$
(0, 45)	$120 \cdot 0 + 180 \cdot 45 = 8100$

Thus, over the feasibility region, the maximum value of $120x + 180y$ is 10,500 and this occurs at the point $(20, 45)$. The minimum value of $120x + 180y$ is 0 and occurs at the origin, that is, when no dune buggies are produced. Therefore, to maximize the monthly profit, the firm should assemble 20 Zoom Buggies and 45 Dune Dees, and thus obtain a profit of $10,500 each month.

The process illustrated in this example is called linear programming because it furnishes a means of finding maximum and minimum values of a linear expression over a feasibility region determined by linear inequalities.

ORAL EXERCISES

State the value of the given expression for the coordinates of the given point. Refer to the graphs shown at the left.

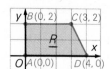

1. $x + y$; A

2. $x + y$; B

3. $x + y$; C

4. $x + y$; D

5. $x - y$; E

6. $x - y$; F

7. $x - y$; G

8. $x - y$; H

9. $x - 2y$; E

10. $x - 2y$; F

11. $x - 2y$; G

12. $x - 2y$; H

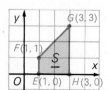

State the requested value for coordinates of points in the given closed region.

13. minimum of $(x + y)$; R

14. maximum of $(x + y)$; R

15. minimum of $(x - y)$; S

16. maximum of $(x - y)$; S

17. minimum of $(x - 2y)$; S

18. maximum of $(x - 2y)$; S

WRITTEN EXERCISES

In Exercises 1–6:

a. Graph the solution set of the system of inequalities.
b. Find the coordinates of the corner points of the graph.
c. Find the value of the linear expression printed in red at each of the corner points.
d. State the maximum and minimum values (if any) of the given linear expression under the given constraints.

A

1. $0 \leq x \leq 5$
   $1 \leq y \leq -x + 8$; $2x - y$

2. $2 \leq x \leq 6$
   $3 \leq y \leq -2x + 16$; $y - x$

3. $y \geq x + 3$
   $y \leq 2x + 1$; $3x + 4y$

4. $1 \leq y \leq 2x - 3$
   $y \geq 2x - 5$; $-2x - y$

5. $0 \leq x \leq 10$
   $0 \leq y \leq 20$; $3x + y$
   $2x + y \leq 32$

6. $0 \leq x \leq 10$
   $0 \leq y \leq 20$; $3x + 2y$
   $2x + y \leq 32$

B   7. a. Explain why the linear expression $4x + 3y$ does not have a maximum value over the solution set of the system:

$$x \geq 0, \, y \geq 0, \, y \geq -x + 3, \, y \leq 2x + 6$$

b. What is the minimum value of $4x + y$ over that solution set?

8. a. Explain why the linear expression $2x + 5y$ does not have a minimum value over the solution set of the system:

$$x + 2y \leq 4, \, y \leq 2 + x, \, -2 \leq x \leq 2$$

b. What is the maximum value of $2x + y$ over the solution set?

Exercises 9 and 10 refer to the following situation:

A manufacturer wishes to produce two commodities, A and B. The number of units of material, labor, and equipment needed to produce one unit of each commodity is shown in the following table. Also shown is the available number of units of each of the items, material, labor, and equipment.

	A	B	Available
Material	3	2	240
Labor	4	1	120
Equipment	2	1	100

9. Find the maximum profit if each unit of commodity A earns a profit of $30 and each unit of B earns $10.

10. Find the maximum profit if each unit of A earns a profit of $30 and each unit of B earns $20.

C   11. Graph the solution set R of the system of inequalities $x \geq 0, \, y \geq 0$, $x + 2y \leq 8, \, 3x + 2y \leq 12$, and on the same coordinate plane graph the line with equation $x + y = p$ for $p = -2, 0, 3, 5$, and 8. Explain why the minimum value of $x + y$ over R is 0 and the maximum is 5.

12. Graph the set R of Exercise 11, and on the same coordinate plane graph the line with equation $x + 2y = p$ for $p = -4, 0, 4, 8$, and 12. For the coordinates of what point(s) does $x + 2y$ have its maximum value over R?

programming in BASIC

EXERCISE

Write a computer program that will assist you in solving a problem in linear programming. Plan to graph the inequalities by hand first, and decide in what order you wish to solve the systems of two linear equations to find the corner points. Then your computer program can find these corner points and evaluate at each one the expression you wish to maximize or minimize.

careers business

Linear programming is used in a great variety of cases in industrial and business operations. Such programming techniques are not only increasingly applied to finding the most economical production of various products, as we saw in Section 4–6, but to purchasing and distribution problems as well, to job assignments, to budgeting, and even to advertising.

It is important to note that often the relationships among the variables of the problem are only probable. For example, in the dune buggy example of Section 4-6, profits on each buggy are assumed to be constant while in fact such profits may vary depending on the sales volume. Linear programming is an approximation to a real-world situation. However, it is a sufficiently accurate mathematical model to be of great use to the world of business.

Mathematics is an essential part of many management training programs.

EXAMPLE   An advertising manager of a company considers the alternatives in advertising various products in two weekly magazines. A half-page advertisement costs $300 in magazine *A* and $250 in magazine *B* per weekly issue. A recent advertising survey indicates that for every issue, 6000 readers will notice the advertisement in magazine *A* and 5000 will see it in *B*. In addition, 2000 readers of *A* and 3000 of *B* per week will usually complete attached questionnaire cards for additional information. In order to profit from the advertising campaign, it was determined that at least 59,000 readers should be reached and at least 29,000 request cards for additional information must be received. How many weekly advertisements should be placed with each magazine in order to minimize the cost for these advertisements?

SOLUTION   Let *x* be the number of weekly advertisements with magazine *A* and *y* the number in magazine *B*. Graph the following equations:

Readers} $6000x + 5000y \geq 59{,}000$
Cards} $2000x + 3000y \geq 29{,}000$
  $x \geq 0$ $y \geq 0$

The feasibility region is shown at the left.

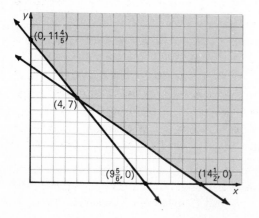

Determining the minimum value of $300x + 250y$, you find that 4 ads should be placed in magazine *A*, and 7 in magazine *B*.

Give the meaning of each of the following.

1. linear programming
2. feasibility region

3. corner point
4. maximize

Objective 1, page 130 Graph the solution set of each system.

5. $2x + 5y \leq 20$
   $x - 3y > 6$

6. $\quad x \geq 0$
   $\quad y \geq 0$
   $4x + 3y \leq 12$

7. $0 \leq x \leq 2$
   $3 \leq y \leq 6$
   $y \leq x + 4$

Objective 2, page 130

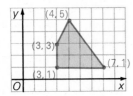

Determine the maximum and minimum values of the given expression over the feasibility region shown at the left.

8. $x + 2y$

9. $2x + y$

10. Find the maximum profit that can be realized on manufacturing x units of product A and y units of product B under the production constraints

$$0 \leq x \leq 100, \ 0 \leq y \leq 200, \ 2x + y \leq 300$$

if there is a profit of $30 on each unit of product A and a profit of $10 on each unit of product B.

Check your answers with those printed at the back of the book.

chapter summary

1. For a **system of two linear equations** in two variables, the graphs of the equations either intersect in a single point or are coincident or parallel lines. Correspondingly, the system has a single solution, an infinite number of solutions, or no solution. A system that has at least one solution is said to be **consistent**; otherwise, it is **inconsistent**.

2. You can solve a system of linear equations in two variables by making transformations that yield equivalent systems, using the *linear-combination method* or the *substitution method*. Transformations that produce an equivalent system of linear equations are the following:

   1. Replace any equation of the system with an equivalent equation in the same variables.
   2. Replace any equation of the system with the sum of that equation and an equation obtained by multiplying both members of another equation of the system by a real number.
   3. In any equation substitute for one variable (a) its value, if known, or (b) an equivalent expression for that variable obtained from another equation of the system.

3. You can also use **determinants** to solve such a system by applying **Cramer's Rule**.

4. Systems of linear equations can be applied to solve problems by translating relationships into a system of equations.

5. The solution set of a system of linear inequalities in two variables is the intersection of open or closed half-planes representing the inequalities.

6. If a linear expression has a maximum or minimum value over a feasibility region which is the intersection of a finite number of closed half-planes and which has corner points, then that value occurs for the coordinates of some corner point.

chapter test 4-1 Graph the given system of equations.

1. $2x - 3y = 0$
   $4x + 5y = 10$

2. $x - 5y = 5$
   $-x + 5y = 3$

4-2 3. Solve by the linear-combination method: $4x - 2y = 9$
   $x + 3y = 4$

4. Solve by the substitution method: $2x + 5y = 1$
   $3x - 4y = 1$

4-3 5. Solve for x: $\begin{vmatrix} 2x & 1 \\ x & 3 \end{vmatrix} = 15$

6. Use Cramer's Rule to solve: $x - 2y = 7$
   $2x + 3y = 6$

4-4 7. A first number is three more than twice a second number, and half the sum of the numbers is five. Find the numbers.

4-5 8. Graph the solution set of the following system.

$$0 \leq x \leq 3$$
$$0 \leq y < x + 2$$

4-6 9. Find the maximum value of $2x + 5y$ subject to the following system of constraints.

$$0 \leq x \leq 5$$
$$0 \leq y \leq 8$$
$$x + 2y \leq 19$$

10. Find the minimum value of $4x - 5y$ subject to the following constraints.

$$y \geq 0$$
$$x + y \leq 1$$
$$y \leq x + 1$$

programmed chapter review

4–1   1. A system of linear equations has either 0, 1, or a(n) __?__ number of solutions.

           2. A system of equations that has at least one solution is called a(n) __?__ system.

           3. A system of two linear equations in two variables has exactly one solution if the graphs of the equations have different __?__ .

4–2   4. Two systems of equations are __?__ if they have the same solution set.

           5. When you multiply both members of an equation by the same constant, and add the resulting expressions to the corresponding members of another equation, you obtain a(n) __?__ __?__ of the two equations.

           6. You can solve a system of linear equations by the __?__-__?__ method and also by the __?__ method.

4–3   7. You can also solve a system of linear equations with the use of __?__ .

           8. $\begin{vmatrix} a & b \\ c & d \end{vmatrix} = $ __?__ .

           9. The rule for writing the solution of a linear system in determinant form is called __?__ __?__ .

4–4   10. You can sometimes solve a practical problem by finding the __?__ __?__ of a system of linear equations.

          11. The two equations used to represent the following problem are __?__ and __?__ .

               "There are 26 students in a mathematics class. The number of boys in the class is five more than one-half the number of girls. How many boys and how many girls are in the class?"

4–5   12. The solution set of a system of linear inequalities is the intersection of open or closed __?__-__?__ .

4–6   13. In linear programming, the inequalities that the variables must satisfy are called __?__ .

          14. In linear programming, to find the maximum or __?__ value of a linear expression, you determine its value at the __?__ points of the __?__ region.

Answer column:

infinite

consistent

slopes

equivalent

linear
combination

linear-combination
substitution

determinants

$ad - bc$

Cramer's Rule

solution set

$x + y = 26;\ x = 5 + \frac{1}{2}y$

half-planes

constraints

minimum
corner
feasibility

. . . a citrus harvest. The expanding population has increased the demand for foodstuffs worldwide. Farming and food processing techniques must keep pace to provide an adequate supply of food.

graphs in space; determinants

systems of equations in three variables

Objectives

After completing the next three sections, you should be able to:
1. Draw graphs of ordered triples and linear equations in space.
2. Determine the x-, y-, and z-intercepts of a given plane and the traces of the plane in the coordinate planes.
3. Draw the space-graph of a given linear equation in three variables.
4. Solve a system of three linear equations in three variables by transforming it into a simple equivalent system.

5-1 *coordinates in space*

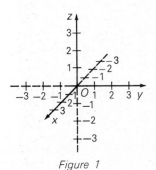

Figure 1

Just as a coordinate system in the two-dimensional plane establishes a one-to-one correspondence between the set of points in the plane and the set of ordered pairs of real numbers, so does a rectangular coordinate system in three-dimensional space establish a one-to-one correspondence between the set of points in space and the set of *ordered triples* of real numbers.

To set up a rectangular coordinate system in space, draw three mutually perpendicular number lines, or axes, passing through a common point O, the origin, of each. The axes are usually labeled x, y, and z, as in Figure 1, with an arrowhead on each to indicate the positive direction, and the same scale ordinarily is used on each.

In order to give spatial perspective to the figure, the angle between the positive x- and y-axes is drawn as a $135°$-angle instead of a $90°$-angle. When equal units are used on all three axes, the units of length on the y- and z-axes are drawn the same, while the unit on the x-axis is *drawn* as if it were two-thirds of the unit on each of the other axes; this "foreshortening" helps give the appearance of depth to the drawing. Also, the negative portion of each axis is often shown as a dashed line.

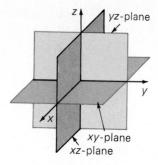

Figure 2

The coordinate axes determine three coordinate planes (Figure 2), each passing through the origin and each containing two of the axes:

1. the *xy*-plane, which contains the *x*- and *y*-axes and is perpendicular to the *z*-axis;
2. the *yz*-plane, which contains the *y*- and *z*-axes and is perpendicular to the *x*-axis;
3. the *xz*-plane, which contains the *x*- and *z*-axes and is perpendicular to the *y*-axis.

The coordinate planes separate space into eight regions, called octants, each determined by the positive part or the negative part of each of the three axes. Each octant is designated by a succession of three plus or minus signs, according as the octant is determined by the positive or negative part of the *x*-axis, the *y*-axis, and the *z*-axis. Thus the $(-, -, +)$-octant (read "the minus minus plus octant") is bounded in part by the negative part of the *x*-axis, the negative part of the *y*-axis, and the positive part of the *z*-axis. The $(+, +, +)$-octant is also called the first octant; the other octants are not numbered.

EXAMPLE   In which octant does the given point lie?

a. $(3, -1, 2)$ **b.** $(-2, -4, -1)$ **c.** $(-1, 2, 2)$

SOLUTION   **a.** $(+, -, +)$ **b.** $(-, -, -)$ **c.** $(-, +, +)$

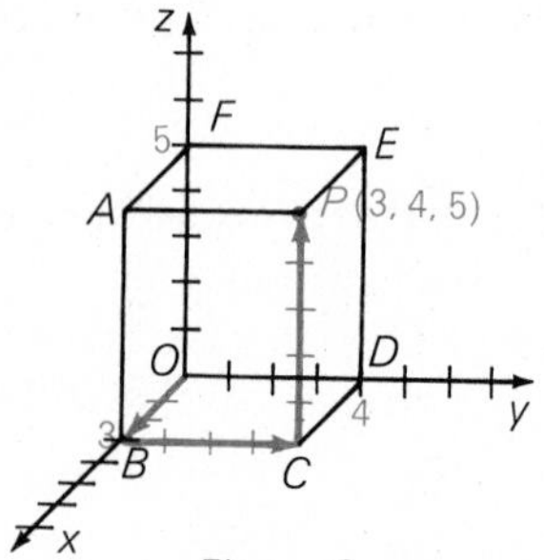

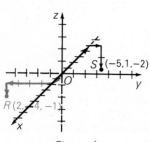

Figure 3

To assign an ordered triple of numbers, or coordinates, to a point such as *P* in Figure 3, draw three planes through *P*, the first (represented by *ABCP*) perpendicular to the *x*-axis, the second (*EDCP*) perpendicular to the *y*-axis, and the third (*AFEP*) perpendicular to the *z*-axis. The numbers paired with the points in which these planes intersect the respective axes are, in order, the *x*-coordinate, the *y*-coordinate, and the *z*-coordinate of *P*. For example, in Figure 3, *P* has coordinates $(3, 4, 5)$.

Together with the coordinate planes, the three planes drawn through *P* form a *rectangular parallelepiped*, or *box*, which we shall call the coordinate box of *P*.

Notice that, starting at the origin, you can arrive at *P* by moving on this box along edges parallel to each axis in succession. One such path is shown by red arrows in Figure 3: *O* to *B*, *B* to *C*, *C* to *P*. This suggests how to locate a point whose coordinates are given. For example, Figure 4 shows the plotting of the point $R(2, -4, -1)$:

1. From *O* move 2 units in the positive *x*-direction along the *x*-axis.
2. Then move -4 units (4 units in the negative direction) parallel to the *y*-axis.
3. Then move -1 unit parallel to the *z*-axis.

Figure 4

The point $S(-5, 1, -2)$ has also been plotted in Figure 4.

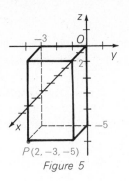

$P(2, -3, -5)$

Figure 5

For better visualization, it is helpful in drawing space figures to show "hidden edges" by dashed segments and visible edges by darkened segments, as illustrated in Figure 5 for the coordinate box of $P(2, -3, -5)$.

ORAL EXERCISES

In Exercises 1–4 state which hidden edges of the given coordinate box you would show as dashed segments for better visualization.

1.

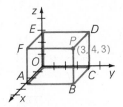

3.

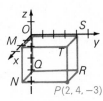

2.

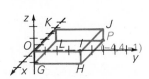

4.

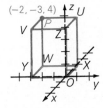

In Exercises 5–28 state the coordinates of the given vertex of a coordinate box shown above.

5. *A*	9. *E*	13. *I*	17. *M*	21. *S*	25. *W*
6. *B*	10. *F*	14. *J*	18. *N*	22. *T*	26. *X*
7. *C*	11. *G*	15. *K*	19. *Q*	23. *U*	27. *Y*
8. *D*	12. *H*	16. *L*	20. *R*	24. *V*	28. *Z*

In which octant does the given point lie?

29. $P(2, 5, -3)$ 31. $R(-3, 1, -5)$ 33. $T(-2, -1, 1)$

30. $Q(4, -1, -1)$ 32. $S(2, 2, 2)$ 34. $U(-3, -4, -6)$

35. The x-coordinate of every point in the yz-plane is __?__ .

36. Each point in the __?__-plane has 0 as its y-coordinate.

37. If the z-coordinate of a point is 0, then the point must lie in the __?__-plane.

38. A point whose x- and y-coordinates are both 0 must lie on the __?__-axis.

39. Explain why the coordinate "box" of $P(3, 4, 0)$ is a rectangle.

40. Explain why the coordinate "box" of $Q(0, 0, 2)$ is a line segment.

A   1-4. Copy each coordinate box given in Oral Exercises 1-4, but show the hidden edges as dashed segments.

Draw a diagram of a coordinate system in space and in the diagram show the coordinate box of the given point. Show the hidden edges as dashed segments and give the coordinates of all the vertices of the box.

5. (5, 3, 4)   9. (−3, 4, 7)
6. (4, 3, 2)   10. (2, −3, 6)
7. (4, 2, −5)   11. (−3, 6, −5)
8. (−2, −4, 3)   12. (−3, −2, −4)

In Exercises 13-18 draw the line segment whose endpoints have the given coordinates.

EXAMPLE   (4, −1, 5); (−3, 4, 1)   SOLUTION

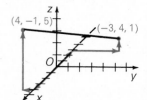

13. (0, 3, 0); (5, 0, 0)
14. (0, 0, 2); (4, 0, 0)
15. (−2, 0, 0); (0, 4, 0)
16. (0, 0, −2); (0, −3, 0)
17. (−2, 3, 6); (4, 5, −6)
18. (2, 5, 4); (−3, 4, 1)

Sketch the triangle in space whose vertices have the given coordinates.

B   19. (4, 0, 0), (0, 5, 0), (0, 0, 3)
20. (0, 2, 0), (3, 0, 0), (0, 0, 6)
21. (−2, 0, 0), (0, 4, 0), (0, 0, −5)
22. (0, 2, 0), (−3, 0, 0), (0, 0, −5)
23. (0, 0, 0), (4, 0, 2), (−3, 0, 3)
24. (0, 0, 0), (−2, −4, 0), (1, 3, 0)

In Exercises 25 and 26, sketch the pyramid whose base vertices are A, B, C, and D, and whose fifth vertex is E. Find the volume of the pyramid given that the volume V of any pyramid is given by the formula $V = \frac{1}{3}Bh$, where B is the area of the base and h is the altitude of the pyramid.

C   25. A(4, 0, 0); B(0, 0, 4); C(−4, 0, 0); D(0, 0, −4); E(0, 8, 0)
26. A(3, 5, 0); B(3, −5, 0); C(−3, 5, 0); D(−3, −5, 0); E(0, 0, 6)

5-2 *graphs of linear equations in three variables*

An equation such as $3x + 2y + 4z = 6$ is called a *linear equation in three variables*. In general, any equation of the form

$$Ax + By + Cz = D,$$

where A, B, C, and D are real constants such that A, B, and C are *not* all 0, is a linear equation in the variables x, y, and z. In our work, *we shall assume that the replacement set of each variable is* $\Re$.

An equation in one or two variables, such as

$$2y = 3 \quad \text{or} \quad 4x - 3z = 5,$$

can be regarded as an equation in three variables for which one or two of the coefficients of the three variables are zero:

$$0x + 2y + 0z = 3 \quad \text{or} \quad 4x + 0y - 3z = 5.$$

The ordered triple $(4, 5, -4)$ is called a *solution* of the linear equation

$$3x + 2y + 4z = 6$$

because the assertion

$$3 \cdot 4 + 2 \cdot 5 + 4 \cdot (-4) = 6$$

is a true statement. In general, a solution of an open sentence in three variables is an ordered triple of values of the variables for which the open sentence is true. Such an ordered triple of numbers is said to satisfy the sentence. The set of *all* ordered triples of real numbers that are solutions of the open sentence is the solution set of the sentence over $\Re$. To denote the solution set of the equation $3x + 2y + 4z = 6$ over $\Re$, we shall use the notation

$$\{(x, y, z): 3x + 2y + 4z = 6\}.$$

In Section 5–1 you saw that an ordered triple of real numbers gives the coordinates of a point in space. The set consisting of those points and only those points whose coordinates satisfy a given open sentence in three variables is the graph of the sentence. We accept the following without proof.

Theorem. In space, the graph of a linear equation in three variables is a plane. Conversely, every plane is the graph of some linear equation in three variables, called an **equation of the plane**.

For example, $x = 0$ for all points in the *yz*-plane and for no other points. Accordingly, the linear equation

$$x = 0$$

is an equation of the *yz*-plane. Similarly,

$$y = 0 \quad \text{and} \quad z = 0$$

are equations of the *xz*-plane and the *xy*-plane, respectively.

Since three noncollinear points determine a plane, you can use the foregoing theorem to graph a linear equation in three variables by finding three noncollinear points whose coordinates satisfy the equation. When possible, it often is easiest to choose the points where the plane cuts the coordinate axes.

EXAMPLE 1   **Sketch (part of) the graph of the equation**

$$3x + y + 2z = 6.$$

SOLUTION   1. To find the coordinates of the point where the graph cuts the *x*-axis, replace *y* and *z* with "0" in the given equation and solve for *x*:

$$3x + y + 2z = 6$$
$$3x + 0 + 2 \cdot 0 = 6$$
$$3x = 6$$
$$x = 2$$

∴ the plane cuts the *x*-axis at the point $A(2, 0, 0)$.

2. Next, replace *x* and *z* with "0" in the given equation and solve for *y*.

$$3x + y + 2z = 6$$
$$3 \cdot 0 + y + 2 \cdot 0 = 6$$
$$y = 6$$

∴ the plane cuts the *y*-axis at the point $B(0, 6, 0)$.

3. Now replace *x* and *y* with "0" in the given equation and solve for *z*:

$$3x + y + 2z = 6$$
$$3 \cdot 0 + 0 + 2z = 6$$
$$2z = 6$$
$$z = 3$$

∴ the plane cuts the *z*-axis at the point $C(0, 0, 3)$.

4. Draw a sketch showing the three points where the plane cuts the three axes, draw the line segments connecting the three points by pairs, and shade the space triangle as shown. This triangle is part of the plane graph of the given equation. **Answer.**

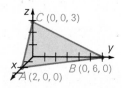

The *x*-coordinate, 2, of the point where the plane of Example 1 cuts the *x*-axis is called the *x-intercept* of the plane. Similarly, the *y-intercept* of the plane is 6 and the *z-intercept* is 3. In general, if a plane intersects the *x*-axis in a *single point,* then the x-coordinate of that point is called the x-intercept of the plane. The y-intercept and z-intercept are defined similarly.

In the graph of Example 1, the points A and B lie in the xy-plane and also in the plane that is the graph of

$$3x + y + 2z = 6.$$

Therefore the line $\overleftrightarrow{AB}$ is the line of intersection of the xy-plane and the graph.

You call a line in which a plane intersects a coordinate plane the trace of the given plane in that coordinate plane. Thus, the trace of the graph of Example 1 in the xy-plane is $\overleftrightarrow{AB}$, in the yz-plane is $\overleftrightarrow{BC}$, and in the xz-plane is $\overleftrightarrow{AC}$.

Since $\overleftrightarrow{AB}$ lies in the xy-plane, the coordinates of its points must satisfy the equation $z = 0$. But $\overleftrightarrow{AB}$ also lies in the graph of $3x + y + 2z = 6$, so the coordinates of its points must satisfy this equation, too. Since there are no other points on both of these planes, you can conclude that $\overleftrightarrow{AB}$ is the solution set of the system of equations:

$$3x + y + 2z = 6$$
$$z = 0$$

If you replace z with "0" in the first equation of the system, you obtain the equivalent system

$$3x + y = 6$$
$$z = 0$$

whose solution set is $\overleftrightarrow{AB}$.

Similarly, the trace $\overleftrightarrow{BC}$ in the yz-plane is the solution set of the system

$$y + 2z = 6$$
$$x = 0$$

and, the trace $\overleftrightarrow{AC}$ in the xz-plane is the solution set of the system

$$3x + 2z = 6$$
$$y = 0.$$

EXAMPLE 2   **a.** Find the x-, y-, and z-intercepts of the graph of $4x + 3z = 12$.
b. Write a linear system of equations whose solution set is the trace of the given graph in each coordinate plane.
c. Sketch the traces, and in your diagram shade part of the given graph.

SOLUTION   **a.** $4x + 3 \cdot 0 = 12; x = 3$. The x-intercept is 3. **Answer.**

$4 \cdot 0 + 3 \cdot 0 = 12; 0 = 12$. This equation is *false* for every value of y. $\therefore$ there is *no* y-intercept, and the graph is parallel to the y-axis. **Answer.**

$4 \cdot 0 + 3z = 12; z = 4$. The z-intercept is 4. **Answer.**

b. 1. Trace in the xy-plane ($\overleftrightarrow{AB}$ in the diagram):

$$z = 0$$
$$x = 3$$

2. Trace in the yz-plane ($\overleftrightarrow{ED}$ in the diagram):

$$x = 0$$
$$z = 4$$

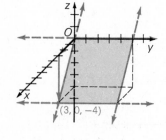

3. Trace in the xz-plane ($\overleftrightarrow{AE}$ in the diagram):

$$y = 0$$
$$4x + 3z = 12$$

c. The space-graph of $4x + 3z = 12$ and its traces are shown at the left.

EXAMPLE 3   **a.** Explain why the space-graph of $4x + 3z = 0$ contains the y-axis.
  b. Sketch part of the graph.

SOLUTION   **a.** For every point on the y-axis, you have $x = 0$ and $z = 0$. Substituting "0" for x and for z in the given equation, you obtain the statement

$$4 \cdot 0 + 3 \cdot 0 = 0, \qquad \text{or} \qquad 0 = 0,$$

which is true for every value of y. Thus, the coordinates of every point on the y-axis satisfy the equation $4x + 3z = 0$, so that the graph of the equation contains the y-axis.

b. Since the graph contains the y-axis, you need to know the coordinates of only one point not on that axis in order to sketch part of the graph. Substituting "3" for x and letting y have the value 0, you obtain

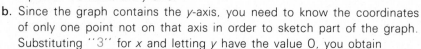

$$4 \cdot 3 + 3z = 0, \qquad \text{or} \qquad z = -4.$$

Therefore, the point with coordinates $(3, 0, -4)$ is on the graph. Sketch a part of the plane containing the y-axis and the point with coordinates $(3, 0, -4)$, as shown in red. **Answer.**

Examples 2 and 3 illustrate the following facts:

> If the coefficient of a variable in an equation of a plane is zero, then:
>   1. The plane is parallel to the axis of that variable if the constant term is not zero;
>   2. The plane contains the axis of that variable if the constant term is zero.

You can apply the foregoing facts in particular to graph a linear equation in three variables when the coefficients of *two* of the variables are zero. For example, in $y = 2.5$ both the coefficient of x and the coefficient of z are zero, but the constant term is not zero. Therefore, the graph is parallel to

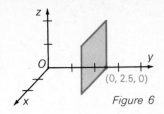

Figure 6

the x-axis and also to the z-axis; that is, the graph is parallel to the xz-plane. You can now sketch the graph (Figure 6) of the equation when you note that the ordered triple (0, 2.5, 0) satisfies the equation.

ORAL EXERCISES

Exercises 1–10 refer to the diagram at the right, which shows part of the graph of the equation $2x - y + 3z = 6$. For this graph, identify:

1. The x-intercept.
2. The y-intercept.
3. The z-intercept.
4. The trace in the xy-plane.
5. The trace in the yz-plane.
6. The trace in the xz-plane.
7. The part of the graph in the $(+, -, +)$-octant.
8. The part of the graph in the $(+, +, +)$-octant.
9. The part of the graph in the $(-, +, -)$-octant.
10. Is the x-intercept a point? How is the x-intercept determined?

State the x-, y-, and z-intercepts of the given equation.

11. $x + y + 3z = 3$
12. $2x + 4y + z = 8$
13. $3x + 4y - 6z = 12$
14. $5x - 2y + 10z = 10$
15. $-3x + 5y - z = -15$
16. $2x - 3y + z = 6$
17. $2x + y - 5z = -5$
18. $x - 7y - 2z = 14$

The space-graph of the given equation either is parallel to or contains one of the coordinate axes. Identify that axis, and tell whether the graph is parallel to it or contains it.

19. $4x - y = 5$
20. $y + 2z = 8$
21. $3x - 5z = 0$
22. $6x + 7y = 0$
23. $-x + z = 1$
24. $3x - 4y = 0$
25. $2z - y = 3$
26. $4y - 3x = 2$

The space-graph of the given equation either is parallel to or coincides with one of the coordinate planes. Identify that coordinate plane, and describe the location of the space-graph with respect to that coordinate plane.

27. $z = 0$
28. $y = -2$
29. $z = 3$
30. $x = 5$
31. $y = 2$
32. $x = 0$
33. $x = -4$
34. $y = 0$

WRITTEN EXERCISES

A **1–8.** For each of the graphs of the linear equations given in Oral Exercises 11–18 above:

    a. Write a system of equations whose solution set is the trace of the plane in each coordinate axis.

    b. Sketch these traces, and in your diagram shade part of the plane.

    9–16. For each of the graphs of the linear equations in Oral Exercises 19–26 above, sketch the traces of the graph in each coordinate plane, and in your diagram shade the part of the graph in the first octant.

In Exercises 17–26 the given equations have graphs that, together with the coordinate planes, enclose a solid in the first octant. Sketch the portions of the graphs on the boundary of the solid.

EXAMPLE $3x + 2y = 6$
               $z = 4$

SOLUTION

B **17.** $y + 3z = 3$; $x = 5$

    18. $2x + 3y = 6$; $z = 4$

    19. $x = 5$; $y = 3$; $z = 4$

    20. $x = 3$; $y = 4$; $z = 4$

    21. $2x - z = 0$; $x = 4$, $z = 3$

    22. $3y - 4z = 0$; $y = 5$, $z = 5$

    23. $x + 2y - z = 0$; $z = 4$ **24.** $2x - y + z = 0$; $y = 6$

C **25.** $3x + 4y = 12$; $x + 2z = 4$ **26.** $3x + 2y = 12$; $y + 3z = 6$

Determine A and B so that the graph of the given equation will contain the points whose coordinates are given.

    27. $Ax + By + 4z = 6$; $(3, 4, 3)$; $(4, 2, 1)$

    28. $Ax + y + Bz = 5$; $(1, 4, -4)$; $(2, -3, 2)$

    29. $3x + Ay + Bz = 12$; $(0, 3, 6)$; $(3, 0, 1)$

    30. $3x + y + Az = B$; $(2, 2, 1)$; $(2, 4, 3)$

5–3 *systems of linear equations in three variables*

A solution of a system of linear equations in three variables over $\mathcal{R}$ is an ordered triple of real numbers that satisfies all equations of the system. The solution set of the system is the set of all its solutions.

    The geometric interpretation of the solution of a system of two equations in two variables (Section 4–1) can be extended to systems of three equations in three variables.

A system such as

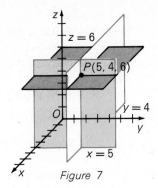

Figure 7

$$x = 5$$
$$y = 4$$
$$z = 6$$

can readily be solved, because you can see by inspection that its one and only solution is (5, 4, 6). Thus, the solution set is $\{(5, 4, 6)\}$. Figure 7 pictures this fact by showing $P(5, 4, 6)$ as the single point on the graphs of all three of the equations.

As Figure 7 suggests, two nonparallel planes intersect in a line, and three such planes *can* intersect in a single point. In that case, a system of three linear equations in three variables represented by the three planes is *consistent*, and the solution is unique.

But such a system is also consistent if the graphs of the equations in such a system consist of:

1. Three different planes intersecting in a single line (Figure 8).
2. Two coincident planes intersecting a third plane in a line (Figure 9).
3. Three coincident planes (Figure 10).

In each of these cases the system has an infinite set of solutions.

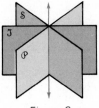

Figure 8

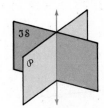

Figure 9

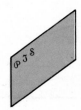

Figure 10

The solution set is the empty set Ø, and the system is *inconsistent*, if the graphs of the equations consist of:

1. Three parallel planes (Figure 11).
2. Two coincident planes parallel to a third plane (Figure 12).
3. Three planes intersecting in three parallel lines (Figure 13).
4. Two parallel planes intersecting a third plane in two parallel lines (Figure 14).

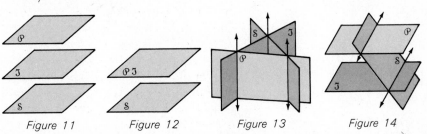

Figure 11   Figure 12   Figure 13   Figure 14

Because it often is difficult to obtain accurate information about coordinates of points of intersection of space figures from flat drawings, you should not ordinarily attempt to solve systems of linear equations in three variables by graphing the equations. Instead, to solve such a system you might transform it into an equivalent system which can be solved by inspection.

The transformations used in solving systems of linear equations in two variables (page 116) are also applicable in solving three-variable systems. In applying transformations, you might use the linear-combination method, the substitution method, or a combination of these. If the transformations yield a *false* statement such as "$0 = 2$", then the system is inconsistent. If they do not yield a false statement but do yield a true statement such as "$0 = 0$", then the solution set is an infinite set.

EXAMPLE   Determine the solution set of the system:

$$
\begin{aligned}
x + 2y + z &= 5 \quad (1) \\
2x - y + z &= 4 \quad (2) \\
3x + y + 4z &= 1 \quad (3)
\end{aligned}
$$

SOLUTION   1. To obtain an equation in which the coefficient of y is 0, multiply each member of the second equation by 2 and add the resulting equation to the first equation.

$$
\begin{array}{ll}
x + 2y + z = 5 & (1) \\
\underline{4x - 2y + 2z = 8} & (2) \times 2 \\
5x + 3z = 13 & (4)
\end{array}
$$

2. To obtain a second equation in which the coefficient of y is 0, add the third equation to the second.

$$
\begin{array}{ll}
2x - y + z = 4 & (2) \\
\underline{3x + y + 4z = 1} & (3) \\
5x + 5z = 5 & (5)
\end{array}
$$

3. The equations obtained in Steps 1 and 2 involve only x and z. You can use the method of transforming two equations in two variables to replace that pair of equations by the equivalent pair shown at the right.

$$
\begin{array}{ll}
5x + 3z = 13 & (4) \\
5x + 5z = 5 & (5)
\end{array}
\quad \text{is equivalent to} \quad
\begin{array}{l}
x = 5 \\
z = -4
\end{array}
$$

4. Replace x with "5" and z with "-4" in the second of the given equations, and solve for y.

$$
\begin{aligned}
2x - y + z &= 4 \quad (2) \\
2 \cdot 5 - y + (-4) &= 4 \\
6 - y &= 4 \\
y &= 2
\end{aligned}
$$

5. Thus you find that the given system is equivalent to the system

$$x = 5$$
$$y = 2$$
$$z = -4$$

whose solution set is $\{(5, 2, -4)\}$.

Checking in the given system, you have:

$$5 + 2 \cdot 2 + (-4) = 5 \checkmark$$
$$2 \cdot 5 - 2 + (-4) = 4 \checkmark$$
$$3 \cdot 5 + 2 + 4(-4) = 1 \checkmark$$

$\therefore$ the solution set is $\{(5, 2, -4)\}$. **Answer.**

ORAL EXERCISES   In Exercises 1–4 state the number by which you would multiply the members of each equation before adding to obtain an equation in which the coefficient of z is 0.

1. $x + 2y - z = 3$
    $2x - y + z = 7$

2. $3x - y + 2z = 1$
    $2x + 3y + 2z = 2$

3. $3x - 9y - 5z = z$
    $6x + 6y - z = 0$

4. $12x - 3y + 6z = 7$
    $4x + 9y + 5z = 2$

5–8. Repeat Exercises 1–4, this time stating values of multipliers so that the coefficient of y in the resulting equation is 0.

9–12. Repeat Exercises 1–4, this time stating values of multipliers so that the coefficient of x is 0.

In Exercises 13–16 state whether the given system of equations in x, y and z is consistent or inconsistent. If it is consistent, state whether the solution is unique or there is an infinite set of solutions. Give reasons for your statements.

13. $x = 2$
    $y = -3$
    $z = 5$

14. $x + y + z = 1$
    $x + y + z = 2$
    $2x + 2y + 2z = 2$

15. $x + y = 0$
    $x - y = 0$
    $z = 0$

16. $x + y = 0$
    $x - y = 0$
    $x = 0$

17–20. Describe the relationship between the graphs of the equations in Exercises 13–16.

In Exercises 1–18 the given system of equations in three variables has a single solution. Find the solution.

A 1. $x + 3y + z = 1$
       $2x - y - z = 6$
       $5x + y + z = 1$

   2. $x + y + z = 1$
       $x + 2y - z = -3$
       $2x + 5y + z = 5$

   3. $-x + y + 2z = 2$
       $2x - y + z = 5$
       $-4x - y + 3z = 3$

   4. $x - y - z = 0$
       $x - 2y + 3z = 2$
       $-2x + 3y + 2z = 2$

   5. $-3x + 2y + z = -6$
       $x + 3y + 2z = 5$
       $4x + 4y + 3z = 13$

   6. $-x + 2y + 3z = 5$
       $3x + y + 2z = -1$
       $2x + 3y - z = 4$

   7. $9x + 5y + 3z = 4$
       $6x + 2y + 4z = 2$
       $-3x + 3y - 7z = 2$

   8. $x - y + 2z = 3$
       $2x + y - z = 3$
       $3x + 2y - 4z = -1$

   9. $3x - y + 2z = 6$
       $-x + y = 2$
       $2x + z = 5$

  10. $x + 3y + 4z = 3$
       $y + z = 3$
       $x - 2z = 9$

  11. $2a - b - c = 3$
       $4a + b - 2c = 3$
       $-a + b + c = 1$

  12. $3a + 3b - c = 1$
       $5a - 4b + c = 7$
       $2a + b - c = 0$

  13. $2x + 3y + 3z = 5$
       $4x + 5y + 3z = 13$
       $3x + 2y - 2z = 13$

  14. $2x + 5y - 2z = -18$
       $7x + 2y - 5z = 3$
       $-2x + 3y + 2z = -14$

B 15. $-\dfrac{4}{x} + \dfrac{1}{y} + \dfrac{3}{z} = 0$

       $-\dfrac{2}{x} + \dfrac{2}{y} + \dfrac{1}{z} = -1$

       $\dfrac{2}{x} + \dfrac{2}{y} + \dfrac{5}{z} = 2$

  16. $\dfrac{3}{x} - \dfrac{4}{y} - \dfrac{2}{z} = -1$

       $\dfrac{1}{x} + \dfrac{2}{y} + \dfrac{1}{z} = 3$

       $\dfrac{2}{x} + \dfrac{2}{y} + \dfrac{2}{z} = 5$

  17. $x - \dfrac{1}{y} + 2z = 8$

       $x + \dfrac{2}{y} + z = 6$

       $3x + \dfrac{1}{y} + 4z = 12$

  18. $\dfrac{1}{x} + y + z = 2$

       $\dfrac{3}{x} - 2y + 3z = 6$

       $\dfrac{1}{x} - y + 2z = 5$

Hint: Compare Exercises 15–18 with Exercises 29–32 on page 119.

In Exercises 19–22 if the given system has exactly one solution, find it; if the system has no solution, state that fact; if the system has an infinite solution set, state that fact.

19. $x + 2y + 3z = 4$
     $x \quad\quad + 2z = 3$
     $\quad\quad 2y + \quad z = 2$

20. $\quad x - \quad y + 2z = 3$
     $-3x + 3y - 3z = 2$
     $-2x + 2y - \quad z = 5$

21. $2x - \quad y + 4z = 2$
     $3x + 4y - \quad z = 1$
     $-x + 6y - 9z = -3$

22. $4x - y + 3z = 1$
     $\quad x + y - \quad z = 2$
     $6x + y + \quad z = 4$

In Exercises 23–26 determine A, B, and C so that the graph of the given equation will contain the points whose coordinates are given.

23. $Ax + By + Cz = 7$; $(0, -1, 3)$; $(2, -1, 0)$; $(1, 0, 2)$

24. $2x + Ay + Bz = C$; $(0, 1, 1)$; $(-2, 0, -7)$; $(1, 0, -1)$

25. $Ax - 2y + Bz = C$; $(2, 0, -2)$; $(-2, -7, 0)$; $(0, 1, 2)$

26. $Ax + By - lz = C$; $(4, 0, 9)$; $(1, -3, 0)$; $(0, 2, 9)$

SELF-TEST 1   Give the meaning of each of the following.

1. coordinate plane
2. octant
3. coordinate box of a point
4. x-intercept of a plane
5. trace of a plane in a coordinate plane

Objective 1, page 141   6. Draw a diagram of a coordinate system in space, and in the diagram show the points $P(2, 1, 4)$ and $Q(-2, 4, 3)$ and the line segment PQ.

Objective 2, page 141   7. Determine the x-, y-, and z-intercepts of the plane with equation $2x - 3y + 6z = 6$.

8. Sketch the trace of the plane $2x - 3y + 6z = 6$ in each coordinate plane.

Objective 3, page 141   9. Draw the portion of the graph of $4x + 5y + 10z = 20$ that lies in the first octant.

Objective 4, page 141   10. Solve the system

$$2x + \quad y + \quad z = 3$$
$$\quad x - \quad y + 2z = -6$$
$$-x + 5y + \quad z = -2$$

by transforming it into a simple equivalent system.

Check your answers with those printed at the back of the book.

careers *economics*

Economists deal with a wide variety of problems in business, government, and international affairs. They study the production, distribution, and consumption of goods. They are concerned with the relationship between supply and demand, and its effect on prices. In government, economists are involved in decisions regarding budgets, taxes, inflation, unemployment, and wage and price guidelines. In international affairs, the issues of trade, tariffs, the balance of payments, currency valuation, and aid to developing nations require knowledge of economics.

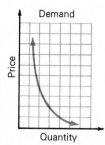

The principle of supply and demand operates during trading sessions of a stock exchange (above) and at the Chicago Board of Trade (below).

EXAMPLE One of the most basic principles in the study of economics is the relationship between supply and demand and its effect on prices. If the price of a certain commodity goes up, then there will be less demand for that item, or consumers will buy smaller quantities of that item. A graph of this relationship looks something like the one on the left. Now look at the producer's point of

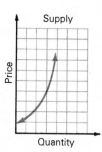

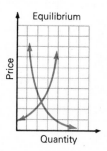

view. If the price of an item increases, then the manufacturing of that item becomes more attractive and producers will supply greater quantities of that item. This is shown in the graph at the center.

You can see that these forces work to balance each other. As the price of an item becomes too high, the supply will become greater than the demand. Then the price will be lowered to attract more buyers for the product. If a price becomes too low, the demand for the item will exceed the supply and the producer can then begin to charge higher prices. The price for which supply and demand are equal is called the equilibrium price, which you can see from the graph at the right is at the point of intersection of the curves.

determinants

After completing the next three sections, you should be able to:
1. Use determinants to solve a system of three linear equations in three variables.
2. Use three variables to solve problems.
3. Use properties of determinants to simplify the expansion of a determinant by minors.

Objectives

5–4 third-order determinants

The determinants introduced in Section 4–3, such as $\begin{vmatrix} a_1 & b_1 \\ a_2 & b_2 \end{vmatrix}$, have two (horizontal) rows, $a_1 \ b_1$ and $a_2 \ b_2$, and two (vertical) columns, $\begin{matrix} a_1 \\ a_2 \end{matrix}$ and $\begin{matrix} b_1 \\ b_2 \end{matrix}$; such a determinant is called a second-order determinant, or a determinant of order 2.

You can use *third-order determinants* in the solution of three linear equations in three variables over $\mathcal{R}$.

For any $a_1, b_1, c_1, a_2, b_2, c_2, a_3, b_3, c_3 \in \mathcal{R}$, the **determinant**

$$D = \begin{vmatrix} a_1 & b_1 & c_1 \\ a_2 & b_2 & c_2 \\ a_3 & b_3 & c_3 \end{vmatrix}$$

has the value

$$a_1 b_2 c_3 + a_2 b_3 c_1 + a_3 b_1 c_2 - a_1 b_3 c_2 - a_2 b_1 c_3 - a_3 b_2 c_1.$$

$$\begin{vmatrix} a_1 & b_1 & c_1 \\ a_2 & b_2 & c_2 \\ a_3 & b_3 & c_3 \end{vmatrix} \begin{matrix} a_1 & b_1 \\ a_2 & b_2 \\ a_3 & b_3 \end{matrix}$$

A convenient way to remember how to evaluate a *third-order* determinant is to copy the 3×3 (read "three by three") array and repeat the first two columns after the third column as shown at the left. Compute the product of the entries along each diagonal arrow as shown below. Add the products found from the descending arrows to the negatives of the products found from the ascending arrows. (This does not work for higher-order determinants.)

$$\begin{matrix} a_1 & b_1 & c_1 & a_1 & b_1 \\ a_2 & b_2 & c_2 & a_2 & b_2 \\ a_3 & b_3 & c_3 & a_3 & b_3 \end{matrix} \qquad \begin{matrix} a_1 & b_1 & c_1 & a_1 & b_1 \\ a_2 & b_2 & c_2 & a_2 & b_2 \\ a_3 & b_3 & c_3 & a_3 & b_3 \end{matrix}$$

$$a_1 b_2 c_3 + b_1 c_2 a_3 + c_1 a_2 b_3 - a_3 b_2 c_1 - b_3 c_2 a_1 - c_3 a_2 b_1$$
$$= a_1 b_2 c_3 + a_2 b_3 c_1 + a_3 b_1 c_2 - a_1 b_3 c_2 - a_2 b_1 c_3 - a_3 b_2 c_1$$

EXAMPLE 1   Evaluate the determinant:

$$D = \begin{vmatrix} 3 & 1 & 2 \\ 4 & 3 & 0 \\ -1 & 3 & -4 \end{vmatrix}$$

SOLUTION

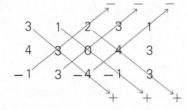

$D = -36 + 0 + 24 - (-6) - 0 - (-16) = 10.$ **Answer.**

If you use transformations, as in Section 5–3, to solve the system

$$a_1 x + b_1 y + c_1 z = d_1$$
$$a_2 x + b_2 y + c_2 z = d_2$$
$$a_3 x + b_3 y + c_3 z = d_3$$

over $\Re$, and let

$$D = \begin{vmatrix} a_1 & b_1 & c_1 \\ a_2 & b_2 & c_2 \\ a_3 & b_3 & c_3 \end{vmatrix}, \; D_x = \begin{vmatrix} d_1 & b_1 & c_1 \\ d_2 & b_2 & c_2 \\ d_3 & b_3 & c_3 \end{vmatrix},$$

$$D_y = \begin{vmatrix} a_1 & d_1 & c_1 \\ a_2 & d_2 & c_2 \\ a_3 & d_3 & c_3 \end{vmatrix}, \; D_z = \begin{vmatrix} a_1 & b_1 & d_1 \\ a_2 & b_2 & d_2 \\ a_3 & b_3 & d_3 \end{vmatrix},$$

you find that, if $D \neq 0$, the system has the unique solution

$$x = \frac{D_x}{D}, \; y = \frac{D_y}{D}, \; z = \frac{D_z}{D}.$$

These equations are called Cramer's Rule for systems of three linear equations in three variables. The determinant D is the determinant of coefficients. If $D = 0$, then either the system is inconsistent or the system has an infinite solution set.

EXAMPLE 2   Use Cramer's Rule to solve the system:

$$2x + y - z = 3$$
$$4x - y + 4z = 0$$
$$- 3y + 2z = 6$$

SOLUTION

$$D = \begin{vmatrix} 2 & 1 & -1 \\ 4 & -1 & 4 \\ 0 & -3 & 2 \end{vmatrix} \begin{matrix} 2 & 1 \\ 4 & -1 \\ 0 & -3 \end{matrix} = -4 + 0 + 12 - 0 - (-24) - 8$$
$$= 24$$

$$D_x = \begin{vmatrix} 3 & 1 & -1 \\ 0 & -1 & 4 \\ 6 & -3 & 2 \end{vmatrix} \begin{matrix} 3 & 1 \\ 0 & -1 \\ 6 & -3 \end{matrix} = -6 + 24 + 0 - 6 - (-36) - 0$$
$$= 48$$

$$D_y = \begin{vmatrix} 2 & 3 & -1 \\ 4 & 0 & 4 \\ 0 & 6 & 2 \end{vmatrix} \begin{matrix} 2 & 3 \\ 4 & 0 \\ 0 & 6 \end{matrix} = 0 + 0 - 24 - 0 - 48 - 24 = -96$$

$$D_z = \begin{vmatrix} 2 & 1 & 3 \\ 4 & -1 & 0 \\ 0 & -3 & 6 \end{vmatrix} \begin{matrix} 2 & 1 \\ 4 & -1 \\ 0 & -3 \end{matrix} = -12 + 0 + (-36) - 0 - 0 - 24$$
$$= -72$$

Thus, you have

$$x = \frac{D_x}{D} = \frac{48}{24} = 2, \; y = \frac{D_y}{D} = \frac{-96}{24} = -4, \; z = \frac{D_z}{D} = \frac{-72}{24} = -3.$$

∴ (as you can check) the solution set is $\{(2, -4, -3)\}$. **Answer.**

WRITTEN EXERCISES Evaluate the given determinant.

A

1. $\begin{vmatrix} 1 & 1 & 1 \\ 1 & 2 & 4 \\ 2 & 1 & 5 \end{vmatrix}$

2. $\begin{vmatrix} 1 & 4 & 1 \\ 2 & 5 & -1 \\ 1 & 1 & 2 \end{vmatrix}$

3. $\begin{vmatrix} 2 & -3 & 1 \\ 1 & -2 & -2 \\ 3 & -5 & -1 \end{vmatrix}$

4. $\begin{vmatrix} 4 & -1 & 2 \\ 2 & 1 & -3 \\ 10 & -1 & 1 \end{vmatrix}$

5. $\begin{vmatrix} 1 & 0 & 2 \\ 0 & 3 & -4 \\ 2 & -1 & 5 \end{vmatrix}$

6. $\begin{vmatrix} 2 & 1 & 6 \\ 0 & 3 & -2 \\ 9 & 0 & 5 \end{vmatrix}$

Use Cramer's Rule to find the solution set of the given system.

7. $\begin{aligned} 2x + y + z &= 5 \\ 4x - 2y - z &= 0 \\ 3x - y + 2z &= 6 \end{aligned}$

8. $\begin{aligned} 2x + y - z &= -4 \\ x + 5y - z &= 2 \\ 2x + 3y + z &= 0 \end{aligned}$

9. $\begin{aligned} x + 4y &= 6 \\ -y + z &= 2 \\ x + z &= 5 \end{aligned}$

10. $\begin{aligned} x + 3y &= 6 \\ 2x + z &= 4 \\ -y + 2z &= -5 \end{aligned}$

11. $\begin{aligned} x + 3y + 4z &= 0 \\ x - 2z &= 8 \\ y + z &= 3 \end{aligned}$

12. $\begin{aligned} 3x - y + 2z &= 0 \\ -x + y &= 4 \\ 2x + z &= 1 \end{aligned}$

In Exercises 13–16 evaluate D. If $D = 0$, state whether the system is inconsistent or the system has an infinite solution set.

B 13. $x + y - z = 2$
      $6x + y + z = 4$
      $4x - y + 3z = 0$

   14. $2x - y + 4z = 2$
      $-x + 6y - 9z = 0$
      $3x + 4y - z = 1$

   15. $2x - 3y + z = 3$
      $10x + y - z = 4$
      $4x + 2y - z = -5$

   16. $2x - 4y + z = 5$
      $x - 2y - 2z = 4$
      $-x + 2y - 3z = -1$

C 17–20. Use determinants to do Exercises 23–26 on page 155.

5–5 *solving problems with three variables*

Systems of linear equations in three variables sometimes appear in the solutions of practical problems.

EXAMPLE   The sum of the length, width, and height of a rectangular box is 16 centimeters, the width is twice the height, and twice the length exceeds the sum of the width and height by 5. Find the length, width, and height of the box.

SOLUTION 1. The problem asks for the length, width, and height of the box.
2. Let the length be l cm, the width w cm, and the height h cm.
3. The sum of the length, width, and height is 16 cm.

$$l + w + h = 16. \tag{1}$$

The width is twice the height: $w = 2h$. $\qquad\qquad$ (2)

Twice the length is 5 more than the sum of the width and height.

$$2l = w + h + 5. \tag{3}$$

4. The system of equations (1), (2), and (3) is equivalent to:

$$l + w + h = 16$$
$$w - 2h = 0$$
$$2l - w - h = 5$$

Transforming this system into the equivalent system

$$l = 7$$
$$w = 6$$
$$h = 3$$

or solving the system by Cramer's Rule is left to you.
5. The check to show that 7 cm, 6 cm, and 3 cm satisfy the requirements for the length, width, and height of the box as described in the problem is also left to you.

∴ the length is 7 cm, the width is 6 cm, and the height is 3 cm. **Answer.**

ORAL EXERCISES   In Exercises 1–6 let *x* represent a first number, *y* a second number, and *z* a third number. In each case translate the stated relationship into an equation in *x*, *y*, and *z*.

1. The sum of the three numbers is 4.

2. If you subtract the third number from the second, you obtain the first.

3. The sum of the third number and four times the second number is equal to the first number.

4. Twice the first number is eleven more than the sum of the other two numbers.

5. The sum of twice the first number and three times the third number is one more than the second number.

6. The second number is equal to the sum of the first number and the third number.

PROBLEMS
A

1. Use the relationships stated in Oral Exercises 1, 2, and 3 to find the three numbers.

2. Use the relationships stated in Oral Exercises 4, 5, and 6 to find the three numbers.

3. The sum of three numbers is 7. One of the numbers is one more than the sum of the other two numbers. It is also four times the difference between the other two numbers. What are the three numbers?

4. The sum of three numbers is 4. One of the numbers is two less than one-half the sum of the other two numbers, but three times their difference. What are the three numbers?

5. In a triangle whose perimeter is 44 centimeters, the length of the longest side is 4 centimeters less than the sum of the lengths of the other sides. Twice the length of the shortest side is 9 centimeters more than the difference between the lengths of the other sides. How long is each side of the triangle?

6. In a certain triangle, the angle of greatest measure measures 75 degrees more than the angle of least measure. If one-third the sum of the degree measures of the smallest and the largest angles is equal to the degree measure of the remaining angle, what is the degree measure of each angle of the triangle?

7. In her wallet, Ms. Thompson has one-dollar, five-dollar, and ten-dollar bills, totaling $171. She has the same number of five-dollar bills as one-dollar and ten-dollar bills put together. If she has 30 bills in all, how many bills of each denomination does she have?

8. Juan has 31 coins, made up of quarters, nickels, and dimes. If he had one more dime, he would have just as many dimes as he has nickels and quarters put together. If the total value of Juan's coins is $4.70, how many coins of each kind does he have?

B 9. Find the three-digit decimal numeral in which the sum of the numbers named by the digits is 12, the number named by the tens digit is twice the sum of the numbers named by the hundreds and units digits, and the sum of the numbers named by the hundreds and tens digits is five times the number named by the units digit.

10. A certain integer is represented by a three-digit decimal numeral in which the sum of the numbers named by the digits is 13. If the digits of the given numeral are reversed, the resulting numeral represents a new integer whose sum with the original integer is 1151. On the other hand, if the new integer is subtracted from the original integer, the difference is 297. What is the original integer?

11. Mr. Leland is older than his wife. In fact, by adding his son's age to his wife's age, you obtain Mr. Leland's age. Five years from now Mr. Leland will be three times as old as his son, but now his age is twice the difference between his wife's and his son's ages. How old are Mr. and Mrs. Leland?

12. In a certain family, the age of the oldest of three children is 4 years less than the sum of the ages of the other two children. Four years ago, the oldest child was three times as old as the youngest, and at the same time the age of the oldest child equaled the sum of the ages of the other two children. How old are the oldest and youngest of the three children?

5–6 *properties of determinants*

In the defining equations

$$\begin{vmatrix} a_1 & b_1 \\ a_2 & b_2 \end{vmatrix} = a_1b_2 - a_2b_1$$

and

$$\begin{vmatrix} a_1 & b_1 & c_1 \\ a_2 & b_2 & c_2 \\ a_3 & b_3 & c_3 \end{vmatrix} = a_1b_2c_3 + a_2b_3c_1 + a_3b_1c_2 - a_1b_3c_2 - a_2b_1c_3 - a_3b_2c_1$$

the sums of products in the right-hand members are called expansions of the determinants. Notice that the first of these expansions shows all possible arrangements of the subscripts 1 and 2 of the letters *a* and *b*, and that the second expansion shows all possible arrangements of the subscripts 1, 2, and 3 of the letters *a*, *b*, and *c*.

The fact that a determinant of order 2 or 3 is a sum of terms involving all possible arrangements of the subscripts of the elements suggests that a determinant of order *n* (*n* > 3), that is, a determinant having *n* rows and *n* columns, can similarly be defined as a sum of terms involving all possible arrangements of the subscripts 1, 2, . . . , n. This is indeed true, but there are no simple arrow diagrams to help us make the rather lengthy computations (120 terms, for instance, in the sum for a determinant of order 5, and 720 for one of order 6!). We therefore omit this definition and give an alternative (but equivalent) definition of a determinant of higher order in terms of determinants of next lower order by using *minors*. The minor of an element in a determinant is defined to be the determinant obtained when you delete the row and column containing the element. For example,

$$\text{the minor of 4 in } \begin{vmatrix} 4 & 3 & -9 \\ 2 & 5 & -2 \\ 7 & 8 & 0 \end{vmatrix} \quad \text{is} \quad \begin{vmatrix} 5 & -2 \\ 8 & 0 \end{vmatrix}.$$

Similarly, the minor of 2 is $\begin{vmatrix} 3 & -9 \\ 8 & 0 \end{vmatrix}$ and of 5 is $\begin{vmatrix} 4 & -9 \\ 7 & 0 \end{vmatrix}$.

Now if you rewrite the right-hand member of the expression defining a third-order determinant on page 157 as

$$a_1 b_2 c_3 - a_1 b_3 c_2 - a_2 b_1 c_3 + a_2 b_3 c_1 + a_3 b_1 c_2 - a_3 b_2 c_1,$$

you can factor it to obtain

$$a_1(b_2 c_3 - b_3 c_2) - a_2(b_1 c_3 - b_3 c_1) + a_3(b_1 c_2 - b_2 c_1).$$

It follows that if you let A_1, A_2, and A_3 represent the minors of a_1, a_2, and a_3, respectively, you can then write

$$\begin{vmatrix} a_1 & b_1 & c_1 \\ a_2 & b_2 & c_2 \\ a_3 & b_3 & c_3 \end{vmatrix} = a_1 A_1 - a_2 A_2 + a_3 A_3.$$

The right-hand member of this latter equation is called the expansion of the determinant by minors of the elements in the first column.

By suitably arranging the terms in the definition of a third-order determinant, you can show that such a determinant can be expanded by minors about any row or any column as follows:

1. Choose a row or column and form the product of each element in the row or column with its minor.

2. Use the product obtained or its negative according as the sum of the number of the row and number of the column containing the element is even or odd.

3. The sum of the resulting numbers is the value of the determinant.

EXAMPLE 1 Expand by minors of elements of the second row and evaluate:

$$\begin{vmatrix} 5 & -1 & -2 \\ 3 & 6 & -7 \\ 2 & -3 & 4 \end{vmatrix}$$

SOLUTION The elements of the second row are 3, 6, and -7. The element 3 is in the second row, first column; since $2 + 1 = 3$ (odd), we use the negative of its product with its minor. Similarly, we use the product of 6 and its minor and the negative of the product of -7 and its minor. Thus,

$$\begin{vmatrix} 5 & -1 & -2 \\ 3 & 6 & -7 \\ 2 & -3 & 4 \end{vmatrix} = -3\begin{vmatrix} -1 & -2 \\ -3 & 4 \end{vmatrix} + 6\begin{vmatrix} 5 & -2 \\ 2 & 4 \end{vmatrix} - (-7)\begin{vmatrix} 5 & -1 \\ 2 & -3 \end{vmatrix}$$

$$= (-3)(-10) + 6(24) + 7(-13) = 83. \quad \textbf{Answer.}$$

We can extend this idea to fourth-order (or higher-order) determinants. For example,

$$\begin{vmatrix} a_1 & b_1 & c_1 & d_1 \\ a_2 & b_2 & c_2 & d_2 \\ a_3 & b_3 & c_3 & d_3 \\ a_4 & b_4 & c_4 & d_4 \end{vmatrix} = a_1A_1 - a_2A_2 + a_3A_3 - a_4A_4,$$

where

$$A_1 = \begin{vmatrix} b_2 & c_2 & d_2 \\ b_3 & c_3 & d_3 \\ b_4 & c_4 & d_4 \end{vmatrix}, \quad A_2 = \begin{vmatrix} b_1 & c_1 & d_1 \\ b_3 & c_3 & d_3 \\ b_4 & c_4 & d_4 \end{vmatrix}, \quad \text{etc.}$$

Cramer's Rule, in addition, extends to the solution of four linear equations in four variables, etc. Thus, the solution of

$$a_1x + b_1y + c_1z + d_1w = e_1$$
$$a_2x + b_2y + c_2z + d_2w = e_2$$
$$a_3x + b_3y + c_3z + d_3w = e_3$$
$$a_4x + b_4y + c_4z + d_4w = e_4$$

is

$$x = \frac{D_x}{D}, \ y = \frac{D_y}{D}, \ z = \frac{D_z}{D}, \ w = \frac{D_w}{D}, \qquad \text{where}$$

$$D = \begin{vmatrix} a_1 & b_1 & c_1 & d_1 \\ a_2 & b_2 & c_2 & d_2 \\ a_3 & b_3 & c_3 & d_3 \\ a_4 & b_4 & c_4 & d_4 \end{vmatrix}, \quad D_x = \begin{vmatrix} e_1 & b_1 & c_1 & d_1 \\ e_2 & b_2 & c_2 & d_2 \\ e_3 & b_3 & c_3 & d_3 \\ e_4 & b_4 & c_4 & d_4 \end{vmatrix}, \quad D_y = \begin{vmatrix} a_1 & e_1 & c_1 & d_1 \\ a_2 & e_2 & c_2 & d_2 \\ a_3 & e_3 & c_3 & d_3 \\ a_4 & e_4 & c_4 & d_4 \end{vmatrix},$$

etc., provided $D \neq 0$.

EXAMPLE 2 **Expand by minors and evaluate:**

$$\begin{vmatrix} 4 & -1 & 1 & 2 \\ 3 & -1 & 0 & 2 \\ 0 & 4 & 0 & 1 \\ 3 & 1 & 1 & 2 \end{vmatrix}$$

SOLUTION Expand by minors of the third column since two elements are 0.

$$1\begin{vmatrix} 3 & -1 & 2 \\ 0 & 4 & 1 \\ 3 & 1 & 2 \end{vmatrix} - 0\begin{vmatrix} 4 & -1 & 2 \\ 0 & 4 & 1 \\ 3 & 1 & 2 \end{vmatrix} + 0\begin{vmatrix} 4 & -1 & 2 \\ 3 & -1 & 2 \\ 3 & 1 & 2 \end{vmatrix} - 1\begin{vmatrix} 4 & -1 & 2 \\ 3 & -1 & 2 \\ 0 & 4 & 1 \end{vmatrix}$$

$$= (24 - 3 - 24 - 3) - (-4 + 24 - 32 + 3)$$
$$= -6 - (-9) = 3. \text{ Answer.}$$

Determinants have some properties that are useful in simplifying their expansion by minors. The properties are presented here without proof. While third-order determinants are used in illustrating them, the properties are valid for determinants of any order.

Property 1. If each element in any row (or each element in any column) of a matrix is 0, then the determinant is equal to 0.

$$\begin{vmatrix} 2 & 1 & 4 \\ 0 & 0 & 0 \\ 1 & 3 & -1 \end{vmatrix} = -0\begin{vmatrix} 1 & 4 \\ 3 & -1 \end{vmatrix} + 0\begin{vmatrix} 2 & 4 \\ 1 & -1 \end{vmatrix} - 0\begin{vmatrix} 2 & 1 \\ 1 & 3 \end{vmatrix}$$

$$= 0 + 0 + 0 = 0$$

Property 2. If any two rows (or any two columns) of a determinant are interchanged, the resulting determinant is the negative of the original determinant.

$$\begin{vmatrix} 1 & 2 & -3 \\ 2 & 1 & 4 \\ 3 & 1 & 2 \end{vmatrix} = 1\begin{vmatrix} 1 & 4 \\ 1 & 2 \end{vmatrix} - 2\begin{vmatrix} 2 & -3 \\ 1 & 2 \end{vmatrix} + 3\begin{vmatrix} 2 & -3 \\ 1 & 4 \end{vmatrix} = 17$$

$$\begin{vmatrix} 2 & 1 & -3 \\ 1 & 2 & 4 \\ 1 & 3 & 2 \end{vmatrix} = -1\begin{vmatrix} 1 & 4 \\ 1 & 2 \end{vmatrix} + 2\begin{vmatrix} 2 & -3 \\ 1 & 2 \end{vmatrix} - 3\begin{vmatrix} 2 & -3 \\ 1 & 4 \end{vmatrix} = -17$$

Property 3. If two rows (or two columns) of a determinant have corresponding elements that are equal, then the determinant is equal to 0.

$$\begin{vmatrix} 1 & 3 & -2 \\ 3 & 2 & 4 \\ 1 & 3 & -2 \end{vmatrix} = -3\begin{vmatrix} 3 & -2 \\ 3 & -2 \end{vmatrix} + 2\begin{vmatrix} 1 & -2 \\ 1 & -2 \end{vmatrix} - 4\begin{vmatrix} 1 & 3 \\ 1 & 3 \end{vmatrix}$$

$$= -3 \cdot 0 + 2 \cdot 0 - 4 \cdot 0 = 0$$

Property 4. If each element in one row (or one column) of a determinant is multiplied by a real number k, then the determinant is multiplied by k.

$$\begin{vmatrix} 1 & 3 & -1 \\ 2 & 1 & 4 \\ 3(2) & 3(-1) & 3(5) \end{vmatrix} = 3 \begin{vmatrix} 1 & 3 & -1 \\ 2 & 1 & 4 \\ 2 & -1 & 5 \end{vmatrix}$$

Verify this by expanding both determinants by minors of the elements in the third row.

Property 5. If each element of one row is multiplied by a real number k and the resulting products are added to the corresponding elements of another row, or each element of one column is multiplied by a real number k and the resulting products are added to the corresponding elements of another column, then the resulting determinant is equal to the original determinant.

$$\begin{vmatrix} 1 & 3 & -2 \\ 0 & 4 & 3 \\ 1 & -2 & 5 \end{vmatrix} = \begin{vmatrix} 1 & 3 & -2 \\ 0 & 4 & 3 \\ 1+3(1) & -2+3(3) & 5+3(-2) \end{vmatrix} = \begin{vmatrix} 1 & 3 & -2 \\ 0 & 4 & 3 \\ 4 & 7 & -1 \end{vmatrix}$$

EXAMPLE 3 Evaluate: $\begin{vmatrix} 2 & -1 & -6 \\ 3 & 4 & 2 \\ 5 & -2 & 3 \end{vmatrix}$

SOLUTION Use the above properties to obtain zeros in the second column. Multiply the first row by 4 and add to the second row.

$$\begin{vmatrix} 2 & -1 & -6 \\ 3+4(2) & 4+4(-1) & 2+4(-6) \\ 5 & -2 & 3 \end{vmatrix} = \begin{vmatrix} 2 & -1 & -6 \\ 11 & 0 & -22 \\ 5 & -2 & 3 \end{vmatrix}$$

Multiply the first row by -2 and add to the third row.

$$\begin{vmatrix} 2 & -1 & -6 \\ 11 & 0 & -22 \\ 5+(-2)(2) & -2+(-2)(-1) & 3+(-2)(-6) \end{vmatrix} = \begin{vmatrix} 2 & -1 & -6 \\ 11 & 0 & -22 \\ 1 & 0 & 15 \end{vmatrix}$$

Expand the last determinant by minors of the second column.

$$\begin{vmatrix} 2 & -1 & -6 \\ 11 & 0 & -22 \\ 1 & 0 & 15 \end{vmatrix} = -(-1)\begin{vmatrix} 11 & -22 \\ 1 & 15 \end{vmatrix} + 0\begin{vmatrix} 2 & -6 \\ 1 & 15 \end{vmatrix} - 0\begin{vmatrix} 2 & -6 \\ 11 & -22 \end{vmatrix}$$

$$= 187 + 0 - 0 = 187. \text{ \textbf{Answer.}}$$

Expand the given determinant by minors of the given row or column and then evaluate.

A 1. $\begin{vmatrix} 2 & 1 & 4 \\ 1 & 3 & -1 \\ 6 & 1 & 1 \end{vmatrix}$; row 1

3. $\begin{vmatrix} 1 & 1 & 2 \\ 2 & -3 & 1 \\ 2 & -2 & 6 \end{vmatrix}$; column 2

2. $\begin{vmatrix} -1 & 1 & 5 \\ -1 & 2 & 4 \\ 3 & 3 & 2 \end{vmatrix}$; row 2

4. $\begin{vmatrix} 3 & 0 & 1 \\ 2 & -1 & 4 \\ 1 & -2 & 2 \end{vmatrix}$; column 1

Evaluate.

5. $\begin{vmatrix} 1 & 6 & -4 & 3 \\ 0 & -2 & -1 & 2 \\ 0 & 3 & 3 & 1 \\ 1 & 5 & 0 & 1 \end{vmatrix}$

6. $\begin{vmatrix} 1 & -1 & 2 & 4 \\ 4 & 0 & 1 & 3 \\ -1 & 0 & 2 & 0 \\ -2 & 1 & 2 & 5 \end{vmatrix}$

Use Cramer's Rule to solve the system.

B 7. $2x - y - w = 1$
$3x + z + w = 1$
$x + y + 2w = 0$
$4x - 3z + 2w = 0$

8. $3x - z + 2w = 0$
$x + 5y + z + w = -2$
$3x - y + 2w = -1$
$x + y + z = 0$

9. Given that

$$a_1x + b_1y = c_1$$
$$a_2x + b_2y = c_2$$

and that $D = \begin{vmatrix} a_1 & b_1 \\ a_2 & b_2 \end{vmatrix}$, $D_x = \begin{vmatrix} c_1 & b_1 \\ c_2 & b_2 \end{vmatrix}$, and $D_y = \begin{vmatrix} a_1 & c_1 \\ a_2 & c_2 \end{vmatrix}$, use properties of determinants to explain why

$$xD = \begin{vmatrix} a_1x & b_1 \\ a_2x & b_2 \end{vmatrix} = \begin{vmatrix} a_1x + b_1y & b_1 \\ a_2x + b_2y & b_2 \end{vmatrix} = \begin{vmatrix} c_1 & b_1 \\ c_2 & b_2 \end{vmatrix} = D_x$$

and

$$yD = \begin{vmatrix} a_1 & b_1y \\ a_2 & b_2y \end{vmatrix} = \begin{vmatrix} a_1 & a_1x + b_1y \\ a_2 & a_2x + b_2y \end{vmatrix} = \begin{vmatrix} a_1 & c_1 \\ a_2 & c_2 \end{vmatrix} = D_y.$$

10. Use properties of determinants to show that, for all real numbers a_1, b_1, c_1, a_2, b_2, and c_2,

$$a_1D_x + b_1D_y = c_1D \quad \text{and} \quad a_2D_x + b_2D_y = c_2D,$$

where D, D_x, and D_y have the same meanings as in Exercise 9.

Give the meaning of each of the following.

1. order of a determinant
2. minor of an element in a determinant
3. expansion of a determinant by minors

Objective 1, page 157   4. Use determinants to solve the system:

$$3x + 5z = 4$$
$$3y + 4z = -1$$
$$5x - 2y + 2z = 0$$

Objective 2, page 157   5. Myron, Nelson, and Pete together have $22. Nelson and Pete together have $2 more than Myron, and Nelson has $1 more than Pete. Use three variables to determine how much money each boy has.

Objective 3, page 157   6. Evaluate:

$$\begin{vmatrix} 1 & 0 & 2 & -1 \\ 2 & 1 & 6 & 0 \\ 3 & 3 & 12 & 6 \\ 1 & 1 & 8 & 1 \end{vmatrix}$$

Check your answers with those printed at the back of the book.

chapter summary

1. A rectangular coordinate system in three-dimensional space assigns an ordered triple of numbers to each point. The three **coordinate axes** determine three **coordinate planes,** and the coordinate planes separate space into eight **octants.**

2. The graph of a linear equation in three variables is a plane. The **x-, y-,** and **z-intercepts** of a plane are the x-, y-, and z-coordinates, respectively, of the points where the plane intersects the x-, y-, and z-axes. A line in which a plane cuts a coordinate plane is called the **trace** of the given plane in that coordinate plane.

3. The transformations used in solving systems of linear equations in two variables are also applicable in solving three-variable systems.

4. Third-order determinants can be used to solve a system of three linear equations in three variables by a method called **Cramer's Rule.**

5. A determinant can be **expanded** by **minors** of the elements in any row or column.

6. Cramer's Rule can be extended to the solution of n linear equations in n variables.

7. You can use properties of determinants in simplifying their expansion by minors.

chapter test   1. Sketch the coordinate box of the point $P(5, 4, -6)$.

2. Sketch the graph of $P(3, 1, 2)$ and $Q(-2, -3, 4)$ and draw the line segment joining these points.

5-2   3. Draw a sketch showing the trace of the graph $x + 3y + 2z = 8$ in each coordinate plane, and shade the part of the graph in the first octant.

5-3   4. Solve by transforming into a simple equivalent system:

$$3x + y - z = 4$$
$$5x - 4y + 6z = 5$$
$$2x + 3y + z = -3$$

5-4   **Solve each system by Cramer's Rule.**

5. $x + 3y + z = 2$ 6. $x - 2y - 3z = -7$
$-2x - y = 7$ $2x + 3y - 4z = 7$
$x + y - z = 0$ $-x - 4y + 3z = -11$

5-5   7. For their hi-fi cassette sets, Alan, Tom, and Barbara have a total of 52 cassettes. If Barbara had 6 more, then she would have as many as both of the boys together. Tom has three more cassettes than Alan. How many cassettes does each of the three have?

5-6   8. Expand by minors of elements of the second column, and then evaluate:

$$\begin{vmatrix} 2 & 6 & 7 \\ 1 & -2 & -3 \\ 3 & 1 & 5 \end{vmatrix}$$

9. Evaluate:

$$\begin{vmatrix} 5 & 10 & 0 & 10 \\ 6 & 3 & 0 & 9 \\ 2 & 1 & 2 & 1 \\ 3 & 2 & 4 & -1 \end{vmatrix}$$

10. Use Cramer's Rule to solve:

$$x - 2y + 2z = 0$$
$$2x + y - w = 8$$
$$y - z + 3w = -8$$
$$-y + z + w = -4$$

programmed chapter review

1. In a rectangular coordinate system in space, the three coordinate axes determine three __?__ planes, and these planes separate space into __?__ octants.

coordinate
8

2. In space, the graph of a linear equation in three variables is a __?__ .

plane

3. If a plane cuts the y-axis in a single point, then the y-coordinate of that point is called the __?__ of the plane.

y-intercept

4. A line in which a plane cuts a coordinate plane is called the __?__ of the given plane in the coordinate plane.

trace

5. Two nonparallel planes intersect in a __?__ , and three such planes can intersect in a single __?__ .

line
point

6. The value of the determinant $\begin{vmatrix} 1 & 0 & 0 \\ 0 & 2 & 0 \\ 0 & 0 & 3 \end{vmatrix}$ is __?__ .

6

7. If John has x nickels, y dimes, and z quarters, and the total value of these coins is $\$1.35$, then

$$\underline{}x + \underline{}y + \underline{}z = 135.$$

5; 10; 25

8. In $\begin{vmatrix} a & b & c \\ d & e & f \\ g & h & i \end{vmatrix}$, the minor of f is __?__ .

$\begin{vmatrix} a & b \\ g & h \end{vmatrix}$

9. $\begin{vmatrix} 2a & 2b & 2c \\ 2d & 2e & 2f \\ 2g & 2h & 2i \end{vmatrix} = \underline{} \begin{vmatrix} a & b & c \\ d & e & f \\ g & h & i \end{vmatrix}$

8

10. $\begin{vmatrix} a & b & c \\ d & e & f \\ d & e & f \end{vmatrix} = \underline{}$

0

cumulative review chapters 1–5

1. Graph {the whole numbers between 7 and 9}.

2. State the axiom justifying $7 + (-7) = 0$.

Simplify each expression.

3. $43 + (-92) + 11$

4. $(-8)(-\frac{1}{4})(5)$

5. $-14 - (-22) - 3$

6. $[-23 + 2(7 - 11)] \div [-3 - 3(5 - 7)]$

7. $(3t^2 - 4t + 5) + (t^2 + 3t - 5)$

8. $(7n^2 + 3n - 2) - (5n^2 + n - 1)$

Solve over $\mathcal{R}$.

9. $5n - 3(n + 2) = n + 6$ 10. $\dfrac{3r}{5} - \dfrac{r}{5} = 18$

11. Graph the solution set over $\mathcal{R}$ of $2z - 3 \le 5(z + 6)$.

12. The vertex angle of an isosceles triangle measures $16°$ more than the sum of the measures of the other two angles. Find the measure of each angle in the triangle.

13. Simplify: $\dfrac{|3 - 7| + |12 - 2|}{2|1 - 2|}$

14. Solve $|3x - 2| \le 10$ over $\mathcal{R}$ and graph the solution set.

15. If $g(x) = \dfrac{2x}{3x - 1}$, find **(a)** $g(0)$, **(b)** $g(-1)$, and **(c)** $g(10)$.

Graph each relation over $\mathcal{R}$.

16. $2x - 3y = 12$ 18. $x - y \le 5$

17. $x + 4y = 8$ 19. $3x + y > 2$

20. Find the slope of the line containing the points $(0, 5)$ and $(-1, 3)$.

21. Find an equation for the line described in Exercise 20.

22. Find an equation for the line with slope $-\frac{2}{3}$ and y-intercept -1.

23. If y varies directly as x, and $y = 6$ when $x = 18$, find y when $x = 6$.

24. Solve by graphing: $2x - y = 3$
$\qquad\qquad\qquad\quad x - 3y = -1$

25. Solve by the linear-combination method: $5x - 2y = 7$
$\qquad\qquad\qquad\qquad\qquad\qquad\qquad\quad x + 2y = -1$

26. Solve by substitution: $3x + 4y = -2$
$\qquad\qquad\qquad\qquad\quad 2x - \ y = 6$

27. Solve using Cramer's Rule: $2x - 3y = -13$
$\qquad\qquad\qquad\qquad\qquad\quad 3x + 5y = 9$

28. Find the maximum value of $3x - y$ subject to the constraints:
$$0 \le x \le 6, \ 0 \le y \le 5, \text{ and } x + y \le 7.$$

29. Sketch the trace of the graph of $2x + y + 3z = 6$ in each coordinate plane, and shade the part of the graph in the first octant.

30. Solve by transforming into a simple equivalent system:
$$x - 2y + z = 5$$
$$2x + y - 3z = -7$$
$$x + 3y + z = 0$$

31. The sum of three numbers is 2. The first number is equal to the sum of the other two, and the third number is the result of subtracting the first from the second. Find the numbers.

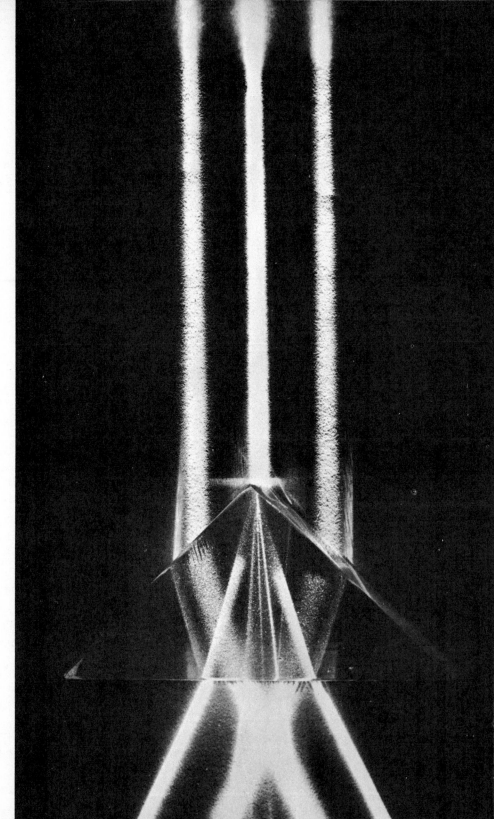

. . . light rays passing through a triangular prism. The study of light and lenses has applications in such diverse fields as astronomy, photography, and optometry.

6

polynomials and rational algebraic expressions

polynomials and their factors

Objectives

After completing the next four sections, you should be able to:
1. Apply the laws of exponents to simplify products and quotients of monomials.
2. Represent a given number in standard notation.
3. Estimate products and quotients.
4. Write a product of polynomials in simple form.
5. Write a polynomial in factored form.

6-1   laws of exponents

You will recall from page 34 that b^n, the nth power of b, where n is a positive integer, denotes a product of n equal factors. That is:

$$b^n = \overbrace{(b \times b \times \ldots \times b)}^{n \text{ factors}}$$

Each factor is b, the *base,* and the number of such factors is n, the *exponent.* The laws for working with positive-integral exponents are summarized in the following theorem.

Theorem. If a and $b \in \mathcal{R}$, and m and n are positive integers, then:

1. $b^m b^n = b^{m+n}$

2. $(b^m)^n = b^{mn}$

3. $(ab)^m = a^m b^m$

4. If $m > n$ and $b \neq 0$, $\dfrac{b^m}{b^n} = b^{m-n}$.

5. If $m < n$ and $b \neq 0$, $\dfrac{b^m}{b^n} = \dfrac{1}{b^{n-m}}$.

6. If $b \neq 0$, $\left(\dfrac{a}{b}\right)^m = \dfrac{a^m}{b^m}$.

7. If $b \notin \{-1, 0, 1\}$, then $b^m = b^n$ if and only if $m = n$.

Knowing the definition of a power and the properties of real numbers, you can see why each of the laws stated in the preceding theorem holds. Consider, for example, the reasoning for Law 1.

$$b^m b^n = \overbrace{(b \times \ldots \times b)}^{m \text{ factors}}\overbrace{(b \times \ldots \times b)}^{n \text{ factors}} \quad \text{Definition of a power}$$

$$= \overbrace{(b \times \ldots \times b)}^{(m+n) \text{ factors}} \quad \text{Associative axiom of multiplication}$$

$$= b^{m+n} \quad \text{Definition of a power}$$

$$b^m b^n = b^{m+n} \quad \text{Transitive property of equality}$$

Laws 1–3 together with the properties of multiplication enable you to simplify a *product* of two or more monomials.

EXAMPLE 1   Simplify each product.

a. $(2x^2 y^3)(-5x^4 y^2)$ b. $(-4p^2 s^4)^3$ c. $(-5m^2 q)^2(-3m^3 q)^3$

SOLUTION   a. $(2x^2 y^3)(-5x^4 y^2) = 2(-5)(x^2 x^4)(y^3 y^2) = -10x^6 y^5$. **Answer.**

b. $(-4p^2 s^4)^3 = (-4)^3(p^2)^3(s^4)^3 = -64p^6 s^{12}$. **Answer.**

c. $(-5m^2 q)^2(-3m^3 q)^3 = (-5)^2(-3)^3(m^2)^2(m^3)^3(q^2 q^3) = -675m^{13} q^5$.

Answer.

You can deduce Laws 4 and 5 from Law 1 with the help of a corollary of the following *basic property of quotients,* which you may recall from an earlier algebra course.

Basic Property of Quotients

For all r, s, t, and $u \in \mathcal{R}$, and t and $u \neq 0$,

$$\frac{rs}{tu} = \frac{r}{t} \cdot \frac{s}{u}.$$

This theorem says that a quotient of products can be written as a product of quotients. If you let (1) $t = 1$, or (2) $r = 1$, you obtain the required corollary.

Corollary. For all r, s, t, and $u \in \mathcal{R}$, and t and $u \neq 0$:

1. $\dfrac{rs}{u} = r \cdot \dfrac{s}{u}$
$\qquad\qquad$
2. $\dfrac{s}{tu} = \dfrac{1}{t} \cdot \dfrac{s}{u}$

PROOF OF LAW 4

First, note that if $m > n$, then $m - n$ is positive (Definition of ">").

$\dfrac{b^m}{b^n} = \dfrac{b^{(m-n)+n}}{b^n}$
$\qquad\qquad$
$(m - n) + n = m$

$\qquad = \dfrac{b^{m-n} \cdot b^n}{b^n}$
$\qquad\qquad$
Law 1 for positive exponents

$\qquad = b^{m-n} \cdot \dfrac{b^n}{b^n}$
$\qquad\qquad$
Corollary above

$\qquad = b^{m-n} \cdot 1$
$\qquad\qquad$
$\dfrac{b^n}{b^n} = 1$

$\qquad = b^{m-n}$
$\qquad\qquad$
Axiom of 1

EXAMPLE 2$\qquad$Simplify each quotient, assuming that no variable equals 0.

a. $\dfrac{-16r^3s^5}{2r^7s^4}$
$\qquad\qquad$
b. $\left(\dfrac{-4x^2}{xz^2}\right)^3$

SOLUTION$\qquad$**a.** $\dfrac{-16r^3s^5}{2r^7s^4} = \left(-\dfrac{16}{2}\right)\left(\dfrac{1}{r^{7-3}}\right)(s^{5-4}) = -8\dfrac{s}{r^4}$.$\quad$Answer.

b. $\left(\dfrac{-4x^2}{xz^2}\right)^3 = \dfrac{(-4)^3(x^2)^3}{(x^3)(z^2)^3} = \dfrac{-64x^6}{x^3z^6} = \dfrac{-64x^3}{z^6}$.$\quad$Answer.

Thus far we have used only *positive* integers as exponents. The laws for exponents will hold for *any* integral exponent with the addition of these definitions:

For all nonzero $b \in \mathcal{R}$ and all positive integers n,

$$b^0 = 1 \qquad \text{and} \qquad b^{-n} = \dfrac{1}{b^n}.$$

EXAMPLE 3   Show that Law 1 holds for $b^{-m}b^{-n}$ when $m = 5$, $n = 2$.

SOLUTION   In order to show that $b^{-5}b^{-2} = b^{-5+(-2)} = b^{-7}$, we have:

$$b^{-5}b^{-2} = \frac{1}{b^5} \cdot \frac{1}{b^2}$$ Definition of b^{-n}

$$= \frac{1}{b^5 \cdot b^2}$$ Basic Property of Quotients

$$= \frac{1}{b^7}$$ Law 1

$$= b^{-7}$$ Definition of b^{-n}

ORAL EXERCISES   Give an equivalent numeral without exponents.

EXAMPLE $\dfrac{2^{-1}}{3^2}$ SOLUTION $\dfrac{2^{-1}}{3^2} = \dfrac{1}{2 \cdot 9} = \dfrac{1}{18}$. Answer.

1. 10^3 4. 3^{-2} 7. $(-4)^{-2}$ 10. 628×10^{-2}

2. $\dfrac{4^5}{4^4}$ 5. $\dfrac{6^3}{6^5}$ 8. $\dfrac{1}{2^{-4}}$ 11. $2(4 - 2)^{-3}$

3. $2^2 \cdot 2^3$ 6. $\left(\dfrac{2}{3}\right)^3$ 9. $\dfrac{2^{-3}}{2^{-4}}$ 12. $\left(\dfrac{2}{3}\right)^{-1} + \dfrac{1}{2}$

State an equivalent expression in which each variable occurs at most once and only positive exponents appear. Assume that all variables with negative exponents do not have 0 as their value.

13. $(5a^2b)(-2b^3)$ 15. $(6x^{-1}y)(x^2y^2)$

14. $(4x^{-2})(2x^2y)$ 16. $(\frac{1}{3}r^3s^4)(9r^2s^{-2})$

WRITTEN EXERCISES   For each product or quotient give an equivalent expression containing only positive exponents. Assume that all variables in denominators or with nonpositive exponents do not have 0 as their value.

A   1. $2x^3(-3x^2)$ 8. $(m^2)^4(2m^3r)$

2. $(4a^{-2})(3a^3)$ 9. $(2ab^2c^3)^2(-5a^2bc^3)^3$

3. $(7x^2y)(-2xy^{-2})$ 10. $(12x^{-1}y^2z)(12^{-2}x^2y^{-1}z^{-2})$

4. $(-8c^3d)(\frac{1}{2}cd^2e^{-1})$

5. $(5rs^{-1}t^3)(-3r^2st)$ 11. $\dfrac{4x^2y^0}{2y^{-1}}$

6. $(-4x^2)(5x^{-3})(10x)^{-1}$

7. $(2pq)^2(-3p^2q)$ 12. $\dfrac{p^0}{p^{-2}}$

13. $\dfrac{16r^3t^2}{-4rt}$ 15. $\dfrac{(-3a^2b)^3}{54(ab^3)^2}$ 17. $\dfrac{x^{-3}y^2}{x^2y^{-4}}$ 19. $\dfrac{x^{-3}y^5z^{-4}}{x^2y^{-2}z^3}$

14. $\dfrac{18k^{-2}m^3}{6k^3m^4}$ 16. $\left(\dfrac{11d^2e^5}{33d^4e^2}\right)^2$ 18. $\dfrac{3^{-2}b^{-1}}{a^{-1}b^2}$ 20. $\dfrac{(2k)^{-2}m^2n}{k^3m^{-1}n^{-2}}$

Simplify each expression.

B 21. $(3a^4)(4b)^3 - (2a^2b)^2(5b)$

22. $(2mr)^2 + (-4m)(6mr)(-r)$

23. $(7c)(-2c) + (2c^2)^2 - (3c)(4c)^3 + \left(\dfrac{6c^4}{c^3}\right)^2$

24. $(2p)^2(-3p) - \dfrac{9(p^3 + q^3)^2}{9(p^3 + q^3)} + q(-5q)^2$

25. Deduce Law 5 from Law 1.

26. Deduce Law 6 from Law 3.

27. Prove that for any positive integer n, $b \in \mathcal{R}$, and $b \neq 0$, $\dfrac{1}{b^{-n}} = b^n$.

28. Prove that for any positive integer n, and a, $b \in \mathcal{R}$ with $ab \neq 0$, $(ab)^{-n} = a^{-n}b^{-n}$.

C 29. Prove that for any nonzero $b \in \mathcal{R}$ and any positive integers m and n, if $m = n$, then $\dfrac{b^m}{b^n} = b^{m-n}$.

30. Prove the Basic Property of Quotients (page 174).

Hint: $\dfrac{rs}{tu} = rs \cdot \dfrac{1}{tu} = (r \cdot s) \cdot \left(\dfrac{1}{t} \cdot \dfrac{1}{u}\right).$

6-2 *standard notation*

We use integer powers of 10 in representing any nonzero real number in *standard notation*. Such a number is given in standard notation (also called scientific notation when used in the expression of measurements) provided it is named as a product,

$$a \times 10^n,$$

where $1 \leq |a| < 10$ and n is an integer. As illustrated by the last three examples in the table at the left, if $n = 0$ (so that $10^n = 1$), then the second factor ordinarily is not written, and if $n \neq 0$ but $a = 1$, then the first factor ordinarily is not written.

In a numeral, each digit reporting the *number of units* of measure contained in a measurement is called a significant digit. Thus, 27.2 and 0.0103 have three significant digits. In each decimal numeral in the table, notice the red caret that is placed after the first significant digit in the numeral. By counting

Decimal notation	Standard notation
-41.5	-4.15×10^1
0.0058	5.8×10^{-3}
3.207	3.207
-1	-1
0.0001	10^{-4}

the number of places *from the caret to the decimal point,* you obtain n. Do you see that n is positive or negative according as you count to the right or to the left from the caret?

You can easily compare numbers when they are represented in standard notation.

EXAMPLE 1 $6.3 \times 10^5 > 9.1 \times 10^4$, because $5 > 4$.

EXAMPLE 2 $5.1 \times 10^3 < 5.2 \times 10^3$, because $5.1 < 5.2$.

It is often convenient to break off, or round off, a lengthy decimal, leaving a numeral that represents an approximation of the number named by the given decimal. Using $\doteq$ to mean ''equals approximately,'' you may write

$$248.13 \doteq 248.1, \qquad 248.13 \doteq 248, \qquad 248.13 \doteq 250,$$

as approximations of 248.13 to the nearest tenth, the nearest unit, and the nearest multiple of 10, respectively. In rounding, use this rule:

> To round off a decimal, add 1 to the last digit retained if the value of the first digit dropped is 5 or more; otherwise leave the retained digits unchanged.

Under this rule, the difference between a number and its approximation (the round-off error) is *at most* half the unit of the last digit retained. For example, the statement $s \doteq 1.32$ is equivalent to

$$1.32 - 0.005 \leq s < 1.32 + 0.005, \qquad \text{or} \qquad 1.315 \leq s < 1.325.$$

You can round off decimals and use standard notation to help you *estimate* products and quotients rapidly.

EXAMPLE 3   **Find a one-significant-digit estimate of A, if**

$$A = \frac{2120 \times 36.94 \times 194}{365.3}.$$

SOLUTION   1. Round off each number to its one-significant-digit approximation.

$$A \doteq \frac{2000 \times 40 \times 200}{400}$$

2. Express the approximation in standard notation.

$$A \doteq \frac{2 \times 10^3 \times 4 \times 10^1 \times 2 \times 10^2}{4 \times 10^2}$$

3. Compute and round off to one significant digit.

$$A \doteq \frac{2 \times 4 \times 2}{4} \times 10^{3+1+2-2}$$

$$\therefore A \doteq 4 \times 10^4 \text{ or } 40,000. \textbf{ Answer.}$$

(To four decimal places, A is actually equal to 41,589.6064.)

Name the given number, using standard notation.

    1. 224.8   **2.** 0.0127   **3.** 452   **4.** 0.01

Name the given number, using decimal notation.

    5. 7.28×10^3 **7.** 4.9×10^{-1}

    6. 1.12×10^{-2} **8.** 7×10^6

State a one-significant-digit approximation of the given number.

    9. 5280   **11.** 0.19

   10. 5820   **12.** 0.0032

State which of the given numerals names the greater number.

   13. 5.37×10^6 or 5.42×10^6 **15.** 5.37×10^6 or 5.37×10^7

   14. 3×10^{-4} or 4×10^{-4} **16.** 3×10^{-3} or 3×10^{-2}

Express each of the following in standard notation.

  A   **1.** 315   **4.** 59.1   **7.** 27,315   **10.** 0.000006

         2. 5172   **5.** 0.036   **8.** 812,215   **11.** 3002

         3. 7.8   **6.** 0.701   **9.** 0.00021   **12.** 4030

Express each of the following using a decimal numeral.

   13. 6.1×10^2 **19.** 2.163×10^{-1}

   14. 8.2×10^3 **20.** 4.008×10^5

   15. 1.03×10^5 **21.** 3.02×10^7

   16. 7.003×10^2 **22.** 5.08×10^8

   17. 5.92×10^{-3} **23.** 3.214×10^{-5}

   18. 8.6×10^{-2} **24.** 6.198×10^{-6}

Express each of the following as a single decimal numeral.

   25. $\dfrac{(8 \times 10^3)(3 \times 10^{-1})}{(6 \times 10^{-2})}$ **27.** $\dfrac{(4.2 \times 10^3)(6.3 \times 10^{-5})}{(2.1 \times 10^4)(3.15 \times 10^{-3})}$

   26. $\dfrac{(6 \times 10^5)(5 \times 10^{-8})}{(3 \times 10^{-5})}$ **28.** $\dfrac{(7.2 \times 10^5)(3.6 \times 10^{-7})}{(2.7 \times 10^{-1})}$

Find a one-significant-digit estimate of the given number.

  B   **29.** $\dfrac{3868 \times 51.08}{4.02 \times 0.0069}$ **30.** $\dfrac{0.0213 \times 0.005827}{23157 \times 4862}$

In BASIC, answers that are not exact are rounded to six significant digits. Also, numbers greater than 999999 are rounded to six digits and expressed in a manner that corresponds exactly to the standard notation described in Section 6-2.

Multiplying 54321 by 12345 exactly gives the product 670,592,745. The program

```
10   PRINT 54321*12345
20   END
```

gives the output 6.70593E+08. The "E+08" means "times 10 with the exponent positive 8." Thus,

$$6.70593E+08 = 6.70593 \times 10^8.$$

To discover how the computer expresses small numbers, try the following programs.

EXERCISES

1.
```
10   FOR N=2 TO 20
20   PRINT "1 /";N;" =";1/N
30   NEXT N
40   END
```

2.
```
10   LET D=10
20   FOR I=1 TO 10
30   PRINT 5/D
40   LET D=D*10
50   NEXT I
60   END
```

3. In the preceding program change line 30 to: 30   PRINT 3.14159/D

6-3   *multiplying polynomials*

You can find the product of two polynomials by using the familiar axioms of addition and multiplication and the first law of exponents. For example, to find the product of the *binomial* $3x - 2$ and the *trinomial* $5x^4 - x^3 + 4x$, you can proceed as follows:

$(3x - 2)(5x^4 - x^3 + 4x)$

$= 3x(5x^4 - x^3 + 4x) - 2(5x^4 - x^3 + 4x)$	Distributive axiom
$= 15x^5 - 3x^4 + 12x^2 - 10x^4 + 2x^3 - 8x$	Distributive axiom and Law 1 of exponents
$= 15x^5 - 13x^4 + 2x^3 + 12x^2 - 8x$	Simplification

You are less likely to make errors in adding like terms, however, if you use a vertical arrangement in multiplying:

$$
\begin{array}{r}
5x^4 - \ , \ x^3 \qquad\ + \ 4x \\
3x \ - \ 2 \\
\hline
15x^5 - \ \ 3x^4 \qquad\quad + 12x^2 \\
- \ 10x^4 + 2x^3 \qquad\quad - 8x \\
\hline
15x^5 - 13x^4 + 2x^3 + 12x^2 - 8x
\end{array}
$$

> To obtain the product of two polynomials, multiply each term of one of the polynomials by each term of the other, and then add all the products.

Three special cases of binomial products that are useful to know are given here:

$$(a + b)^2 = a^2 + 2ab + b^2$$
$$(a - b)^2 = a^2 - 2ab + b^2$$
$$(a + b)(a - b) = a^2 - b^2 \ .$$

EXAMPLE Write $(2x^2 - 5y)^2$ as a polynomial in simple form.

SOLUTION $(2x^2 - 5y)^2 = (2x^2)^2 - 2(2x^2)(5y) + (5y)^2 = 4x^4 - 20x^2y + 25y^2$.

Answer.

ORAL EXERCISES Express each product as a polynomial in simple form.

1. $(2t)(3t)$ 3. $(3z)(2z)^2$ 5. $(a + b)^2$ 7. $(c - 1)(c + 1)$
2. $(-4a)^2$ 4. $(5x)(-2x)^3$ 6. $(y - 1)^2$ 8. $(r + 2q)(r - 2q)$

WRITTEN EXERCISES Write each product as a polynomial in simple form.

A 1. $(a + 1)(a - 3)$ 6. $(0.4y + 2)(0.4y + 2)$
2. $(x^2 - 3)5x^2$ 7. $(x^{3a} - 5)^2$
3. $(p + 3q)^2$ 8. $(m + 2)^3$
4. $(\frac{2}{3}m - 5)(\frac{2}{3}m + 5)$ 9. $(2a - b)^3$
5. $(b^3 + 3)^2$ 10. $(x - 1)(x + 1)^2$

B 11. $(2x + 1)(3x^2 - x + 6)$ 17. $(x - 3y)^4$
12. $(3x - 4)^2(x + 4)$ 18. $5a^3 \left(\dfrac{2}{a} + \dfrac{4}{a^2} - \dfrac{5}{a^3} \right)$
13. $(s + t)^2(s^2 - t^2)$
14. $(k - n)^2(3k^2 + 2n^2)$ 19. $-2t^2 \left(-t^2 + \dfrac{3}{4} - \dfrac{1}{2t} + \dfrac{2}{t^2} \right)$
15. $ab(a + b)^3$
16. $(2x + 3)^2(x - 4)^2$ 20. $(t^3 + t^2) \left(1 + \dfrac{2}{t} - \dfrac{3}{t^2} \right)$

Express each product as a sum.

21. $(3a^{-2} + 1)^2$

22. $(4x^{-3} + 2)(4x^{-3} - 2)$

23. $(7 - x^{-3})^2$

24. $(y^{-2} + 1)(y^2 - 2)^2$

In Exercises 25–29 find the value of a that makes the given equation a true statement for all real values of the variable x. Check your result.

EXAMPLE $(5x + a)(3x - a) = 15x^2 - 4x - a^2$

SOLUTION $15x^2 - 2ax - a^2 = 15x^2 - 4x - a^2$

$$-2ax = -4x$$
$$a = 2$$

CHECK $(5x + 2)(3x - 2) = 15x^2 - 4x - 2^2$

$15x^2 - 4x - 4 = 15x^2 - 4x - 4 \checkmark$ $\qquad \therefore a = 2$. Answer.

25. $(x + a)(2x - a) = 2x^2 + 3x - a^2$

26. $(3x - a)(x + 2a) = 3x^2 + 10x - 2a^2$

27. $(ax - 3)(2ax + 3) = 2a^2x^2 - 12x - 9$

28. $(5 - 3ax)(5 + 2ax) = -6a^2x^2 + 20x + 25$

C 29. $(4x - a)(2x^2 - 3x + a^2) = 8x^3 - 2x^2(6 + a) + 2x(2a^2 - 3) - a^3$

30. Solve $(x - 1)^3 = 9x(x - 4) + (x - 4)^3$ for x.

programming in BASIC

Up to now, we have used separate, unrelated variables. BASIC also provides for *lists* of variables. These variables are called *subscripted variables,* and their use often corresponds to that of subscripted variables in algebra. For example, we can write a general fourth-degree polynomial in x as:

$$a_1x^4 + a_2x^3 + a_3x^2 + a_4x + a_5$$

In BASIC, these coefficients may be represented by:

$$A(1), A(2), A(3), A(4), A(5)$$

Moreover, the subscript may itself be a variable. This makes it easy to READ in a list of DATA:

```
10   FOR I = 1 TO 5
20   READ A(I)
30   NEXT I
40   DATA 1, −2, 3, 5, 1
```
. . . .

This makes $A(1) = 1$, $A(2) = -2$, and so on. DATA statements may go anywhere in the program. The READ statement takes values from the DATA list in the order in which the variables appear in the program.

Study the following program that will find the coefficients of the sum of two polynomials. (Recall Section 2–1.) By changing the DATA statements, you can use it for different problems. Notice that N is the degree of the polynomial of higher degree and hence the degree of the sum.

```
10   READ N
20   FOR I=1 TO N+1
30   READ A(I)
40   NEXT I
50   FOR I=1 TO N+1
60   READ B(I)
70   NEXT I
80   FOR I=1 TO N+1
90   PRINT A(I)+B(I);" ";
100  NEXT I
110  DATA (Higher degree)
120  DATA (Coef. of 1st polynomial)
130  DATA (Coef. of 2d polynomial)
140  END
```

Two examples:

$$3x^3 + 4x^2 - 7x + 5$$
$$\underline{6x^3 \qquad\qquad + 5x}$$

```
110  DATA 3
120  DATA 3,4,-7,5
130  DATA 6,0,5,0
```

$$x^4 \qquad\qquad + 3x^2 + 5x$$
$$\underline{\qquad x^3 + 2x^2 \qquad + 5}$$

```
110  DATA 4
120  DATA 1, 0, 3, 5, 0
130  DATA 0,1,2,0,5
```

Notice that the data must have a coefficient for each of $N + 1$ terms in each polynomial, including zeros where necessary.

Subscripted variables as described here can be used for $I = 1$ to 10. If more than 10 are needed, a DIMension statement must be used as described on page 184.

You probably don't need to use a computer just to add polynomials, but an interesting program can be made for multiplying polynomials.

First notice that if M and N are the degrees of the factor polynomials, the product will have the degree $M + N$ and may have up to $M + N + 1$ terms. For example, consider the product of $(a_1x^3 + a_2x^2 + a_3x + a_4)$ and $(b_1x^3 + b_2x^2 + b_3x + b_4)$. The coefficients of the product can be written as shown below:

No. of term		Sum of subscripts
1	a_1b_1	2
2	$a_1b_2 + a_2b_1$	3
3	$a_1b_3 + a_2b_2 + a_3b_1$	4
4	$a_1b_4 + a_2b_3 + a_3b_2 + a_4b_1$	5
5	$\cancel{a_1b_5} + a_2b_4 + a_3b_3 + a_4b_2 + \cancel{a_5b_1}$	6
6	$\cancel{a_1b_6} + \cancel{a_2b_5} + a_3b_4 + a_4b_3 + \cancel{a_5b_2} + \cancel{a_6b_1}$	7
7	$\cancel{a_1b_7} + \cancel{a_2b_6} + \cancel{a_3b_5} + a_4b_4 + \cancel{a_5b_3} + \cancel{a_6b_2} + \cancel{a_7b_1}$	8

The terms that are crossed out are zero because $a_5 = b_5 = a_6 = b_6 = a_7 = b_7 = 0$. However, keeping the terms in the pattern suggests a way of using nested loops to find the coefficients of the product.

Notice that the sum of the subscripts in the terms of each coefficient is one more than the number of that term in the product.

To allow for polynomial factors up to degree 9 (10 terms), we must provide for up to 19 terms in the product. To use the pattern of coefficients shown earlier, we must allow for up to 19 terms for A(I) and B(I) by including the DIMension statement as shown in the following program. We must use DIM when there are more than 10 values for a subscripted variable. The statement reserves enough space in the computer for these values.

```
10   DIM A[19],B[19]
20   READ M,N
30   FOR I=N+1 TO M+N+1
40   LET A[I]=0
50   LET B[I]=0
60   NEXT I
70   FOR I=1 TO M+1
80   READ A[I]
90   NEXT I
100  FOR I=1 TO N+1
110  READ B[I]
120  NEXT I
130  DATA 1 (Deg. of 1st poly., M)
140  DATA 1 (Deg. of 2d poly., N≤M)
150  DATA 1,1 (Coef. of 1st poly.)
160  DATA 1,1 (Coef. of 2d poly.)
170  FOR I=1 TO M+N+1
180  LET S=0
190  FOR J=1 TO I
200  LET S=S+A[J]*B[I+1−J]
210  NEXT J
220  PRINT S;" ";
230  NEXT I
240  END
```

In line 170, I is the number of the term in the product; and in line 200, I + 1 is the sum of the subscripts.

EXERCISES

1. If you RUN the multiplication program above as listed, the output will be

1   2   1

which represents $x^2 + 2x + 1$. Make that polynomial the first factor by making these changes and RUN the program again:

```
130  DATA   2
150  DATA   1, 2, 1
```

Continue changing lines 130 and 150 in this way up to

```
130  DATA   9
```

and observe the pattern of your results.

2. Find the product shown at the top of page 181 by using these DATA statements in the previous program:

```
130  DATA  4
140  DATA  1
150  DATA  5, −1, 0, 4, 0
160  DATA  3, −2
```

3. Rewrite the multiplication program to use INPUT statements instead of READ and DATA statements.

4. Write a program that will use subscripted variables to store the prices of four items and will allow you to compute bills for orders for numbers of one or more of the items.

6-4 *factoring a polynomial*

In Section 6–2 you saw that:

I. $\qquad a^2 - b^2 = (a - b)(a + b)$ Difference of squares

II. $a^2 - 2ab + b^2 = (a - b)(a - b) = (a - b)^2$

III. $a^2 + 2ab + b^2 = (a + b)(a + b) = (a + b)^2$

A polynomial, such as any of those in I–III, that can be expressed as a product of two or more *polynomials of lower positive degree* is said to be reducible. Each of the latter polynomials is called a factor of the given polynomial. To factor a polynomial over a designated set (the factor set), you express it as a product of polynomials belonging to the factor set. Unless stated otherwise, we assume only integral coefficients for the factors of a polynomial with integral coefficients.

EXAMPLE 1   Factor the polynomial $6xy + 21y^2$.

SOLUTION   You can easily observe that $3y$ is the monomial of greatest coefficient and degree that is a factor of each term in the given polynomial. Then by the distributive law, we have

$$6xy + 21y^2 = 3y(2x + 7y). \textbf{Answer.}$$

In Example 1, $3y$ is called the greatest monomial factor of the given polynomial because it is the monomial with the *greatest* numerical coefficient and the *greatest* degree that is a factor of each term of the polynomial. The other factor, $2x + 7y$, cannot be reduced to a product of factors of lower positive degree, and is hence irreducible. Moreover, since it is irreducible and its greatest monomial factor is 1, $2x + 7y$ is called a prime polynomial.

A polynomial is said to be factored completely when it has been expressed as the product of a constant and one or more prime polynomials or powers of prime polynomials. In Example 1 the constant is 3, and the prime polynomials are y and $2x + 7y$.

EXAMPLE 2   Factor each polynomial completely.

a. $6x^4 - 150x^2$

b. $3a^5 - 6a^4b + 3a^3b^2$

SOLUTION   a. $6x^4 - 150x^2 = 6x^2(x^2 - 25) = 6x^2(x - 5)(x + 5)$.   Answer.

b. $3a^5 - 6a^4b + 3a^3b^2 = 3a^3(a^2 - 2ab + b^2) = 3a^3(a - b)^2$.   Answer.

Every reducible *quadratic trinomial* of the form $ax^2 + bx + c$ has two binomial factors, of the form $Ax + B$ and $Cx + D$. Since

$$(Ax + B)(Cx + D) = ACx^2 + (BC + AD)x + BD,$$

the problem of factoring such a trinomial is to find values of the coefficients A, B, C, and D such that

$$AC = a, \qquad AD + BC = b, \qquad \text{and} \qquad BD = c.$$

EXAMPLE 3   Factor $6x^2 + 7x + 2$.

SOLUTION   First, you might analyze the coefficients as follows: Since the coefficient a (AC) of x^2 is positive, we know that A and C must both be of the same sign, and likewise since the constant term c (BD) is positive, B and D must be of the same sign. (Two numbers are of the "same sign" if both are positive or both are negative; they are of "opposite signs" if one is positive and the other negative.) Since the coefficient b ($AD + BC$) of x is also positive, A and C cannot have the opposite sign of D and B or else AD and BC would both be negative. Hence A, B, C, and D must all be of the same sign, which we can take to be positive. Since $AC = 6$ and $BD = 2$, the possible factors are:

$$
\begin{array}{cccccccc}
A & B & C & D & & AC & AD + BC & BD \\
\downarrow & \downarrow & \downarrow & \downarrow & & \downarrow & & \downarrow \\
(6x & + 2)(& x & + 1) & = & 6x^2 + & 8x & + 2 \\
(6x & + 1)(& x & + 2) & = & 6x^2 + & 13x & + 2 \\
(3x & + 2)(2x & & + 1) & = & 6x^2 + & 7x & + 2 \\
(3x & + 1)(2x & & + 2) & = & 6x^2 + & 8x & + 2 \\
\end{array}
$$

The combination of factors shown in red makes $AD + BC = b$, or 7.
∴ in factored form, $6x^2 + 7x + 2 = (3x + 2)(2x + 1)$.   Answer.

Notice that in Example 3, if we had chosen A, B, C, and D as all negative instead of positive, the result would have been equivalent. That is,

$$[-3x + (-2)][-2x + (-1)] = 6x^2 + 7x + 2.$$

EXAMPLE 4   Factor $8y^2 - 2y - 3$.

SOLUTION   Let us abbreviate the possible factors by writing only the coefficients.

8		−3		−2
$A \times C$		$B \times D$		$AD + BC$
4	2	1	−3	$-12 + 2 = -10$
4	2	−1	3	$12 - 2 = 10$
4	2	3	−1	$-4 + 6 = 2$
4	2	−3	1	$4 - 6 = -2$

Hence the factors are $(4y - 3)$ and $(2y + 1)$, and

$$8y^2 - 2y - 3 = (4y - 3)(2y + 1). \textbf{ Answer.}$$

Of course, as soon as you find the correct factors to make

$$AC = a, \ AD + BC = b, \text{ and } BD = c,$$

there is no point in going through the other possibilities.

EXAMPLE 5   Factor $x^2 - 3x + 1$.

SOLUTION

1	1	−3
$A \times C$	$B \times D$	$AD + BC$
1 1	1 1	2
1 1	−1 −1	−2

Since there are no other different factorizations possible, $x^2 - 3x + 1$ is irreducible. **Answer.**

Two other factor patterns that are useful to know in addition to the three at the beginning of this section are:

IV. $a^3 + b^3 = (a + b)(a^2 - ab + b^2)$ Sum of cubes
V. $a^3 - b^3 = (a - b)(a^2 + ab + b^2)$ Difference of cubes

EXAMPLE 6   Factor $64x^3 + 27$.

SOLUTION   Using formula IV with $a = 4x$ and $b = 3$, we have

$$64x^3 + 27 = (4x + 3)(16x^2 - 12x + 9). \textbf{ Answer.}$$

Tell whether the given polynomial is reducible or irreducible. If it is irreducible, state whether or not it is a prime polynomial.

1. $2y^2 + 3y$ 3. $5a - 10$ 5. $2p^2q + p$

2. $6x^2$ 4. $5a - 1$ 6. $m^3 - 3$

State the greatest monomial factor of the given polynomial.

7. $2a^2 - 6a$ 10. $25y^2 - 15$

8. $3xy - x$ 11. $17n^2q^5 - 34n^3q$

9. $6r^2s^3t + 18rs^2t$ 12. $3a^2bc^2 - 12ab^2c + 9a^3b^3c^3$

Identify the given polynomial as a difference of squares, a difference of cubes, a sum of cubes, or the square of a binomial.

13. $x^2 - 16$ 19. $s^4 - 25$

14. $a^3 - 27$ 20. $r^2 - 10r + 25$

15. $36 - m^2$ 21. $x^4 + 16x^2 + 64$

16. $c^3 + 125$ 22. $a^2 - 4ab + 4b^2$

17. $4y^2 - 9$ 23. $x^2y^2 - 4xy + 4$

18. $x^2 + 4x + 4$ 24. $p^2q^2 - 6pq + 9$

Factor completely the given polynomial. Write "prime" for any that cannot be factored over the set of polynomials with integral coefficients.

A   1–18. Each of the polynomials in Oral Exercises 7–24.

B   19. $6 - c - c^2$ 27. $z(a - b) + t(a - b)$

20. $5x^2 - 30x + 32$ 28. $3y(x + 5) - 21(x + 5)$

21. $18y^2 - 83y + 9$ 29. $16r^4 + 24r^2q^2 + 9q^4$

22. $x^2 - 35xy + 300y^2$ 30. $36x^4 - 60x^2y^2 + 25y^4$

23. $p^6 - 64$ 31. $c^2 + cd - 3c - 3d$

24. $c^3d^6 + a^3$ 32. $(n - 1)^2 - r^2$

25. $8 - 27y^6$ 33. $y^3 + 4y^2 - 9y - 36$

26. $x^2 + 4$ 34. $16a^3 - 2$

C   35. $2y^{2a} + y^a - 15$ 37. $(a - 2b)^3 - (a - 2b)^5$

36. $3x^{4y} - 10x^{2y} + 3$ 38. $(x^2 + x - 2)^2 - (x^2 - x - 6)^2$

39. $9x^4 - 7x^2y^2 + y^4$
   Hint: $9x^4 - 7x^2y^2 + y^4 = (9x^4 - 6x^2y^2 + y^4) - x^2y^2$

40. $25x^4 - 11x^2y^2 + y^4$

You can use INT to test whether or not a number is a factor of another number. For example:

```
10   PRINT "INPUT N";
20   INPUT N
30   FOR F=1 TO N
40   LET Q=N/F
50   IF Q <> INT(Q) THEN 70
60   PRINT F;
70   NEXT F
80   END
```

RUN this for N=60. Notice that there are no factors between N/2 and N. Now change the program to include:

```
25   PRINT 1;
30   FOR F=2 TO N/2
75   PRINT N
```

RUN this revised program for values of N from 61 to 72. You will see that the factors occur in pairs except when N is a perfect square. Then the square root is printed only once.

BASIC has a special built-in function for finding the positive square root of a positive number, SQR(X). Try the program at the left.

```
10   FOR N=2 TO 10
20   PRINT N,SQR(N)
30   NEXT N
40   END
```

Now change line 30 in the factoring program above to

```
30   FOR F=2 TO SQR(N)
```

and observe the results.

EXERCISES

1. Write a program that will print out all the pairs of factors of a given number N, including 1 and N.
2. Write a program that will store the pairs of factors of N in subscripted variables L(I) and M(I).
3. Write a program that will factor $Ax^2 + Bx + C$, $A > 0$, by finding and storing pairs of factors of A in L(H) and M(H) and pairs of positive and negative factors of C in R(K) and S(K). Test

$$B = L(I) * S(J) + M(I) * R(J)$$

to make factors (L(I)X + R(J))(M(I)X + S(J)).
4. a. Write a program that will print out primes less than 100, beginning with 3.

   Hint:
   ```
   10   FOR N=3 TO 99 STEP 2
   20   FOR F=3 TO SQR(N) STEP 2
   ```

   b. Put a counter (LET K=K+1) in the program and count the number of primes from 3 to 99, from 101 to 199, from 201 to 299, and so on up to the set from 1901 to 1999, by changing line 10.

Give the meaning of each of the following.

1. standard notation
2. first significant digit
3. round-off error
4. reducible polynomial
5. irreducible polynomial
6. prime polynomial

Objective 1, page 173 Give an equivalent expression in which each variable occurs at most once, using only positive exponents. Assume that all variables in denominators or with negative exponents do not have value 0.

7. $(5x^{-8})(-4x^5)$

8. $\dfrac{15x^3y^{-2}z^5}{12x^{-2}y^{-2}z^{-3}}$

Objective 2, page 173 Express in standard notation.

9. 3751

10. 0.000125

Objective 3, page 173 11. Find a one-significant-digit estimate of $\dfrac{52.16 \times 192.6}{0.00315 \times 0.497}$.

Objective 4, page 173 12. Write $(4x^5 - 2x^4 + 5x^2)(2x - 1)$ as a polynomial in simple form.

Objective 5, page 173 Factor completely.

13. $x^2 - 3x - 10$

14. $x^3 - 8y^3$

Check your answers with those printed at the back of the book.

applications of factoring

Objectives | After completing the next two sections, you should be able to:
1. Solve polynomial equations by factoring.
2. Solve problems involving factorable polynomial equations.
3. Solve polynomial inequalities by factoring.

6–5 *solving equations by factoring*

The quadratic polynomial in the equation

$$2x^2 + 5x - 3 = 0$$

can be factored as

$$(2x - 1)(x + 3).$$

Then it is a simple matter to find the solution set of the given equation by using the theorem which states that *a product of real numbers is zero if and only if at least one of the factors is zero.*

> **Theorem.** For all a and $b \in \Re$, $ab = 0$ if and only if $a = 0$ or $b = 0$.

PROOF

I. The "if" part says that if either a or b is zero, then $ab = 0$. This follows directly from the multiplication property of zero, that is: $a \cdot 0 = 0 \cdot a = 0$.

II. The "only if" part says that if $ab = 0$, then at least one of a and b is zero. The reasoning goes as follows:

Suppose $b \neq 0$. We want to show that a must then be zero.

1. $ab = 0$	Hypothesis
2. $ab \left(\dfrac{1}{b} \right) = 0 \cdot \dfrac{1}{b}$	Multiplication property of equality
3. $a \left(b \cdot \dfrac{1}{b} \right) = 0$	Associative axiom and multiplication property of zero
4. $a \cdot 1 = 0$	Axiom of multiplicative inverses
5. $a = 0$	Axiom of 1

From the theorem above we know that the equation at the beginning of the section,

$$2x^2 + 5x - 3 = 0, \quad \text{or} \quad (2x - 1)(x + 3) = 0,$$

is equivalent to the statement that either $2x - 1 = 0$, or $x + 3 = 0$. Solving these two linear equations, we obtain

$$x = \tfrac{1}{2} \quad \text{or} \quad x = -3.$$

Checking, you find that each of these values satisfies the original equation. Hence the solution set is $\{\tfrac{1}{2}\} \cup \{-3\} = \{\tfrac{1}{2}, -3\}$.

EXAMPLE 1 Solve $y^3 - y^2 = 6y$.

SOLUTION

1. First rewrite the equation into an equivalent equation with one member 0.
$$y^3 - y^2 - 6y = 0$$

2. Factor completely.
$$y(y^2 - y - 6) = 0$$
$$y(y - 3)(y + 2) = 0$$

3. Solve the compound sentence:

$$y = 0 \quad \text{or} \quad y - 3 = 0 \quad \text{or} \quad y + 2 = 0$$
$$y = 0 \quad \text{or} \quad y = 3 \quad \text{or} \quad y = -2$$

4. Check each solution in the *original* equation, $y^3 - y^2 = 6y$.

$$0 - 0 = 0 \quad \Big| \quad 3^3 - 3^2 = 6 \cdot 3 \quad \Big| \quad (-2)^3 - (-2)^2 = 6(-2)$$
$$0 = 0 \checkmark \quad \Big| \quad 27 - 9 = 18 \checkmark \quad \Big| \quad -8 - 4 = -12 \checkmark$$

$\therefore$ the solution set is $\{0, 3, -2\}$. **Answer.**

EXAMPLE 2   In a community park a rectangular swimming pool and walk are to be built on a piece of ground 20 meters long and 8 meters wide. The pool is to be surrounded by a paved walk that is twice as wide at the ends as at the sides of the pool. If the area of the pool is $\frac{3}{5}$ that of pool-plus-paving, how wide is the walk (a) at either side and (b) at either end?

SOLUTION   1. The problem asks for the widths of the walk at either side and at either end of the pool.

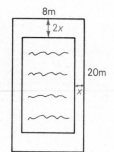

2. Let x = width of walk along either side, and
   $2x$ = width of walk at either end.
   Then the dimensions of the pool (in meters) are $(8 - 2x)$ and $(20 - 4x)$.

3. The area of the pool is $\frac{3}{5}$ that of the pool-plus-paving.
$$(8 - 2x)(20 - 4x) = \tfrac{3}{5}(8 \times 20)$$

4. $160 - 72x + 8x^2 = 96$
   $8x^2 - 72x + 64 = 0$
   $x^2 - 9x + 8 = 0$
   $(x - 8)(x - 1) = 0$
   $x - 8 = 0$ or $x - 1 = 0$
   $x = 8$ or $x = 1$

Since the entire plot is only 8 m wide, the solution $x = 8$ is not possible. Hence, $x = 1$ is the only possibility.

5. The width of the pool is 6 m $(8 - 2x)$ and the length is 12 m $(20 - 4x)$. The area of the pool is $(6 \times 12) = 96$ sq m which is $\frac{3}{5}$ that of pool-plus-paving, $\frac{3}{5}(8 \times 20)$.

∴ the walk is 1 m wide at each side and 2 m wide at each end. **Answer.**

WRITTEN EXERCISES   Determine the solution set of the given equation.

A   1. $x^2 - 9 = 0$

2. $x^2 - 121 = 0$

3. $y^2 + 6y + 9 = 0$

4. $x^2 - 10x + 25 = 0$

5. $a^2 + 4a + 3 = 0$

6. $m^2 - 6m + 8 = 0$

7. $x^2 - 2x - 15 = 0$

8. $r^2 + 5r - 14 = 0$

9. $3x^2 - 48 = 0$

10. $18a^2 = 6a$

11. $6x^2 + 7x + 2 = 0$

12. $15x^2 - 26x + 8 = 0$

13. $(y + 3)(y - 3) = 7$

14. $(n + 2)(n - 2) = 3n$

15. $s^2 = 8s - 12$

16. $9x = 2 - 26x^2$

B   17. $(5 - x)^2 + x^2 = 13$

18. $(5 - 2y)^2 = 10 - y^2$

Solve each equation for x. Assume that a, b, $n \neq 0$.

19. $x^2 - ax - 56a^2 = 0$

20. $2b^2x^2 + 13bx = 24$

21. $x^3 - x^2 - 6x = 0$

22. $2x^4 - 10x^2 + 8 = 0$

23. $x^4 + 144 = 25x^2$

24. $x^5 - 10x^3 + 9x = 0$

C 25. $a^2x + b = b^2x + a$

26. $5x^3 + 8x^2 = 5x + 8$

27. $ax - a^2 + b^2 - bx = 2a - 2b$

28. $6nx - 2 = 4x - 5a + 3a^2$

29. Explain the error in the solution of this problem:

$$y^2 - 3y + 2 = 6$$
$$(y - 1)(y - 2) = 6$$
$$y - 1 = 6 \quad \text{or} \quad y - 2 = 6$$
$$y = 7 \quad \text{or} \quad y = 8$$
$$\therefore \{7, 8\} \text{ is the solution set.}$$

PROBLEMS

A

1. Find the positive number whose square is 32 more than 4 times the number.

2. If the square of Mark's age exceeds 9 times his age by 360, what is his age?

3. Find four consecutive positive integers such that the sum of the squares of the first and fourth is 65.

4. Find three consecutive positive odd integers such that the square of the sum of the first two exceeds the square of the third by 63.

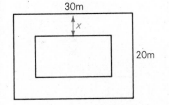

30m

20m

x

5. A room 20 meters wide and 30 meters long is being tiled, starting in the center. If $\frac{1}{3}$ of the tile has been laid, leaving an untiled strip of uniform width along the edges of the room, how wide is the strip?

6. If the area of a triangle is 63 square centimeters, and the length of the base is 4 centimeters shorter than twice the length of the altitude, how long are the base and altitude?

In Exercises 7 and 8 use the fact that if an object is launched vertically upward with a starting velocity of v_0 meters per second from an altitude of h_0 meters, its altitude (in meters) after t seconds is given by this formula: $h = v_0 t - 4.9 t^2 + h_0$

B

7. A missile is launched vertically from gound level with a velocity of 1960 meters per second. In how many seconds will it return to the ground?

8. If a missile is launched vertically with a starting velocity of 2500 meters per second from a cliff 50 meters above the sea, how long (to the nearest second) will it take the missile to descend to an altitude of 50 meters above sea level?

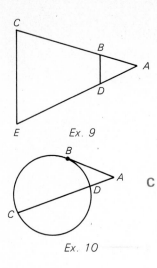

Ex. 9

Ex. 10

9. In the figure, $m(\overline{AC})$ (read "the measure of the segment A, C") is 12; $m(\overline{AD}) = 6$; and $m(\overline{DE}) = 3 \cdot m(\overline{AB})$. Find $m(\overline{AB})$, given that $\dfrac{m(\overline{AB})}{m(\overline{BC})} = \dfrac{m(\overline{AD})}{m(\overline{DE})}$.

10. In the figure at the left, $m(\overline{AB}) = 4$, and $m(\overline{AC}) - m(\overline{AD}) = 6$. Find $m(\overline{AC})$, given that $m(\overline{AC}) \cdot m(\overline{AD}) = (m(\overline{AB}))^2$.

11. A truck and a sedan leave a filling station at the same time and travel south and east, respectively. After an hour they are 39 kilometers apart. If the sedan travels at an average speed that is 6 kilometers per hour greater than twice that of the truck, find the speed of each.

12. Find all real numbers a such that $x^2 + 2ax + a + 6 = 0$ has two equal roots. (*Hint:* Let R be a root. Then $(x - R)^2 = x^2 + 2ax + a + 6$.)

6–6 *solving inequalities by factoring*

You know that for a and $b \in \mathcal{R}$, if $ab > 0$ then a and b are of the same sign, while if $ab < 0$, then a and b are of opposite signs. You can use these facts to solve an inequality in which one member consists of a reducible quadratic polynomial and the other is 0.

EXAMPLE 1 **Find and graph the solution set of $x^2 - 2x > 8$ over $\mathcal{R}$.**

SOLUTION
$$x^2 - 2x > 8$$
$$x^2 - 2x - 8 > 0$$
$$(x - 4)(x + 2) > 0$$

The inequality is satisfied if and only if $x - 4$ and $x + 2$ both have the same sign.

Both factors positive	or	*Both factors negative*
$x - 4 > 0$ and $x + 2 > 0$		$x - 4 < 0$ and $x + 2 < 0$
$x > 4$ and $x > -2$		$x < 4$ and $x < -2$
The intersection of these two solution sets is $\{x: x > 4\}$.		The intersection of these two solution sets is $\{x: x < -2\}$.

∴ the solution set of the given inequality is the union

$$\{x: x > 4\} \cup \{x: x < -2\}. \quad \textbf{Answer.}$$

-5 -4 -3 -2 -1 0 1 2 3 4 5 6

EXAMPLE 2 **Find and graph the solution set of** $y^2 - 2y < 3$ **over** $\Re$.

SOLUTION
$$y^2 - 2y < 3$$
$$y^2 - 2y - 3 < 0$$
$$(y - 3)(y + 1) < 0$$

The inequality is satisfied if and only if $y - 3$ and $y + 1$ have opposite signs:

$y - 3 > 0$ and $y + 1 < 0$ or $y - 3 < 0$ and $y + 1 > 0$
$y > 3$ and $y < -1$ $y < 3$ and $y > -1$
$\{y\colon y > 3\} \cap \{y\colon y < -1\} = \emptyset$ $\{y\colon y < 3\} \cap \{y\colon y > -1\}$
                                                 $= \{y\colon -1 < y < 3\}$

$\therefore$ the solution set of the given inequality is the union

$$\emptyset \cup \{y\colon -1 < y < 3\} = \{y\colon -1 < y < 3\}. \quad \text{Answer.}$$

WRITTEN EXERCISES **Find the solution set of each inequality over** $\Re$ **and draw its graph.**

A   1. $x^2 - 9x < 0$

     2. $4a - 2a^2 < 0$

     3. $(y + 3)(y - 4) \geq 0$

     4. $(m + 8)(m - 1) > 0$

     5. $x^2 + 4x - 21 \leq 0$

     6. $x^2 - 3x - 8 < 2$

     7. $c^2 - 36 \leq 0$

     8. $49 \geq d^2$

B   9. $y^3 - 16y < 0$

   10. $x^3 - 9x > 0$

   11. $r^3 \geq 6r^2 - 9r$

   12. $10m^2 > 25m + m^3$

   13. $b^2 + 1 < 0$

   14. $a^2 + 1 > 0$

C   15. $y^4 \geq 81$

   16. $16 \leq x^4$

SELF-TEST 2 **Solve each equation by factoring.**

Objective 1, page 190   1. $x^2 + 3x - 54 = 0$ 2. $20y^2 - 15 = 13y$

Objective 2, page 190   3. Find three consecutive positive even integers such that the product of the first two increased by the product of the last two gives 200 as a result.

Objective 3, page 190   4. Find the solution set of $x^2 + 4x > 5$ over $\Re$ and draw its graph.

Check your answers with those printed at the back of the book.

rational algebraic expressions

After completing the next six sections, you should be able to:

1. Simplify a rational expression by factoring its numerator and denominator.
2. Find the quotient and remainder when one polynomial is divided by another.

Objectives

3. Express a product or quotient of rational expressions as a rational expression in lowest terms.
4. Transform a sum or difference of rational expressions into an equivalent rational expression in lowest terms.
5. Solve problems involving equations with rational coefficients and fractional equations.

6-7 *simplifying rational expressions*

Just as any number which is the quotient of two integers is called a rational number, so the quotient of two polynomials is called a rational expression or, more fully, a rational algebraic expression. In neither case can the divisor be zero.

The following theorem enables you to reduce a fraction to lowest terms, that is, to express it as an equivalent fraction whose numerator and denominator have no common factors except 1 and -1.

Theorem. For all r, s, and $t \in \mathcal{R}$, s and $t \neq 0$,

$$\frac{r}{s} = \frac{r \div t}{s \div t}, \quad \text{and} \quad \frac{r}{s} = \frac{r \cdot t}{s \cdot t}.$$

For example,

$$\frac{56}{42} = \frac{56 \div 14}{42 \div 14} = \frac{4}{3}, \quad \text{and} \quad \frac{\frac{2}{3}}{\frac{5}{6}} = \frac{\frac{2}{3} \cdot 6}{\frac{5}{6} \cdot 6} = \frac{4}{5}.$$

Likewise you can simplify a rational expression by factoring the numerator and denominator completely and then dividing both by all their common prime factors. The rational expression is said to be simplified, or in lowest terms.

EXAMPLE 1   Simplify $\dfrac{y^5 - y^4 - 6y^3}{y^3 - 2y^2 - 3y}$.

SOLUTION $\dfrac{y^5 - y^4 - 6y^3}{y^3 - 2y^2 - 3y} = \dfrac{y^3(y^2 - y - 6)}{y(y^2 - 2y - 3)} = \dfrac{y \cdot y^2(y + 2)(y - 3)}{y(y + 1)(y - 3)}$

Dividing numerator and denominator by the product $y(y - 3)$ of all their common prime factors (that is, their greatest common factor), you obtain

$$\frac{y^2(y + 2)}{y + 1} \qquad (y \notin \{0, 3, -1\}). \quad \text{Answer.}$$

EXAMPLE 2 Simplify $(28 - 7a)^{-1}(64 - a^3)$.

SOLUTION $(28 - 7a)^{-1}(64 - a^3) = \dfrac{64 - a^3}{28 - 7a} = \dfrac{(4 - a)(16 + 4a + a^2)}{7(4 - a)}$

$$= \frac{a^2 + 4a + 16}{7} \qquad (a \neq 4). \quad \text{Answer.}$$

Hereafter in this book it will be assumed, usually without comment, that the replacement sets of the variables in a fraction include no numbers for which the denominator is zero.

WRITTEN EXERCISES   Simplify the given expression.

A   1. $45(5)^{-3}$

2. $-108(10)^{-2}$

3. $\dfrac{4ab^2}{-20a^2s}$

4. $\dfrac{-12m^6t^4}{9m^3t^2}$

5. $6^{-1}(9x - 18)$

6. $2^{-2}(12 - 28b^2)$

7. $4x(8x + 24)^{-1}$

8. $(5x + 2)(-10x - 4)^{-1}$

9. $\dfrac{3 - a}{(a - 3)^3}$

10. $(4 - y)^3(y - 4)^{-5}$

11. $(5 - x)^2(x - 5)^{-4}$

12. $(2x^2y - 4xy^2)(x - 2y)^{-1}$

13. $(3b^3c + 6b^2c^2)(b + 2c)^{-2}$

14. $\dfrac{p^4 - p^3}{p^2 - 1}$

15. $(a^2 - 1)^{-1}(a^2 - 3a + 2)$

16. $\dfrac{1 - 4m + 4m^2}{4m^2 - 1}$

17. $\dfrac{y^2 + 5y - 6}{(y - 1)^2(y + 6)}$

18. $(3p - 3q)(3p^2 - 2pq - q^2)^{-1}$

19. $\dfrac{x^3 - 1}{2x^2 + 2x - 4}$

20. $\dfrac{s^3 + t^3}{s^2 - st + t^2}$

B   21. $\dfrac{-(r - s)(s - t)(r - t)}{(t - s)(t - r)(s - r)}$

22. $\dfrac{(a - b)^{-3}}{(b - a)^{-5}}$

23. $\dfrac{5x - 20x^3}{10x^4 + 5x^3 - 10x(1 + 2x)}$

24. $\dfrac{196m - 4m^3}{2m^3 - 6m - 42 + 14m^2}$

C   25. $\dfrac{(a^2 + 1)^2(3a - 1)^2(9a) - (3a - 1)^3(4a^3 + 4a)}{(a^2 + 1)^4}$

26. $\dfrac{(x^3 + 8)(3x + 6) - (x^2 - 4)(x^2 + 4x + 4)(x^2 - 2x + 4)}{(x + 2)^2}$

27. Prove the theorem stated on page 196.

28. Prove that for all a, b, and $c \in \mathcal{R}$, a, b, and $c \neq 0$,

$$\frac{\dfrac{a}{b}}{\dfrac{a}{c}} = \frac{c}{b}.$$

6–8 *dividing one polynomial by another*

The following theorem enables you to replace a rational number named by an improper fraction with an equivalent mixed numeral which names the sum of an integer and a proper fraction.

Theorem. For all a, b, and $c \in \mathcal{R}$, $c \neq 0$,

$$\frac{a + b}{c} = \frac{a}{c} + \frac{b}{c}.$$

Thus,

$$\frac{29}{8} = \frac{24 + 5}{8} = \frac{\overset{a}{\overbrace{3 \cdot 8}} + \overset{b}{\overset{\downarrow}{5}}}{\underset{\underset{c}{\uparrow}}{8}} = \frac{3 \cdot 8}{8} + \frac{5}{8} = 3 + \frac{5}{8}, \text{ or } 3\frac{5}{8}.$$

Likewise, using the above theorem along with the division algorithm, you obtain

$$
\begin{array}{r}
151 \\
28\overline{)4233} \\
\underline{28} \longleftarrow \text{subtract } 1 \times 28 \\
143 \\
\underline{140} \longleftarrow \text{subtract } 5 \times 28 \\
33 \\
\underline{28} \leftarrow \text{subtract } 1 \times 28 \\
5
\end{array}
$$

$$\frac{4233}{28} = \frac{151 \cdot 28 + 5}{28} = \frac{151 \cdot 28}{28} + \frac{5}{28} = 151 + \frac{5}{28}, \text{ or } 151\frac{5}{28}.$$

In more advanced mathematics it often becomes necessary to transform a rational expression, by similar means, into the *sum of a polynomial and another rational expression*. The process, called division, consists of successively subtracting a monomial multiple of the divisor from the dividend until you finally obtain *either the remainder zero or a polynomial of lower degree than that of the divisor*.

EXAMPLE 1 Transform $\dfrac{2x - 5x^2 + 6x^3 - 5}{2x + 1}$ into a sum by division.

SOLUTION Before dividing, first arrange the terms of both dividend and divisor in order of decreasing degree.

$$\begin{array}{r} 3x^2 - 4x + 3 \\ 2x + 1 \overline{\smash{\big)}\ 6x^3 - 5x^2 + 2x - 5} \end{array}$$

$$6x^3 + 3x^2 \quad \longleftarrow\text{——————subtract } 3x^2(2x + 1)$$

$$-8x^2 + 2x$$

$$-8x^2 - 4x \longleftarrow\text{———subtract } -4x(2x + 1)$$

$$6x - 5$$

$$6x + 3 \leftarrow\text{subtract } 3(2x + 1)$$

$$-8$$

$$\therefore \frac{2x - 5x^2 + 6x^3 - 5}{2x + 1} = 3x^2 - 4x + 3 + \frac{-8}{2x + 1}. \quad \textbf{Answer.}$$

The following example illustrates the division process for polynomials involving two variables. In this case you first arrange the terms in order of decreasing degree in *one* of the variables.

EXAMPLE 2   **Divide $2s^3 + 5s^2t - 4t^3$ by $2s^2 + st - 2t^2$.**

SOLUTION   As given, the terms are in order of decreasing degree in the variable *s*. Note that the dividend has no first-degree term in *s*. When dividing, insert any such "missing" term with a 0 as its coefficient.

$$\begin{array}{r} s + 2t \\ 2s^2 + st - 2t^2 \overline{\smash{\big)}\ 2s^3 + 5s^2t + 0st^2 - 4t^3} \end{array}$$

$$2s^3 + s^2t - 2st^2$$

$$4s^2t + 2st^2 - 4t^3$$

$$4s^2t + 2st^2 - 4t^3$$

$$0$$

$$\therefore \frac{2s^3 + 5s^2t - 4t^3}{2s^2 + st - 2t^2} = s + 2t. \quad \textbf{Answer.}$$

The quotient of a polynomial and a monomial can be expressed as the sum of the quotients obtained by dividing each term of the polynomial by the monomial.

EXAMPLE 3   **Express $\dfrac{9y^4 + 27y^3 - y^2 + 12}{3y^3}$ as a sum by division.**

SOLUTION   Divide each term in the dividend by the monomial divisor:

$$\frac{9y^4 + 27y^3 - y^2 + 12}{3y^3} = 3y + 9 - \frac{1}{3y} + \frac{4}{y^3}. \quad \textbf{Answer.}$$

Express the given quotient as a sum by division.

1. $\dfrac{8x + 4}{2}$ 3. $\dfrac{2a + b}{a}$ 5. $\dfrac{12t^8 - 8t^3 + 4}{4t^4}$

2. $\dfrac{27a^2 - 9a}{3}$ 4. $\dfrac{-3y^2 + xy}{y}$ 6. $\dfrac{2x^2y^2 - xy + 3}{xy}$

WRITTEN EXERCISES   Transform the given rational expression into a sum by dividing.

A   1. $\dfrac{28x^4 + 36x^2y - 16xy}{4x}$ 7. $\dfrac{15n^2 - n - 6}{5n + 3}$

2. $\dfrac{5m^3t^2 - 15m^2t^3 + 10t^4}{5mt}$ 8. $\dfrac{6y^2 + 2y - 28}{3y + 7}$

3. $\dfrac{a^2b - a^2b^2 + 3ab}{-ab}$ 9. $\dfrac{8x^3 - 4x + 1}{2x - 1}$

4. $\dfrac{16r^2st + 24rs^2t - rst^3 + t^4}{rst}$ 10. $\dfrac{6b^3 + 11b^2 - 4b - 4}{3b - 2}$

5. $\dfrac{y^2 + 15y + 36}{y + 3}$ 11. $\dfrac{y^2 - 6}{y + 3}$

6. $\dfrac{6x^2 + 11x - 35}{3x - 5}$ 12. $\dfrac{x^2 - 4}{x - 1}$

B   13. $\dfrac{x^2 - a}{x - a}$ 17. $\dfrac{x^4 - 4x^3 + 2x^4 + 4x + 1}{x^2 - 2x - 1}$

14. $\dfrac{y^3 - b^3}{y - b}$ 18. $\dfrac{2y^4 - 9y^3 + 6 + 6y - 14y^2}{2 - 3y - y^2}$

15. $\dfrac{3 + 2x - 2x^3}{1 - x}$ 19. $\dfrac{4x^3 + 6x^2y - 2y^3}{2x^2 + xy - y^2}$

16. $\dfrac{4 - y^3 - 4y}{2 + y}$ 20. $\dfrac{9a^4 + 3a^3b - 5a^2b^2 + ab^3}{3a^3 + 2a^2b - ab^2}$

C   21. Is $2x + 3$ a factor of $6x^3 + 11x^2 + x - 3$? Justify your answer.

22. Is $3x - 2$ a factor of $6x^3 - x^2 - 5x + 3$? Justify your answer.

23. Determine k so that $x + 2$ is a factor of $x^2 + kx + 10$.

24. Determine k so that $y - 3$ is a factor of $y^3 - ky^2 - 6y$.

25. Determine the values of a and b so that

$$\frac{y^2 + ay - 11}{y + 3} = y - b + \frac{1}{y + 3}.$$

26. Determine the values of a and b so that

$$\frac{2x^3 - 4x^2 + ax - 4}{x - 2} = 2x^2 + b + \frac{2}{x - 2}.$$

6-9 *multiplying and dividing rational expressions*

You can multiply two rational expressions by using the same rule as that for multiplying rational numbers.

> For all r, s, t, and $u \in \mathcal{R}$, t and $u \neq 0$,
>
> $$\frac{r}{t} \times \frac{s}{u} = \frac{rs}{tu}.$$

EXAMPLE 1   Simplify $\dfrac{p^2 - 3p - 4}{p^3} \cdot \dfrac{p^2 + 2p}{2p - 8}$.

SOLUTION $\dfrac{p^2 - 3p - 4}{p^3} \cdot \dfrac{p^2 + 2p}{2p - 8} = \dfrac{(p - 4)(p + 1)}{p^3} \cdot \dfrac{p(p + 2)}{2(p - 4)}$

$$= \frac{p(p - 4)(p + 1)(p + 2)}{p(p - 4)2p^2}$$

$$= \frac{p^2 + 3p + 2}{2p^2}. \quad \text{Answer.}$$

The relationship between multiplication and division (page 23) and the fact that the reciprocal of $\dfrac{s}{u}$ is $\dfrac{u}{s}$ if $s \neq 0$ and $u \neq 0$ lead to the following result.

> **Theorem.**   For all r, s, t, and $u \in \mathcal{R}$, s, t, and $u \neq 0$,
>
> $$\frac{r}{t} \div \frac{s}{u} = \frac{r}{t} \cdot \frac{u}{s} = \frac{ru}{ts}.$$

EXAMPLE 2   Simplify $\dfrac{v^2 + 4v + 4}{v^3 - 9v} \div \dfrac{v^2 - 4}{v^2 + 2v - 15}$.

SOLUTION $\dfrac{v^2 + 4v + 4}{v^3 - 9v} \div \dfrac{v^2 - 4}{v^2 + 2v - 15} = \dfrac{v^2 + 4v + 4}{v^3 - 9v} \cdot \dfrac{v^2 + 2v - 15}{v^2 - 4}$

$$= \frac{(v + 2)(v + 2)}{v(v + 3)(v - 3)} \cdot \frac{(v + 5)(v - 3)}{(v - 2)(v + 2)}$$

$$= \frac{(v + 2)(v + 5)}{v(v + 3)(v - 2)}$$

$$= \frac{v^2 + 7v + 10}{v^3 + v^2 - 6v}. \quad \text{Answer.}$$

EXAMPLE 3 Simplify $(3x + x^{-1}) \div \left(2 - \dfrac{x}{2}\right)$.

SOLUTION $\quad \dfrac{3x + x^{-1}}{2 - \dfrac{x}{2}} = \dfrac{3x + \dfrac{1}{x}}{2 - \dfrac{x}{2}} = \dfrac{\dfrac{3x^2 + 1}{x}}{\dfrac{4 - x}{2}} = \dfrac{3x^2 + 1}{x} \cdot \dfrac{2}{4 - x} = \dfrac{2(3x^2 + 1)}{x(4 - x)}$

$\qquad\qquad\qquad\qquad\qquad\qquad\qquad\qquad\quad = \dfrac{2 + 6x^2}{4x - x^2} \quad$ Answer.

WRITTEN EXERCISES Express each product or quotient in lowest terms.

A 1. $\dfrac{4x^2}{3}\left(\dfrac{9}{x}\right)^3$

2. $\dfrac{15y^3}{6}\left(\dfrac{3}{10y^2}\right)^2$

3. $\dfrac{7k^3}{3} \div \dfrac{14k^2}{6}$

4. $\dfrac{15p^2q}{4p} \div \dfrac{10q^3}{8}$

5. $\dfrac{s^2 - 4}{2} \div \dfrac{s + 2}{12}$

6. $\dfrac{(x + 3)^2}{x - 3} \div \dfrac{5}{(x^2 - 9)}$

7. $(2x^3)(7y)^{-1}(14y^2)(4x)^{-2}$

8. $(2a^2b^3)(4ab^2)^{-1}(5a^3b^5)(15b^2)^{-1}$

9. $\dfrac{m^2 + 3m}{m^2 + 2m - 3} \cdot \dfrac{m + 1}{m}$

10. $\dfrac{p^2 - 16}{2p + 8} \cdot \dfrac{5}{p - 4}$

11. $\dfrac{3x^2 - 27}{x^2 + 6x + 9} \cdot \left(\dfrac{3}{4x + 12}\right)^{-1}$

12. $\dfrac{y^2 - 4y}{y^2 + 2y} \cdot \dfrac{(y^2 - 9y + 20)^{-1}}{y^2 - 3y - 10}$

13. $\dfrac{2b - 14}{b^2 - 2b - 35} \div \dfrac{6b^3}{b^2 - 25}$

14. $\dfrac{2x^2 - 11x + 15}{2x^2 + x - 15} \div \dfrac{(x + 3)^{-1}}{2}$

B 15. $\dfrac{12x^2 - 3}{2} \cdot (2x + 1)^{-2} \cdot \left(\dfrac{6}{2x + 1}\right)^{-1}$

16. $\dfrac{p^2 - 4q^2}{p + 2q} \cdot (p + 2q)^{-2} \div \dfrac{2p}{p + 2q}$

C 17. Explain why the set of rational numbers is closed under multiplication.

18. Explain why the set of rational numbers is closed under division, excluding division by 0.

19. Prove that for all $r, s, t,$ and $u \in \Re, s, t,$ and $u \neq 0,$

$$\dfrac{r}{t} \div \dfrac{s}{u} = \dfrac{ru}{ts}.$$

20. Prove that for $x_1 > 0, x_2 > 0, y_1$ and $y_2 \in \Re.$

$$\dfrac{y_1}{x_1} > \dfrac{y_2}{x_2} \text{ if and only if } y_1x_2 > y_2x_1.$$

careers   *optometry*

Optometrists test their patients' vision and can prescribe eyeglasses or contact lenses, eye exercises, and treatment other than drugs or surgery. They often supply eyeglasses, and fit and repair frames.

Training for this profession is specialized, requiring two years of preoptometry training and four years of optometry school. Preoptometry education includes courses in mathematics, physics, biology, and chemistry.

The optometrist above is fitting frames for a patient. The technician below is grinding a lens according to an optometrist's prescription.

EXAMPLE · Optometrists fit their patients with lenses to correct their vision. The diagram below shows a convex or converging lens. Lenses of this type are used to correct farsightedness.

Object   Focal point   Image

Suppose the focal length of the lens, or the distance from its center to the point where the light rays converge, is 20 cm. An object is placed 30 cm from the center of the lens. How far from the lens will the image be formed?

SOLUTION   From physics we have the following relationship:

$$\frac{1}{\text{distance to object}} + \frac{1}{\text{distance to image}} = \frac{1}{\text{focal length}}$$

Substituting the values for this lens:

$$\frac{1}{30} + \frac{1}{D_i} = \frac{1}{20}$$

$$\frac{1}{D_i} = \frac{1}{20} - \frac{1}{30}$$

$$\frac{1}{D_i} = \frac{1}{60}$$

$$D_i = 60 \text{ cm}$$

Thus, the image will be formed 60 cm from the lens.

6-10 *adding and subtracting rational expressions*

Two rational numbers having the same denominator can be added or subtracted in accordance with the following theorem (see pages 23 and 25).

For all a, b, and $c \in \mathcal{R}$, $c \neq 0$,

$$\frac{a}{c} + \frac{b}{c} = \frac{a + b}{c} \quad \text{and} \quad \frac{a}{c} - \frac{b}{c} = \frac{a - b}{c}.$$

The same rule applies in the case of rational expressions. For example,

$$\frac{3x^2}{x^2 - 1} - \frac{x + 2}{x^2 - 1} = \frac{3x^2 - x - 2}{x^2 - 1} = \frac{(3x + 2)(x - 1)}{(x + 1)(x - 1)} = \frac{3x + 2}{x + 1}.$$

If the denominators differ, then you must find a common denominator before adding or subtracting. Just as with fractions, it is simplest to use the least common denominator (LCD), that is, the polynomial of least degree and least positive constant factor that has each denominator as a factor.

EXAMPLE 1   Simplify $\dfrac{a^2}{a - 1} - \dfrac{3}{2} + \dfrac{2a - 4}{2a - 2}$.

SOLUTION   To find the LCD, first factor the denominators completely.

$$\frac{a^2}{a - 1} - \frac{3}{2} + \frac{2a - 4}{2(a - 1)}. \qquad \therefore \text{ the LCD is } 2(a - 1).$$

Next replace each rational expression with an equivalent one having the LCD as denominator, and then simplify:

$$\frac{2a^2}{2(a - 1)} - \frac{3(a - 1)}{2(a - 1)} + \frac{2a - 4}{2(a - 1)} = \frac{2a^2 - 3a + 3 + 2a - 4}{2(a - 1)}$$

$$= \frac{2a^2 - a - 1}{2(a - 1)} = \frac{(2a + 1)(a - 1)}{2(a - 1)}$$

$$= \frac{2a + 1}{2} \qquad (a \neq 1). \quad \textbf{Answer.}$$

EXAMPLE 2   Simplify $\dfrac{x^{-2} - y^{-2}}{x^{-1}y^{-1}}$.

SOLUTION $\dfrac{x^{-2} - y^{-2}}{x^{-1}y^{-1}} = \dfrac{\dfrac{1}{x^2} - \dfrac{1}{y^2}}{\dfrac{1}{x} \cdot \dfrac{1}{y}} = \dfrac{\dfrac{y^2}{x^2y^2} - \dfrac{x^2}{x^2y^2}}{\dfrac{1}{xy}} = \dfrac{\dfrac{y^2 - x^2}{x^2y^2}}{\dfrac{1}{xy}} = \dfrac{y^2 - x^2}{x^2y^2} \cdot \dfrac{xy}{1}$

$$= \frac{(y^2 - x^2)xy}{(xy)(xy)} = \frac{y^2 - x^2}{xy}. \quad \textbf{Answer.}$$

WRITTEN EXERCISES Simplify the given rational expression.

A 1. $\dfrac{x}{x+3} + \dfrac{3}{x+3}$

2. $\dfrac{6}{4y-2} - \dfrac{2y+4}{4y-2}$

3. $\dfrac{3}{6a^2} - \dfrac{9}{2a}$

4. $\dfrac{9}{3xa} - \dfrac{1}{x^2}$

5. $\dfrac{6b}{3b} - \dfrac{b}{2b} + \dfrac{1}{18}$

6. $\dfrac{x}{xy} + \dfrac{y}{xz} - \dfrac{z}{yz}$

7. $\dfrac{y-3}{6} + \dfrac{2y-5}{3}$

8. $\dfrac{4x+1}{4} - \dfrac{3x+2}{6}$

9. $\dfrac{1}{2b^2} + \dfrac{2b+1}{3b} - \dfrac{2-3b}{4b}$

10. $\dfrac{t+4}{6t} + \dfrac{1}{10t} - \dfrac{3+5t}{5t}$

11. $2 - 5(x+3)^{-1}$

12. $\dfrac{x + yx^{-1}}{1 + x^{-1}}$

13. $\dfrac{b + 1 - \dfrac{2}{b}}{b + 4b^{-1} + 4}$

14. $\dfrac{m - m^{-1}}{1 + 4m^{-1} - 5m^{-2}}$

15. $\dfrac{xy}{x^2 - y^2} - \dfrac{y}{x+y}$

16. $\dfrac{c+4}{2c^2 - 2c} - \dfrac{5}{2c-2}$

B 17. $\dfrac{p+q}{p^2 + 2pq + q^2} - \dfrac{2p}{p^2 - q^2}$

18. $\dfrac{a}{a-b} + \dfrac{a^2 + b^2}{b^2 - a^2} + \dfrac{b}{a+b}$

19. $x^2 - 1 + \dfrac{2x+3}{x^2 - 1}$

20. $\dfrac{1}{x+y} + \dfrac{xy - 2y^2}{x^3 + y^3}$

21. $\left(4 + \dfrac{3}{t^2 - 1}\right)^{-1}\left(1 + \dfrac{t}{t-1}\right)$

22. $\left(2 - \dfrac{7x+2}{x^2 - 1}\right)\left(x - 3 - \dfrac{5}{x+1}\right)^{-1}$

C 23. $\left(\dfrac{3}{3-x} + \dfrac{9x}{x^2 - 9}\right)\left(\dfrac{x^2 - x - 6}{2x - 3}\right)\left(\dfrac{3x+6}{x+3}\right)^{-1}$

24. $1 + (x + x^{-1})^{-1}$

25. $[y + (y + y^{-1})^{-1}]^{-1}$

26. $\dfrac{(a+b)(a^{-1} - b^{-1})}{(a-b)(a^{-1} + b^{-1})}$

27. Explain why the set of rational numbers is closed under addition.

28. Explain why the set of rational numbers is closed under subtraction.

6-11   *using polynomials with rational coefficients*

The mathematical description of practical problem situations often involves equations whose members are polynomials with rational coefficients.

EXAMPLE 1   One high-speed computer system can prepare the weekly payroll of a large concern in 10 hours. A faster system can do the job in 6 hours. If both systems were in operation, how rapidly could the payroll be processed?

SOLUTION   1. The problem asks for the number of hours required for the systems to process the payroll together.

2. Let x represent the number of hours for the systems to process the payroll together.

$\frac{1}{10}$ = rate of the first system (one-tenth of the job in one hour).

$\frac{1}{6}$ = rate of the second system (one-sixth of the job in one hour).

1 = total work done together (one whole job) in x hours.

3. $\underline{\text{Total work}}$ is $\underline{\text{part}}$ done by the first plus $\underline{\text{part}}$ done by the second.

$$1 \quad = \quad \tfrac{1}{10}x \quad + \quad \tfrac{1}{6}x$$

4. $$30 \cdot 1 = 30 \cdot \tfrac{1}{10}x + 30 \cdot \tfrac{1}{6}x$$

$$30 = 3x + 5x$$

Completing Step 4 is left to you to find that working together the systems would require $3\frac{3}{4}$ hours. Checking the work (Step 5) is also left to you.

A percent is equivalent to a fraction whose denominator is 100. For example, $41\% = \frac{41}{100}$, or 0.41, and $165\% = \frac{165}{100}$, or 1.65. When you multiply a number called the base (**b**), by a percent (**r**), the product is called the percentage (**p**). The formula $p = br$ is a basic tool in solving many problems in science and business.

EXAMPLE 2   A 20-cubic-centimeter solution of alcohol in water is 60% alcohol. At most, how many cubic centimeters of a 42% solution can be added if the final solution is to be at least 50% alcohol?

SOLUTION   1. The problem asks for the maximum number of cubic centimeters of the 42% solution to be added.

2. Let y denote the number of cubic centimeters of the 42% solution to be added. Then

$20 + y$ = the number of cubic centimeters in the final solution.

$0.50(20 + y)$ = 50% of the final solution.

$0.42y$ = the amount of alcohol in the added solution.

$0.60(20)$ = the amount of alcohol in the original solution.

3.   Alcohol in the final solution

Alcohol in original solution	plus	alcohol in added solution	is at least	50% of the final solution.
0.60(20)	+	0.42y	$\geq$	0.50(20 + y)

4. Multiplying each member of the inequality by 100, you find:

$$60(20) + 42y \geq 50(20 + y)$$

By solving this inequality, show that *at most* 25 cubic centimeters of the 42% solution can be added. Check your work.

PROBLEMS

A

1. The average of two numbers is 35. If one of the numbers is two-fifths as great as the other, determine the numbers.

2. The average of two numbers is 9. If one of the numbers is 2 less than three-halves the other, determine the numbers.

3. Eva can type a company's invoices in 20 minutes, while Ed takes 30 minutes. How long would it take them to do the job together?

4. At a certain college, a sociologist finds that the ratio of the number of undergraduate students to the number of graduate students is 3:2. She plans to interview 300 of the students. How many persons of each group must she select, if her sample is to have the same distribution of under-graduate and graduate students as the college?

5. One sewage treatment plant can process a day's sewage in 15 hours. Another plant can complete the treatment in 20 hours. If both plants are in operation, how long does it take to process the day's sewage?

6. A sensory nerve stimulated by a light source carries an impulse from the eye to the brain in 0.0015 seconds. The brain then relays the impulse along the motor nerve network to the fingers in 0.01 seconds. If the distance the impulse travels to the brain is 18 centimeters less than $\frac{1}{3}$ the distance from the brain to the fingers, what is the speed of the impulse?

7. A party of mountaineers started at the 4190-meter level and climbed to the top of Mt. Blanc, the highest mountain in Europe. It took them 10 hours to reach the summit and return to their starting position, counting a one-hour rest at the top. If the party ascended at an average rate of 120 meters per hour and descended at an average of twice that rate, what is the height of Mt. Blanc?

8. A certain type of cream contains 20% butterfat. At least how much skimmed milk (no butterfat) must be added to 1 liter of the cream to make a mixture which is at most 5% butterfat?

B

9. Equal volumes of two different liquids evaporate at different, but constant rates. If the first is totally evaporated in 6 weeks, and the second in 5 weeks, when will the second be $\frac{1}{2}$ the volume of the first?

10. How much water must be evaporated from 500 liters of a 3% salt solution to obtain a 5% salt solution?

C **11.** A chemist has 4 liters of a 10% ethyl alcohol solution. She wants to add enough of a 50% ethyl alcohol solution to obtain a 30% solution. After adding the 50% solution, she discovers that the container was mislabeled and that she has actually added distilled water. How much pure ethyl alcohol must she now add to get a 30% solution?

12. A speeder going 120 kilometers per hour passes a state trooper parked by the side of the thruway. The trooper gives chase; within $1\frac{1}{2}$ minutes he has reached a speed of 150 km/h and has gone 0.25 kilometers. If he continues at this speed, how long does it take him to overtake the speeder?

6–12 *fractional equations*

An equation involving one or more rational expressions in which a variable appears in the denominator is called a **fractional equation**.

To solve the fractional equation

$$1 + \frac{30}{a^2 - 9} - \frac{5}{a - 3} = 0, \quad (1)$$

you can begin by multiplying both members of the equation by the LCD, $(a + 3)(a - 3)$, or $a^2 - 9$:

$$(a^2 - 9)\left(1 + \frac{30}{a^2 - 9} - \frac{5}{a - 3}\right) = (a^2 - 9) \cdot 0$$

Then you have:

$$a^2 - 9 + 30 - 5(a + 3) = 0$$
$$a^2 + 21 - 5a - 15 = 0$$
$$a^2 - 5a + 6 = 0 \quad (2)$$
$$(a - 3)(a - 2) = 0$$
$$a = 3, a = 2$$

Checking the solution set $\{3, 2\}$ of Equation (2) in the original Equation (1), we have:

$$1 + \frac{30}{3^2 - 9} - \frac{5}{3 - 3} \overset{?}{=} 0 \quad \bigg| \quad 1 + \frac{30}{2^2 - 9} - \frac{5}{2 - 3} \overset{?}{=} 0$$

$$1 + \frac{30}{0} - \frac{5}{0} \overset{?}{=} 0 \quad \bigg| \quad 1 + (-6) - (-5) \overset{?}{=} 0$$

$$\bigg| \quad 0 = 0 ✔$$

Since $a = 3$ produces zero divisors, 3 is not an admissible root of Equation (1). Hence, although the solution set of Equation (2) is $\{3, 2\}$, the solution set of Equation (1) is simply $\{2\}$.

Thus you can see that when you transform a fractional equation by multiplying both members by their LCD, the resulting equation is not necessarily equivalent to the original one. The solution set of the transformed equation will, however, include all the roots of the original equation. *Always check the roots back in the original equation to see which ones are admissible.*

EXAMPLE 1   If Jane can paint a certain room in 7 hours, and Becky and Jane together can paint the room in 4 hours, how long would it take Becky alone to paint the room?

SOLUTION

1. The problem asks for the number of hours required for Becky to paint the room alone.

2. Let h = the number of hours required by Becky to paint the room alone.

   Then $\dfrac{1}{h}$ = the part of the total job Becky can do in 1 hour.

   $\dfrac{1}{7}$ = the part of the job Jane can do in 1 hour.

   1 = the entire job, which Jane and Becky can do jointly in 4 hours.

3. Total job is part done by Jane plus part done by Becky in 4 hours.

$$1 \;=\; \frac{1}{7}(4) \;+\; \frac{1}{h}(4)$$

$$1 \;=\; \frac{4}{7} + \frac{4}{h}$$

4. Multiplying both members by the LCD, $7h$, we have:

$$7h = \left(\frac{4h + 28}{7h}\right)7h$$

$$7h = 4h + 28$$
$$3h = 28$$
$$h = 9\tfrac{1}{3}.$$

5. Check:

$$1 \overset{?}{=} \tfrac{1}{7}(4) + \frac{1}{\frac{28}{3}}(4)$$
$$1 \overset{?}{=} \tfrac{4}{7} + \tfrac{3}{28}(4)$$
$$1 \overset{?}{=} \tfrac{4}{7} + \tfrac{3}{7}$$
$$1 = 1 \checkmark$$

∴ Becky alone would take $9\tfrac{1}{3}$ hours.   **Answer.**

EXAMPLE 2   A plane is to dust the crops in a field measuring 1 kilometer wide and 1.2 kilometer long. If the ratio of the time it takes to fly the length of the field with a 10 kilometer-per-hour tailwind to the time required to fly back against that same wind is 8:9, what is the speed of the plane in still air?

SOLUTION

1. The problem asks for the speed of the plane in still air.

2.   Let r = speed of the plane in still air.
   $r + 10$ = speed of the plane with tailwind.
   $r - 10$ = speed of the plane against tailwind.
   t = time to fly the length with the wind.
   t' = time to fly the length against the wind.

   Then $\dfrac{t'}{t} = \dfrac{9}{8}$.

3. $\underbrace{\text{Time} \times \text{rate with wind}}_{t(r + 10)} = \underbrace{\text{distance}}_{1.2} = \underbrace{\text{time} \times \text{rate against wind}}_{t'(r - 10)}$

4. Dividing both members of $t(r + 10) = t'(r - 10)$ by $t(r - 10)$, you obtain:

$$\frac{r + 10}{r - 10} = \frac{t'}{t} = \frac{9}{8}$$

Multiply both members of $\frac{r + 10}{r - 10} = \frac{9}{8}$ by $8(r - 10)$:

$$8(r + 10) = 9(r - 10)$$
$$r = 170$$

5. Check the solution.

∴ the speed of the plane in still air is 170 km/h. **Answer.**

WRITTEN EXERCISES Determine the solution set over $\Re$. Recall that a check is essential.

A 1. $\dfrac{3}{5x} - \dfrac{1}{2x} = 1$

6. $\dfrac{r^2 + 16}{r^2 - 16} - \dfrac{r}{r + 4} = -\dfrac{4}{r - 4}$

2. $\dfrac{1}{y^2} + \dfrac{5}{6y} = \dfrac{2}{3}$

7. $\dfrac{3}{x} + \dfrac{6}{x - 1} = \dfrac{x + 13}{x^2 - x}$

3. $\dfrac{3}{2a} + \dfrac{5}{a} = 4$

8. $\dfrac{5}{2y + 6} - 2 = \dfrac{1 - 2y}{4y}$

4. $\dfrac{3t - 1}{5t - 4} = \dfrac{2}{3}$

9. $\dfrac{x + 2}{2x - 6} = \dfrac{x}{2} - \dfrac{3}{3 - x}$

5. $\dfrac{2}{m + 2} = \dfrac{m}{2 - m} + \dfrac{m^2 + 4}{m^2 - 4}$

10. $\dfrac{z}{z - 1} + 1 = \dfrac{1}{z - 1} - 3$

B 11. $\dfrac{3a + 1}{a^2 - 9} + \dfrac{a + 3}{3 - a} = \dfrac{1 - 5a}{a + 3}$

15. $2a - b = 5$

12. $\dfrac{2}{1 - c^2} = \dfrac{c}{c - 1} - \dfrac{8}{c + 1}$

$\dfrac{a + 4}{b + 9} = \dfrac{3}{4}$

13. $\dfrac{9 - 5y}{2} - 1 = x$

16. $x + y = 6$

$y + 3 = \dfrac{x}{3}$

$\dfrac{10x + y}{x + y} = \dfrac{5}{2}$

14. $\dfrac{x + 2y}{3} - \dfrac{2x - y}{3} = -3$

17. $\dfrac{x + y}{3} = \dfrac{x - y}{2} + 1$

$\dfrac{3x - 2y}{4} - \dfrac{3x + 2y}{4} = \dfrac{3}{4}$

$\dfrac{10x + y}{10y + x} = \dfrac{7}{4}$

Graph the solution set over the set of real numbers.

18. $\dfrac{x-2}{4} + 1 + \dfrac{x}{6} \geq 0$

19. $\dfrac{y+5}{12} - \dfrac{3+y}{8} < 1$

20. $y^2 - \frac{3}{4}y < \frac{5}{2}$

21. $x^2 + \frac{3}{2}x > 1$

22. $t^2 - \frac{8}{3}t < 1$

C   23. $\frac{2}{5}x + \frac{1}{3}y \leq 1$

$x - \frac{2}{3}y \geq 2$

24. $\dfrac{x}{6} + \dfrac{y}{3} > -1$

$\dfrac{x}{2} - y < -3$

Find the solution set over $\Re$.   Recall that a check is essential.

25. $3(2x)^{-1} - 3(4y)^{-1} = 2$
$4(3x)^{-1} - 11(9y)^{-1} = 4$

26. $4(-2x)^{-1} + (3y)^{-1} = -8$
$2(3x)^{-1} - (2y)^{-1} = -2$

27. $\dfrac{2x-1}{x+3} + \dfrac{1}{x^2+x-6} = \dfrac{x-4}{2-x}$

28. $\dfrac{y+1}{y+3} - \dfrac{y+2}{y+4} = \dfrac{y+3}{y+5} - \dfrac{y+4}{y+6}$

PROBLEMS

A

1. A walk of 9 kilometers would have taken Mary 45 minutes less if she had increased her usual rate of walking by 1 kilometer per hour. Find her usual rate of walking.

2. The cold water faucet can fill a tub in 30 minutes. With both the cold and the hot water faucets running, the tub can be filled in 20 minutes. How long does it take the hot water faucet alone to fill the tub?

3. Two numbers are in the ratio $3:8$. If the first number is increased by 4 and the second decreased by 6, the resulting numbers are in the ratio $1:2$. Find the original numbers.

4. A fraction equals $\frac{5}{6}$. The numerator is 4 more than $\frac{2}{3}$ the denominator. Find the reciprocal of the original fraction.

5. A group attending a conference on energy conservation rented a block of hotel rooms in advance for $\$360$. When 4 members were unable to attend, each one who did go had to pay $\$4.50$ more to make up the $\$360$. How many people attended?

6. A strike of part-time agricultural workers was settled when pickers earning $\$90$ per week were granted an increase of 25 cents per hour. As a result, it took each worker 4 hours less to earn his former weekly salary. How many hours per week did each one work before the hourly raise?

7. The Harvard crew, while practicing on the Charles River for the annual Henley regatta, takes 20 minutes to row a 5-kilometer course upstream, and 12 minutes to row the same course downstream. What is their rate in still water? [*Hint:* Let r = rate of boat in still water and c = rate of current.]

8. In still water two women can paddle a canoe 12 kilometers per hour. If it takes them 6 hours to paddle 32 kilometers up a river and then return, what is the rate of the river's current?

B   9. Three carpenters can build a cabinet in 8 hours, while they and a fourth carpenter can do the job in 6 hours. If the three carpenters work 1 hour and then are joined by the fourth, how long will it take the four of them to complete the job?

10. The difference of the reciprocals of two consecutive positive odd integers is $\frac{2}{99}$. Find the integers.

C   11. Between two Navajo villages in Arizona, one stretch of the road is paved and the rest is gravel. The gravel stretch is one kilometer longer than the paved stretch. A man drives the paved stretch at 60 kilometers per hour and the gravel stretch at 45 kilometers per hour. His average rate going from one village to the other is 50 kilometers per hour. Find the distance between the two villages.

12. A plane flies with a tailwind from London to Zurich at an average speed of 550 kilometers per hour. Against the same wind, it makes the return trip at a rate of 450 kilometers per hour. Find the effective speed for the round trip.

SELF-TEST 3   Give the meaning of each of the following.

1. rational number

2. rational algebraic expression

3. fraction in lowest terms

4. fractional equation

Objective 1, page 196   5. Simplify $\dfrac{y^3 - 4y}{y^2 + 2y}$ by factoring its numerator and denominator.

Objective 2, page 196   6. Transform $\dfrac{-7 + 4x^2 - 4x + x^4}{-3 - 2x + x^2}$ into the sum of a polynomial and a rational expression in which the dividend has degree less than that of the divisor.

Objective 3, page 196   7. Express $\dfrac{x^2 - 3x - 4}{2x + 4} \div \dfrac{3x - 12}{x + 2}$ in lowest terms.

Objective 4, page 196   8. Transform $\dfrac{x}{x - 3} - \dfrac{4}{x + 3} - \dfrac{18}{x^2 - 9}$ into an equivalent rational expression in lowest terms.

Objective 5, page 196   9. If one oil well yields enough oil to fill a tank in two days, and another yields enough to fill the tank in six days, how long would it take the two wells to yield enough oil to fill two such tanks?

10. Solve $\dfrac{10}{x^2 - 25} + \dfrac{1}{x + 5} + 1 = 0$ over $\mathcal{R}$.

Check your answers with those printed at the back of the book.

chapter summary

1. Laws for working with positive integral exponents are extended to any integral exponent by defining b^0 and b^{-n} ($b \neq 0, n > 0$):

$$b^0 = 1, \quad \text{and} \quad b^{-n} = \frac{1}{b^n}.$$

2. A numeral is given in **standard notation** when it is expressed as a product, $a \times 10^n$, where $1 \leq |a| < 10$ and n is an integer.

3. A polynomial is **reducible** if it can be expressed as a product of two or more polynomials of lower positive degree; otherwise, it is **irreducible**. The **greatest monomial factor** of a polynomial is the monomial with greatest numerical coefficient and greatest degree that is a factor of each term of the polynomial. If a polynomial is irreducible and its greatest monomial factor is 1, then the polynomial is a **prime polynomial.**

4. For a and $b \in \mathcal{R}$, $ab = 0$ if and only if $a = 0$ or $b = 0$.

5. For a and $b \in \mathcal{R}$, $ab > 0$ if and only if a and b are of the same sign, and $ab < 0$ if and only if a and b are of opposite signs.

6. To reduce a rational expression to **lowest terms**, you can factor the numerator and denominator completely and then divide both by all their common factors.

7. By using the division algorithm, you can transform a nonzero rational expression into the sum of a polynomial and a rational expression in which the degree of the numerator is less than that of the denominator.

8. Operations can be performed with rational expressions by using the corresponding rules for operations with rational numbers.

chapter test

6-1 Write as an equivalent expression containing only positive exponents. Assume that all variables in denominators or with nonpositive exponents do not have 0 as their value.

1. $(3x^5y^{-2}z)(-5x^{-2}y^{-3}z^{-1})$ 2. $\dfrac{x^{-3}y^{-2}z^0}{x^3y^{-2}}$

6-2   3. Write 0.000257 in standard notation.

4. Find a one-significant-digit estimate of A, if $A = \dfrac{4217 \times 0.308}{21.6}$.

6-3   5. Write $(x^4 - 2x^2 + 3x)(x - 4)$ as a polynomial in simple form.

6-4 **Factor completely.**

6. $x^2 + 2xy - 80y^2$ 7. $16x^3 - 2$

6-5   Solve over $\mathcal{R}$ for x by factoring.

     8. $x^2 + 3x - 54 = 0$ **9.** $x^3 - 4x = 0$

6-6   Find the solution set of the given inequality over $\mathcal{R}$ and draw its graph.

     10. $x^2 - x > 12$ **11.** $x^2 + x < 2$

6-7   Simplify the given expression.

     12. $\dfrac{x^3 - 1}{x^3 + x^2 + x}$ **13.** $\dfrac{(y^2 - 4)^{-1}}{(y + 2)^{-2}}$

6-8   **14.** Express $\dfrac{x^3 + 2x - 1}{x^2 + x - 3}$ as a sum by dividing.

6-9   Express in lowest terms.

     15. $\dfrac{a^2 - b^2}{a - b} \cdot \dfrac{2ab}{a^2 + ab}$ **16.** $\dfrac{x^4 - 16}{x + 2} \div \dfrac{x^2 + 4}{5}$

6-10 Simplify the given expression.

     17. $\dfrac{a}{a^2 - 4} + \dfrac{3}{a + 2}$

     18. $\dfrac{x - 3}{(x - 1)(x - 2)} - \dfrac{x - 4}{(x - 1)(x - 3)}$

6-11 **19.** The average of two numbers is 10, and one of the numbers is 1 less than $\frac{3}{4}$ of the other. Find the numbers.

6-12 **20.** Solve $\dfrac{(x - 1)^2}{x} - \dfrac{1 - 2x}{x} = 2$ over $\mathcal{R}$.

programmed chapter review

6-1   **1.** If $b \in \mathcal{R}$, $b \neq 0$, and n is a positive integer, then $b^0 = $ __?__ and $b^{-n} = $ __?__ . $1;\ \dfrac{1}{b^n}$

     2. A numeral without exponents that is equivalent to $\dfrac{2^{-3}}{3^{-2}}$ is __?__ . $\dfrac{9}{8}$

     3. If x and $y \neq 0$, an expression in simple form equivalent to $(3x^{-4}y^{-2})(6x^2y^5)$ but with only positive exponents is __?__ . $\dfrac{18y^3}{x^2}$

6-2   **4.** In standard notation, you would represent 147 as __?__ and 0.00023 as __?__ . 1.47×10^2 2.3×10^{-4}

     5. A one-significant-digit estimate of 4.2087×524 is __?__ .   2000

6–3 **6.** A polynomial in simple form equivalent to $(3x - 2y)(5x + 4y)$ is __?__ .

$15x^2 + 2xy - 8y^2$

6–4 **7.** A polynomial that can be expressed as a product of two or more polynomial factors of lower __?__ degree is said to be __?__ .

positive
reducible

8. If a polynomial is irreducible and its greatest monomial factor is 1, then the polynomial is a __?__ polynomial.

prime

9. In completely factored form, you can write $4x^3 - 9xy^2$ as __?__ .

$x(2x + 3y)(2x - 3y)$

6–5 **10.** If $(x + 3)(2x - 5) = 0$ then either $x = $ __?__ or $x = $ __?__ .

$-3; \frac{5}{2}$

6–6 **11.** If $ab < 0$, then either $a < 0$ and b __?__ 0, or $a > 0$ and b __?__ 0.

$>$
$<$

6–7 **12.** The quotient of two polynomials is called a __?__ (algebraic) expression.

rational

13. A fraction whose numerator and denominator have no common factors except 1 and -1 is said to be in __?__ terms.

lowest

6–8 **14.** In dividing one polynomial by another, you continue the process until you obtain either the remainder __?__ or a polynomial of __?__ degree than that of the divisor.

0
lower

6–9 **15.** You can multiply two rational expressions by using the rule that $\frac{r}{t} \times \frac{s}{u} = r$__?__ $\div t$__?__ .

$s; u$

16. To divide one rational expression by another, you can use the rule that $\frac{r}{t} \div \frac{s}{u} = r$__?__ $\div t$__?__ .

$u; s$

6–10 **17.** To add or subtract rational expressions having the same denominator, you can use the rules that $\frac{a}{c} + \frac{b}{c} = $ __?__ $\div c$ and $\frac{a}{c} - \frac{b}{c} = $ __?__ $\div c$.

$(a + b)$
$(a - b)$

18. To add or subtract rational expressions having different denominators, it is simplest to express them with their __?__ common denominator.

least

6–11 **19.** A __?__ is equivalent to a fraction whose denominator is 100.

percent

6–12 **20.** When you transform a fractional equation by multiplying both members by the least common denominator, the resulting equation __?__ (is/is not) always equivalent to the original equation.

is not

Helgafell, a volcano dormant for at least 5,000 years, erupted on the island of Heimaey, near the coast of Iceland, in 1973. Volcanoes are one force in our environment over which we have no control.

sequences and series

arithmetic sequences and series

Objectives

After completing the next three sections, you should be able to:
1. Determine an arithmetic sequence when the first term and a rule for computing each successive term from the preceding term are given.
2. Find a specified term of an arithmetic sequence when two terms, or one term and the common difference, are given.
3. Find the sum of a given arithmetic series.
4. Solve practical problems involving arithmetic sequences and series.

7-1 arithmetic sequences

Sue had $18 in her savings account. Having a summer job, she resolved to add $20 to the account each week. Starting with the initial amount, and continuing through five successive deposits, the number of dollars in the account formed the following *sequence:*

$$18, 38, 58, 78, 98, 118.$$

The numbers in a sequence are called the terms of the sequence. In the sequence given above, the first term is 18, the second is 38, and so on. A sequence such as this one, which has a last term, is called a finite sequence. A sequence such as

$$18, 38, 58, 78, 98, 118, \ldots,$$

which you think of as continuing forever, has no last term and is called an infinite sequence.

The sequences shown on page 217 are called *arithmetic* (pronounced ar-ith-**met**-ic in this usage) *sequences*. An arithmetic sequence, or an arithmetic progression, is any sequence in which each term after the first is obtained by adding a fixed number, called the common difference, to the preceding term. In the sequence 18, 38, 58, 78, 98, 118, the common difference is 20. The terms in an arithmetic sequence are said to be in arithmetic progression.

EXAMPLE 1   The first three terms of an arithmetic sequence are $-7, -3, 1$. What are the common difference and the fourth term of this sequence?

SOLUTION   1. To find the common difference, subtract any term from its successor.

$$(-3) - (-7) = 4 \quad \text{[or } 1 - (-3) = 4\text{]}$$

∴ the common difference is 4   **Answer.**

2. To find the fourth term, add the common difference to the third term.

$$1 + 4 = 5$$

∴ the fourth term is 5. **Answer.**

To refer to the terms of any sequence, you often use subscript notation. For instance, you might call the first term of a sequence a_1, the second term a_2, and so on, with a_n denoting the nth term.

You can use this subscript notation to write a rule for forming the successive terms of an arithmetic sequence. In the sequence 18, 38, 58, 78, 98, 118, . . . ,

$$a_1 = 18, \quad a_2 = 38 = a_1 + 20, \quad a_3 = a_2 + 20.$$

In general:

> If the first term of an arithmetic sequence is a_1, and the common difference is d, then the successive terms are obtained from the rule
>
> $$a_{n+1} = a_n + d, \quad n = 1, 2, 3, \ldots .$$

EXAMPLE 2   Name the first term and give a rule for finding the successive terms in the arithmetic sequence 23, 19, 15, ...

SOLUTION $a_1 = 23$
$d = a_2 - a_1 = 19 - 23 = -4$ [or $d = a_3 - a_2 = 15 - 19 = -4$]

Therefore, successive terms are computed according to the rule

$$a_{n+1} = a_n + (-4) = a_n - 4. \text{ **Answer.**}$$

ORAL EXERCISES State the common difference and the fourth term of the given arithmetic sequence.

1. 2, 6, 10, . . .   3. −5, −3, −1, . . .   5. 6, 4, 2, . . .

2. 1, 6, 11, . . .   4. −1, −$\frac{1}{2}$, 0, . . .   6. 1, $\frac{1}{2}$, 0, . . .

State the first and third terms of the arithmetic sequence whose second term and common difference are given.

7. $a_2 = 5, d = 3$ 9. $a_2 = -4, d = 3$ 11. $a_2 = 0, d = -3$

8. $a_2 = 3, d = 5$ 10. $a_2 = -1, d = 6$ 12. $a_2 = -1, d = -2$

In Exercises 13–18 the first term of a sequence and a rule for finding successive terms are given.

a. State the second and third terms.

b. State whether or not the sequence is an arithmetic progression.

13. $a_1 = 3, a_{n+1} = 2a_n$ 16. $a_1 = 2, a_{n+1} = (a_n - 2)^2$

14. $a_1 = -1, a_{n+1} = a_n^2$ 17. $a_1 = -3, a_{n+1} = a_n + 13$

15. $a_1 = 1, a_{n+1} = (a_n - 1)^2$ 18. $a_1 = 7, a_{n+1} = a_n - 2$

19. In the sequence $a_1, a_2, a_3,$ must one or the other of the statements "$a_1 \leq a_2 \leq a_3$," and "$a_1 \geq a_2 \geq a_3$" be true? Explain.

20. If the sequence a_1, a_2, a_3 is an arithmetic sequence, must one or the other of the statements "$a_1 \leq a_2 \leq a_3$," and "$a_1 \geq a_2 \geq a_3$" be true? Explain.

WRITTEN EXERCISES Determine the first four terms in an arithmetic sequence having the given values for a_1 and d.

A

1. $a_1 = 7, d = 2$ 4. $a_1 = 2, d = -3$

2. $a_1 = -5, d = 3$ 5. $a_1 = -3, d = 1.5$

3. $a_1 = 9, d = -4$ 6. $a_1 = 7.5, d = -2.5$

Find the first two terms of the arithmetic sequence whose third term and common difference are given.

7. $a_3 = 6, d = 4$ 10. $a_3 = -1, d = -5$

8. $a_3 = -2, d = 3$ 11. $a_3 = -3.2, d = 0.3$

9. $a_3 = 5, d = -2$ 12. $a_3 = 4.7, d = -2.1$

Give a rule for finding successive terms in the given finite sequence. Is the sequence an arithmetic progression?

13. 2, 5, 8, 11   16. 2, 6, 18, 54

14. 4, 2, 0, −2   17. 1, 1 · 2, 1 · 2 · 3, 1 · 2 · 3 · 4

15. 1, 3, 6, 10   18. 4, −2, 1, −$\frac{1}{2}$

B 19. Find the first eight terms of the sequence in which $a_1 = 1$, $a_2 = 1$, and $a_{n+2} = a_n + a_{n+1}$ for $n = 1, 2, 3, \ldots$.

20. Find the first six terms of the sequence in which $a_1 = 1$, $a_2 = 1$, and $a_{n+2} = a_n + 2a_{n+1}$ for $n = 1, 2, 3, \ldots$.

In Exercises 21–26:

a. Write the sequence whose terms are obtained by performing the indicated operation on the terms of the arithmetic sequence $-4, -1, 2, 5$.

b. Is the resulting sequence an arithmetic progression? Explain.

21. Multiply each term by 5.   23. Square each term.

22. Multiply each term by 0.   24. Subtract 4 from each term.

25. Multiply each term by a nonzero real number k.

26. Add a real number k to each term.

C 27. For what value(s) of x will $x + 2$, $3x + 1$, and $4x - 5$, in this order, form an arithmetic sequence?

28. If $a_1, a_2, a_3, \ldots$ is an arithmetic progression, show that

$$a_2 + a_6 = a_3 + a_5 = 2a_4.$$

7–2 *arithmetic means*

To determine a particular term of an arithmetic sequence, $a_1, a_2, a_3, \ldots$, such as a_{20}, it is not necessary to compute each preceding term. Notice that you have:

$$a_1$$
$$a_2 = a_1 + d = a_1 + 1d$$
$$a_3 = a_2 + d = (a_1 + d) + d = a_1 + (d + d) = a_1 + 2d$$
$$a_4 = a_3 + d = (a_1 + 2d) + d = a_1 + (2d + d) = a_1 + 3d$$

and so on. This suggests the following fact:

The nth term of an arithmetic sequence whose first term is a_1 and whose common difference is d is

$$a_n = a_1 + (n - 1)d.$$

EXAMPLE 1 Find the twentieth term in the arithmetic sequence: $-3, 2, 7, \ldots$

SOLUTION $a_1 = -3$, $d = 7 - 2 = 5$. Since $a_n = a_1 + (n - 1)d$,

$$a_{20} = -3 + (20 - 1) \cdot 5 = -3 + 19 \cdot 5 = 92.$$

$\therefore a_{20} = 92$. Answer.

The terms between two given terms of an arithmetic sequence are called *arithmetic means* between the given terms. For example, the set of three arithmetic means between 18 and 98 is {38, 58, 78}, because

$$18, 38, 58, 78, 98$$

is an arithmetic sequence.

EXAMPLE 2   **Find the four arithmetic means between the terms 5 and 25.**

SOLUTION   You can schematically represent the part of the sequence from the term 5 to the term 25 as follows:

$$5, \_\_\_, \_\_\_, \_\_\_, \_\_\_, 25$$

First, determine d for the sequence whose first term is 5 and whose sixth term is 25. Replacing a_n with "25," a_1 with "5," and n with "6" in $a_n = a_1 + (n - 1)d$, you find:

$$25 = 5 + (6 - 1)d$$
$$25 = 5 + 5d$$
$$d = 4$$

The required means are found by successive additions of 4:

$$5, 9, 13, 17, 21, 25$$

∴ the four arithmetic means are 9, 13, 17, 21. **Answer.**

EXAMPLE 3   **What is the first term of an arithmetic sequence whose fifth term is 2 and whose ninth term is 8?**

SOLUTION.   Schematically the sequence looks like this:

$$\_\_\_, \_\_\_, \_\_\_, \_\_\_, 2, \_\_\_, \_\_\_, \_\_\_, 8$$

1. To find the common difference, consider the part of the sequence beginning with the term 2; in this sequence, the *fifth* term is then 8, and so:

$$a_5 = a_1 + (5 - 1)d$$
$$8 = 2 + 4d$$
$$d = 1\tfrac{1}{2}$$

2. To find the first term of the original sequence, you can use:

$$a_5 = a_1 + (5 - 1)d$$
$$2 = a_1 + (4)(1\tfrac{1}{2})$$
$$2 = a_1 + 6$$
$$a_1 = -4$$

∴ the first term of the given sequence is -4. **Answer.**

A single arithmetic mean inserted between two numbers is the average, or *the* arithmetic mean, of the two numbers. For example, the arithmetic mean of 4 and 10 is 7, which is $\frac{1}{2}(4 + 10)$. Proving that the arithmetic mean of two numbers a and b is $\frac{1}{2}(a + b)$ is left to you (Exercise 33, page 223).

ORAL EXERCISES

In the arithmetic sequence $-11, -7, -3, 1, 5, 9$, name the arithmetic mean(s) between:

1. -11 and -3 3. -3 and 5   5. -3 and 9
2. -7 and 1   4. 1 and 9   6. -11 and 5

State the arithmetic mean of the given numbers.

7. -11 and -3 11. -3 and 9   15. 0 and 20
8. -7 and 1   12. -11 and 5   16. 5 and 15
9. -3 and 5   13. -7 and 9   17. a and $-a$
10. 1 and 9   14. -23 and 23   18. a and $3a$

WRITTEN EXERCISES

Find the value of a_n for the given values of a_1, d, and n in an arithmetic sequence.

A
1. $a_1 = 1, d = 3, n = 21$ 4. $a_1 = 33, d = -3, n = 12$
2. $a_1 = 3, d = 2, n = 10$ 5. $a_1 = 6, d = 10, n = 48$
3. $a_1 = -2, d = -5, n = 7$ 6. $a_1 = 3, d = 7, n = 1001$

Find the specified term a_n of the indicated arithmetic sequence.

7. 5, 8, 11, . . . ; a_{16} 11. $-9, -2, 5, . . . ; a_{31}$
8. 2, 8, 14, . . . ; a_{26} 12. 13, 2, -9, . . . ; a_{53}
9. 5, 3, 1, . . . ; a_{14} 13. $-11, -5.5, 0, . . . ; a_{230}$
10. 6, 1, -4, . . . ; a_{49} 14. 1.00, 0.95, 0.90, . . . ; a_{150}

Insert the stated number of arithmetic means between the given numbers.

15. Three, between 9 and -11 18. Ten, between -15 and -4
16. Seven, between 5 and 23   19. Three, between -8 and -9
17. Five, between -8 and 4   20. Seven, between 2 and -2

Find the missing terms in the indicated arithmetic sequence.

21. 3, _?_, 15, _?_, _?_   24. -25, _?_, _?_, _?_, -7
22. -2, _?_, 10, _?_, _?_   25. _?_, 7, _?_, _?_, -14
23. _?_, 40, _?_, _?_, 19   26. _?_, _?_, $21\frac{1}{2}$, _?_, $10\frac{1}{2}$

B 27. Which term of the arithmetic sequence $-1, 5, 11, \ldots$ is 125?

28. Which term of the arithmetic sequence $4, -1, -6, \ldots$ is -141?

29. For what value of x is -3 the arithmetic mean of x and $4x - 1$?

30. For what value of y is 1 the arithmetic mean of $y - 8$ and $y + 6$?

31. For what value of s is s the arithmetic mean of -2 and $s + 7$?

32. For what value of t is t the arithmetic mean of $7t$ and $3t - 4$?

C 33. Prove that if a, c, b is an arithmetic sequence, then $c = \frac{1}{2}(a + b)$. [Thus, *the* arithmetic mean of a and b is $\frac{1}{2}(a + b)$.]

34. Show that if a and b are both even integers or both odd integers, then their arithmetic mean is an integer.

35. Show that if a and b are integers and if one is even and one is odd, then their arithmetic mean is not an integer.

36. Show that if $a < b$ and if the arithmetic mean of a and b is m, then $a < m < b$.

PROBLEMS

A 1. An editor takes a position at $\$7400$ a year. She receives annual increases in salary of $\$350$. What will her salary be during her twelfth year of service?

2. A young man's annual salary increased for six years in arithmetic progression. If his salary the first year was $\$5600$ and his salary the sixth year was $\$8100$, what was his salary during each of the other years?

3. A Vacation Savings Club, which helps members to save money for their vacations, requires each member to deposit $\$10$ the first week and to increase his deposit by $\$2$ weekly for eleven weeks. How much is the final (twelfth) deposit?

4. Mr. and Mrs. Fritz open a savings account when their daughter is in the fifth grade to provide for her college education. If they deposit $\$1500$ the first year and increase their deposits by $\$150$ each year after that, how much will they deposit when their daughter is in the 10th grade?

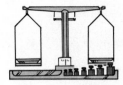

5. The seven weights in a set for an analytic balance are in arithmetic progression. If the next to heaviest is 21 grams and the lightest 1 gram, what are the other weights?

6. Some boys on the beach decide to form a human pyramid having one person fewer in each successive layer. If there are 9 boys in the bottom (or first) layer, how many are in the fifth layer?

7. The annual cost of repairs after the first year for a certain automobile increases $\$70$ each year. If the cost of repairs during the first year is $\$115$, how much will be spent on repairs during the 6th year?

8. John repays some money that he owes his sister by making monthly payments. The first payment is $15 and every succeeding payment is $5 more than that of the preceding month. How much does he give his sister the 10th month?

B   **9.** A student taking a test consisting of ten questions is told that each question after the first is worth two credits more than the preceding question. If the third question is worth fifteen credits, how much is the last question worth?

10. A builder finds that his profit from the sale of the first house in a development is $-$500 (he loses $500). His profit on the sale of the second house is $-$150. On selling more houses in the development, he finds that each additional house sold increases his profit per house by $350. How many houses did he sell if his profit on the last house was $1600?

11. A woman driving along an interstate toll road at 90 kilometers per hour (25 meters per second) applies the brake as she approaches a tollbooth and comes to a complete stop in 25 seconds. If the speed at which she is traveling at the end of successive seconds falls off in arithmetic progression, how fast was she traveling at the end of the twelfth second after braking?

12. At the end of one year, the trade-in value of a certain automobile is $700 less than the original cost. Each year thereafter the trade-in value decreases by $250. If the original cost of the automobile is $4200, what is the trade-in value at the end of n years? When is the trade-in value 0?

7–3 *arithmetic series*

From the terms of any given sequence, such as

$$4, 7, 10, 13, 16,$$

you can construct an associated sequence S_1, S_2, S_3, S_4, S_5 of *sums:*

$$S_1 = 4,$$
$$S_2 = 4 + 7 = 11$$
$$S_3 = 4 + 7 + 10 = 21$$
$$S_4 = 4 + 7 + 10 + 13 = 34$$
$$S_5 = 4 + 7 + 10 + 13 + 16 = 50$$

Each of the indicated sums S_1, S_2, S_3, S_4, and S_5 is called a *series* associated with the sequence 4, 7, 10, 13, 16.

In general, given any sequence

$$a_1, a_2, a_3, \ldots$$

with n or more terms, the associated series of n terms, S_n, is

$$S_n = a_1 + a_2 + a_3 + \cdots + a_n.$$

The Greek letter Σ (sigma), called the summation sign, is used to abbreviate the writing of a series. For example, to abbreviate the series

$$S_5 = 4 + 7 + 10 + 13 + 16,$$

first observe that 4, 7, 10, 13, 16 is an arithmetic sequence with nth term, or general term, $4 + (n - 1)3$. Therefore, the series can be denoted by the symbol:

$$\sum_{n=1}^{5} [4 + (n - 1)3]$$

(read "the summation of $4 + (n - 1)3$ from $n = 1$ to $n = 5$"). This means that you successively replace n with numerals "1," "2," "3," "4," "5," and then write an expression denoting the sum of the resulting values. The letter n is called the index (plural, indexes or indices) and the replacement set of n is the range of summation. Note that any letter, such as i, j, k, m, or n, may be chosen as the index.

EXAMPLE 1 Write $\displaystyle\sum_{k=0}^{5} 5k$ in expanded form.

SOLUTION Replace k with the numerals "0," "1," "2," "3," "4," and "5," in turn and write the sum.

$$\sum_{k=0}^{5} 5k = 5(0) + 5(1) + 5(2) + 5(3) + 5(4) + 5(5). \quad \textbf{Answer.}$$

EXAMPLE 2 Use summation notation to write the series

$$1 + 5 + 9 + 13 + 17 + 21 + 25.$$

SOLUTION Each term is of the form $1 + 4(n - 1) = 1 + 4n - 4 = 4n - 3$. Since there are seven terms,

$$1 + 5 + 9 + 13 + 17 + 21 + 25 = \sum_{n=1}^{7} (4n - 3). \quad \textbf{Answer.}$$

A series, such as $1 + 5 + 9 + 13 + 17 + 21 + 25$, whose terms are in arithmetic progression is called an arithmetic series. Because

$$1 + 5 + 9 + 13 + 17 + 21 + 25 = 91,$$

we say that the value, or sum, of this series is 91.

You can find a formula for the sum of any arithmetic series by noticing that there are two ways to obtain the terms of the series:

(1) Start with the first term a_1 and successively add the common difference d.

(2) Start with the nth term a_n and successively subtract d.

Thus,

(1) $S_n = a_1 + (a_1 + d) + (a_1 + 2d) + \cdots + [a_1 + (n-1)d]$;

(2) $S_n = a_n + (a_n - d) + (a_n - 2d) + \cdots + [a_n - (n-1)d]$.

Adding the corresponding members of these equations, you obtain

$$2S_n = (a_1 + a_n) + (a_1 + a_n) + (a_1 + a_n) + \cdots + (a_1 + a_n),$$

where $a_1 + a_n$ occurs n times. Hence,

$$2S_n = n(a_1 + a_n),$$

or

$$S_n = \frac{n}{2}(a_1 + a_n).$$

EXAMPLE 3   **Find the sum of the first one-hundred positive odd integers.**

SOLUTION $a_1 = 1$, $d = 2$, $n = 100$,

$$a_n = a_1 + (n-1)d = a_{100} = 1 + (100-1)2 = 199$$

and

$$S_{100} = \frac{100}{2}(1 + 199) = 10{,}000. \quad \textbf{Answer.}$$

Note: Example 3 illustrates the following interesting fact: *The sum of the first n positive odd integers is n^2* (see Exercise 30, page 228).

In applying the formula for S_n in Example 3, we used the fact that $a_n = a_1 + (n-1)d$. Thus $S_n = \frac{n}{2}(a_1 + a_n) = \frac{n}{2}[a_1 + a_1 + (n-1)d]$, or

$$S_n = \frac{n}{2}[2a_1 + (n-1)d].$$

In finding the two formulas for S_n for an arithmetic series, you have proved the following theorem.

> **Theorem.** If S_n is the sum of the first n terms of an arithmetic sequence whose first term is a_1, whose common difference is d, and whose nth term is a_n, then
>
> $$S_n = \frac{n}{2}(a_1 + a_n) \quad \text{and} \quad S_n = \frac{n}{2}[2a_1 + (n-1)d].$$

State the value of S_1, S_2, and S_3 for the given sequence.

1. $1, 2, 3, \ldots, n$
2. $1, 3, 5, \ldots, 2n - 1$
3. $-2, -4, -6, \ldots, -2n$
4. $5, 10, 15, \ldots, 5n$
5. $-1, 0, 1, \ldots, n - 2$
6. $5, 6, 7, \ldots, n + 4$

In Exercises 7–14 read the symbol, and then state the indicated series in expanded form.

7. $\sum_{k=1}^{5} k$
9. $\sum_{i=0}^{3} (-i)$
11. $\sum_{m=-1}^{2} (m - 2)$
13. $\sum_{j=3}^{6} (j + 3)$

8. $\sum_{k=1}^{4} 3k$
10. $\sum_{i=2}^{6} 5i$
12. $\sum_{n=2}^{4} (3 - n)$
14. $\sum_{j=10}^{12} (2j + 1)$

State the first term, the common difference, and the number of terms of the given arithmetic series.

15. $\sum_{n=1}^{6} 3n$
16. $\sum_{m=1}^{10} (4m - 1)$
17. $\sum_{k=3}^{9} (-k + 6)$
18. $\sum_{i=2}^{10} 5(i + 3)$

Use the formula $S_n = \frac{n}{2}(a_1 + a_n)$ to state the sum of the given arithmetic series.

19. $2 + 4 + 6 + 8$
20. $1 + 2 + 3 + 4 + 5 + 6 + 7 + 8$

Find the sum of the arithmetic progression having the given data.

A

1. $a_1 = 8, a_n = 18, n = 6$
2. $a_1 = -4, a_n = 17, n = 8$
3. $a_1 = 9, a_n = -31, n = 9$
4. $a_1 = 0, a_n = 42, n = 7$
5. $a_1 = 4, d = 5, n = 8$
6. $a_1 = -7, d = 6, n = 10$
7. $a_1 = 8, d = -5, n = 11$
8. $a_1 = 0, d = -3, n = 9$

9–18. Find the sum of the arithmetic series given in Oral Exercises 9–18.

Write each of the following expressions in summation notation.

19. $3 + 8 + 13 + 18$
20. $5 + 8 + 11 + 14$
21. $-5 - 2 + 1 + 4 + 7$
22. $7 + 3 - 1 - 5 - 9$

Find the second term of the arithmetic series having the given data.

B

23. $d = -3, n = 12, S_n = -114$
24. $d = 4, n = 10, S_n = 150$
25. $a_1 = 13, a_n = -20, S_n = -42$
26. $a_1 = -40, a_n = 8, S_n = -144$

C **27.** Show that if a and b are real numbers and r and s are integers such that $r \leq s$, then $\displaystyle\sum_{i=r}^{s} (ai + b)$ is an arithmetic series having $s - r + 1$ terms and a as its common difference.

28. The **average of n numbers** $a_1, a_2, \ldots, a_n$ is $\dfrac{1}{n}(a_1 + a_2 + \cdots + a_n)$. Show that if these numbers are in arithmetic progression, then the average of the first and last terms is equal to the average of all n terms.

29. Show that the sum of the first n positive integers is $\dfrac{n(n + 1)}{2}$.

30. Show that the sum of the first n positive odd integers is n^2.

PROBLEMS

A   **1.** In a psychology lecture hall, there are 27 seats in the first row and 2 seats more in each following row. How many seats are there in the front 12 rows?

2. How much did an environmental engineer earn in ten years if her starting salary was $9,500 and she received annual increases of $650?

3. The clock in a courthouse tower chimes as many times as the hour. How many times does it chime between 7:00 AM and 6:00 PM, inclusive?

4. If the taxi rate is 50¢ for the first kilometer and 30¢ for each additional kilometer, what is the fare from downtown to the airport, 10 km away?

5. If a state income tax is 2% on the first thousand dollars of net income, 3% on the second thousand, and so on in arithmetic progression, what is the total tax paid on a net income of $15,000?

6. Juanita went to work as a teller in a bank at a salary of $6200 per year, and received yearly increases of $300. If she saved 10% of her income, how much had she saved after 7 years?

B   **7.** The builder in Exercise 10, page 224 sold 7 houses in the development mentioned. What was his total profit on these 7 houses?

8. A well-drilling firm charges $2.00 to drill the first meter, $2.10 for the second meter, and so on in arithmetic progression. At this rate, how much does the firm charge to drill a well 110 meters deep?

9. Find the sum of the positive integers that are less than 100 and are divisible by 3.

10. Find the sum of the positive integers that are less than 100 and are *not* divisible by 5.

C   **11.** Sue Smith and Jack Rogers started to work at the same time and at the same yearly salary. Sue's employer agreed to increase her salary $300 *per year* at the end of every half-year, while Jack's boss agreed to raise his salary $600 *per year* at the end of each year. By how much did Sue's total salary exceed Jack's over a ten-year period?

12. A letter carrier delivered daily for 30 days 4 more letters each day than on the previous day. The total delivery for the first 20 days of the period was the same as that for the last 10 days. How many letters did she deliver during the whole period?

SELF-TEST 1 Give the meaning of each of the following.

1. infinite sequence
2. arithmetic progression
3. common difference

4. arithmetic means
5. series

Objective 1, page 217

6. Determine the first five terms in an arithmetic sequence having -11 as its first term and 6 as its common difference.

Objective 2, page 217

7. Determine the thirteenth term in an arithmetic sequence in which $a_1 = 23$ and $a_2 = 16$.

Objective 3, page 217

8. Find the sum of the arithmetic series $\sum\limits_{j=1}^{9} (10j - 3)$.

Objective 4, page 217

9. John decided to develop his muscles by lifting 5 kilograms the first day of the month and increasing the amount by 0.5 kilograms each succeeding day. At this rate, how much would he be lifting on the thirtieth day of the month?

10. How many bricks are there in a pile one brick thick if there are 25 bricks in the bottom row, 23 in the next row, and so on in arithmetic progression, with 3 in the top row?

Check your answers with those printed at the back of the book.

programming in BASIC

Study the following program. It will print out the first n terms of an arithmetic sequence when you input values for a_1, d, and n.

```
10  PRINT "INPUT A1,D,N";
20  INPUT A1,D,N
30  FOR I=1 TO N−1
40  PRINT A1;",";
50  LET A1=A1+D
60  NEXT I
70  PRINT A1
80  END
```

EXERCISES

1. Write a program that will print out the nth term of an arithmetic sequence when you input values for a_1, d, and n.

2. Write a program that will print out the first n terms of an arithmetic series and the sum of those terms when you input values for a_1, d, and n.

3. Triangular numbers are the numbers.

$$1$$

$$1 + 2 = 3$$

$$1 + 2 + 3 = 6$$

and so on.

Write a program that will print out the first n triangular numbers.

4. The Fibonacci numbers are the numbers in the sequence

$$1, 1, 2, 3, 5, 8, \ldots$$

where each number after the second is the sum of the two preceding numbers. Write a program that will print out the first n Fibonacci numbers.

geometric sequences and series

After completing the next three sections, you should be able to:

Objectives

1. Find a specified term of a geometric sequence when two terms, or one term and the common ratio, are given.
2. Insert any number of geometric means between two given numbers.
3. Find the sum of a given geometric series.
4. Solve practical problems involving geometric sequences and series.

7-4 *geometric sequences*

In Section 7–1 you learned that in an arithmetic sequence each term after the first is obtained by adding a fixed number, the common difference, to the preceding term. Notice that in the sequence

$$2, 10, 50, 250$$

each term after the first is obtained by *multiplying* the preceding term by a fixed number, namely 5.

$$a_2 = 10 = 2 \cdot 5 = a_1 \cdot 5$$
$$a_3 = 50 = 10 \cdot 5 = a_2 \cdot 5$$
$$a_4 = 250 = 50 \cdot 5 = a_3 \cdot 5$$

Thus,
$$a_{n+1} = a_n \cdot 5 \quad \text{for } n = 1, 2, 3.$$

Any sequence in which each term after the first is the product of the preceding term and a fixed number is called a geometric sequence or a geometric progression. The fixed number is called the common ratio. In general:

> In a geometric sequence whose first term is a_1 and whose common ratio is r, successive terms are obtained from the rule
>
> $$a_{n+1} = a_n \cdot r, \qquad n = 1, 2, 3, \ldots .$$

The terms of a geometric sequence are said to be in geometric progression.

EXAMPLE 1   The first three terms of a geometric sequence are 48, 18, 6. Find the common ratio and the fourth term of this sequence.

SOLUTION   1. To find the common ratio, divide any one term into its successor.

$$18 \div 48 = \tfrac{1}{3} \qquad [\text{or } 6 \div 18 = \tfrac{1}{3}]$$

∴ the common ratio is $\tfrac{1}{3}$. **Answer.**
2. To find the fourth term, multiply the third term by the common ratio.

$$6 \times \tfrac{1}{3} = 2$$

∴ the fourth term is 2. **Answer.**

To discover a formula for the general term in any geometric sequence, let us continue the equations on page 230 for the terms of the geometric sequence 2, 10, 50, 250, . . . in the following way.

$$a_2 = a_1 \cdot 5 = a_1 \cdot 5^1$$
$$a_3 = a_2 \cdot 5 = a_1 \cdot 5^2$$
$$a_4 = a_3 \cdot 5 = a_1 \cdot 5^3$$

Do you see that the nth term ($n > 1$) of the sequence is given by the formula

$$a_n = a_1 \cdot 5^{n-1}?$$

Now consider a geometric sequence whose first term is a_1 and whose common ratio is r. The first few terms of the sequence are

$$a_1, a_1 r^1, a_1 r^2, a_1 r^3, a_1 r^4,$$

so that the nth term is given by

$$a_n = a_1 r^{n-1}, \qquad n > 1.$$

Notice that this formula applies, whatever value r may have. Of course, if the value of r is 0, all terms after the first are also 0.

Does the preceding formula apply in case n is 1? In that case, you find

$$a_1 = a_1 r^{1-1}, \qquad \text{or} \qquad a_1 = a_1 r^0.$$

For this formula to be valid, r^0 must be 1. In fact, as you saw on page 175, for every nonzero real number r, r^0 is defined to be 1. With this definition you can state the following fact:

The nth term of a geometric sequence whose first term is a_1 and whose common ratio is a nonzero number r is

$$a_n = a_1 r^{n-1}.$$

In finding the terms of a geometric progression, you may use the following table.

Short Table of Powers

N	N^2	N^3	N^4	N^5
1	1	1	1	1
2	4	8	16	32
3	9	27	81	243
4	16	64	256	1,024
5	25	125	625	3,125
6	36	216	1,296	7,776
7	49	343	2,401	16,807
8	64	512	4,096	32,768
9	81	729	6,561	59,049
10	100	1,000	10,000	100,000
11	121	1,331	14,641	161,051
12	144	1,728	20,736	248,832
13	169	2,197	28,561	371,293
14	196	2,744	38,416	537,824
15	225	3,375	50,625	759,375
16	256	4,096	65,536	1,048,576
17	289	4,913	83,521	1,419,857
18	324	5,832	104,976	1,889,568
19	361	6,859	130,321	2,476,099
20	400	8,000	160,000	3,200,000

EXAMPLE 2   Find the sixth term of the geometric progression

$$-2, -22, -242, \ldots.$$

SOLUTION $a_1 = -2$, $r = -22 \div (-2) = 11$.

Since $a_n = a_1 r^{n-1}$,

$$a_6 = -2(11)^{6-1}, \quad \text{or} \quad a_6 = -2(11)^5.$$

From the preceding table, $11^5 = 161,051$ and

$$a_6 = -2(161,051) = -322,102. \quad \textbf{Answer.}$$

ORAL EXERCISES In Exercises 1–12 if the given sequence is an arithmetic progression, give the common difference; if it is a geometric progression, give the common ratio. If it is neither an arithmetic nor a geometric sequence, state this fact.

1. $1, 3, 7, 15$ 5. $1, 1, 1, 1$ 9. $4, 2, 1, \frac{1}{2}$
2. $1, 0, 1, 0$ 6. $-2, 2, -2, 2$ 10. $3, 1, \frac{1}{3}, \frac{1}{9}$
3. $1, -1, 1, -1$ 7. $1, 2, 4, 8$ 11. a, abc, ab^2c^2, ab^3c^3
4. $1, 0, 0, 0$ 8. $2, 4, 8, 16$ 12. $a - b, a, a + b, a + 2b$

State the numeral with which you would replace the __?__ so that the resulting progression forms **(a)** an arithmetic sequence, and **(b)** a geometric sequence.

13. $3, 6,$ __?__   15. __?__ $, 2, 4$
14. $5, -10,$ __?__   16. __?__ $, 3, -9$

Use the table on page 232 as needed to state the first three terms of the geometric sequence whose first term and common ratio are given.

17. $a_1 = 6, r = 6$ 19. $a_1 = 3, r = 3$ 21. $a_1 = \frac{1}{2}, r = \frac{1}{2}$
18. $a_1 = 36, r = 6$ 20. $a_1 = 27, r = 3$ 22. $a_1 = \frac{2}{3}, r = \frac{2}{3}$

WRITTEN EXERCISES Find the first four terms of the given geometric sequence.

A
1. $a_1 = 1, r = 4$ 3. $a_1 = \frac{1}{2}, r = -3$ 5. $a_1 = \frac{27}{4}, r = \frac{2}{3}$
2. $a_1 = 2, r = 3$ 4. $a_1 = -2, r = \frac{1}{3}$ 6. $a_1 = \frac{8}{25}, r = \frac{5}{2}$

Find the nth term of the indicated geometric sequence for the given value of n.

7. $a_1 = 3, r = -2, n = 5$ 9. $a_1 = 2, r = -\frac{1}{9}, n = 6$
8. $a_1 = 15, r = -1, n = 21$ 10. $a_1 = -3, r = \frac{1}{4}, n = 5$

Find the specified term in the given geometric sequence.

B
11. Eighth, in $\frac{1}{16}, -\frac{1}{8}, \frac{1}{4}, \ldots$ 13. Ninth, in $20, -2, 0.2, \ldots$
12. Sixth, in $1, 4, 16, \ldots$ 14. Seventh, in $0.0003, 0.03, 3, \ldots$

C
15. Use the table on page 232 to determine x if $2^x = 1,048,576$. (*Hint:* Find 1,048,576 in the table.)

16. Use the table on page 232 to determine x if $3^x = 59,049$. (*Hint:* See Exercise 15.)

17. If $a_1, a_2, \ldots, a_n$ is a geometric sequence, is $a_n, a_{n-1}, \ldots, a_2, a_1$ also a geometric sequence? Justify your answer.

18. If $a_1, a_2, a_3, \ldots$ is a geometric sequence, is $a_1, a_3, a_5, \ldots$ also a geometric sequence? Justify your answer.

SEQUENCES AND SERIES 233

PROBLEMS A

1. If you were given a gift of $1 on your first birthday, and the gift was doubled on each following birthday, how much would you receive on your twenty-first birthday? (*Hint:* Use the fact that $2^{20} = (2^4)^5 = 16^5$ together with the table on page 232.)

2. How many ancestors of the eleventh generation does a person have, assuming that there is no duplication?

3. There are seven forests; in each are seven owls. Each owl kills seven mice. Each mouse would have eaten seven ears of corn. Each ear of corn will produce seven measures of grain. How much grain is saved?

4. A large company has a telephone communication system in the event of a blizzard in which one person calls five persons of Group A, each of whom then calls five persons of Group B. Each of these twenty-five persons then calls five persons of Group C, and so on through Groups D and E. How many persons are there in Group E?

5. A man sends out four letters on Saturday, with instructions to the recipients to write letters to two friends on the following Saturday, asking them to do likewise. If there are no duplications and no one breaks the chain, how many letters are sent on the sixth Saturday?

6. The value of a certain rare coin increases by one-tenth each year. If the coin is worth $3.00 now, what will be its approximate value in 5 years?

B

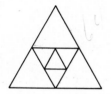

7. A side of an equilateral triangle is 64 centimeters long. A second equilateral triangle is inscribed in it by joining the midpoints of the sides of the first triangle. The process is continued, as shown in the accompanying diagram. Find the perimeter of the sixth *inscribed* equilateral triangle.

8. A tank contains 5000 cubic centimeters of gas. On its first stroke, a pump removes $\frac{1}{5}$ of the gas, leaving $\frac{4}{5}$ of 5000 cubic centimeters of gas in the tank. On the second stroke, the pump removes $\frac{1}{5}$ of the remaining gas, and so on. How much gas is left in the tank after the sixth stroke of the pump?

In Exercises 9–11 use the following compound-interest law: P dollars earning interest at $r\%$ $\left(\dfrac{r}{100}\right)$ per year compounded d times a year amounts to $P\left(1 + \dfrac{r}{100d}\right)^{d}$ at the end of one year and to $P\left(1 + \dfrac{r}{100d}\right)^{nd}$ at the end of n years.

9. Explain why the successive amounts computed at the end of each interest period according to the compound-interest law form a geometric progression. What is the common ratio of the progression?

10. The interest rate in a certain bank is 8% compounded semiannually. If you deposit $10,000 in an account and make no other deposits or withdrawals, how much money will be in your account at the end of two years?

11. Find the compound interest due at the end of 5 years if $2000 is invested at 10% compounded annually.

7-5   *geometric means*

The terms between two given terms of a geometric sequence are called geometric means between the given terms. For example, in the sequence

$$-2, 6, -18, 54, -162,$$

$6, -18,$ and 54 are the three geometric means between -2 and -162.

EXAMPLE 1   **Find the two geometric means between the terms 3 and 375.**

SOLUTION   Schematically, the sequence looks like this: 3, _____, _____, 375. To determine r, replace a_1 with "3," a_n with "375," and n with "4" in

$$a_n = a_1 r^{n-1}$$
$$375 = 3r^{4-1}$$
$$125 = r^3$$
$$r = 5 \text{ (from the table on page 232 or from memory)}$$

To complete the sequence, multiply 3 by 5 and the result by 5:

$$3, 15, 75, 375.$$

$\therefore$ the required means are 15 and 75. **Answer.**

EXAMPLE 2   **Find the second term of a geometric sequence whose third term is 36 and whose fifth term is 4. Give all possible correct answers.**

SOLUTION   A diagram of the sequence is _____, _____, 36, _____, 4.

1. To find r, determine the common ratio of the sequence whose first term is 36 and whose third term is 4:

$$a_3 = a_1 r^{3-1}$$
$$4 = 36r^2$$
$$\tfrac{1}{9} = r^2$$
$$r = \tfrac{1}{3} \quad \text{or} \quad r = -\tfrac{1}{3}$$

2. Working from the term 36 with a common ratio of $\tfrac{1}{3}$, you find that the sequence is

$$324, 108, 36, 12, 4;$$

if the common ratio is $-\tfrac{1}{3}$, the sequence is

$$324, -108, 36, -12, 4.$$

$\therefore$ the second term is either 108 or -108. **Answer.**

Examples 1 and 2 on page 235 illustrate the two situations that occur when you wish to solve over $\mathfrak{R}$ an equation of the form

$$r^n = b,$$

where n is a positive integer and b is a positive real number. In case n is odd, the equation has one real root, which is a positive number. Thus, the equation

$$r^3 = 125 \text{ has the single real root 5.}$$

In case n is even, the equation has two real roots, one a positive number and the other a negative number. Both roots have the same absolute value. For instance,

$$r^2 = \tfrac{1}{9} \text{ has the two real roots } \tfrac{1}{3} \text{ and } -\tfrac{1}{3}.$$

Now suppose that b is a negative number. For example, what are the roots in $\mathfrak{R}$ of

$$r^3 = -125?$$

Do you see that the one and only real root is -5? On the other hand,

$$r^2 = -\tfrac{1}{9}$$

has no real root because the square of every real number is either 0 or a positive number.

The preceding discussion suggests the following theorem, which we shall accept without proof.

Theorem. For all real numbers b:

1. If n is a positive odd integer, then the equation $r^n = b$ has one and only one real root.
2. If n is a positive even integer, then $r^n = b$ has:
   - i. one real root if b is 0;
   - ii. two real roots with the same absolute value if b is a positive number;
   - iii. no real root if b is a negative number.

A single geometric mean inserted between two numbers is called the geometric mean or mean proportional of the numbers. If the real number m is the geometric mean of two nonzero real numbers a and b, then a, m, b is a geometric sequence and

$$\frac{m}{a} = \frac{b}{m}.$$
$$\therefore m^2 = ab.$$

Since m^2 is positive, a and b must be both positive or both negative. If both a and b are positive, then the geometric mean of the numbers is usually defin‿d to be the *positive* root of the equation $m^2 = ab$, whereas if both a and b are negative, then their geometric mean is the *negative* root of the equation.

EXAMPLE 3   Find the geometric mean of **18 and 50.**

SOLUTION   The required mean satisfies the equation $m^2 = 18 \cdot 50$, or

$$m^2 = 900.$$
$$m = 30 \quad \text{or} \quad m = -30.$$

$\therefore$ the geometric mean of 18 and 50 is 30. **Answer.**

ORAL EXERCISES   In Exercises 1–10 let m denote the geometric mean of the given numbers. State **(a)** the value of m^2, and **(b)** the value of m.

EXAMPLE $-2, -8$

SOLUTION   a. $m^2 = 16$ b. $m = -4$

1. 2, 18   3. $-4, -1$ 5. $\frac{1}{2}, 50$ 7. $-2, -50$ 9. $a^2, a^2 b^4$
2. 1, 9   4. $-4, -16$ 6. $-\frac{2}{3}, -6$ 8. $\frac{5}{6}, 30$ 10. $a^2, 4$

In Exercises 11–16 find all the real roots of the given equation. You may use the table on page 232.

11. $x^3 = 64$ 13. $x^2 = 64$ 15. $x^5 = -243$
12. $x^3 = -125$ 14. $x^4 = 625$ 16. $x^4 = -256$

17. Explain why there is no real number which is a geometric mean of the numbers -1 and 9.

18. Explain why 0 is the geometric mean of any real number and 0.

WRITTEN EXERCISES   Find the common ratio of a geometric sequence of real numbers having the indicated terms. Give all possible correct answers.

A   1. $a_1 = 3, a_4 = 24$ 5. $a_2 = 3, a_4 = 147$
    2. $a_1 = -2, a_4 = 54$ 6. $a_3 = -4, a_5 = -1$
    3. $a_1 = 108, a_4 = -4$ 7. $a_3 = -2, a_7 = -2$
    4. $a_1 = 40, a_4 = 5$ 8. $a_5 = 17, a_9 = 272$

9–16. Write the first five terms of each geometric series having the terms indicated in Exercises 1–8.

Insert the given number of real geometric means between the given numbers and write the resulting geometric sequence. Give all possible correct answers.

17. Two, between 1 and 125
18. Two, between -1 and -27
19. Two, between $-\frac{1}{2}$ and $\frac{1}{16}$
20. Two, between 6 and $-\frac{3}{32}$
21. Three, between $-\frac{2}{9}$ and -18
22. Three, between $\frac{3}{25}$ and $\frac{25}{27}$
23. Three, between $\frac{2}{9}$ and $\frac{9}{128}$
24. Three, between $-\frac{5}{8}$ and $-\frac{2}{125}$

B 25. Which term in the geometric progression $\frac{1}{24}, -\frac{1}{6}, \frac{2}{3}, \ldots$ is $\frac{512}{3}$?

26. Which term in the geometric progression $-80, 20, -5, \ldots$ is $\frac{5}{64}$?

27. The first term of a geometric sequence is 162, the common ratio is $\frac{1}{3}$, and there is a term $a_n = \frac{2}{9}$. What is the value of n?

28. If the first term of a geometric sequence is -5 and the common ratio is 4, for what value of n is $a_n = -1280$?

29. If the third term of a geometric sequence is $\frac{1}{4}$ and the common ratio is 2, what is the ninth term?

30. The fifth term of a geometric sequence is $\frac{3}{4}$ and the common ratio is $\frac{3}{2}$. What is the first term?

31. The seventh term of a geometric sequence is 1875 and the fifth term is 75. What is the first term?

32. If the fourth term of a geometric sequence is $\frac{5}{3}$ and the seventh term is $-\frac{625}{81}$, what is the third term?

33. A dealer bought a painting for $20,000 and three years later sold it for $26,620. Assuming that the value increased geometrically each year, find the average rate per year at which the value of the painting increased.

34. An investor purchased some Amalgamated Petroleum Enterprises stock for $40,000 and two years later sold it for $31,684. Assuming that the value decreased geometrically each year, find the average rate per year at which the value of the stock decreased.

35. Show that if b is the geometric mean of a and c, then b^2 is the geometric mean of a^2 and c^2.

36. From the result of Exercise 35 deduce that the squares of the terms of a geometric progression also form a geometric progression.

C 37. Show that the reciprocals of the terms of a geometric sequence in which $a_1 \neq 0$ and $r \neq 0$ also form a geometric sequence.

38. Show that if $a_1, a_2, a_3, \ldots$ and $b_1, b_2, b_3, \ldots$ are geometric sequences, then $a_1b_1, a_2b_2, a_3b_3, \ldots$ also is a geometric sequence.

39. a. Explain why the geometric mean of a^2 and b^2 is $|ab|$.

b. Then prove that if $|a| \neq |b|$, the arithmetic mean of a^2 and b^2 is greater than the geometric mean of a^2 and b^2. [*Hint:* $(|a| - |b|)^2 > 0$.]

40. Use the result of Exercise 39 to prove that for any three different positive real numbers a, b, and c,

$$(a^2 + b^2)(b^2 + c^2)(c^2 + a^2) > 8a^2b^2c^2.$$

7–6 *geometric series*

A series, such as $3 + 6 + 12 + 24$, whose terms are in geometric progression is called a *geometric series*. To find an expression for the sum S_n of a geometric series of n terms, first write S_n in expanded form and below it write the product of $-r$ and S_n as follows:

$$S_n = a_1 + a_1r + a_1r^2 + \cdots + a_1r^{n-2} + a_1r^{n-1}$$
$$-rS_n = \quad\quad - a_1r - a_1r^2 - a_1r^3 - \cdots \quad - a_1r^{n-1} - a_1r^n$$

Then add the corresponding members of these equations to obtain

$$S_n - rS_n = a_1 + (a_1r_1 - a_1r_1) + (a_1r^2 - a_1r^2) + \cdots$$
$$+ (a_1r^{n-1} - a_1r^{n-1}) - a_1r^n.$$

Since $a_1r - a_1r = 0$, $a_1r^2 - a_1r^2 = 0$, and so on, you have

$$S_n - rS_n = a_1 - a_1r^n,$$
$$(1 - r)S_n = a_1 - a_1r^n.$$
$$\therefore S_n = \frac{a_1 - a_1r^n}{1 - r}, \quad r \neq 1.$$

EXAMPLE 1 **Find the sum of the terms of the sequence**

3, 6, 12, 24.

SOLUTION Replace a_1 with "3," r with "2," and n with "4" in $S_n = \dfrac{a_1 - a_1r^n}{1 - r}$:

$$S_4 = \frac{3 - 3(2)^4}{1 - 2}$$

$$S_4 = \frac{3 - 48}{-1} = \frac{-45}{-1} = 45$$

$$\therefore S_4 = 45. \quad \textbf{Answer.}$$

Note that $a_1 r^n = r(a_1 r^{n-1}) = ra_n$. Hence, from $S_n = \dfrac{a_1 - a_1 r^n}{1 - r}$,

$$S_n = \dfrac{a_1 - ra_n}{1 - r}, \qquad r \neq 1.$$

EXAMPLE 2   Find the sum of a geometric series whose first term is 2, whose last (nth) term is 13122, and whose common ratio is 3.

SOLUTION   Replace a_1 with "2," a_n with "13122" and r with "3" in $S_n = \dfrac{a_1 - ra_n}{1 - r}$.

$$S_n = \dfrac{2 - (3)(13122)}{1 - (3)}$$

$$= \dfrac{2 - 39366}{-2} = 19682. \quad \textbf{Answer.}$$

The following theorem summarizes the results obtained in this section.

Theorem. If S_n is the sum of the first n terms of a geometric sequence whose first term is a_1, whose common ratio is r, and whose nth term is a_n, then

$$S_n = \dfrac{a_1 - a_1 r^n}{1 - r} \quad \text{and} \quad S_n = \dfrac{a_1 - ra_n}{1 - r}, \qquad r \neq 1.$$

ORAL EXERCISES   State whether the given series is an arithmetic series, a geometric series, both, or neither.

1. $1 + 2 + 3 + 4 + 5$
2. $1 + 1 + 1 + 1 + 1$
3. $1 - 1 + 1 - 1 + 1$

4. $1 + 2 + 3 + 5 + 8$
5. $2 + 6 + 18 + 54$
6. $-9 + 3 - 1 + \frac{1}{3} - \frac{1}{9}$

In Exercises 7–14 name the first term, the common ratio, the number of terms, and the last term of the given geometric series.

7. $40 - 20 + 10 - 5$

8. $300 + 30 + 3 + 0.3$

9. $\displaystyle\sum_{k=1}^{5} 3(-1)^{k-1}$

11. $\displaystyle\sum_{i=4}^{6} 2^i$

13. $\displaystyle\sum_{j=1}^{4} 9(-\tfrac{1}{3})^{j-1}$

10. $\displaystyle\sum_{k=1}^{4} 2(3)^{k-1}$

12. $\displaystyle\sum_{i=0}^{4} 5(\tfrac{1}{3})^i$

14. $\displaystyle\sum_{j=-1}^{1} -2(\tfrac{1}{4})^j$

State the numeral with which you would replace the __?__ so that the resulting series is **(a)** arithmetic and **(b)** geometric.

15. $7 + 14 +$ __?__

16. $-2 + 4 +$ __?__

17. $2 +$ __?__ $+ 8$

18. __?__ $+ 5 + 10$

WRITTEN EXERCISES   Find the sum of the terms of the indicated geometric sequence.

A
1. $2, 6, 18, \ldots$ to 5 terms
2. $5, 10, 20, \ldots$ to 6 terms
3. $-2, -10, -50, \ldots$ to 6 terms
4. $-12, -36, -108, \ldots$ to 5 terms

5. $1, -4, 16, \ldots$ to 6 terms
6. $-1, 3, -9, \ldots$ to 6 terms
7. $\frac{1}{27}, \frac{1}{9}, \frac{1}{3}, \ldots$ to 8 terms
8. $\frac{3}{16}, \frac{3}{4}, 3, \ldots$ to 7 terms

Find the sum of the given geometric series.

9. $\displaystyle\sum_{i=1}^{5} 3(2)^{i-1}$

10. $\displaystyle\sum_{i=1}^{4} 5(3)^{i-1}$

11. $\displaystyle\sum_{k=1}^{6} -2(\tfrac{1}{4})^{k-1}$

12. $\displaystyle\sum_{k=1}^{5} 3(-\tfrac{1}{2})^{k-1}$

13. $\displaystyle\sum_{j=1}^{5} 9(-\tfrac{1}{3})^{j-1}$

14. $\displaystyle\sum_{j=1}^{10} 2^{j-1}$

In Exercises 15–26 three of the five real numbers a_1, a_n, r, n, and S_n for a geometric sequence are given. Find the two numbers that are not given.

B
15. $a_1 = 8, r = -3, n = 5$
16. $a_1 = -5, r = 2, n = 7$
17. $a_n = 225, r = 5, n = 5$
18. $a_n = \frac{3}{2}, r = 9, n = 4$
19. $r = \frac{2}{5}, n = 4, S_n = 40\frac{3}{5}$
20. $r = -2, n = 5, S_n = -33$

21. $a_1 = \frac{5}{9}, r = -3, S_n = -\frac{100}{9}$
22. $a_1 = 5, r = -2, a_n = 80$
23. $a_1 = 3, a_n = 48, S_n = 33$
24. $a_1 = -56, a_n = \frac{7}{4}, n = 6$
25. $a_1 = -2, n = 3, S_n = -\frac{7}{2}$
26. $a_1 = 3, n = 3, S_n = \frac{19}{3}$

$$\left[\textit{Hint:} \text{ For Exercises 25 and 26, use the fact that } \frac{1-r^3}{1-r} = 1 + r + r^2. \right]$$

In Exercises 27–30 let S_n be the sum of the first n terms of a geometric sequence whose first term, nth term, and common ratio are a_1, a_n, and r, respectively ($r \neq 1$). Show that:

C
27. $a_1 = S_n(1 - r) + ra_n$

28. $a_1 = \dfrac{S_n(1 - r)}{1 - r^n}$

29. $r = \dfrac{S_n - a_1}{S_n - a_n}$ $(S_n \neq a_n)$

30. $a_n = \dfrac{a_1 - S_n(1 - r)}{r}$ $(r \neq 0)$

PROBLEMS

A

1. A string of licorice 3 meters long was passed in succession to 5 boys. Each took $\frac{1}{5}$ of the licorice which was in the string when he received it. How long was the string when it reached the last boy?

2. If there have been no intermarriages, how many ancestors have you had in the eight generations preceding you?

3. In a lottery, the first ticket drawn paid a prize of $30,000. Each succeeding ticket paid half as much as the preceding one. If six tickets were drawn, what was the total of prize money paid?

4. At the age of 65, a woman began receiving yearly payments from a pension fund. On each succeeding birthday, she received 90% of the amount she received the preceding year. If the amount she received at age 69 brought the total to $40,951, how much did she receive at the age of 65?

5. A side of an equilateral triangle is 40 centimeters long. The midpoints of the sides are joined to form an inscribed equilateral triangle, and the process is continued. Find the sum of the perimeters of the first six equilateral triangles in the resulting figure.

6. A certain circular saw makes a total of 131 revolutions in the first five seconds after the motor is turned off. In any one second, its speed is three-fifths of its speed during the preceding second. What was its speed in revolutions per second at the time the motor was turned off?

7. The half-life of the Uranium 230 isotope is 20.8 days, that is, one-half of a given amount of Uranium 230 decomposes every 20.8 days. How much of an initial amount of 1000 grams of the isotope will be left after 208 days?

B

8. Show that by depositing $100 at the beginning of each quarter-year in a credit union that pays interest at the rate of 8% per year compounded quarterly, you will have

$$\frac{100[(1.02)^5 - 1.02]}{0.02}$$

dollars before depositing $100 at the beginning of your second year.

9. At the end of each half-year, a bank pays 6% per year interest on money left on deposit from the beginning of the half-year. Suppose that you wish to accumulate $2000 by the end of a three-year period during which you deposit a fixed number d of dollars in your account at the beginning of each half-year and make no withdrawals. Show that d must satisfy the equation

$$2000 = \frac{d[(1.03)^7 - 1.03]}{0.03}.$$

10. "As I was going to St. Ives, I met a man with seven wives. Each wife had seven sacks. Each sack had seven cats. Each cat had seven kits. Kits, cats, sacks, and wives, how many were going to St. Ives?" Of course, none of them were going to St. Ives, since the speaker *met* them on his way there. But how many of them were there?

11. With one grain of wheat on the first square of a chess board, two on the second, four on the third, and so on, the amount on a square being doubled for each successive square, how many grains in all would there be on the first twenty squares? How many on the twenty-first square alone?

SELF-TEST 2   Give the meaning of each of the following.

1. geometric progression
2. common ratio

3. geometric means
4. geometric series

Objective 1, page 230

5. Find the first four terms of a geometric sequence if the first term is $\frac{5}{2}$ and the common ratio is $\frac{2}{3}$.
6. Find the sixth term of the geometric sequence $-1, -8, -64, \dots$.

Objective 2, page 230

7. Insert three real geometric means between 8 and $\frac{1}{2}$. Give all possible correct answers.

Objective 3, page 230

8. Find the sum of the geometric series

$$\sum_{i=1}^{5} 375(-\tfrac{1}{5})^{i-1}.$$

Objective 4, page 230

9. Each year, a manufacturing plant increased its production by 10% of the amount it produced the preceding year. If it produced 500,000 units the first year, how many units did it produce the fourth year?
10. If the half-life of an unstable element is 12 minutes, how much of an original amount of 32 milligrams would be left after one hour?

Check your answers with those printed at the back of the book.

programming in BASIC

EXERCISES

1. Write a program that will print out the first n terms of a geometric sequence when you input values of a_1, r, n.
2. Write a program that will print out the nth term of a geometric sequence when you input values of a_1, r, n.
3. Write a program that will print out the first n terms of a geometric series and the sum of those terms when you input values of a_1, r, n.
4. Write a program that will print out the arithmetic mean and the geometric mean of two numbers, p and q.

careers *environmental protection*

The engineer above is testing the contents of wastewater with a carbon infrared analyzer. The picture below illustrates another environmental concern—wildlife preservation. The conservationist is stocking a lake with trout.

Concern over the pollution of the environment has increased greatly in recent years, and the number of careers in environmental protection has increased as well. Air-pollution control is one area of environmental protection. This field includes determining the effects of pollutants on human health and the environment, setting standards for acceptable levels of pollutants, enforcing those standards, and developing ways to meet them. Similar tasks occur in the fields of water- and noise-pollution control.

Other functions of environmental workers include: the management of solid wastes—recycling what can be used and properly disposing of other materials; the study of pesticides—their efficiency, side effects, and safety level; and the study of the effects of exposure to radiation for long periods of time. Workers in all of these fields are trying to make the earth a better and safer place to live.

EXAMPLE   In order to meet emission standards set by the Environmental Protection Agency, a certain company must remove at least 80% of the particles from the smoke pouring out of its smokestack. If each filter removes 20% of the particles passing through it, how many of these filters will the company have to install in its smokestack?

SOLUTION   Let x be the amount of particles originally in the smoke. After passing through the first filter, there are $0.8x$ particles; after passing through the second, $(0.8)(0.8)x$ particles, and so on. As you can see, this is a geometric sequence with $r = 0.8$:

(the amount after the first filter)	and	(the amount after the nth filter)
$a_1 = 0.8x$		$a_n = (0.8)^{n-1}a_1 = (0.8)^n x$

Thus, the number of filters needed will be n, where

$$(0.8)^n x \leq 0.20x.$$

Since

$$(0.8)^7 = 0.2097152 \quad \text{and} \quad (0.8)^8 = 0.16777216,$$

the company will need 8 filters.

infinite sequences and series

Objectives | After completing the next two sections, you should be able to:
1. Find the absolute value of the difference between the limit of a convergent sequence and a term in the sequence.
2. Find the sum of a convergent geometric series.

7-7   *limit of a sequence*

Figure 1 pictures the first few terms of the infinite sequence

$$1, 1\tfrac{1}{2}, 1\tfrac{3}{4}, 1\tfrac{7}{8}, \ldots, 2 - (\tfrac{1}{2})^{n-1}, \ldots$$

Figure 1

n	a_n	$\lvert 2 - a_n \rvert$
1	1	1
2	$1\tfrac{1}{2}$	$\tfrac{1}{2}$
3	$1\tfrac{3}{4}$	$\tfrac{1}{4}$
4	$1\tfrac{7}{8}$	$\tfrac{1}{8}$
. . .	. . .	. . .

This figure suggests that the graphs of the terms of the given sequence eventually crowd in on the graph of 2. Notice that if you think of each term of the sequence as an approximation of 2, then the error of approximation, that is, the absolute value of the error that you make in considering a_n to be 2, is $(\tfrac{1}{2})^{n-1}$. As shown in the table at the left, this error is halved each time n is increased by 1. Therefore, by choosing n large enough, you can make the error less than any given positive number, however small. For this reason, we say that the *limit* of the sequence is 2, and we write

$$\lim_{n \to \infty} [2 - (\tfrac{1}{2})^{n-1}] = 2,$$

read, "the limit of $2 - (\tfrac{1}{2})^{n-1}$ as n increases without bound is 2." An infinite sequence which has a limit is said to converge or to be convergent.

EXAMPLE   Find the limit of the sequence $2, 1\tfrac{1}{2}, 1\tfrac{1}{3}, 1\tfrac{1}{4}, \ldots, 1 + \dfrac{1}{n}, \ldots$

SOLUTION   Make a sketch showing the first few terms of the sequence on a number line, as shown below.

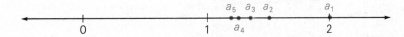

The diagram suggests that the limit is 1; in fact, the error made in considering the *n*th term a_n to be 1 is $\lvert a_n - 1 \rvert$, or $\dfrac{1}{n}$, and $\dfrac{1}{n}$ is as small a positive number as you like if n is great enough.

$$\therefore \lim_{n \to \infty} \left(1 + \frac{1}{n}\right) = 1. \quad \text{Answer.}$$

Notice how the successive terms of the sequence

$$1, 1\tfrac{1}{2}, 1\tfrac{3}{4}, 1\tfrac{7}{8}, \ldots, 2 - (\tfrac{1}{2})^{n-1}, \ldots$$

compare with each other. Because

$$1 \le 1\tfrac{1}{2} \le 1\tfrac{3}{4} \le 1\tfrac{7}{8} \ldots,$$

you say that the sequence is *nondecreasing*. Any sequence in which each term is less than or equal to the following term is called a nondecreasing sequence.

The sequence

$$2, 1\tfrac{1}{2}, 1\tfrac{1}{3}, 1\tfrac{1}{4}, \ldots, 1 + \frac{1}{n}, \ldots,$$

on the other hand, is *nonincreasing*, because

$$2 \ge 1\tfrac{1}{2} \ge 1\tfrac{1}{3} \ge 1\tfrac{1}{4} \ldots.$$

Any sequence in which each term is greater than or equal to the following term is called a nonincreasing sequence.

Notice also that each term of the sequence

$$1, 1\tfrac{1}{2}, 1\tfrac{3}{4}, 1\tfrac{7}{8}, \ldots, 2 - (\tfrac{1}{2})^{n-1}, \ldots$$

is less than 2 in absolute value, and that each term of the sequence

$$2, 1\tfrac{1}{2}, 1\tfrac{1}{3}, 1\tfrac{1}{4}, \ldots, 1 + \frac{1}{n}, \ldots$$

is less than or equal to 2 in absolute value. Whenever there exists a number which equals or exceeds the *absolute value* of *every* term of a sequence, you say that the sequence is bounded by the number. Thus, each of the sequences given above is bounded by 2. Of course, each of the sequences is also bounded by 10, for example.

The fact that both of the sequences

$$1, 1\tfrac{1}{2}, 1\tfrac{3}{4}, 1\tfrac{7}{8}, \ldots, 2 - (\tfrac{1}{2})^{n-1}, \ldots$$

and

$$2, 1\tfrac{1}{2}, 1\tfrac{1}{3}, 1\tfrac{1}{4}, \ldots, 1 + \frac{1}{n}, \ldots$$

are convergent illustrates the last axiom needed to characterize the set $\mathcal{R}$ of real numbers. This assumption is stated below.

Axiom of Completeness

Every bounded, nondecreasing (or nonincreasing) sequence of real numbers converges, and its limit is a real number.

Not all infinite sequences converge. An infinite sequence that does not have a limit is said to diverge or to be divergent. For example, the sequence

$$3, 9, 27, \ldots, 3^n, \ldots$$

diverges because it contains terms that are arbitrarily large in absolute value. Do you see that this sequence is nondecreasing but that it is not bounded? The sequence

$$1, -1, 1, -1, \ldots, (-1)^{n-1}, \ldots$$

is also divergent because its terms are alternately 1 and -1. Do you see that this sequence is bounded, but that it is neither nondecreasing nor nonincreasing?

ORAL EXERCISES

In Exercises 1–10 state whether or not the given sequence seems to be convergent. If so, make a reasonable guess of the limit.

1. $\dfrac{1}{3}, \dfrac{1}{9}, \dfrac{1}{27}, \ldots, \dfrac{1}{3^n}, \ldots$

2. $-1, 2, -3, \ldots, (-1)^n n, \ldots$

3. $1, -\dfrac{1}{2}, \dfrac{1}{3}, \ldots, (-1)^{n-1}\dfrac{1}{n}, \ldots$

4. $0, \dfrac{1}{2}, \dfrac{2}{3}, \ldots, \dfrac{n-1}{n}, \ldots$

5. $1, 3, 5, \ldots, 2n - 1, \ldots$

6. $2, -4, 6, \ldots, (-1)^{n+1}2n, \ldots$

7. $\dfrac{1}{2}, \dfrac{4}{5}, \dfrac{9}{10}, \ldots, \dfrac{n^2}{n^2 + 1}, \ldots$

8. $2\frac{2}{3}, 2\frac{8}{9}, 2\frac{26}{27}, \ldots, 3 - (\frac{1}{3})^n, \ldots$

9. $0, 1, 0, 1, \ldots, \frac{1}{2} + (-1)^n\frac{1}{2}, \ldots$

10. $1\frac{1}{2}, -1\frac{1}{3}, 1\frac{1}{4}, \ldots, (-1)^{n+1}\left(1 + \dfrac{1}{n + 1}\right), \ldots$

11–20. State whether the sequences given in Oral Exercises 1–10 are nondecreasing, nonincreasing, or neither.

21–30. State whether or not the sequences given in Oral Exercises 1–10 are bounded.

31. Can a sequence be convergent even though it is neither nondecreasing nor nonincreasing? Give an example or a reason.

32. Can a sequence be convergent even though it is not bounded? Give an example or a reason.

WRITTEN EXERCISES In Exercises 1–10 a formula for the *n*th term a_n, and the limit L, of an infinite sequence are given. Find a_n and $|L - a_n|$ for $n = 1, 2, 3,$ and 4, and then write a general formula for $|L - a_n|$.

EXAMPLE $a_n = 4 - (-1)^n \left(\dfrac{1}{n^2}\right); L = 4$

SOLUTION

n	a_n	$\lvert L - a_n\rvert$
1	5	$\lvert 4 - 5\rvert = 1$
2	$3\frac{3}{4}$	$\lvert 4 - 3\frac{3}{4}\rvert = \frac{1}{4}$
3	$4\frac{1}{9}$	$\lvert 4 - 4\frac{1}{9}\rvert = \frac{1}{9}$
4	$3\frac{15}{16}$	$\lvert 4 - 3\frac{15}{16}\rvert = \frac{1}{16}$

$$|L - a_n| = \left| 4 - 4 + (-1)^n \left(\dfrac{1}{n^2}\right)\right|$$

$$= \dfrac{1}{n^2}. \text{ Answer.}$$

A

1. $a_n = 5 + \dfrac{1}{n^2}; L = 5$

2. $a_n = -3 - \dfrac{1}{n}; L = -3$

3. $a_n = 2 - (0.3)^n; L = 2$

4. $a_n = -1 + (0.6)^n; L = -1$

5. $a_n = 1 + \dfrac{n + 1}{n}; L = 2$

6. $a_n = \dfrac{n^2 - 1}{n^2}; L = 1$

7. $a_n = 4 - (\frac{1}{3})^n; L = 4$

8. $a_n = 3 + (\frac{1}{4})^n; L = 3$

9. $a_n = 0.3[1 + (0.2)^n]; L = 0.3$

10. $a_n = 7.2[1 - (0.1)^n]; L = 7.2$

B 11–20. In Written Exercises 1–10 find the least positive value of *n* for which $|L - a_n| < \frac{1}{10}$.

Sophie Germain
1776–1831

Sophie Germain became interested in mathematics as a child in Paris. Confined to her library during the French Revolution and the Terror, she studied mathematics against her family's objections. She became a student of the mathematician Lagrange, and later won the grand prize offered by the Academy of Science for her presentation of the mathematical theory of the vibration of elastic surfaces. Her work led to her recognition as one of the founders of the field of mathematical physics. Sophie Germain won the respect of other mathematicians of the time. She attended the meetings of the Institut de France, but was denied membership in the Academy of Science because only men were accepted.

7–8 *infinite geometric series*

Figure 2 pictures the numbers

$$1, \; 1 + \tfrac{1}{2}, \; 1 + \tfrac{1}{2} + \tfrac{1}{4}, \; 1 + \tfrac{1}{2} + \tfrac{1}{4} + \tfrac{1}{8},$$

and suggests three facts:

1. The more terms you add in the infinite series

$$1 + \tfrac{1}{2} + \tfrac{1}{4} + \tfrac{1}{8} + \tfrac{1}{16} + \cdots + (\tfrac{1}{2})^{n-1} + \cdots,$$

the greater is the sum obtained.
2. The sum never exceeds 2, no matter how many terms you add.
3. If enough terms are added, the sum will approximate 2 as closely as you may demand.

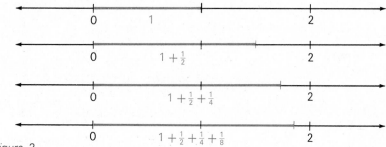

Figure 2

You can never add all the terms, so that you cannot refer to the "sum of the infinite series" without first defining what you mean by such a sum. To define the sum of the *infinite geometric series*

$$1 + \tfrac{1}{2} + \tfrac{1}{4} + \tfrac{1}{8} + \tfrac{1}{16} + \cdots + (\tfrac{1}{2})^{n-1} + \cdots,$$

consider the sequence of *partial sums*

$$S_1 = 1, \; S_2 = 1 + \tfrac{1}{2}, \; S_3 = 1 + \tfrac{1}{2} + \tfrac{1}{4},$$

and in general

$$S_n = 1 + \tfrac{1}{2} + \tfrac{1}{4} + \cdots + (\tfrac{1}{2})^{n-1} = \sum_{i=1}^{n} (\tfrac{1}{2})^{i-1}, \qquad n \geq 1.$$

Since S_n is the sum of the first n terms of a geometric sequence whose first term is 1 and whose common ratio is $\tfrac{1}{2}$, you have:

$$S_n = \frac{[1 - 1(\tfrac{1}{2})^n]}{1 - \cdot \tfrac{1}{2}} = 2 - \frac{1}{2^{n-1}}$$

Hence (see page 245), $\qquad \lim_{n \to \infty} S_n = 2.$

Accordingly, we *define* the sum of this infinite series to be 2, and we write

$$1 + \tfrac{1}{2} + \tfrac{1}{4} + \cdots + (\tfrac{1}{2})^{n-1} + \cdots = 2, \quad \text{or} \quad \sum_{i=1}^{\infty} (\tfrac{1}{2})^{i-1} = 2.$$

In general, for any infinite series $a_1 + a_2 + \cdots + a_n + \ldots$,

$$S_n = \sum_{i=1}^{n} a_i$$

is called a partial sum. If the sequence $S_1, S_2, \ldots, S_n, \ldots$ of partial sums converges and if $\lim\limits_{n \to \infty} S_n = S$, then the sum of the infinite series

$$a_1 + a_2 + \cdots + a_n + \cdots$$

is defined to be S. You write

$$\sum_{k=1}^{\infty} a_k = S,$$

and you say that the series converges or is convergent.

On the other hand, if the sequence of partial sums diverges, then the series diverges or is divergent, and its sum is *not* defined. For example, the series

$$1 + 2 + 3 + 4 + \cdots + n + \cdots$$

diverges, because the sequence of partial sums

$$1, 3, 6, 10, \ldots, \frac{n(n + 1)}{2}, \ldots$$

diverges. The series

$$1 - 1 + 1 - 1 + \ldots$$

also is divergent because the sequence of partial sums $1, 0, 1, 0, \ldots$ is a divergent sequence.

Consider each of the following cases for any infinite geometric series,

$$a_1 + a_1 r + a_1 r^2 + \ldots.$$

Case 1. $a_1 = 0$. In this case, every term of the series is 0, so that the series is $0 + 0 + 0 + \ldots$, which has the sum 0.

Case 2. $a_1 \neq 0$ and $r = 1$. In this case, every term of the series is a_1, so that the series is $a_1 + a_1 + a_1 + \ldots$. This series diverges because the sequence of partial sums $a_1, 2a_1, \ldots$ diverges.

Case 3. $a_1 \neq 0$ and $r = -1$. In this case, the terms of the series are alternately a_1 and $-a_1$, so that the series is $a_1 - a_1 + a_1 - a_1 + \ldots$. This series diverges because the sequence of partial sums, $a_1, 0, a_1, 0, \ldots$ diverges.

Case 4. $a_1 \neq 0$ and $|r| \neq 1$. In this case, the nth partial sum is

$$S_n = \frac{a_1}{1 - r} - \frac{a_1}{1 - r} r^n.$$

If $|r| < 1$, then r^n $\left(\text{and therefore, } \left|\frac{a_1}{1 - r} r^n\right|\right)$ can be made to approximate 0 as closely as you wish by taking n great enough. Because $\left|S_n - \frac{a_1}{1 - r}\right| = \left|\frac{a_1}{1 - r} r^n\right|$, it follows that

$$S = \lim_{n \to \infty} S_n = \frac{a_1}{1 - r}, \qquad |r| < 1.$$

If $|r| > 1$, $|r^n|$ increases steadily with n; so r^n does not have a limit as n increases without bound and neither does S_n.

The following theorem summarizes these cases.

Theorem. The infinite geometric series

$$a_1 + a_1 r + a_1 r^2 + \ldots$$

converges and has the sum $\dfrac{a_1}{1 - r}$ if $|r| < 1$. If $a_1 = 0$, the series converges and has the sum 0. If $|r| \geq 1$ and $a_1 \neq 0$, the series diverges.

EXAMPLE Determine the sum of the infinite geometric series

$$\frac{9}{10} + \frac{9}{10^2} + \frac{9}{10^3} + \ldots$$

SOLUTION $a_1 = \dfrac{9}{10}$, $r = \dfrac{1}{10}$, $|r| < 1$. Since $S = \dfrac{a_1}{1 - r}$, you have

$$S = \frac{\frac{9}{10}}{1 - \frac{1}{10}} = \frac{\frac{9}{10}}{\frac{9}{10}} = 1. \quad \text{Answer.}$$

The series $\dfrac{9}{10} + \dfrac{9}{10^2} + \dfrac{9}{10^3} + \ldots$ is often written as the infinite decimal

$0.999 \ldots$, or $0.\overline{9}$, where the bar shows that the indicated digit is repeated without end. Thus, you have

$$0.999 \ldots = 0.\overline{9} = 1$$

and similarly, for example,

$$3.\overline{9} = 4, \qquad 5.6\overline{9} = 5.7, \qquad \text{and} \qquad 0.75\overline{9} = 0.76.$$

State the first term and the common ratio of the given infinite geometric series. Does the series converge?

1. $100 + 50 + 25 + \ldots$

2. $-1 + \frac{1}{3} - \frac{1}{9} + \ldots$

3. $4 - 4 + 4 - \ldots$

4. $2 + 2 + 2 + \ldots$

5. $\frac{1}{1000} - \frac{1}{100} + \frac{1}{10} - \ldots$

6. $\frac{9}{4} + \frac{3}{4} + \frac{1}{4} + \ldots$

7. $30 + 3 + 0.3 + \ldots$

8. $1 + 2 + 4 + \ldots$

9. $2 + 0.002 + 0.000002 + \ldots$

10. $0.7 - 0.07 + 0.007 - \ldots$

11–20. State the value of S_1, S_2, and S_3 for each infinite geometric series in Oral Exercises 1–10.

Give an example that shows that each of the following statements is false.

21. Every infinite geometric series converges.

22. Any infinite geometric series in which the common ratio is a positive number has a positive sum.

23. An infinite geometric series whose first term is positive and less than 1 must converge.

24. An infinite geometric series whose terms are alternately positive and negative numbers cannot diverge.

WRITTEN EXERCISES

A **1–10.** Find the sum of each of the convergent series in Oral Exercises 1–10. If the series is not convergent, so state.

Find the sum of the given infinite geometric series.

11. $\displaystyle\sum_{i=1}^{\infty} -2(\tfrac{1}{3})^{i-1}$

12. $\displaystyle\sum_{i=1}^{\infty} 3(-\tfrac{1}{2})^{i-1}$

13. $\displaystyle\sum_{i=1}^{\infty} 5(\tfrac{2}{3})^{i-1}$

14. $\displaystyle\sum_{j=1}^{\infty} 9(\tfrac{1}{4})^{j-1}$

15. $\displaystyle\sum_{m=1}^{\infty} 7(0.8)^{m-1}$

16. $\displaystyle\sum_{m=1}^{\infty} 6(0.3)^{m-1}$

In Exercises 17–24 two of the three numbers a_1, r, and S for a convergent infinite geometric series are given. Find the number not given.

17. $a_1 = 5$, $r = \frac{1}{3}$

18. $a_1 = -2$, $r = \frac{2}{3}$

19. $a_1 = -3$, $r = -\frac{1}{2}$

20. $a_1 = 7$, $r = -\frac{5}{6}$

21. $a_1 = 0.4$, $r = 0.2$

22. $a_1 = 15$, $r = -0.5$

23. $a_1 = 7$, $S = 11$

24. $r = -\frac{4}{5}$, $S = 20$

In Exercises 25–34 find the value of the given repeating decimal.

EXAMPLE $0.\overline{42}$

SOLUTION $0.\overline{42} = 0.42 + 0.42(0.01) + 0.42(0.01)^2 + \cdots$
$\therefore a_1 = 0.42$ and $r = 0.01$.

$$S = \frac{a_1}{1 - r} = \frac{0.42}{1 - 0.01} = \frac{0.42}{0.99} = \frac{0.03 \times 14}{0.03 \times 33} = \frac{14}{33}$$

$\therefore 0.\overline{42} = \frac{14}{33}$. **Answer.**

25. $0.\overline{4}$ 27. $0.\overline{03}$ 29. $0.\overline{427}$

26. $0.\overline{7}$ 28. $0.\overline{01}$ 30. $0.\overline{316}$

B   31. $3.\overline{2}$ (*Hint:* $3.\overline{2} = 3 + 0.\overline{2}$)   32. $15.\overline{6}$ 33. $1.3\overline{8}$ 34. $2.0\overline{9}$

35. Explain why an infinite arithmetic series with nonzero terms must diverge.

36. Write an infinite geometric series having $\dfrac{1}{1 - x}$ as its sum when it converges, and state the values of x for which it converges.

In Exercises 37 and 38, find the values of x for which the given geometric series converges, and find the sum when the series converges.

37. $5 + 15x + 45x^2 + \cdots$ 38. $2 - \dfrac{x^3}{4} + \dfrac{x^6}{32} - \cdots$

C   39. Show that the sum of a convergent infinite geometric series is positive if a_1 is positive and is negative if a_1 is negative.

40. Show that for any convergent geometric series in which a_1 is positive, $S > \frac{1}{2}a_1$.

PROBLEMS

A   1. A physicist found that a tennis ball dropped on a concrete floor rebounds on each bounce $\frac{2}{3}$ of the height from which it fell. If it is dropped from a height of 50 meters, how far will it travel before coming to rest?

2. A rubber ball dropped from a height of 20 meters rebounded on each bounce $\frac{5}{8}$ of the height from which it fell. How far did it travel before coming to rest?

3. Moving along a straight path, a tortoise traveled 2 meters in 1 minute. In the next minute, he moved 1 meter. Similarly, in each succeeding minute, he traveled half as far as he had in the preceding minute. If the tortoise could keep moving forever in this way, how far would he travel?

4. Air resistance causes the path of each swing (after the first) of a pendulum bob to be 0.9 as long as that of the preceding swing. If the path of the first swing is 15 centimeters long, find the total distance traveled by the bob in coming to rest.

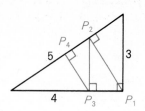

B   **5.** The length of each side of an equilateral triangle is 12 centimeters. The midpoints of its sides are joined to form an inscribed equilateral triangle and the process is continued. Find the sum of the perimeters of the triangles if the process is continued without end.

6. In a right triangle with dimensions of 3 cm, 4 cm, and 5 cm, perpendicular segments $\overline{P_1P_2}$, $\overline{P_2P_3}$, $\overline{P_3P_4}$, and so on, are constructed as indicated at the left. Determine the sum of the lengths of all the constructed perpendicular segments.

C   **7.** If $|x| < 1$, find the sum S of the series $1 + 2x + 3x^2 + 4x^3 + \ldots$. (*Hint:* Consider $S - xS$.)

8. Find the fallacy in the following argument.

Let $S = 1 + 3 + 3^2 + 3^3 + \ldots$
$$= 1 + 3(1 + 3 + 3^2 + \ldots) = 1 + 3 \cdot \frac{1}{1-3} = 1 - \left(\frac{3}{2}\right)$$
$$\therefore S = -\frac{1}{2}.$$

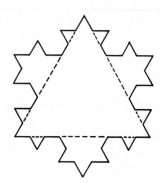

9. A "snowflake" curve is constructed as follows: The sides of an equilateral triangle are trisected, and the middle third of the trisection serves as a base for a new equilateral triangle, following which this segment is deleted from the figure. The process is continued. If the side of the initial equilateral triangle is of length 1, what is the area enclosed by the snowflake curve if the process is continued without end?

10. Show that the figure described in Problem 9 has no perimeter, that is, that the curve is of unbounded length.

SELF-TEST 3   Give the meaning of each of the following.

1. limit of an infinite sequence
2. convergent infinite sequence
3. divergent infinite sequence
4. nondecreasing sequence
5. nonincreasing sequence
6. bounded sequence
7. partial sum of an infinite series
8. sum of an infinite series
9. convergent infinite series
10. divergent infinite series

In Exercises 11 and 12 the nth term a_n and the limit L of an infinite sequence are given. Find a_4, $|L - a_4|$, and $|L - a_n|$.

Objective 1, page 245   **11.** $a_n = 7 - \frac{2}{n^2}$; $L = 7$ **12.** $a_n = \frac{n+2}{2n}$; $L = \frac{1}{2}$

In Exercises 13 and 14 find the sum of the given infinite geometric series.

Objective 2, page 245   **13.** $\frac{1}{2} - \frac{1}{3} + \frac{2}{9} - \ldots$ **14.** $\sum_{j=1}^{\infty} -4(0.6)^j$

Check your answers with those printed at the back of the book.

chapter summary

1. An **arithmetic sequence**, or **arithmetic progression**, is any sequence in which each term after the first is obtained by adding a fixed number, d, called the **common difference**, to the preceding term. For an arithmetic sequence, you have

$$a_{n+1} = a_n + d \quad \text{and} \quad a_n = a_1 + (n-1)d \text{ for } n = 1, 2, 3, \ldots.$$

2. The terms between two given terms of an arithmetic sequence are called **arithmetic means** between the given terms; a single arithmetic mean between two numbers is the **average**, or **the arithmetic mean**, of the two numbers.

3. The sum of the first n terms of a given sequence is the associated series, S_n. For an arithmetic series, you have

$$S_n = \frac{n}{2}(a_1 + a_n) = \frac{n}{2}[2a_1 + (n-1)d].$$

4. You can use the **summation sign** to abbreviate the writing of a series, using an **index** to indicate the **range of summation**. Thus,

$$a_1 + a_2 + \cdots + a_n = \sum_{i=1}^{n} a_i.$$

5. A **geometric sequence**, or **geometric progression**, is any sequence in which each term after the first is the product of the preceding term and a fixed number, r, called the **common ratio**. For a geometric sequence, you have $a_{n+1} = a_n \cdot r$ and $a_n = a_1 r^{n-1}$, $n = 1, 2, 3, \ldots.$

6. The terms between two given terms of a geometric sequence are called **geometric means** between the given terms. A single geometric mean between two numbers is called a **geometric mean** or **mean proportional** of the two numbers; *the* geometric mean of two positive numbers is usually defined to be positive, and of two negative numbers to be negative.

7. A series whose terms are in geometric progression is called a geometric series. For a geometric series, you have

$$S_n = \frac{a_1 - a_1 r^n}{1 - r} = \frac{a_1 - r a_n}{1 - r}, \qquad r \neq 1.$$

8. An infinite sequence has a **limit** L if you can make the error of approximation, $|L - a_n|$, less than any positive number, however small, by choosing n great enough. Any infinite sequence which has a limit is said to **converge**, or to be **convergent**; if the sequence does not converge, it is said to **diverge**, or to be **divergent**.

9. **Axiom of Completeness:** Every bounded, nondecreasing (or nonincreasing) sequence of real numbers converges, and its limit is a real number.

10. For any infinite series $a_1 + a_2 + \cdots + a_n + \ldots$, $S_n = \sum_{i=1}^{n} a_i$ is called a **partial sum.** If the sequence $S_1, S_2, \ldots, S_n, \ldots$ of partial sums converges to S, then the infinite series is said to **converge,** or to be **convergent,** and its **sum** is defined to be S.

11. For an infinite geometric series with $|r| < 1$, you have the sum

$$S = \frac{a_1}{1 - r}.$$

chapter test   7-1

1. Determine the first four terms in an arithmetic sequence in which a_2 is 8 and the common difference d is -3.

2. Give a rule for finding successive terms in the arithmetic progression $-9, -4, 1, 6$.

7-2

3. If $a_1 = 3$ and $d = 4$ for an arithmetic sequence, find a_{26}.

4. Insert three arithmetic means between -5 and 7.

7-3

5. Find the value of the sum S_9 for the arithmetic sequence

$$12, 15, 18, \ldots.$$

6. Find the value of $\sum_{k=1}^{5} (3k + 4)$.

7-4

7. If $a_1 = 10$ and $r = -2$ for a geometric sequence, find a_8.

8. If you could lift 4 kilograms on your fifth birthday, and $\frac{3}{2}$ times as much on each succeeding birthday as on the preceding birthday, how much could you lift on your tenth birthday?

7-5

9. Insert two geometric means between -3 and 192.

7-6

10. Find the sum of the terms of the geometric sequence for which $a_1 = -4$, $r = 3$, and $n = 6$.

7-7

11. If the nth term a_n, of an infinite sequence is $\dfrac{2n - 1}{3n + 1}$ and its limit L is $\frac{2}{3}$, find a_8, $|L - a_8|$ and $|L - a_n|$.

7-8

12. (a) Write $0.\overline{73}$ as a geometric series and (b) find its value.

programmed chapter review

7-1 1. Any sequence in which each term after the first is obtained by adding a fixed number, called the _?_ _?_, to the preceding term is a(n) _?_ sequence.

common difference
arithmetic

2. The sequence 1, _?_, 9, 13 is an arithmetic sequence.

5

7-2 3. In an arithmetic sequence for which $a_1 = 5$ and $d = 3$, $a_{21} = $ _?_.

65

4. The two arithmetic means between -4 and 5 are _?_ and _?_.

-1;
2

7-3 5. The index in $\sum\limits_{i=1}^{4} a_i$ is _?_, and the range of summation is _?_.

i
$\{1, 2, 3, 4\}$

6. For an arithmetic series in which $a_1 = 3$ and $a_{10} = 21$, $S_{10} = \frac{?}{2}(3 + $ _?_ $)$.

10; 21

7-4 7. For the geometric sequence $\frac{6}{5}$, 2, $\frac{10}{3}$, the common ratio is _?_.

$\frac{5}{3}$

8. In a geometric sequence for which $a_1 = -5$ and $r = -2$, $a_6 = $ _?_.

160

7-5 9. The two geometric means between 5 and -40 are _?_ and _?_.

-10;
20

7-6 10. If S_n is the sum of the first n terms of a geometric series for which the first term is a_1 and the common ratio is r, $r \neq 1$, then $S_n = \dfrac{a_1 - a_1 r^{?}}{1 - r}$.

n

11. For a geometric series in which $a_1 = 6$, $a_n = \frac{2}{3}$, and $r = \frac{1}{3}$, $S_n = $ _?_.

$\frac{26}{3}$

7-7 12. An infinite sequence which has a _?_ is said to be convergent.

limit

13. The limit L of the sequence for which $a_n = 6 - \dfrac{1}{n^2}$ is 6, and $|L - a_n| = $ _?_.

$\frac{1}{n^2}$

7-8 14. If the limit of the partial sums of an infinite series is S, then the series is said to _?_, and its sum is defined to be _?_.

converge; S

15. $0.\overline{2}$ can be written as an infinite _?_ series, and its sum is _?_.

geometric
$\frac{2}{9}$

Weather and climate affect many aspects of our lives. Meteorologists study and sometimes attempt to alter weather patterns.

radicals and irrational numbers

power functions, roots, and radicals

Objectives

After completing the next five sections, you should be able to:
1. Use power functions in solving variation problems.
2. Determine all real nth roots of a given real number.
3. Determine all rational roots of an equation with integral coefficients.
4. Express a rational number by a terminating or repeating decimal numeral, and express such a numeral as a fraction.
5. Find rational and irrational numbers between any two given real numbers.

8-1   power functions and variation

A function f defined by an equation of the form

$$f(x) = x^n$$

is called a power function. When $n = 1$, the function is simply the linear function $f = \{(x, y): y = x\}$. Figure 1 shows the graphs of power functions for the values $n = 1, 2, 3,$ and 4.

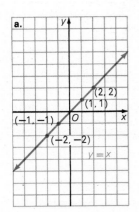

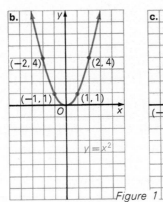

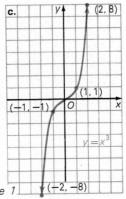

Figure 1

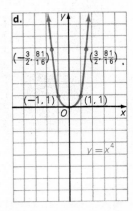

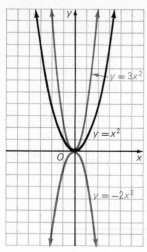

Figure 2

A comparison of the graphs in (a) and (c) of Figure 1 indicates the fact that when *n* is *odd*, the graph of $y = x$ is symmetric with respect to the *origin*. Thus when the function contains the ordered pair (a, b) it also contains the pair $(-a, -b)$; a function with this property is said to be an odd function.

When *n* is *even*, as in (b) and (d) of Figure 1, the graph is symmetric with respect to the *vertical axis*. Thus when the function contains (a, b), it also contains $(-a, b)$; such a function is called an even function.

Closely related to the power function is the function defined by

$$y = ax^n, n > 0, a \neq 0.$$

This function is termed a variation. We say that *y varies directly as*, or *is directly proportional to*, the nth power of x, and that *a* is the constant of variation, or proportionality. When $n = 1$, the function becomes the direct variation $y = ax$ (see page 91).

Figure 2 shows a comparison of the graphs of $y = 3x^2$ and $y = -2x^2$ with that of the power function $y = x^2$.

The concept of variation arises frequently in problems related to the physical world.

EXAMPLE 1   The distance that a body near the earth's surface will fall from rest varies directly as the square of the number of seconds it has been falling. If a boulder falls from a cliff a distance of 176 meters in 6 seconds, approximately how far will it fall in 4 seconds?

SOLUTION   Let d = distance (in meters), t = time (in seconds), and a = constant of variation. Then the problem can be solved by either of the following methods.

METHOD I	METHOD II
$d = at^2$	$d_1 = at_1^2;\ d_2 = at_2^2$
$176 \doteq a(6)^2;\ a \doteq \frac{176}{36} = \frac{44}{9}$	$\frac{d_1}{t_1^2} = \frac{d_2}{t_2^2}$
$d \doteq \frac{44}{9}t^2$	$\frac{176}{6^2} = \frac{d_2}{4^2}$
When $t = 4$,	$d_2 \doteq \frac{176 \times 16}{36} \doteq 78.2.$
$d \doteq \frac{44}{9}(4)^2 \doteq 78.2.$	

∴ the boulder falls approximately 78.2 meters in 4 seconds. **Answer.**

In the preceding Example, the constant of proportionality a is $\frac{1}{2}$ times the acceleration due to gravity at the surface of the earth: $a = \frac{1}{2}g \doteq \frac{44}{9} \doteq 4.9$ so that $g \doteq 9.8$ m/s². The corresponding constant at the surface of the moon is $g \doteq 1.6$ m/s². The distance an object falls under the influence of gravity is given by

$$d = \tfrac{1}{2}gt^2.$$

State **(a)** whether the graph of the given function is symmetric with respect to the vertical axis or the origin, and **(b)** whether the function is odd or even.

1. $f(x) = x^3$

2. $f(x) = x^4$

3. $f: x \rightarrow 2x$

4. $\{(x, y): y = -5x^2\}$

5. $g(x) = -2x^9$

6. $\{(x, y): y = x^3\}$

7. At the surface of the earth, where $g \doteq 9.8$ m/s^2, state the approximate distance a rock will fall from the edge of a cliff in 1 second; in 2 seconds.

8. At the surface of the moon, where $g \doteq 1.6$ m/s^2, what would be the corresponding distances in Exercise 7?

WRITTEN EXERCISES Graph the two given functions on the same set of axes.

A
1. $\{(x, y): y = x^2\}$; $\{(x, y): y = 2x^2\}$

2. $\{(x, y): y = 2x^2\}$; $\{(x, y): y = -\frac{1}{2}x^2\}$

3. $\left\{(x, y): y = \frac{x^3}{2}\right\}$; $\left\{(x, y): y = -\frac{x^3}{4}\right\}$

4. $\{(x, y): y = \frac{1}{6}x^3\}$; $\{(x, y): y = -\frac{1}{6}x^3\}$

5. $f(x) = \frac{1}{2}x^4$; $g(x) = -\frac{1}{2}x^4$

6. $f(x) = -\frac{1}{16}x^5$; $g(x) = -\frac{1}{5}x^5$

Find the value of a for which the given point lies on the graph of $y = ax^2$.

7. $(2, 4)$

8. $(3, -8)$

9. $(-2, 7)$

10. $(3, -36)$

11. $(\frac{1}{3}, \frac{1}{4})$

12. $(\frac{3}{7}, -\frac{6}{7})$

13. If y varies directly as x^2, and y is 6 when x is 2, find y when x is 4.

14. If A varies directly as r^2 and A is π when r is $\frac{1}{2}$, find A when r is 5.

B
15. If s varies directly as v^3 and s is 27 when v is $\frac{1}{3}$, find s when v is 2.

16. If x varies directly as the square of y, and y is proportional to z, what happens to the value of x when z is doubled?

17. If s varies directly as t^4, what happens to the value of s when t is halved?

18. If $p = aq^5$, what happens to the value of p when q is tripled?

C
19. For what values of a is $\left(a, \dfrac{a}{2}\right) \in \{(x, y): y = ax^2, a \neq 0\}$?

20. If $\left(k, \dfrac{k}{4}\right) \in f = \{(x, y): y = kx^2, k > 0\}$, for what value of y is $(8, y) \in f$ a true statement?

A   **1.** The value of a diamond varies directly as the square of its weight. If a 2-carat diamond is worth $2000, what is the value of a diamond weighing 3 carats?

2. The power required to propel a boat varies as the cube of its speed. If a certain motorboat needs 4×10^2 kilowatts to run at a steady speed of 10 kilometers per hour, how many kilowatts are needed to run the boat at 15 kilometers per hour?

3. The distance a body falls from a position of rest varies directly as the square of the number of seconds it falls. If near the surface of the moon a body falls 7.2 meters in 3 seconds, how far will it fall in 6 seconds?

4. The energy of a 1-kilogram satellite orbiting at 28,000 kilometers per hour is equivalent to 3×10^6 calories of heat. If the amount of heat varies directly as the square of the velocity, find the heat equivalent of the energy of this satellite orbiting at 40,000 kilometers per hour.

5. The power expended by heat in an electric circuit of fixed resistance is directly proportional to the square of the measure of the current. If a circuit expends 180 watts when a current of 6 amperes is flowing, what is the heat expended when the current is 10 amperes?

6. The maximum deflection of a beam is directly proportional to the cube of its length. If a maximum deflection of 0.003 centimeters occurs in a beam 10 meters long, find the deflection in a 4-meter beam.

7. The moment of inertia of a square plate 3 centimeters wide is 6.75. What is the moment of inertia of a square plate 6 centimeters wide if the moment of inertia varies as the fourth power of the width of the plate?

8. The crushing load of a circular pillar with a 25-centimeter diameter is 200 tonnes. Find the crushing load of a pillar of the same height and material but with a diameter of 35 centimeters if the crushing load is directly proportional to the fourth power of the diameter.

9. The work done in stretching a spring is directly proportional to the square of the elongation. If 16 joules of work are done in stretching a spring $\frac{1}{2}$ meter beyond its natural length of 3 meters, find the work done in stretching it to be a length of 4 meters.

10. The amount of silt carried by a stream is directly proportional to the sixth power of its velocity. A certain stream carries 200 tonnes of silt per day. Determine the amount of silt it would carry if its velocity were doubled.

8–2   *the real nth roots of a number*

By observing the graphs in Figures 3, 4, and 5 of the power functions specified by (1) $f(x) = x^2$, (2) $g(x) = x^3$, and (3) $h(x) = x^4$, you can answer questions such as the following about the members of f, g, and h.

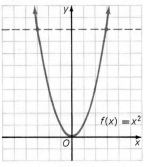

Figure 3

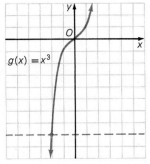

Figure 4

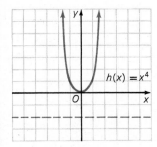

Figure 5

(1) How many values in the domain of f are paired with the value $f(x) = 9$ in the range? That is, how many values of x satisfy the equation $x^2 = 9$?

(2) How many values in the domain of g are paired with the value $g(x) = -8$ in the range? That is, how many solutions are there of the equation $x^3 = -8$?

(3) Are there any real values of x such that the pair $(x, -2) \in h$? That is, are there any real values of x that satisfy $x^4 = -2$?

The abscissas of the points shown by red dots on the graphs in Figures 3 and 4 indicate the values of x that satisfy the given equation in each case. In Figure 5 you can see that, since -2 is not an element of the range, there is no pair $(x, -2)$ in h, and hence there is no real solution to $x^4 = -2$.

Each solution of the equation $x^n = b$, for n a positive integer, is called an nth root of b. Thus, 3 and -3 are the 2nd roots (or *square roots*) of 9, and -2 is the 3rd (or *cube*) root of -8.

The facts concerning the *real* nth roots of b, as suggested by Figures 3, 4, and 5, are summarized in the following table.

Number and Nature of Real nth Roots of b

	$b > 0$	$b < 0$	$b = 0$
n **even**	one positive root one negative root	no real roots	one root, namely, 0
n **odd**	one positive root	one negative root	one root, namely, 0

The symbol $\sqrt[n]{b}$ (read "the nth root of b") denotes the principal nth root of b, that is:

1. The *nonnegative* nth root of b if n is even and $b \geq 0$. For example, we write

$$\sqrt[2]{36} = 6, \ -\sqrt[2]{36} = -6, \ \sqrt[4]{0} = 0.$$

2. The single real nth root of b if n is odd. For example,

$$\sqrt[3]{8} = 2, \ -\sqrt[3]{8} = -2.$$

Notice that we are talking about only the *real* nth roots of b; that is, in the set of real numbers, $\sqrt[4]{-16}$ is not defined.

The symbol $\sqrt[n]{b}$ is called a radical; b is the radicand and n the index. (The index 2 for the square root is usually omitted.) Always be careful to include all of the desired radicand under the radical sign. Thus,

$$\sqrt{36 - 9} = \sqrt{27} = 3\sqrt{3}, \quad \text{whereas} \quad \sqrt{36} - 9 = 6 - 9 = -3.$$

Notice that $\sqrt[3]{(-2)^3} = -2$, but $\sqrt[4]{(-2)^4} = 2$, because a radical of even index denotes a *nonnegative* root. In general,

$$\sqrt[n]{b^n} = b \text{ if } n \text{ is odd, and } \sqrt[n]{b^n} = |b| \text{ if } n \text{ is even.}$$

State the value of the indicated principal root.

1. $\sqrt[3]{8}$ 3. $\sqrt[3]{-27}$ 5. $\sqrt[7]{(-2)^7}$ 7. $\sqrt[4]{\frac{1}{16}}$

2. $\sqrt[4]{0}$ 4. $\sqrt[5]{-1}$ 6. $\sqrt[6]{(-4)^6}$ 8. $\sqrt[3]{-\frac{1}{125}}$

State the real roots of the given equation.

9. $x^2 = 36$ 11. $3x^3 = -24$ 13. $64x^4 - 1 = 0$

10. $2x^2 = 5$ 12. $5x^2 = 1$ 14. $x^9 - 7 = 0$

Express each radical as a decimal to the nearest tenth, by using Tables 3 and 4 in the Appendix.

A   1. $\sqrt{5}$ 3. $\sqrt{1.2}$ 5. $\sqrt[3]{26}$ 7. $\sqrt{\frac{13}{5}}$

2. $-\sqrt{7}$ 4. $\sqrt{0.64}$ 6. $\sqrt[3]{-53}$ 8. $\sqrt[3]{(-2)^5}$

Solve over the set of rational numbers.

EXAMPLE 1 $1.44x^2 - 1 = 0$

SOLUTION $1.44x^2 - 1 = 0$

$$x^2 = \frac{1}{1.44} = \frac{100}{144}$$

$$x = \pm\frac{10}{12} = \pm\frac{5}{6}$$

$\therefore$ the solution set is $\{\frac{5}{6}, -\frac{5}{6}\}$. Answer.

9. $36x^2 = 25$ 11. $27r^3 - 343 = 0$ 13. $1.21x^2 - 1 = 0$

10. $64y^2 = 16$ 12. $1 - 625x^4 = 0$ 14. $1.96n^2 - 1.21 = 0$

Find all real values of the variable for which the given statement is true.

EXAMPLE 2 $\sqrt{(x - 3)^2} = x - 3$

SOLUTION   Since $\sqrt{(x - 3)^2}$ denotes a nonnegative number, the equation is true if and only if $x - 3$ is nonnegative; that is, $x - 3 \geq 0$, or $x \geq 3$. Answer.

15. $\sqrt{x - 1} = 0$ 18. $\sqrt[4]{(y - 3)^4} = |y - 3|$

16. $\sqrt[4]{4 - y} = 0$ 19. $\sqrt[3]{(t - 1)^3} = t - 1$

17. $\sqrt{(x + 1)^2} = x + 1$ 20. $\sqrt{4 - x^2} \in \mathcal{R}$

B   21. $\sqrt[4]{(x - 5)^2} = \sqrt{x - 5}$ 23. $\sqrt[3]{-27y^{15}} = -3y^5$

22. $\sqrt{q^2 + 1} = q + 1$ 24. $\sqrt{-(x + 3)} \in \mathcal{R}$

Determine the solution set over $\mathcal{R}$.

25. $\sqrt[4]{t^4} - t = 10$ 26. $x - \sqrt{x^2 - 22} = 0$

27. If $x^2 + y^2 = 43$, $xy = -3$, and $x - y < 0$, find the value of $x - y$.

28. If $(r - s)^2 = 7$, $rs = 14$, and $r > 0$, find the value of $\dfrac{1}{r} + \dfrac{1}{s}$.

C 29. a. Prove: If $0 < x < 1$, then $0 < x^2 < x$ and $0 < x^3 < x$.
    b. Use the results of (a) to explain why the graphs of both $y = x^2$ and $y = x^3$ are below that of $y = x$ in the interval $0 < x < 1$.

30. Prove: If $a > b > 0$, then $\sqrt{a} > \sqrt{b}$.
    Hint: $a - b = (\sqrt{a} + \sqrt{b})(\sqrt{a} - \sqrt{b})$.

8–3 *the roots of a polynomial equation*

A *rational number* has been defined (page 196) as any number that can be represented in the form $\dfrac{a}{b}$, where a and b are integers, $b \neq 0$.

You know that $\sqrt{4}$ is a rational number because $\sqrt{4} = \frac{2}{1}$, but what about $\sqrt{5}$? Since $\sqrt{5}$ is a root of the equation $x^2 - 5 = 0$, we can answer the question by using the following theorem concerning the rational roots, if any, of such a polynomial equation. (Note first that the leading coefficient of a polynomial is the coefficient of the term of highest degree.)

> **Theorem.** Let $f(x)$ be a simplified polynomial with integral coefficients. If the equation $f(x) = 0$ has a rational root $\dfrac{p}{q}$ that is in lowest terms, then p must be an integral factor of the constant term, and q an integral factor of the leading coefficient, of $f(x)$.

EXAMPLE 1 If $f(x) = 4x^3 + 4x^2 - x - 1$, list the possible rational roots of $f(x) = 0$; then find which, if any, actually satisfy that equation.

SOLUTION The numerator of any rational root $\dfrac{p}{q}$ must be an integral factor of -1, and the denominator an integral factor of 4. That is, $p \in \{1, -1\}$ and $q \in \{1, -1, 2, -2, 4, -4\}$. Hence the possible rational roots $\dfrac{p}{q}$ are

$$\pm\tfrac{1}{4}, \ \pm\tfrac{1}{2}, \ \pm 1.$$

Next, check each possible value for $\dfrac{p}{q}$ in $f(x)$ to see which, if any, satisfy $f(x) = 0$.

$$f(\tfrac{1}{4}) = -\tfrac{15}{16}; \qquad f(\tfrac{1}{2}) = 0; \qquad f(1) = 6;$$
$$f(-\tfrac{1}{4}) = -\tfrac{9}{16}; \quad f(-\tfrac{1}{2}) = 0; \quad f(-1) = 0.$$

$\therefore$ the rational roots of $4x^3 + 4x^2 - x - 1 = 0$ are $\tfrac{1}{2}$, $-\tfrac{1}{2}$ and -1.

Answer.

EXAMPLE 2   If $f(x) = x^2 - 5$, determine the rational roots, if any, of $f(x) = 0$.

SOLUTION   A rational root $\dfrac{p}{q}$ must satisfy $p \in \{5, -5, 1, -1\}$ and $q \in \{1, -1)$.

Hence $\dfrac{p}{q} \in \{5, -5, 1, -1\}$. Checking in $f(x)$:

$$f(5) = f(-5) = 20 \neq 0;$$
$$f(1) = f(-1) = -4 \neq 0.$$

$\therefore x^2 - 5 = 0$ has no rational roots.   **Answer.**

Real numbers that are not rational are called irrational numbers. Example 2 establishes the fact that $\sqrt{5}$ and $-\sqrt{5}$, which are the roots of $x^2 - 5 = 0$, are irrational numbers. In general, for any positive integer b and any integer $n > 1$, you can show, by considering the equation $x^n = b$, that $\sqrt[n]{b}$ is an irrational number unless b is the nth power of an integer.

Example 3 below illustrates the following fact: *The sum, difference, product, or quotient of a rational number and an irrational number is an irrational number.* (Exceptions: $0 \cdot x$ and $\dfrac{0}{x}$, where x is irrational.)

EXAMPLE 3   Determine whether $2 + 3\sqrt{5}$ is a rational or an irrational number.

SOLUTION   If $2 + 3\sqrt{5}$ is a rational number, there must be integers a and b, $b \neq 0$, such that

$$2 + 3\sqrt{5} = \frac{a}{b}$$

or

$$\sqrt{5} = \frac{a - 2b}{3b}.$$

Since $a - 2b$ and $3b$ are both integers and $b \neq 0$, $\dfrac{a - 2b}{3b}$ is a rational number. But we know that $\sqrt{5}$ is an irrational number. Thus we have been led to a contradiction, and accordingly, our hypothesis that $2 + 3\sqrt{5}$ is a rational number must be false. Hence $2 + 3\sqrt{5}$ is irrational.   **Answer.**

ORAL EXERCISES   Name all the rational numbers that fulfill the conditions required of rational roots of the given equation.

1. $x^2 - 3 = 0$
2. $x^2 + 5 = 0$
3. $2y^2 - 3 = 0$
4. $m^3 + 5m - 4 = 0$
5. $a^3 + a - 6 = 0$

6. $b^2 + 16 = 0$
7. $2y^4 - 3y^2 + y - 1 = 0$
8. $3x^3 - x^2 + 4 = 0$
9. $-x^5 + 32 = 0$
10. $10x^2 + 4x - 5 = 0$

WRITTEN EXERCISES In Exercises 1–10 prove that the given number is irrational by showing that it is a root of a simplified polynomial equation which has no rational roots.

EXAMPLE $\sqrt[3]{\frac{3}{5}}$

SOLUTION $\sqrt[3]{\frac{3}{5}}$ is a root of $x^3 = \frac{3}{5}$, or

$$5x^3 - 3 = 0.$$

Any rational root $\dfrac{p}{q}$ of this equation must satisfy $p \in \{3, -3, 1, -1\}$

and $q \in \{5, -5, 1, -1\}$. Hence $\dfrac{p}{q} \in \{\frac{3}{5}, -\frac{3}{5}, 3, -3, \frac{1}{5}, -\frac{1}{5}, 1, -1\}$.
Check each possibility:

$$5(\pm\tfrac{3}{5})^3 - 3 \overset{?}{=} 0; \ \pm\tfrac{27}{25} - 3 \neq 0.$$
$$5(\pm 3)^3 - 3 \overset{?}{=} 0; \ \pm 135 - 3 \neq 0.$$
$$5(\pm\tfrac{1}{5})^3 - 3 \overset{?}{=} 0; \ \pm\tfrac{1}{25} - 3 \neq 0.$$
$$5(\pm 1)^3 - 3 \overset{?}{=} 0; \ \pm 5 - 3 \neq 0.$$

$\therefore$ the equation has no rational roots, and so $\sqrt[3]{\frac{3}{5}}$ must be an irrational number. **Answer.**

A 1. $\sqrt{2}$ 6. $\sqrt[3]{-6}$

2. $\sqrt{21}$ 7. $\sqrt[4]{\frac{3}{5}}$

3. $-\sqrt{\frac{2}{3}}$ 8. $\sqrt[5]{-\frac{3}{11}}$

4. $-\sqrt{\frac{1}{15}}$ 9. $\sqrt[6]{\frac{13}{9}}$

5. $\sqrt[3]{7}$ 10. $-\sqrt[7]{\frac{4}{15}}$

Use the method of Example 3 to show that the given number is irrational. Assume it is known that $\sqrt{2}$, $\sqrt{3}$, $\sqrt[3]{4}$, and $\sqrt{7}$ are irrational.

11. $\sqrt{2} - 3$ 13. $\dfrac{\sqrt[3]{4}}{3}$

12. $\frac{1}{4}(\sqrt{3} + 5)$ 14. $-\dfrac{2}{\sqrt{7}}$

Find the rational roots, if any, of the given equation.

B 15. $t^3 + t^2 - 4t - 4 = 0$ 17. $2x^4 - 15x = 13(x^2 + x^3)$

16. $4y^3 + 4y^2 - y = 1$ 18. $6r(2r^3 + 1) = r^2(20r + 1)$

C 19. Prove that any rational root of $x^3 + bx^2 + cx + d = 0$, where b, c, and d are integers, must be an integer.

20. Given $P(x) = ax^3 + bx^2 + cx + d$, where a, b, c, and d are integers. If $P(x) = 0$ has a root $\dfrac{p}{q}$, where p and q are relatively prime integers, prove that p is a factor of d and that q is a factor of a by justifying the following steps.

1. $a\left(\dfrac{p}{q}\right)^3 + b\left(\dfrac{p}{q}\right)^2 + c\left(\dfrac{p}{q}\right) + d = 0$
2. $ap^3 + bp^2q + cpq^2 + dq^3 = 0$
3. $p(ap^2 + bpq + cq^2) = -dq^3 = d(-q^3)$
4. p is a factor of the integer represented by $d(-q^3)$.
5. p is a factor of d.
6. $q(bp^2 + cpq + dq^2) = a(-p^3)$
7. q is a factor of $a(-p^3)$.
8. q is a factor of a.

8–4 *decimal numerals for rational numbers*

To find a decimal numeral for a rational number, first express the number as the quotient of two integers and then perform the indicated division.

EXAMPLE 1 Express as a decimal numeral **(a)** $1\frac{3}{8}$; and **(b)** $\frac{1}{22}$. Check your answer in Part **(a)**.

SOLUTION **a.** $1\frac{3}{8} = \frac{11}{8} = 11 \div 8$

$$
\begin{array}{r}
1.375 \\
8)\overline{11.000} \\
\underline{8} \\
30 \\
\underline{24} \\
60 \\
\underline{56} \\
40 \\
\underline{40} \\
0
\end{array}
$$

b. $\frac{1}{22} = 1 \div 22$

$$
\begin{array}{r}
.0454545 \\
22)\overline{1.0000000} \\
\underline{88} \\
120 \\
110 \\
100 \\
88 \\
120 \\
110 \\
100 \\
88 \\
120 \\
110 \\
10
\end{array}
$$

CHECK $1.375 = 1 + \dfrac{3}{10} + \dfrac{7}{100} + \dfrac{5}{1000}$

$ = \dfrac{1000 + 300 + 70 + 5}{1000}$

$ = \dfrac{1375}{1000} = \dfrac{11}{8}$ ✓

$\therefore 1\frac{3}{8} = 1.375$. **Answer.**

You can see that in Example 1(a), the division process effectively terminates when the remainder 0 occurs, since thereafter only "0"'s appear in the quotient. Accordingly, the decimal numeral for $\frac{11}{8}$ is called a terminating decimal.

In Example 1(b), however, the remainder 0 never occurs. As a result, the quotient consists of an endlessly *repeating block of digits*, or repetend: 45. The decimal numeral for $\frac{1}{22}$ is an example of a repeating (or periodic) decimal, which we usually denote as follows:

$$\tfrac{1}{22} = 0.0\overline{45}$$

The bar indicates the block of digits that repeats without end.

Example 1 illustrates the following facts concerning the result when an integer p is divided by a positive integer q:

1. The remainder at each step in the process may be any element of $\{0, 1, 2, \ldots, q - 1\}$.
2. After only 0's are left in the dividend, within at most $q - 1$ steps either 0 occurs as a remainder and the division process stops, or one of the possible nonzero remainders recurs, initiating a repeating sequence of dividends in the algorithm process, and hence a repeating block of digits in the quotient.
3. If the repetend is $\overline{0}$, the quotient is a terminating decimal; otherwise, the quotient is a repeating decimal.

The decimal representation of any rational number $\dfrac{p}{q}$ either terminates or has a repetend of fewer than q digits. Conversely, every terminating or repeating decimal represents a rational number.

You can use either of the following two methods to convert a repeating decimal to a common fraction.

EXAMPLE 2   Express $0.\overline{378}$ as a ratio of two integers.

METHOD I

SOLUTION   Use the formula on page 251 for the sum of an infinite geometric series.

$$0.\overline{378} = 0.378 + 0.378(.001) + 0.378(.001)^2 + \cdots,$$

so that $a_1 = 0.378$ and $r = .001$.

$$S = \frac{a_1}{1 - r} = \frac{0.378}{1 - .001} = \frac{0.378}{.999} = \frac{42}{111}. \text{ Answer.}$$

Let $N = 0.\overline{378}$.

$$1000\,N = 378.\overline{378}$$
$$N = 0.\overline{378}$$
$$\overline{}$$
$$1000N - N = 378$$
$$999N = 378$$
$$N = \frac{378}{999} = \frac{42}{111}. \quad \text{Answer.}$$

WRITTEN EXERCISES Express as a decimal numeral.

A 1. $\frac{7}{40}$ 5. $\frac{23}{60}$

   2. $\frac{3}{16}$ 6. $-\frac{15}{14}$

   3. $\frac{5}{3}$ 7. $\frac{2}{175}$

   4. $-\frac{7}{11}$ 8. $\frac{10}{21}$

Use the method of the check in Example 1(a) to express the given decimal as a ratio of relatively prime integers.

   9. 2.154   12. −0.00046

  10. 5.777   13. 0.20502

  11. 0.039   14. −1.0044

Use Method I of Example 2 to express the given decimal as a common fraction in lowest terms.

B 15. $0.\overline{7}$ 17. $1.2\overline{14}$

  16. $-0.\overline{32}$ 18. $0.\overline{425}$

Use Method II of Example 2 to express the given decimal as a common fraction in lowest terms.

  19. $-3.\overline{714}$ 21. $61.28\overline{125}$

  20. $-5.8\overline{21}$ 22. $0.0003\overline{9}$

C 23. Show that if a fraction in lowest terms can be represented by a terminating decimal, its denominator can have only powers of 2 and 5 as factors.

  24. Show that if a fraction in lowest terms has only powers of 2 and 5 as factors of its denominator, then it can be represented by a terminating decimal.

  25. Find a common fraction in lowest terms having 11 as denominator and $0.\overline{4d}$ as decimal representation, where d is a digit such that $0 < d < 10$.

8-5 *decimals for irrational numbers*

The axiom of completeness (page 246) for the set of real numbers can be used to show that every real number has a decimal representation, and conversely. Since the rational numbers are the real numbers named by terminating or repeating decimals, the irrational numbers must be the real numbers represented by the nonterminating, nonrepeating decimals.

It is possible to find successive digits in the infinite decimal representing an irrational number such as $\sqrt{2}$ by various methods. In the geometric method in Figure 9, where the interval from 1 to 2 is subdivided into tenths, you can see that

$$1.4 < \sqrt{2} < 1.5.$$

You can verify this algebraically as follows:

$$(1.4)^2 \overset{?}{<} (\sqrt{2})^2 \overset{?}{<} (1.5)^2$$

$$1.96 < 2 < 2.25 \checkmark$$

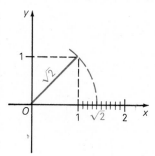

Figure 9

Next, if the same interval were divided into hundredths and you could observe the location of $\sqrt{2}$, you would find, and again verify by comparing squared members of the following inequality, that

$$1.41 < \sqrt{2} < 1.42.$$

By further subdividing the unit interval into thousandths, ten-thousandths, etc., you could obtain as many additional digits in the decimal for $\sqrt{2}$ as you desire. In accordance with the usual round-off rules (page 178), when you write $\sqrt{2} \doteq 1.414$, you mean

$$1.414 - 0.0005 \le \sqrt{2} < 1.414 + 0.0005.$$

Notice that, for example, the decimal numeral

$$0.2121121112\ldots,$$

which consists, from the decimal point on, of a succession of "2"'s, separated first by one "1", then by two "1"'s, then three "1"'s, and so on, is neither terminating nor repeating. It therefore represents an irrational number. No such pattern is known for the decimal expansion of the irrational number $\sqrt{2}$.

Using decimal representations, you can illustrate the following property of density of the set of real numbers.

Property of Density

Between any two real numbers, there is another real number.

In fact, between any two real numbers there are both rational and irrational numbers.

EXAMPLE   **a.** Find a rational number between $4.\overline{5211}$ and $4.\overline{521}$.
          b. Find an irrational number between $\sqrt{2}$ and $1.41515515551\ldots$.

SOLUTION **a.** $4.\overline{5211} < 4.5212 < 4.\overline{521}$; ∴ a rational number between $4.\overline{5211}$ and $4.\overline{521}$ is 4.5212. **Answer.**

           b. Since by Table 3 in the Appendix you have $\sqrt{2} < 1.415$, you can see that $\sqrt{2} < 1.4150505505550\ldots < 1.41515515551\ldots$, and $1.4150505505550\ldots$ is one such irrational number. **Answer.**

ORAL EXERCISES   State whether the given number is rational or irrational.

1. $\dfrac{7}{4}$

2. $2.0\overline{14}$

3. $\dfrac{\sqrt{3}}{2}$

4. $-5 + 3.\overline{625}$

5. $\sqrt{3}\,(6.\overline{923})$

6. $1.415\overline{155}$

7. $5.6464464446\ldots$

8. $2.1313313331\ldots$

9. The sum of the numbers in Exercises 7 and 8.

10. The difference of the numbers in Exercises 7 and 8.

WRITTEN EXERCISES   Find the first three digits in the decimal for each given number.

A   1. $\sqrt{3}$

    2. $-\sqrt{5}$

    3. $\sqrt[3]{2}$

    4. $\sqrt[3]{10}$

Between the two given numbers find **(a)** a rational number; and **(b)** an irrational number.

5. $\frac{3}{5}$ and $\frac{7}{10}$

6. $\frac{2}{3}$ and $\frac{5}{6}$

7. $\frac{8}{5}$ and 1.7

8. $-\frac{28}{9}$ and -3.2

9. $0.\overline{26}$ and $\frac{3}{11}$

10. $-3\frac{1}{5}$ and $-\frac{17}{5}$

B   11. $\sqrt{5}$ and 2.237

    12. $\sqrt{2}$ and $0.85\sqrt{3}$

    13. $-\pi$ and $-\frac{394}{125}$ $(\pi \doteq 3.14159)$

    14. $\sqrt{\frac{23}{10}}$ and $\sqrt[3]{\frac{7}{2}}$

C 15. Explain why the set of rational numbers has the property of density; that is, between any two rational numbers $\dfrac{p}{q}$ and $\dfrac{r}{s}$ there is another rational number.

16. Explain why the set of rational numbers does not have the property of completeness by giving a bounded, nondecreasing sequence of rational numbers that converges to an *irrational* number.

SELF-TEST 1 Give the meaning of each of the following.

1. power function
2. odd function
3. even function
4. variation
5. principal nth root

6. radicand
7. index of a radical
8. leading coefficient
9. repeating decimal
10. irrational number

Objective 1, page 259 11. If y varies directly as x^2, and $y = 7$ when $x = 2$, find y when $x = 4$.

Objective 2, page 259 12. Determine (a) $\sqrt[4]{(-\frac{4}{9})^2}$; and (b) $\sqrt[3]{-\frac{27}{8}}$.

Objective 3, page 259 13. Determine all rational roots of $2x^3 + 9x^2 + 7x - 6 = 0$.

Objective 4, page 259 14. Express $\frac{5}{9}$ as a terminating or repeating decimal.

15. Express $0.\overline{172}$ as a common fraction.

Objective 5, page 259 16. Find (a) a rational number and (b) an irrational number between 23.112 and 23.113.

Check your answers with those printed at the back of the book.

The Bernoulli Family
17th–18th centuries

This Swiss family produced more mathematicians than any other family in the history of mathematics. Within four generations about a dozen members achieved distinction in mathematics and physics. Of these, brothers Jacques I (1654–1705) and Jean I (1667–1748) were the most famous.

Jacques's main interest was in calculus, probability, and graphs; one curve even bears his name—the "Lemniscate of Bernoulli," described by the polar equation $r^2 = a \cos 2\theta$.

Jean helped a great deal to spread the calculus throughout Europe. He also published works in chemistry, physics, and astronomy. His son Daniel (1700–1782) has been called "the founder of mathematical physics."

careers *meteorology*

Meteorology is the study of atmospheric phenomena. In addition to weather forecasting, there are many other specializations in the field, such as climatology (the study of average weather patterns), the design of meteorological instruments, and the study of the chemical composition and physical properties of the atmosphere.

Meteorologists work in a variety of situations. In many countries government and military weather stations employ a large number of meteorologists. The operations of commercial airlines, aerospace industries, and insurance companies rely upon weather information and other atmospheric data. A number of meteorologists teach and do research at universities. The knowledge and skills of meteorologists are also needed in the field of air pollution control.

EXAMPLE   Thermal wind in the atmosphere results from temperature differences within a layer of air. To find the direction and speed of a wind at a particular altitude above the ground, meteorologists find the sum of the *vectors* (see Section 16–5) representing the thermal wind and the wind at the surface.

If the wind at the surface is from the south at 10 km/h and the thermal wind between the surface and an altitude of 5450 m is from the west at 15 km/h, what is the velocity of the wind at an altitude of 5450 m?

SOLUTION   The diagram at the right is a vector representation of the speed and direction of the winds. We can use the Pythagorean Theorem (page 333) to find the speed of the resultant wind, w:

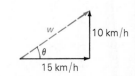

$$w^2 = 100 + 225$$
$$w^2 = 325$$
$$w = \sqrt{325} = 5\sqrt{13} \doteq 18.1 \text{ km/h}$$

Top: A member of the Naval Weather Service Command studies weather maps. Center: A meteorologist monitors the weather on a radarscope. Bottom: A satellite picture of a weather pattern is produced by an Automatic Picture Transmission receiver.

operating with radicals

Objectives

After completing the next four sections, you should be able to:
1. Use properties of radicals to simplify algebraic expressions.
2. Solve equations involving radicals.
3. Solve quadratic equations by completing the square and by using the quadratic formula.

8–6 *properties of radicals*

Notice that

$$\sqrt[3]{8 \cdot 27} = \sqrt[3]{216} = 6, \quad \text{and} \quad \sqrt[3]{8} \cdot \sqrt[3]{27} = 2 \cdot 3 = 6,$$

and therefore

$$\sqrt[3]{8 \cdot 27} = \sqrt[3]{8} \cdot \sqrt[3]{27}.$$

Likewise,

$$\sqrt{\frac{64}{16}} = \sqrt{4} = 2 \quad \text{and} \quad \frac{\sqrt{64}}{\sqrt{16}} = \frac{8}{4} = 2,$$

and therefore

$$\sqrt{\frac{64}{16}} = \frac{\sqrt{64}}{\sqrt{16}}.$$

These examples illustrate the following theorem concerning certain properties of radicals.

Theorem. For all a, b, $\sqrt[n]{a}$, and $\sqrt[n]{b} \in \mathcal{R}$:

$$1. \ \sqrt[n]{ab} = \sqrt[n]{a} \cdot \sqrt[n]{b} \qquad 2. \ \sqrt[n]{\frac{a}{b}} = \frac{\sqrt[n]{a}}{\sqrt[n]{b}} \quad (b \neq 0)$$

PROOF OF 1

First, note that $\sqrt[n]{ab}$ denotes the *principal* nth root of ab.

1. $(\sqrt[n]{a} \cdot \sqrt[n]{b})^n = (\sqrt[n]{a})^n \cdot (\sqrt[n]{b})^n = a \cdot b$ (Why?)
2. $\therefore \ \sqrt[n]{a} \cdot \sqrt[n]{b}$ is an nth root of $a \cdot b$. (Why?)
3. If n is even, then a and b must both be nonnegative and accordingly the principal nth root of each of these numbers is nonnegative. Hence their product, $\sqrt[n]{a} \cdot \sqrt[n]{b}$, is nonnegative and must therefore represent the *principal* nth root of $a \cdot b$, $\sqrt[n]{ab}$.
4. If n is odd, and $a \cdot b \geq 0$, then $\sqrt[n]{a} \cdot \sqrt[n]{b} \geq 0$, and also $\sqrt[n]{ab} \geq 0$. Hence $\sqrt[n]{a} \cdot \sqrt[n]{b} = \sqrt[n]{ab}$.

The proof of the case in which n is odd and exactly one of a and b is negative, as well as Part 2 of the theorem, will be left as Exercises 29–31, page 278.

If we let $b = a$ in Part 1 we have $\sqrt[n]{a^2} = \sqrt[n]{a} \cdot \sqrt[n]{a} = (\sqrt[n]{a})^2$. This illustrates a special case ($m = 2$) of the following useful theorem concerning another property of radicals.

> **Theorem.** For all b and $\sqrt[n]{b} \in \Re$, and m and n positive integers,
> $$\sqrt[n]{b^m} = (\sqrt[n]{b})^m.$$

EXAMPLE 1   Evaluate **(a)** $\sqrt[3]{(-64)^2}$; and **(b)** $\sqrt[4]{(81)^3}$.

SOLUTION   a. $\sqrt[3]{(-64)^2} = (\sqrt[3]{-64})^2 = (-4)^2 = 16$. Answer.

b. $\sqrt[4]{(81)^3} = (\sqrt[4]{81})^3 = 3^3 = 27$. Answer.

The following theorem enables you to replace the index of a radical with a lesser index.

> **Theorem.** For k and m integers and all b and $\sqrt[km]{b} \in \Re$,
> $$\sqrt[km]{b} = \sqrt[k]{\sqrt[m]{b}} = \sqrt[m]{\sqrt[k]{b}}.$$

For example,
$$\sqrt[8]{36} = \sqrt[4\cdot2]{36} = \sqrt[4]{\sqrt[2]{36}} = \sqrt[4]{6}.$$

The theorems of this section, together with other number properties, enable you to *simplify* a radical of index n according to the following criteria:

1. The index is as small as possible.
2. There are no radicands containing a fraction or a negative exponent, or radicals appearing in a denominator.
3. No radicand contains the nth power of an integer or polynomial other than 1.

The term rationalizing the denominator is often used to describe the process of transforming a term involving radicals and fractions into an equivalent term with the expression for the denominator free of radicals. (See Example 2(b).)

EXAMPLE 2   Simplify each expression:

a. $\sqrt[6]{64x^7}$ b. $\dfrac{2}{\sqrt{2a}}$ c. $\sqrt[5]{\dfrac{128}{b}}$ d. $\sqrt[3]{x^{-3} + (2y)^{-3}}$

SOLUTION   a. $\sqrt[6]{64x^7} = \sqrt[6]{64x^6 \cdot x} = 2x\sqrt[6]{x}$. Answer.

b. $\dfrac{2}{\sqrt{2a}} = \dfrac{2\sqrt{2a}}{\sqrt{2a}\,\sqrt{2a}} = \dfrac{2\sqrt{2a}}{2a} = \dfrac{\sqrt{2a}}{a}$. Answer.

c. $\sqrt[5]{\dfrac{128}{b}} = \dfrac{\sqrt[5]{32}\,\sqrt[5]{4}\,\sqrt[5]{b^4}}{\sqrt[5]{b}\,\sqrt[5]{b^4}} = \dfrac{2\,\sqrt[5]{4b^4}}{b}$ Answer.

d. $\sqrt[3]{x^{-3} + (2y)^{-3}} = \sqrt[3]{\dfrac{1}{x^3} + \dfrac{1}{(2y)^3}}$

$\qquad\qquad = \sqrt[3]{\dfrac{8y^3 + x^3}{8x^3y^3}} = \dfrac{\sqrt[3]{8y^3 + x^3}}{2xy}$.   Answer.

ORAL EXERCISES   Express each of the following in simplified form.

1. $\sqrt{12}$ 3. $\sqrt{8}$ 5. $\sqrt[3]{-64}$ 7. $-\sqrt{\dfrac{9a^2}{4}}$ 9. $\sqrt[3]{8^{-4}}$

2. $\sqrt{18}$ 4. $\sqrt[3]{54}$ 6. $\sqrt[3]{-24}$ 8. $-\sqrt{\dfrac{3b^3}{9}}$ 10. $\sqrt[3]{27^{-2}}$

WRITTEN EXERCISES   Using Tables 3 and 4 in the Appendix, give approximations correct to the nearest hundredth of each of the following numbers.

EXAMPLE 1 $\dfrac{5 + \sqrt{2}}{\sqrt{3}} = \dfrac{5 + \sqrt{2}}{\sqrt{3}} \cdot \dfrac{\sqrt{3}}{\sqrt{3}} = \dfrac{5\sqrt{3} + \sqrt{6}}{3} \doteq \dfrac{5(1.732) + 2.449}{3}$

$\qquad\qquad\qquad\qquad\qquad\qquad\qquad\qquad\qquad \doteq 3.70.$ Answer.

EXAMPLE 2 $\sqrt[3]{184} = \sqrt[3]{8}\,\sqrt[3]{23} = 2\,\sqrt[3]{23} \doteq 2(2.844) \doteq 5.69.$ Answer.

A   1. $2\sqrt{162}$ 3. $\tfrac{2}{3}\sqrt{243}$ 5. $\sqrt{45}\,\sqrt{\tfrac{3}{5}}$ 7. $\dfrac{\sqrt[3]{-108}}{\sqrt[3]{2}}$

2. $\sqrt{1\tfrac{1}{8}}$ 4. $\sqrt{0.91}$ 6. $\sqrt[3]{\tfrac{3}{4}}\,\sqrt[3]{\tfrac{40}{3}}$ 8. $\dfrac{\sqrt[3]{25}}{\sqrt[3]{-625}}$

Express each of the following in simple radical form. State restrictions, if any, on the values of the variables for the radicals to denote real numbers.

9. $\sqrt[3]{\tfrac{16}{125}}$ 15. $\sqrt[4]{\dfrac{a^4}{b^3}}$ 19. $\sqrt[5]{\dfrac{20}{x + h}}$

10. $\sqrt[4]{\tfrac{81}{8}}$

11. $\tfrac{3}{4}\sqrt[3]{\tfrac{2}{3}}$ 16. $\sqrt[4]{\dfrac{2a^4b^2c}{5x^3yz^5}}$ 20. $\sqrt[7]{\dfrac{3y^4}{32x^2z^3}}$

12. $5\sqrt{\tfrac{4}{7}}$ 17. $\dfrac{1}{\sqrt{a^2 + b^2}}$ 21. $\sqrt[6]{32x^{-8}y^{12}}$

13. $\sqrt[3]{\tfrac{24}{343}}$

14. $3\sqrt[3]{\tfrac{5}{2}}$ 18. $\dfrac{1}{\sqrt{2x^2 + 3}}$ 22. $2\sqrt[3]{-12x^{-2}y^{-3}}\,\sqrt[3]{-2x^{-5}}$

Express each of the following as a fraction with the expression for the numerator free of radicals.

B 23. $\sqrt{\dfrac{2x}{5}}$ 25. $\sqrt[3]{\dfrac{6(x+1)^8}{3(x+1)}}$ 27. $\sqrt[4]{7(t^2+3)}$

24. $\sqrt{\dfrac{7a}{5}}$ 26. $\sqrt[3]{\dfrac{4(y+2)^9}{12(y+2)^4}}$ 28. $\sqrt[6]{5(v^2+4)}$

Assuming that a and b denote real numbers and that n represents a positive integer, prove each of the following statements, subject to the indicated additional restrictions.

C 29. $\sqrt[n]{ab} = \sqrt[n]{a}\,\sqrt[n]{b}$; n odd, and exactly one of the numbers a, b negative. (*Hint:* First show that $\sqrt[n]{ab}$ and $\sqrt[n]{a}\,\sqrt[n]{b}$ both denote nonpositive numbers.)

30. $\sqrt[n]{\dfrac{a}{b}} = \dfrac{\sqrt[n]{a}}{\sqrt[n]{b}}$; $a \geq 0$, $b > 0$.

31. $\sqrt[n]{\dfrac{a}{b}} = \dfrac{\sqrt[n]{a}}{\sqrt[n]{b}}$; n odd; $\dfrac{a}{b} < 0$.

32. $\sqrt[n]{b^m} = (\sqrt[n]{b})^m$; $\sqrt[n]{b}$ denotes a real number, m a positive integer.

33. $\sqrt[n]{b^{-m}} = (\sqrt[n]{b})^{-m}$; $b \neq 0$; $\sqrt[n]{b}$ denotes a real number; m a positive integer. (*Hint:* Apply the quotient property of radicals to $\sqrt[n]{b^{-m}}$ or $\sqrt[n]{\dfrac{1}{b^m}}$ and use the result of Exercise 32.)

PROBLEMS   Express each answer in simple radical form, and then approximate it to the nearest integer. Where needed, use $\pi \doteq \frac{22}{7}$.

A   1. Find the time T in seconds for a complete swing of a pendulum whose length L is 4 meters. $\left(T = 2\pi\sqrt{\dfrac{L}{9.8}}\right)$

2. Determine (in kilometers per second) the escape velocity V at the surface of a planet whose radius R is 6400 kilometers and on which the acceleration due to gravity g is $\frac{1}{105}$ kilometers per second per second. $(V = \sqrt{2gR})$

3. The altitude h of a cone with volume 284 cubic centimeters is 11 centimeters. Find the radius r. $(V = \frac{1}{3}\pi r^2 h)$

4. Find the length d of a diameter of a sphere whose volume is 792 cubic meters. $(V = \frac{1}{6}\pi d^3)$

5. The maximum height h (in meters) attained by an object fired with an initial vertical velocity of v meters per second is given by $h = \dfrac{v^2}{19.6}$ (neglecting air resistance). Find the velocity required to shoot a projectile to an altitude of 3000 meters.

6. A sky diver left her plane at 3,500 meters and fell freely to an altitude of 700 meters, where she opened her parachute. Determine the time t (in seconds) that she fell before opening her chute, if the distance d (in meters) fallen in free flight is $d = 4.9t^2$.

B   **7.** Find the circumference of a circle whose area is 98 square centimeters.

8. A man derives a dollars from his business one year and b dollars the next. By varying the use of his resources, he can determine a and b according to the formula $b = 10000 - \dfrac{a^2}{4900}$. If he wants to take \$6400 next year, how much can he take this year?

9. A cube and a sphere have the same surface area, 40.0 square meters. What is the ratio of their volumes? (For a sphere of radius r, surface area S, and volume V, $S = 4\pi r^2$ and $V = \frac{4}{3}\pi r^3$.)

10. According to Kepler's third law of planetary motion, the cubes of the average distances of the planets from the sun are proportional to the squares of their times of one revolution around the sun. If Mars is one-sixth as far from the sun as Saturn, find the ratio of their times of revolution.

8–7   *operations with radicals*

A sum of radicals can be simplified in accordance with the following rules:

1. First simplify each radical in the sum.
2. Then combine radical terms containing the *same index and radicand,* using the distributive law.

EXAMPLE 1   **Simplify** $a\sqrt[4]{16a} + 3\sqrt[4]{a^5} - a\sqrt[4]{2401}$.

SOLUTION
$$
\begin{aligned}
a\sqrt[4]{16a} + 3\sqrt[4]{a^5} - a\sqrt[4]{2401} &= a\sqrt[4]{2^4 \cdot a} + 3\sqrt[4]{a^4 \cdot a} - a\sqrt[4]{7^4} \\
&= 2a\sqrt[4]{a} + 3a\sqrt[4]{a} - 7a \\
&= 5a\sqrt[4]{a} - 7a \\
&= a(5\sqrt[4]{a} - 7). \textbf{ Answer.}
\end{aligned}
$$

To simplify a product or quotient involving radicals, you can use the theorems in the preceding section.

EXAMPLE 2   **Simplify** $(\sqrt[3]{a^2} - 1)(\sqrt[3]{a} + a)$.

SOLUTION
$$
\begin{aligned}
(\sqrt[3]{a^2} - 1)(\sqrt[3]{a} + a) &= \sqrt[3]{a^3} + a\sqrt[3]{a^2} - \sqrt[3]{a} - a \\
&= a + a(\sqrt[3]{a})^2 - \sqrt[3]{a} - a \\
&= a(\sqrt[3]{a})^2 - \sqrt[3]{a} \\
&= \sqrt[3]{a}(a\sqrt[3]{a} - 1). \textbf{ Answer.}
\end{aligned}
$$

EXAMPLE 3 Rationalize the denominator of $\dfrac{x}{\sqrt{x} - 2}$.

SOLUTION *Plan:* Use the formula for the difference of squares,
$$(a - b)(a + b) = a^2 - b^2.$$

$$\frac{x}{\sqrt{x} - 2} = \frac{x(\sqrt{x} + 2)}{(\sqrt{x} - 2)(\sqrt{x} + 2)} = \frac{x(\sqrt{x} + 2)}{x - 4}. \quad \text{Answer.}$$

Using radicals, you can factor certain quadratic polynomials which are irreducible over the set of polynomials with *integral* coefficients.

EXAMPLE 4 Factor $x^2 - 18$ completely over the set of polynomials with *real* coefficients.

SOLUTION $x^2 - 18 = x^2 - (\sqrt{18})^2 = (x - \sqrt{18})(x + \sqrt{18}).$

$\therefore x^2 - 18 = (x - 3\sqrt{2})(x + 3\sqrt{2}).$ Answer.

WRITTEN EXERCISES Simplify each expression and then use Table 3 or 4 in the Appendix to evaluate to the nearest hundredth.

A
1. $\sqrt{32} + 5\sqrt{2}$
2. $2\sqrt{54} - 3\sqrt{6}$
3. $\frac{1}{2}\sqrt{48} - 3\sqrt{75} - \frac{3}{4}\sqrt{192}$

4. $\frac{1}{3}\sqrt{28} - 2\sqrt{\frac{25}{7}} + 12\sqrt{9\frac{1}{7}}$
5. $2\sqrt[3]{\frac{40}{6}} + 5\sqrt[3]{27} - \sqrt[3]{\frac{135}{6}}$
6. $\sqrt[3]{-0.027} + 7\sqrt[3]{\frac{3}{10}} - \sqrt[3]{37.5}$

Express in simple form.

7. $x\sqrt{9x} - 8\sqrt{16x^3} + \sqrt{121x^3}, \, x \geq 0$
8. $\sqrt{27y^4} - 2\sqrt{12y^4} + 3\sqrt{72y^4}$
9. $2\sqrt[4]{3x^8} - 2\sqrt[4]{48x^8} + \sqrt[4]{243}$
10. $\sqrt[3]{-40x^2} + x\sqrt[3]{5x^5} - \sqrt[3]{625x^5}$
11. $2\sqrt{6}(\sqrt{3} - 4\sqrt{12})$
12. $(\sqrt{5} - \sqrt{16})(\sqrt{5} + \sqrt{16})$
13. $(\sqrt{3} + \sqrt{7})^2$
14. $(2\sqrt{5} - \sqrt{9})^2$
15. $(3\sqrt{11} - 2)(4\sqrt{11} + 5)$

16. $(\sqrt[4]{2} + 3)(\sqrt[4]{2} - 1)$
17. $\dfrac{4}{\sqrt{7} + 3}$
18. $\dfrac{5}{1 - \sqrt{6}}$
19. $\dfrac{-8}{\sqrt{14} - 3}$
20. $\dfrac{11}{4\sqrt{2} - 9}$

B
21. $(\sqrt[3]{3} - \sqrt[3]{5})(\sqrt[3]{9} + \sqrt[3]{15} + \sqrt[3]{25})$
22. $(\sqrt[3]{7} + \sqrt[3]{2})(\sqrt[3]{49} - \sqrt[3]{14} + \sqrt[3]{4})$
23. $(\sqrt[3]{x} + \sqrt[3]{y})(\sqrt[3]{x^2} - \sqrt[3]{xy} + \sqrt[3]{y^2})$
24. $(\sqrt[3]{a} - \sqrt[3]{b})(\sqrt[3]{a^2} + \sqrt[3]{ab} + \sqrt[3]{b^2})$

25. $\dfrac{1}{\sqrt[3]{7} + \sqrt[3]{2}}$
26. $\dfrac{1}{\sqrt[3]{5} - \sqrt[3]{3}}$

27. $\dfrac{4}{\sqrt{x+3}-2}$ **28.** $\dfrac{2}{3-\sqrt{x-1}}$

By assigning the given values to the variables, show that:

29. $\sqrt{x+y} \neq \sqrt{x} + \sqrt{y}$; $x = 36, y = 64$.

30. $\sqrt[3]{x-y} \neq \sqrt[3]{x} - \sqrt[3]{y}$; $x = 27, y = 8$.

31. $\dfrac{1}{\sqrt[3]{x}} + \dfrac{1}{\sqrt[3]{y}} \neq \dfrac{1}{\sqrt[3]{x+y}}$; $x = 1, y = 1$.

32. $\dfrac{\sqrt[3]{x+y}}{\sqrt[3]{x}} \neq \sqrt[3]{\dfrac{y}{x}}$; $x = 1, y = 1$.

Factor completely over the set of polynomials with real coefficients.

C **33.** $x^2 + \sqrt{8}x + 2$ **35.** $x^3 + 81$ **37.** $x^2 + 4xy + 4y^2 - 3$

   34. $x^2 - \sqrt{12}x + 3$ **36.** $x^3 - 16$ **38.** $r^2 - 2rs + s^2 - 8$

8–8   *equations involving radicals*

To solve an equation in which one term contains a variable in a radicand, you first isolate that term on one side of the equality sign. Then you can raise both members to the power of the radical index, and solve the resulting equation.

EXAMPLE 1   Solve $y + \sqrt{y-2} - 4 = 0$.

SOLUTION

$$y + \sqrt{y-2} - 4 = 0$$
$$y - 4 = -\sqrt{y-2} \qquad (1)$$
$$(y-4)^2 = (-\sqrt{y-2})^2 \qquad (2)$$
$$y^2 - 8y + 16 = y - 2$$
$$y^2 - 9y + 18 = 0$$
$$(y-6)(y-3) = 0$$
$$y = 6, \; y = 3$$

CHECK   For $y = 6$: $6 + \sqrt{6-2} - 4 \overset{?}{=} 0$ | For $y = 3$: $3 + \sqrt{3-2} - 4 \overset{?}{=} 0$

$6 + 2 - 4 \neq 0$ | $3 + 1 - 4 = 0$

$\therefore$ the solution set is $\{3\}$. **Answer.**

Can you explain why an "extraneous value" appeared, that is, why the "squared" Equation (2) is not equivalent to the given equation? Think of the equation $x = 3$ and the equation obtained by squaring both members, $x^2 = 9$; the latter has *two* real solutions, $x = 3$ and $x = -3$, while the former has only *one*, $x = 3$.

In general, for two functions $P(x)$ and $Q(x)$, and n a positive integer, the solution set of the equation $P(x) = Q(x)$ is a subset of the solution set of $[P(x)]^n = [Q(x)]^n$. The following theorem summarizes the facts.

> **Theorem.** For n a positive integer and a and $b \in \mathcal{R}$:
>
> 1. If $a = b$, then $a^n = b^n$.
> 2. If $a^n = b^n$ and n is odd, then $a = b$.
> 3. If $a^n = b^n$ and n is even, then $a = \pm b$.

If more than one term in an equation contains a variable in a radicand, you may have to repeat the process of isolating a radical term.

EXAMPLE 2   Solve $\sqrt{x - 3} = \sqrt{2} - \sqrt{x}$ over $\mathcal{R}$.

SOLUTION
$$\sqrt{x - 3} = \sqrt{2} - \sqrt{x}$$
$$(\sqrt{x - 3})^2 = (\sqrt{2} - \sqrt{x})^2$$
$$x - 3 = 2 - 2\sqrt{2x} + x$$
$$-5 = -2\sqrt{2x}$$
$$(-5)^2 = (-2\sqrt{2x})^2$$
$$25 = 8x$$
$$\tfrac{25}{8} = x$$

CHECK
$$\sqrt{\tfrac{25}{8} - 3} \overset{?}{=} \sqrt{2} - \sqrt{\tfrac{25}{8}}$$
$$\sqrt{\tfrac{1}{8}} \overset{?}{=} \sqrt{2} - 5\sqrt{\tfrac{1}{8}}$$
$$\tfrac{1}{4}\sqrt{2} + \tfrac{5}{4}\sqrt{2} \overset{?}{=} \sqrt{2}$$
$$\tfrac{3}{2}\sqrt{2} \neq \sqrt{2}$$

$\therefore$ the solution set is $\varnothing$. **Answer.**

Example 2 illustrates the fact that the solution set of $P(x) = Q(x)$ may be empty even though $[P(x)]^n = [Q(x)]^n$ has one or more real roots. Actually in this case you can tell by inspecting the given equation that there can be no real value of x for which $P(x) = Q(x)$; the proof is left as Exercise 33.

WRITTEN EXERCISES   Solve each equation over $\mathcal{R}$.

A
1. $\sqrt{m} - 6 = 0$
2. $\sqrt{t} - 5 = 0$
3. $\sqrt[3]{y + 2} = 3$
4. $\sqrt[3]{v + 1} = 4$
5. $\sqrt{5x + 1} + 7 = 14$

6. $\sqrt{1 + 2r} - 8 = -3$
7. $4 + \sqrt[4]{\dfrac{a}{2}} = 7$
8. $\sqrt[4]{\dfrac{b}{3}} - 4 = 2$

9. $\sqrt[3]{y^{-1}} = -3$

10. $\sqrt[3]{a^2} + 6 = 15$

11. $\frac{1}{3}\sqrt{b^5} - 1 = 80$

12. $4\sqrt[3]{v^{-1}} + 8 = 0$

13. $\sqrt[4]{x^2 + x + 9} = 3$

14. $\sqrt[3]{s^2 - 1} - 2 = 0$

15. $\sqrt{2y - 6} = 3 - y$

16. $\sqrt{2(x + 6)} = x + 2$

17. $\sqrt{p^2 - 4} = p + 8$

18. $\sqrt{9 + a^2} = 5 - a$

19. $12 + 3\sqrt[3]{2n} = 0$

20. $12 + 2\sqrt{3n} = 0$

21. $4 + 5\sqrt{10n} = 0$

22. $5 - 3\sqrt[3]{2n + 1} = 0$

23. $\sqrt{k - 7} = \sqrt{k} - 1$

24. $\sqrt{s - 10} + \sqrt{s} = 2$

25. $\sqrt{q + 6} + \sqrt{q} = 3$

26. $\sqrt{r + 2} + \sqrt{r} = 1$

Solve each of the following for the variable shown in red.

B 27. $r = \sqrt[3]{\dfrac{3w}{\pi 4d}}$

28. $r = \sqrt[3]{\dfrac{2mM}{C}}$

29. $c = \sqrt{a^2 + b^2}$

30. $\sqrt{x + a} = \sqrt{x} + \sqrt{a},\ a > 0$

31. $v = \dfrac{1}{2}\sqrt{1 + \dfrac{T}{d}}$

32. $\dfrac{1}{d} = \sqrt{\dfrac{4F}{d} - 3F^2}$

33. Argue that over $\mathfrak{R}$ the equation $\sqrt{x - 3} = \sqrt{2} - \sqrt{x}$ has no solution because the left-hand member is not defined for $x < 3$ and the left-hand member is greater than the right-hand member for $x \geq 3$.

C 34. Prove: If r and s denote real numbers and $r^3 = s^3$, then:
   a. r and s are both zero, both positive, or both negative.
   b. $r = s$.
   Hint: Use the result of part (a) and $r^3 - s^3 = (r - s)(r^2 + rs + s^2)$.

35. Prove: If r and s denote real numbers and $r^4 = s^4$, then:
   a. r and s are both zero, or r and s are both nonzero.
   b. $r = s$ or $r = -s$.
   Hint: Use the fact that $r^4 - s^4 = (r^2 - s^2)(r^2 + s^2)$.

8-9 the quadratic formula

You learned in Section 6–5 how to solve a quadratic equation of the form $ax^2 + bx + c = 0$, $a \neq 0$, in which the left-hand member can be factored over the integers. For example:

$$x^2 - 36 = 0 \qquad\qquad 2x^2 - 5x + 2 = 0$$
$$(x + 6)(x - 6) = 0 \qquad (2x - 1)(x - 2) = 0$$
$$x = 6 \text{ or } x = -6 \qquad x = \tfrac{1}{2} \text{ or } x = 2$$

You can see by inspection that the quadratic equation $3y^2 + 9y + 1 = 0$ cannot be solved by factoring the left member over the integers. If, however, we could put the equation in the form

$$(x + d)^2 = f \qquad (d \text{ and } f \in \mathfrak{R}, \ f \geq 0),$$

it could be easily solved as follows:

$$x + d = \pm\sqrt{f}$$
$$x = -d \pm \sqrt{f}$$

EXAMPLE 1   Solve $(x - \sqrt{3})^2 = 12$.

SOLUTION

$$(x - \sqrt{3})^2 = 12$$
$$x - \sqrt{3} = \pm\sqrt{12}$$
$$x = \sqrt{3} \pm 2\sqrt{3}$$
$$x = 3\sqrt{3} \text{ or } x = -\sqrt{3}.$$

$\therefore$ the solution set is $\{3\sqrt{3}, -\sqrt{3}\}$.   **Answer.**

To transform any quadratic equation

$$(1) \qquad ax^2 + bx + c = 0 \qquad (a, b, \text{ and } c \in \mathfrak{R}, a \neq 0)$$

into the desired form $(x + d)^2 = f$, or

$$(2) \qquad x^2 + 2dx + d^2 = f,$$

let us first rewrite (1) equivalently as

$$(3) \qquad x^2 + \frac{b}{a}x = -\frac{c}{a}.$$

Next, by equating the coefficients of x in Equations (2) and (3), we can find an expression for d, and hence for d^2, in terms of a and b. We can then express the left member of Equation (3) in the desired form $(x + d)^2$; that is, we can **complete the square** in that member, as follows:

$$2d = \frac{b}{a}, \qquad \text{so} \qquad d = \frac{b}{2a} \qquad \text{and} \qquad d^2 = \frac{b^2}{4a^2}.$$

Add $\dfrac{b^2}{4a^2}$ to both members of Equation (3):

$$(4) \qquad x^2 + \frac{b}{a}x + \frac{b^2}{4a^2} = -\frac{c}{a} + \frac{b^2}{4a^2}$$

$$(5) \qquad \left(x + \frac{b}{2a}\right)^2 = \frac{b^2 - 4ac}{4a^2}$$

$$(6) \qquad x + \frac{b}{2a} = \pm\sqrt{\frac{b^2 - 4ac}{4a^2}}$$

$$(7) \qquad x = -\frac{b}{2a} \pm \frac{\sqrt{b^2 - 4ac}}{2a}$$

$$(8) \qquad x = \frac{-b \pm \sqrt{b^2 - 4ac}}{2a}$$

Equation (8) is known as the **quadratic formula.** You can see from the quadratic formula that for x to be a real number, it is necessary that we have $b^2 - 4ac \geq 0$.

EXAMPLE 2 Solve $3y^2 + 9y + 1 = 0$ by (a) completing the square, and (b) using the quadratic formula.

SOLUTION **a.** $3y^2 + 9y + 1 = 0$; $a = 3$, $b = 9$; $\dfrac{b^2}{4a^2} = \dfrac{81}{36} = \dfrac{9}{4}$.

$$y^2 + 3y \qquad = -\frac{1}{3}$$

$$y^2 + 3y + \frac{9}{4} = -\frac{1}{3} + \frac{9}{4}$$

$$\left(y + \frac{3}{2}\right)^2 = \frac{-4 + 27}{12} = \frac{23}{12}$$

$$y + \frac{3}{2} = \pm\sqrt{\frac{23}{12}} = \pm\frac{1}{2}\sqrt{\frac{23}{3}} = \pm\frac{1}{6}\sqrt{69}$$

$$y = -\tfrac{3}{2} \pm \tfrac{1}{6}\sqrt{69}$$

∴ the solution set is $\{-\tfrac{3}{2} + \tfrac{1}{6}\sqrt{69}, \ -\tfrac{3}{2} - \tfrac{1}{6}\sqrt{69}\}$. **Answer.**

b. $a = 3$, $b = 9$, $c = 1$:

$$y = \frac{-9 \pm \sqrt{81 - 12}}{6}$$

$$= -\tfrac{3}{2} \pm \tfrac{1}{6}\sqrt{69}.$$

∴ the solution set is $\{-\tfrac{3}{2} + \tfrac{1}{6}\sqrt{69}, \ -\tfrac{3}{2} - \tfrac{1}{6}\sqrt{69}\}$. **Answer.**

ORAL EXERCISES Read each equation equivalently in the form $ax^2 + bx + c = 0$, with $a > 0$.

1. $6x^2 = 4x + 3$
2. $x^2 = 2 + 3x$
3. $5x = x^2$
4. $3x^2 = 8$
5. $6 = 2x - x^2$

6. $\frac{3}{2}x = 7x^2 + 9$
7. $-2x = 10 - x^2$
8. $4 - 3x - x^2 = 0$
9. $0 = 3 + \frac{5}{3}x - x^2$
10. $2x = 3x^2 - 1$

In Exercises 1–16 give irrational results in simple radical form and also as decimals correct to tenths.

Solve by completing the square.

A
1. $t^2 - 6t - 5 = 0$
2. $y^2 - 4y - 11 = 0$
3. $v^2 - 8v - 3 = 0$
4. $k^2 - 10k + 10 = 0$

5. $3s^2 + 15s + 15 = 0$
6. $2d^2 - 6d - 60 = 0$
7. $6x^2 = 12 - 11x$
8. $11y = 10y^2 - 8$

9–16. Solve the equations in Exercises 1–8 by using the quadratic formula.

Solve over $\mathcal{R}$ by any method.

B
17. $3.5y^2 - 1.1y - 0.6 = 0$
18. $0.13 = 0.07k - 0.2k^2$
19. $\dfrac{2}{a-1} + \dfrac{1}{a+1} = 4$
20. $\dfrac{3}{b-2} - \dfrac{1}{b+2} = 2$
21. $5x^2 + x + 3 = 0$

22. $3u^2 + 2u + 1 = 0$
23. $k^2 - 8k + 2 = 0$
24. $t^2 + 12t - 3 = 0$
25. $d^2 + 2d = \sqrt{3}$
26. $m^2 - 4m = \sqrt{5}$

C
27. $v^4 + 4v^2 - 2 = 0$
28. $3 - 6r^3 - r^6 = 0$

29. $(u^3 + 1)^2 - 2(u^3 + 1) - 3 = 0$
30. $(x^2 + x)^2 - 3(x^2 + x) - 4 = 0$

31. Show that if $c \neq 0$, an alternative form of the quadratic formula is

$$x = \frac{2c}{-b \pm \sqrt{b^2 - 4ac}}.$$

32. Prove that if each root of $ax^2 + bx + c = 0$, $a \neq 0$, is the reciprocal of the other, then $a = c$.

PROBLEMS Unless otherwise directed, express irrational results in simple radical form.

A
1. One base of a trapezoid measures 5 centimeters more than the other, while the altitude is $\frac{4}{3}$ times as long as the shorter base. Find the lengths of the bases if the area is 100 square centimeters.

2. The volume of a rectangular box 4 centimeters high is 84 cubic centimeters. If the perimeter of the base is 20 centimeters, find the dimensions of the box.

3. For the most pleasing effect, the ratio of the width of a rectangle to its length should equal the ratio of its length to the sum of its length and width. With this "Divine Proportion" in mind, design a rectangular picture frame with a perimeter of 60 centimeters. Give the dimensions to the nearest tenth of a centimeter.

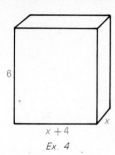

6

$x + 4$

x

Ex. 4

4. A rectangular prism is 6 centimeters high, and it is 4 centimeters longer than it is wide. If the volume of the prism is 42 cubic centimeters, find its width and length.

5. The volumes of two spheres differ by $\frac{800}{3}\pi$ cubic meters and the lengths of their radii differ by 5 meters. Find the length of the radius of the smaller sphere. $(V = \frac{4}{3}\pi r^3)$

6. From a rectangular sheet of metal 20 centimeters long and 12 centimeters wide an open rectangular box is made by cutting squares of equal area from the four corners and folding up the ends. If the area of the base of the box is 48 square centimeters, find the total area of the discarded squares.

B

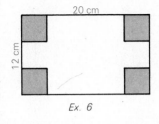

20 cm

12 cm

Ex. 6

7. As a result of tire trouble on the return leg of a 360-kilometer round trip that took 5 hours, Ms. Gorham's average speed coming home was 30 kilometers per hour less than her average speed going. If she had been able to maintain the same average speed coming home as going, what would her total driving time have been?

8. For any positive integer n, $n!$ is the product $1 \cdot 2 \cdot 3 \cdots n$. Determine the value for which $n! = 56(n - 2)!$. (*Hint:* $n! = n(n - 1) \cdot (n - 2)!$ for $n \geq 3$.)

9. The sum of the squares of the first n consecutive integers, i.e., $1^2 + 2^2 + 3^2 + \cdots + n^2$, is given by $\dfrac{n(n + 1)(2n + 1)}{6}$. The sum of the cubes of the first n integers is given by $\left[\dfrac{n(n + 1)}{2}\right]^2$. Determine all values of n for which the sums of the first n squares is equal to $\frac{3}{10}$ times the sum of the first n cubes.

10. An artist is to draw two rectangular diagrams of equal width. One is square; the height of the other is $\frac{1}{2}$ centimeter less than its width. If each dimension of each diagram is to be photo-reduced $\frac{1}{3}$ and the combined area of the two reduced diagrams is to be $13\frac{1}{3}$ square centimeters, what should be the dimensions of each diagram before reduction?

programming in BASIC

EXERCISES

1. Write a program that will print the roots of a quadratic equation by using the quadratic formula. Be sure to include a special print-out if
$$b^2 - 4ac < 0.$$

2. Modify the preceding program to test whether or not $b^2 - 4ac$ is a perfect square. If it is not, print an intermediate step like this (for 3, 9, 1):

$$R1 = (-9 + / 69) / 6 = -.115563$$
$$R2 = (-9 - / 69) / 6 = -2.88444$$

(If you wish, you can mark over the first / to make a square-root sign.)

SELF-TEST 2 Give the meaning of each of the following.

1. rationalizing the denominator
2. completing the square

Express in simple radical form:

Objective 1, page 275

3. $\sqrt[3]{-16x^{-4}}$

4. $\sqrt{48} - \frac{1}{2}\sqrt{27} + \frac{3}{2}\sqrt{75}$

5. $(7\sqrt[3]{5} - 2)(7\sqrt[3]{5} + 2)$

6. $\dfrac{1}{\sqrt{4a^2 + 1}}$

Solve over $\Re$.

Objective 2, page 275

7. $\sqrt{1 + 2n^2} - 8 = -3$

8. $\sqrt[3]{\dfrac{3x^{-2}}{8}} = 3$

Objective 3, page 275

9. Solve by completing the square: $4x^2 - 12x - 7 = 0$

10. Use the quadratic formula to solve: $3x^2 - 5x - 4 = 0$

Check your answers with those printed at the back of the book.

chapter summary

1. The graph of the **power function** defined by $p(x) = x^n$, with n an *even* positive integer, is **symmetric with respect to the vertical axis** and has a **minimum point** at the origin. If n is an *odd* positive integer, the graph contains the origin and is **symmetric with respect to the origin.**

2. Whenever a function is specified by an equation of the form $y = ax^n$, $a \neq 0$, we say that y **varies directly as** x^n or that y is **directly proportional to the nth power of x.**

3. For every positive integer n, any solution of $x^n = b$ is an *nth root of b.* The **radical** $\sqrt[n]{b}$ denotes the *principal nth root of b.* If n is odd, $\sqrt[n]{b^n} = b$; if n is even, $\sqrt[n]{b^n} = |b|$.

4. If a rational root of a *polynomial equation in simple form* with integral coefficients is expressed in lowest terms $\dfrac{p}{q}$, with $q \neq 0$, then p must be an integral factor of the constant term and q an integral factor of the leading coefficient. Any other real root of the equation is an **irrational number.**

5. The **property of density** of the real numbers asserts that between any two real numbers, there is always another real number.

6. A number can be represented by a terminating or a repeating decimal if and only if it is a rational number.

7. If n is a positive integer, and a, b, $\sqrt[n]{a}$, and $\sqrt[n]{b}$ denote real numbers, then:

$$\sqrt[n]{ab} = \sqrt[n]{a}\sqrt[n]{b} \qquad \text{and} \qquad \sqrt[n]{\frac{a}{b}} = \frac{\sqrt[n]{a}}{\sqrt[n]{b}}, \quad b \neq 0$$

If m is also a positive integer, $\sqrt[n]{b^m} = (\sqrt[n]{b})^m$.

8. You can write the **sum or difference of radicals** *having the same index and the same radicand* as a single term by using the distributive property. You can write the **product or quotient of radicals** *having the same index* as a single term by applying the product or quotient property of radicals.

9. To solve an **irrational equation,** isolate a radical as one member and raise each member to the power corresponding to the root index.

10. The **quadratic formula,** $x = \dfrac{-b \pm \sqrt{b^2 - 4ac}}{2a}$, enables you to solve any quadratic equation of the form $ax^2 + bx + c = 0$, $a \neq 0$.

chapter test and review

8-1
1. If s varies directly as t^4 and $s = 5$ when $t = 3$, find s when $t = 6$.

2. The distance a body falls from a position of rest varies directly as the square of the number of seconds it falls. If a body falls 1.2 meters in $\frac{1}{2}$ second, how far will it fall in $1\frac{1}{2}$ seconds?

8-2
3. Solve $x^2 - 1.21 = 0$ over $\mathcal{R}$.

8-3
4. Find the rational roots, if any, of $2x^3 - x^2 - 7x + 6 = 0$.

8-4
5. Find a decimal numeral for **(a)** $\frac{7}{20}$, and **(b)** $\frac{2}{13}$.

6. Express $0.\overline{121}$ as a common fraction in lowest terms.

8-5
7. Determine whether 6.9 is greater than or less than $\sqrt{48}$.

8. Find **(a)** a rational number and **(b)** an irrational number between $127.48\overline{2}$ and $127.48\overline{3}$.

Simplify.

8-6
9. $(3\sqrt[3]{-12xy^2})(4\sqrt[3]{-3x^2y})$

10. $\dfrac{\sqrt[4]{2x^{-1}}}{\sqrt[4]{64x^{-5}}}$

8-7
11. $5\sqrt{27} + 2\sqrt{3}$

12. $-\sqrt[3]{-6\frac{2}{3}} - \sqrt[3]{125} + 2\sqrt[3]{\frac{5}{6}}$

13. $(3 - \sqrt{2})(\sqrt{6} - \sqrt{3})$

14. $\dfrac{4}{3\sqrt{5} - \sqrt{6}}$

8-8
15. Solve over $\mathcal{R}$: $2 - x - 2\sqrt{x + 1} = 0$

8-9
16. Solve by completing the square: $4x^2 - 20x + 9 = 0$

17. Use the quadratic formula to solve: $2x^2 + 3x - 7 = 0$

This painting en-
titled HAT is one of the
series "Hommage à l'Hexagone"
by Victor Vasarely. Although painted
on a flat surface, the shading creates a three-
dimensional effect. Try looking at the picture
from different angles—do you see the same shapes?

290

complex numbers and polynomial functions

the set of complex numbers

After completing the next five sections, you should be able to:
1. Simplify a square-root radical whose radicand is a negative number.
2. Find the sum, difference, product and quotient (divisor not zero) of two given complex numbers.

Objectives
3. Use the discriminant of a quadratic equation to determine the nature of its roots.
4. Use relations between the roots and coefficients of a quadratic equation to determine the sum and product of the roots when the equation is given, and vice versa.

9-1 *imaginary numbers*

Over the set of positive real numbers, the linear equation

$$x + 1 = 0$$

has no solution. However, when you extend the replacement set of x to contain negative as well as positive numbers, the given equation has a single solution, namely, -1.

Over the set $\Re$ of all real numbers, the quadratic equation

$$x^2 + 1 = 0$$

has no solution. Can we extend the replacement set of x to contain new numbers which will satisfy this equation? About 400 years ago, mathematicians proposed the introduction of a number, i, with the property that

$$i^2 + 1 = 0,$$

or

$$i^2 = -1.$$

Thus, i is a solution of the equation $x^2 + 1 = 0$.

The fact that $i^2 = -1$ suggests that you write

$$\sqrt{-1} = i$$

and call i "a square root of -1."

By requiring that multiplication continue to have the commutative and associative properties, you can discover how to multiply real numbers and i. Study the following examples:

$$3 \cdot i = 3i; \quad 4(5i) = (4 \cdot 5)i = 20i; \quad 2i(-3) = 2(-3)i = -6i;$$
$$(7i)(2i) = (7 \cdot 2)(i \cdot i) = 14i^2 = 14(-1) = -14;$$
$$(-i)(i) = -i^2 = -(-1) = 1;$$
$$(3i)^2 = (3i)(3i) = 3^2 i^2 = 9(-1) = -9.$$

Since for any $r > 0$,

$$(\sqrt{r}\, i)^2 = (\sqrt{r})^2 i^2 = r(-1) = -r,$$

it is natural to make this definition:

For every positive real number r, $\sqrt{-r} = i\sqrt{r}$.

EXAMPLE 1 $\quad \sqrt{-12} = \sqrt{12}\, i = 2\sqrt{3}\, i$, or $2i\sqrt{3}$. **Answer.**

The last form of the answer in Example 1 is often used to avoid the error of writing $\sqrt{3i}$ for $\sqrt{3}\, i$.

The preceding suggests the following fact: *For every nonzero real number b, bi is a number whose square is $-b^2$; that is, $(bi)^2 = -b^2$.* For $b \neq 0$, we call bi a pure imaginary* number. The number i is called the imaginary unit. We define $0 \cdot i$ to be 0.

Do you see that the product of a nonzero real number and a pure imaginary number is a pure imaginary number, but the product of two pure imaginary numbers is a real number? When you simplify successive powers of i, you find the values repeating in cycles of four, according to the pattern $i, -1, -i, 1$.

---

*The term "imaginary" is an unfortunate relic of seventeenth-century uneasiness about these numbers; it does not imply any doubt about the existence of the numbers. They are in fact of great importance in many branches of mathematics.

$$i^1 = i \qquad\qquad i^5 = i^4 \cdot i = 1 \cdot i = i$$
$$i^2 = -1 \qquad\qquad i^6 = i^4 \cdot i^2 = 1 \cdot -1 = -1$$
$$i^3 = i^2 \cdot i = -1 \cdot i = -i \qquad i^7 = i^4 \cdot i^3 = 1 \cdot -i = -i$$
$$i^4 = i^2 \cdot i^2 = -1 \cdot -1 = 1 \qquad i^8 = i^4 \cdot i^4 = 1 \cdot 1 = 1$$

Notice also that $i(-i) = (-i)i = 1$. Thus, i and $-i$ are reciprocals; that is,

$$\frac{1}{i} = -i \qquad \text{and} \qquad \frac{1}{-i} = i.$$

You can use this fact in computing a quotient in which the divisor is a pure imaginary number.

$$\frac{14}{8i} = \frac{14}{8} \cdot \frac{1}{i} = \frac{7}{4} \cdot -i = -\frac{7}{4}i$$

$$\frac{12}{i^3} = \frac{12}{-i} = 12\,\frac{1}{-i} = 12 \cdot i = 12i$$

To simplify a square-root radical whose radicand is a negative number, take these steps:

1. Express the radical as the product of a real number and i.
2. Then use the properties of the *real roots of real numbers* (Chapter 8) to simplify this product.

EXAMPLE 2
$$\sqrt{-25} + \sqrt{-20} = i\sqrt{25} + i\sqrt{20}$$
$$= 5i + 2\sqrt{5}\,i$$
$$= (5 + 2\sqrt{5})i. \quad \textbf{Answer.}$$

Notice the use of the distributive property in Example 2.

EXAMPLE 3
$$\sqrt{-2} \cdot \sqrt{-50} = i\sqrt{2} \cdot i\sqrt{50}$$
$$= \sqrt{2 \cdot 50} \cdot i^2 = \sqrt{100} \cdot (-1) = -10. \quad \textbf{Answer.}$$

Notice that if you wrote $\sqrt{-2} \cdot \sqrt{-50} = \sqrt{-2 \cdot -50} = \sqrt{100} = 10$, you would be applying properties that have been proved only for radicals denoting *real numbers*, and you would in fact obtain an incorrect result. This is why it is important to follow the order of operations indicated above.

EXAMPLE 4
$$\frac{3}{\sqrt{-12}} = \frac{3}{i\sqrt{12}} = \frac{3i}{\sqrt{12}} = -\frac{3i}{2\sqrt{3}}$$
$$= -\frac{3i \cdot \sqrt{3}}{2\sqrt{3} \cdot \sqrt{3}} = -\frac{3\sqrt{3}\,i}{2 \cdot 3} = -\frac{\sqrt{3}\,i}{2}$$
$$= -\frac{\sqrt{3}}{2}i. \quad \textbf{Answer.}$$

Express each of the following in the form b or bi, where b is a real number.

1. $3i \cdot 2$
6. $-i(2i)$
11. $\dfrac{2i}{3i}$
16. $\sqrt{-18}$

2. $4i \cdot 5$
7. $-i(-i)$
12. $\dfrac{-4i}{5i}$
17. $\dfrac{-1}{i}$

3. $2i(-4)$
8. $3i(-5i)$
13. $\sqrt{-36}$
18. $\dfrac{2}{-i}$

4. $-3i(-3)$
9. $\dfrac{12i}{4}$
14. $\sqrt{-7}$
19. $\dfrac{2}{3i}$

5. $4i\left(\dfrac{i}{2}\right)$
10. $\dfrac{-9i}{3}$
15. $\sqrt{-8}$
20. $\dfrac{7}{-4i}$

Name the two roots of the given equation.

EXAMPLE $t^2 + 9 = 0$

SOLUTION $3i$ and $-3i$. Answer.

21. $x^2 + 4 = 0$
23. $y^2 + 50 = 0$
25. $4z^2 + 9 = 0$

22. $x^2 + 16 = 0$
24. $y^2 + 27 = 0$
26. $25t^2 + 121 = 0$

WRITTEN EXERCISES   Simplify. Assume that x denotes a positive real number.

A

1. i^{10}
11. $\sqrt{-\frac{2}{3}}$
18. $\dfrac{5\sqrt{-125}}{2\sqrt{-5}}$

2. i^{28}
12. $\sqrt{-\frac{5}{6}}$

3. i^7
13. $\sqrt{-3}\sqrt{-12}$
19. $\dfrac{3}{\sqrt{-3}}$

4. i^{21}
14. $\sqrt{-8}\sqrt{-125}$

5. $(i\sqrt{17})^2$
15. $\dfrac{i\sqrt{27}}{i\sqrt{3}}$
20. $\dfrac{5}{\sqrt{-5}}$

6. $(i\sqrt{11})^2$

7. $\sqrt{-7}$
21. $2\sqrt{-3} + 7\sqrt{-27}$

8. $\sqrt{-3}$
16. $\dfrac{i\sqrt{2}}{i\sqrt{8}}$
22. $5\sqrt{-2} + 2\sqrt{-8}$

9. $2\sqrt{-45}$
23. $7\sqrt{-18} - 2\sqrt{-2}$

10. $3\sqrt{-28}$
17. $\dfrac{2\sqrt{-12}}{3\sqrt{-3}}$
24. $4\sqrt{-12} - 5\sqrt{-3}$

B

25. $\sqrt{-\frac{2}{3}} - \sqrt{-\frac{3}{2}}$
27. $\dfrac{1}{i} + \dfrac{1}{i^2} + \dfrac{1}{i^3} + \dfrac{1}{i^4}$

26. $-\sqrt{-\frac{1}{9}} - \sqrt{-\frac{1}{6}}$
28. $i + 2i^2 + 3i^3 + 4i^4$

29. $\sqrt{-x^2} + \sqrt{-4x^2} - \sqrt{-9x^2}$

30. $\sqrt{-x^2} - \sqrt{-\dfrac{x^2}{4}} - \sqrt{-\dfrac{x^2}{9}}$

31. $\sqrt{-x^3} + \sqrt{-x^2} + \sqrt{-x}$

32. $\sqrt{-2x^6} + \sqrt{-8x^6} - \sqrt{-18x^6}$

9–2 *complex numbers; addition and subtraction*

The real numbers together with the pure imaginary numbers form a set in which you can compute products (Section 9–1). But to be able to add two numbers in this set, such as 2 and $7i$ you have to invent another new number, namely, $2 + 7i$, which is neither a real number nor a pure imaginary number. In fact, to assign a sum to any real number a and any pure imaginary number bi, you have to invent a number

$$a + bi,$$

which is called a complex number. If $b \neq 0$, $a + bi$ is also called an imaginary number. You call a, the *real part*, and b, the *imaginary part*, of $a + bi$.

We shall use the letter $\mathcal{C}$ to refer to the set of all complex numbers. In $\mathcal{C}$, equality of numbers is defined as follows:

> If a, b, c, and d are real numbers, then $a + bi = c + di$ if and only if $a = c$ and $b = d$.

Notice that $9 + 6i \neq 6 + 9i$, because $9 \neq 6$.

By identifying the real number a with the complex number $a + 0i$, you can say that every real number belongs to $\mathcal{C}$. Similarly, from the agreement $0 + bi = bi$, it follows that every pure imaginary number is also a complex number.

To define the sum

$$(a + bi) + (c + di),$$

we are guided by the requirement that the familiar properties of sums and products in $\mathcal{R}$ continue to be true in $\mathcal{C}$. For example, if the commutative and associative properties of addition are valid in $\mathcal{C}$ and if multiplication in $\mathcal{C}$ is distributive with respect to addition, then

$$(5 + 3i) + (4 + 2i) = (5 + 4) + (3i + 2i)$$
$$= (5 + 4) + (3 + 2)i$$
$$\therefore (5 + 3i) + (4 + 2i) = 9 + 5i.$$

The previous example suggests the following:

Definition of Addition in $\mathbb{C}$

If a, b, c, and d are real numbers, then

$$(a + bi) + (c + di) = (a + c) + (b + d)i.$$

To simplify notation, the symbol $a + (-b)i$ is often written $a - bi$. Thus,

$$(3 - 5i) + (-1 + 2i) = (3 - 1) + (-5 + 2)i = 2 - 3i.$$

The following facts are true in $\mathbb{C}$. (See Exercises 21 and 22 page 298.)

1. The **additive identity element** is $0 + 0i$, or 0. For example, $(6 + 7i) + (0 + 0i) = 6 + 7i$.
2. For all real numbers c and d, the **negative** or **additive inverse**, of $c + di$ is $-c - di$; that is,

$$-(c + di) = -c - di.$$

For example, $-(2 - 5i) = -2 + 5i$.

Because the relationship between addition and subtraction (page 20) is preserved in $\mathbb{C}$, you can use fact **2** above to obtain the rule for subtracting one complex number from another. You have:

$$(a + bi) - (c + di) = (a + bi) + (-c - di)$$
$$\therefore (a + bi) - (c + di) = (a - c) + (b - d)i.$$

Complex numbers such as $2 + 3i$ and $2 - 3i$ are called *complex conjugates*. Thus, for any real numbers a and b, the complex conjugate of $a + bi$ is $a - bi$; conversely, the complex conjugate of $a - bi$ is $a + bi$.

EXAMPLE   Find (a) the sum and (b) the difference of $7 + 5i$ and its conjugate.

SOLUTION   The conjugate of $7 + 5i$ is $7 - 5i$.

a. $(7 + 5i) + (7 - 5i) = (7 + 7) + (5 - 5)i$
   $\therefore (7 + 5i) + (7 - 5i) = 14$. **Answer.**

b. $(7 + 5i) - (7 - 5i) = (7 - 7) + (5 + 5)i$
   $\therefore (7 + 5i) - (7 - 5i) = 10i$. **Answer.**

This example suggests the following theorem. Its proof is left as Exercise 23, page 298.

Theorem. For all real numbers a and b:

$$(a + bi) + (a - bi) = 2a$$
$$(a + bi) - (a - bi) = 2bi$$

Therefore, the sum of a complex number $a + bi$ and its complex conjugate is a real number; if $b \neq 0$, their difference is a pure imaginary number.

ORAL EXERCISES State (a) the additive inverse and (b) the complex conjugate of the given complex number.

1. $2 + 5i$ 3. $-1 + 2i$ 5. $\sqrt{2} - 8i$ 7. 4

2. $3 + 4i$ 4. $7 - 3i$ 6. $-6 - \sqrt{5}\,i$ 8. $2i$

9–16. In each of Exercises 1–8 state the sum of the given complex number and its complex conjugate.

17–24. In each of Exercises 1–8 state the difference of the given complex number and its complex conjugate.

WRITTEN EXERCISES Determine (a) the sum and (b) the difference (second subtracted from first) of the given complex numbers.

A   1. $5 + 8i, 2i$ 5. $1 + 7i, 5 + 6i$

2. $7 + 10i, -4i$ 6. $-3 + 4i, 2 - 8i$

3. $-6i, 2 + i$ 7. $3 - \sqrt{-16}, \sqrt{-9} + 2$

4. $i, 3 - i$ 8. $-2\sqrt{-49} + 4, 5 - \sqrt{-1}$

Determine (a) the sum and (b) the difference of the given complex number and its complex conjugate.

9. $5 - 3i$ 11. $-i - 1$ 13. $5 - \sqrt{-25}$

10. $-2 + 7i$ 12. $-2i + 3$ 14. $-3 + \sqrt{-36}$

Determine real numbers x and y for which the given equation is true.

15. $(1 - i) + (x + yi) = -2 + 7i$ 17. $x - 3yi = 2i + (1 + 4i)$

16. $(-4 + 2i) + (x + yi) = 3 - 4i$ 18. $5x + yi = 4 + (11 - i)$

B   19. $-2i(3x - y) + (x - 2y + 3) = \dfrac{2}{i}$

20. $x - y - 6 + \dfrac{2x + y}{i} = 0$

C **21.** Prove: For all real numbers a and b,

$$(a + bi) + (0 + 0i) = a + bi \text{ and } (0 + 0i) + (a + bi) = a + bi.$$

22. Prove: For all real numbers a and b,

$$(a + bi) + (-a - bi) = 0 + 0i.$$

23. Prove the theorem stated on page 297.

24. Prove: The complex conjugate of the sum of two complex numbers is the sum of their complex conjugates.

9-3 *complex numbers; multiplication and division*

Granted that the commutative, associative, and distributive properties of multiplication are to hold in $\mathcal{C}$, you can compute products of complex numbers by following the pattern for products of binomials over $\mathcal{R}$ (page 181). Here is an example:

$$(5 + 3i)(4 + 2i) = 5(4 + 2i) + 3i(4 + 2i)$$
$$= (20 + 10i) + (12i + 6i^2)$$
$$= (20 - 6) + (10i + 12i)$$
$$\therefore (5 + 3i)(4 + 2i) = 14 + 22i.$$

This example leads us to the following:

Definition of Multiplication in $\mathcal{C}$

If a, b, c, and d are real numbers, then

$$(a + bi)(c + di) = (ac - bd) + (ad + bc)i.$$

In particular, for $b = 0$, this definition gives you the following rule for multiplying a real and a complex number:

$$a(c + di) = ac + adi.$$

Thus, $1(c + di) = 1 \cdot c + 1 \cdot di = c + di$, so that 1, or $1 + 0i$, is the **multiplicative identity element** in $\mathcal{C}$.

Notice that, by the definition of multiplication in $\mathcal{C}$,

$$(a + bi)(a - bi) = (a^2 + b^2) + (-ab + ab)i = a^2 + b^2.$$

Hence we have the following result:

> **Theorem.** For all real numbers a and b,
>
> $$(a + bi)(a - bi) = a^2 + b^2.$$

Therefore the product of a complex number and its complex conjugate is a real number.

Because equality, addition, and multiplication of complex numbers have been defined so that the properties of equality, addition, and multiplication for the set of real numbers (pages 29 and 30) are also valid when restated for the set of complex numbers, concepts and methods based on these properties apply in working with complex numbers.

The following examples show how you can use the foregoing theorem to express the reciprocal of a complex number and the quotient of two complex numbers (divisor not zero) in the standard form, $a + bi$ (see Exercises 23–24, page 300).

EXAMPLE 1 **Express the reciprocal of $2 - 5i$ in the form $a + bi$.**

SOLUTION *Plan.* Multiply the numerator and denominator of $\dfrac{1}{2 - 5i}$ by the complex conjugate of the denominator.

$$\frac{1}{2 - 5i} = \frac{1}{(2 - 5i)}\frac{(2 + 5i)}{(2 + 5i)} = \frac{2 + 5i}{4 + 25} = \frac{2 + 5i}{29}$$

$$= \frac{2}{29} + \frac{5}{29}i. \quad \text{Answer.}$$

EXAMPLE 2 **Express $\dfrac{2 + 3i}{7 + 4i}$ in standard form, $a + bi$.**

SOLUTION $\dfrac{2 + 3i}{7 + 4i} = \dfrac{(2 + 3i)(7 - 4i)}{(7 + 4i)(7 - 4i)}$

$$= \frac{(14 + 12) + (-8 + 21)i}{49 + 16} = \frac{26 + 13i}{65}$$

$$= \frac{2}{5} + \frac{1}{5}i. \quad \text{Answer.}$$

WRITTEN EXERCISES Determine the product of the given complex numbers.

A

1. $4 - i, 4 + i$

2. $1 + 6i, 5 - 7i$

3. $-2 - 3i, -2 + 3i$

4. $-3 + 5i, 7 - i$

5. $-\frac{1}{2} + \frac{1}{2}\sqrt{3}\,i, -\frac{1}{2} - \frac{1}{2}\sqrt{3}\,i$

6. $-\frac{1}{2} + \frac{1}{2}\sqrt{3}\,i, -\frac{1}{2} + \frac{1}{2}\sqrt{3}\,i$

7. $-\frac{1}{2} - \frac{1}{2}\sqrt{3}\,i, -\frac{1}{2} - \frac{1}{2}\sqrt{3}\,i$

8. $\frac{1}{2} + \frac{1}{2}i, \frac{1}{2} + \frac{1}{2}i$

Express in the form $a + bi$, where a and b are real numbers.

9. $\dfrac{4 - i}{2 + i}$

10. $\dfrac{1 + 6i}{5 - 7i}$

11. $\dfrac{-2 - 3i}{4 - 3i}$

12. $\dfrac{-3 + 5i}{7 - i}$

13. $\dfrac{1}{-\frac{1}{2} + \frac{1}{2}\sqrt{3}\,i}$

14. $\dfrac{1}{-\frac{1}{2} - \frac{1}{2}i}$

B 15. $\left(\dfrac{3 - i}{2 + i}\right)^2 - (4 - 5i)$

16. $1 + 3i - \left(\dfrac{2 + 5i}{5 - 2i}\right)^2$

17. $\dfrac{(1 + i)(2 - 3i)}{4 + i}$

18. $\dfrac{1 - 5i}{(2 + i)(3 - i)}$

Solve over $\mathbb{C}$.

19. $(2 - 6i)z = 3i$

20. $(4 - 5i)z = 2$

21. $2iz + (3 - i)(3 + i) = 0$

22. $(i + 1)z - (4 + i)(5 - i) = 0$

C 23. By multiplying both numerator and denominator by the complex conjugate of the denominator, show that for all real numbers a and b not both of which are zero,

$$\frac{1}{a + bi} = \frac{a}{a^2 + b^2} - \frac{b}{a^2 + b^2}i.$$

24. Show that for all real numbers a, b, c, d, where c and d are not both zero,

$$\frac{a + bi}{c + di} = \frac{ac + bd}{c^2 + d^2} + \frac{bc - ad}{c^2 + d^2}i.$$

25. Show that the complex conjugate of the product of two complex numbers is the product of their complex conjugates.

9–4 *the nature of the roots of a quadratic equation*

The quadratic formula developed in Section 8–9 can be used to determine the solution set of a quadratic equation over $\mathbb{C}$.

EXAMPLE 1   Solve $x^2 + 3x + 5 = 0$ over $\mathbb{C}$.

SOLUTION $x = \dfrac{-b \pm \sqrt{b^2 - 4ac}}{2a}$; $a = 1$, $b = 3$, $c = 5$.

$x = \dfrac{-3 \pm \sqrt{3^2 - 4 \cdot 1 \cdot 5}}{2 \cdot 1} = \dfrac{-3 \pm \sqrt{-11}}{2}$

$= \dfrac{-3 \pm \sqrt{11}\,i}{2} = -\dfrac{3}{2} \pm \dfrac{\sqrt{11}}{2}i$

CHECK $\left(-\dfrac{3}{2} + \dfrac{\sqrt{11}}{2}i\right)^2 + 3\left(-\dfrac{3}{2} + \dfrac{\sqrt{11}}{2}i\right) + 5$

$$= \left(\dfrac{9}{4} - \dfrac{11}{4}\right) - \dfrac{3\sqrt{11}}{2}i - \dfrac{9}{2} + \dfrac{3\sqrt{11}}{2}i + 5 = 0 \checkmark$$

$\left(-\dfrac{3}{2} - \dfrac{\sqrt{11}}{2}i\right)^2 + 3\left(-\dfrac{3}{2} - \dfrac{\sqrt{11}}{2}i\right) + 5$

$$= \left(\dfrac{9}{4} - \dfrac{11}{4}\right) + \dfrac{3\sqrt{11}}{2}i - \dfrac{9}{2} - \dfrac{3\sqrt{11}}{2}i + 5 = 0 \checkmark$$

$\therefore$ the solution set is $\left\{ -\dfrac{3}{2} + \dfrac{\sqrt{11}}{2}i, \ -\dfrac{3}{2} - \dfrac{\sqrt{11}}{2}i \right\}$. **Answer.**

The number $b^2 - 4ac$, which is named under the radical sign in the quadratic formula, is called the **discriminant** of the quadratic equation $ax^2 + bx + c = 0$. We denote it by D.

If a, b, and c are real numbers, the discriminant indicates the nature of the roots of the equation.

Theorem. For all real numbers b and c, and all nonzero real numbers a, the quadratic equation $ax^2 + bx + c = 0$ has:

(1) two different real roots if $b^2 - 4ac > 0$;
(2) one double real root if $b^2 - 4ac = 0$;
(3) two imaginary complex conjugate roots if $b^2 - 4ac < 0$.

The discriminant also enables you to tell whether the roots of a quadratic equation with *rational coefficients* are rational numbers. If a, b, and c are rational numbers, $a \neq 0$, $\dfrac{-b \pm \sqrt{b^2 - 4ac}}{2a}$ denotes a rational number if and only if $\sqrt{b^2 - 4ac}$ is rational (Section 8–3). But $\sqrt{b^2 - 4ac}$ is rational if and only if $b^2 - 4ac$ is the square of a rational number. Thus:

A quadratic equation with rational coefficients has rational roots if and only if its discriminant is the square of a rational number.

EXAMPLE 2   Determine the nature of the roots of $3x^2 + 2x - 6 = 0$.

SOLUTION $3x^2 + 2x - 6 = 0$; $a = 3$, $b = 2$, $c = -6$.
$D = b^2 - 4ac = 2^2 - 4(3)(-6) = 76$.

Since $D > 0$, there are two unequal real roots.
Since D is not the square of a rational number, the roots are irrational numbers. **Answer.**

In the domain of a function f, any value of x which satisfies the equation $f(x) = 0$ is said to be a *zero* of f. Notice that "zeros of the function f," and "roots of the equation $f(x) = 0$," are just different ways of referring to the same numbers.

EXAMPLE 3   **What is the nature of the zeros of**

$$\{(x, y): y = x^2 - 2\sqrt{5}x + 5\}?$$

SOLUTION $x^2 - 2\sqrt{5}\,x + 5 = 0;\ a = 1,\ b = -2\sqrt{5},\ c = 5.$
$D = b^2 - 4ac = (-2\sqrt{5})^2 - 4 \cdot 1 \cdot 5 = 20 - 20 = 0.$

Since $D = 0$, there is one real zero (a double zero).
Although D is the square of a rational number ($0 = 0^2$), the real zero is an irrational number because b is irrational. **Answer.**

If $b^2 - 4ac > 0$, then $\sqrt{b^2 - 4ac} > 0$. Thus, $ax^2 + bx + c = 0$ has two different real roots because

$$\frac{-b + \sqrt{b^2 - 4ac}}{2a} \neq \frac{-b - \sqrt{b^2 - 4ac}}{2a}.$$

But if $b^2 - 4ac = 0$, then $\sqrt{b^2 - 4ac} = 0$, and hence the roots of $ax^2 + bx + c = 0$ are real and equal:

$$\frac{-b + 0}{2a} = \frac{-b - 0}{2a} = -\frac{b}{2a}.$$

We call $-\dfrac{b}{2a}$ a *double* root of the equation.

If $b^2 - 4ac < 0$, then $\sqrt{b^2 - 4ac}$ is a pure imaginary number. In this case,

$$\sqrt{b^2 - 4ac} = \sqrt{|b^2 - 4ac|}\ i,$$

so that the roots of $ax^2 + bx + c = 0$ are the complex conjugates:

$$-\frac{b}{2a} + \frac{\sqrt{|b^2 - 4ac|}}{2a}\ i \quad \text{and} \quad -\frac{b}{2a} - \frac{\sqrt{|b^2 - 4ac|}}{2a}\ i.$$

Example 1 on page 300 illustrates this case.

WRITTEN EXERCISES   Without solving the equation, determine the nature of its roots.

A   1. $x^2 - x - 12 = 0$ 5. $t^2 + 2t - 7 = 0$

        2. $x^2 + x - 30 = 0$ 6. $x^2 - 3x - 3 = 0$

        3. $y^2 + y + 30 = 0$ 7. $2\sqrt{2}x^2 - 5x + \sqrt{2} = 0$

        4. $y^2 + y + 12 = 0$ 8. $\sqrt{3}x^2 - 2x = 0$

Determine whether the given function over $\mathcal{R}$ has one, two, or no real zeros. For each real zero, state whether or not it is a rational number.

9. $\{(x, y): y = 2x^2 + 2\sqrt{2}x + 1\}$ 11. $f: x \rightarrow x^2 + 2x + 5$

10. $\{(x, y): y = -6x^2 + x + 1\}$ 12. $f: x \rightarrow x^2 + 3x - 6$

Solve over the set $\mathcal{C}$ of complex numbers.

13. $z^2 - 9z + 20 = 0$ 15. $u^2 + u + 4 = 0$

14. $2z^2 + 3z + 2 = 0$ 16. $u^2 + 2u + 2 = 0$

Determine the values of k for which the given function over $\mathcal{R}$ will have the indicated number of real zeros.

B   17. $\{(x, y): y = x^2 + kx + 3\}$; 1

18. $\{(x, y): y = x^2 + kx + (k + 3)\}$; 1

19. $\{(x, y): y = x^2 + 6x - k\}$; 0

20. $\{(x, y): y = x^2 + 4x - k\}$; 2

Solve over the set $\mathcal{C}$ of complex numbers.

C   21. $t^2 + 2it + 3 = 0$ 22. $s^2 + 2(i - 1)s - 1 - 2i = 0$

programming in BASIC

EXERCISES

1. Write a program that will test values of discriminants and give print-outs similar to the following:

RUN

INPUT A($<>$0), B, C?1,1,-6
(1)X↑2 + (1)X + (-6) = 0 HAS TWO DIFFERENT REAL ROOTS.

RUN

INPUT A($<>$0), B, C?1,2,1
(1)X↑2 + (2)X + (1) = 0 HAS ONE DOUBLE REAL ROOT.

RUN

INPUT A($<>$0), B, C?1,3,5
(1)X↑2 + (3)X + (5) = 0 HAS TWO IMAGINARY COMPLEX CONJUGATE ROOTS.

2. Modify the program you wrote for the exercises on page 287 to print the roots like this if $D < 0$:

$$R1 = -.5 + .866025I$$
$$R2 = -.5 - .866025I$$
for 1, 1, 1

9-5 relations between roots and coefficients of a quadratic equation

Do you recall (page 191) that the compound sentence

$$x - 3 = 0 \qquad \text{or} \qquad x + 2 = 0$$

is equivalent to the equation $(x - 3)(x + 2) = 0$? In general, if any real or complex numbers r_1 and r_2 are the roots of a quadratic equation in x, then the quadratic equation must be equivalent to $(x - r_1)(x - r_2) = 0$, or

$$x^2 - (r_1 + r_2)x + r_1 r_2 = 0.$$

By transforming the equation $ax^2 + bx + c = 0$, $a \neq 0$, to the equivalent form

$$x^2 + \frac{b}{a}x + \frac{c}{a} = 0.$$

you can deduce (Exercise 21, page 306) the following property:

Property of the Sum and Product of the Roots of a Quadratic Equation

The solution set of the equation $ax^2 + bx + c = 0$, $a \neq 0$, is $\{r_1, r_2\}$ if and only if $r_1 + r_2 = -\dfrac{b}{a}$ and $r_1 r_2 = \dfrac{c}{a}$.

EXAMPLE 1 Is $\left\{ \dfrac{1 + \sqrt{2}}{2}, \dfrac{1 - \sqrt{2}}{2} \right\}$ the solution set of $4x^2 - 4x - 1 = 0$?

SOLUTION $4x^2 - 4x - 1 = 0$; $a = 4$, $b = -4$, $c = -1$; $-\dfrac{b}{a} = 1$, $\dfrac{c}{a} = -\dfrac{1}{4}$.

$$r_1 + r_2 = \frac{1 + \sqrt{2}}{2} + \frac{1 - \sqrt{2}}{2} = 1 = -\frac{b}{a} \checkmark$$

$$r_1 r_2 = \frac{1 + \sqrt{2}}{2} \times \frac{1 - \sqrt{2}}{2} = -\frac{1}{4} = \frac{c}{a} \checkmark$$

$\therefore \left\{ \dfrac{1 + \sqrt{2}}{2}, \dfrac{1 - \sqrt{2}}{2} \right\}$ is the solution set of $4x^2 - 4x - 1 = 0$.

Answer.

EXAMPLE 2   Find a quadratic equation whose roots are $1 + \sqrt{3}i$ and $1 - \sqrt{3}i$.

SOLUTION $(1 + \sqrt{3}i) + (1 - \sqrt{3}i) = 2 = -\dfrac{b}{a}$

$(1 + \sqrt{3}i)(1 - \sqrt{3}i) = 1 + 3 = 4 = \dfrac{c}{a}$

Let $a = 1$; then $b = -2$ and $c = 4$.

$\therefore x^2 - 2x + 4 = 0$. **Answer.**

CHECK   Show that the roots of $x^2 - 2x + 4 = 0$ are $1 \pm \sqrt{3}i$ by using the quadratic formula. This check is left to you.

ORAL EXERCISES

State the sum and product of the roots of the given equation.

1. $x^2 + 2x + 3 = 0$ 3. $4x^2 + 5x + 7 = 0$ 5. $2x^2 - 3x = 0$
2. $x^2 + 5x + 4 = 0$ 4. $2x^2 - 3x - 6 = 0$ 6. $4x^2 + 5x = 0$

State a quadratic equation of the form $x^2 + bx + c = 0$ whose roots, r_1 and r_2, have the given sum and product.

7. $r_1 + r_2 = -3,\ r_1 r_2 = 2$ 9. $r_1 + r_2 = 3,\ r_1 r_2 = 0$
8. $r_1 + r_2 = -1,\ r_1 r_2 = 4$ 10. $r_1 + r_2 = 0,\ r_1 r_2 = -\sqrt{5}$

WRITTEN EXERCISES

Write a quadratic equation having the given solution set.

A   1. $\{-2, -1\}$ 5. $\{1 + \sqrt{2}, 1 - \sqrt{2}\}$ 9. $\{1 + i, 1 - i\}$
     2. $\{-3, -4\}$ 6. $\{3 + \sqrt{3}, 3 - \sqrt{3}\}$ 10. $\{2 + 5i, 2 - 5i\}$
     3. $\{2, 4\}$ 7. $\{4\sqrt{2}, 0\}$ 11. $\{2i, 0\}$
     4. $\{5, 3\}$ 8. $\{3 - \sqrt{5}, 0\}$ 12. $\{-3i, 0\}$

If one root of the given equation is the given value, find the other root and the value of p.

B   13. $3x^2 + 4x + p = 0;\ \frac{1}{3}$ 15. $2s^2 + 20s + p = 0;\ 5 + \sqrt{7}$
     14. $2x^2 - 3x + p = 0;\ \frac{1}{2}$ 16. $3t^2 - 12t + p = 0;\ 2 - \sqrt{3}$

17. If the roots of the equation $y^2 - 5y + p = 0$ are equal, find the roots and the value of p.

18. One root of $x^2 + qx - 6 = 0$ is the negative of the other. Find the roots and the value of q.

C **19.** Without solving the equation, find the sum of the reciprocals of the roots of $3x^2 + 5x - 4 = 0$.

20. Show that if $a + bi \neq 0 + 0i$ then $(a + bi)(x + yi) = 0$ if and only if $x + yi = 0 + 0i$.

21. Show that if

$$r_1 = \frac{-b + \sqrt{b^2 - 4ac}}{2a} \quad \text{and} \quad r_2 = \frac{-b - \sqrt{b^2 - 4ac}}{2a},$$

then $r_1 + r_2 = -\dfrac{b}{a}$ and $r_1 r_2 = \dfrac{c}{a}$.

22. Show that if r_1 and r_2 are the roots of $ax^2 + bx + c = 0$, $a \neq 0$, then

$$r_1^2 + r_2^2 = \frac{b^2 - 2ac}{a^2}.$$

SELF-TEST 1 Give the meaning of each of the following.

1. pure imaginary number
2. complex number
3. imaginary number

4. imaginary part of $a + bi$
5. complex conjugate of $a + bi$
6. discriminant of $ax^2 + bx + c = 0$

Objective 1, page 291   **7.** Simplify $\dfrac{12}{3\sqrt{-16}}$.

Objective 2, page 291   **8.** If $r = 1 + 2i$ and $s = 3 - 4i$, express in the form $a + bi$.

  a. $r + s$ **b.** $r - s$ **c.** $r \times s$ **d.** $r \div s$

Objective 3, page 291   **9.** By evaluating the discriminant, determine whether the roots are real or imaginary. If they are real, state whether they are rational or irrational.

  a. $2x^2 - x - 15$ **b.** $x^2 - 8x + 15$

Objective 4, page 291   **10. a.** What are **(a)** the sum and **(b)** the product of the roots, r_1 and r_2, of the equation $4x^2 - 3x - 2 = 0$?

  b. What are the values of b and c if the sum and product of the roots, r_1 and r_2, of $x^2 + bx + c = 0$ are $r_1 + r_2 = 3$ and $r_1 r_2 = -4$?

Check your answers with those printed at the back of the book.

quadratic functions and their graphs

Objectives

After completing the next three sections, you should be able to:
1. Find an equation of the line of symmetry and the coordinates of the vertex of the graph of an equation of the form $y = a(x - h)^2 + k$, and determine whether the vertex is a maximum or a minimum point.
2. Sketch the graph of a given quadratic function.
3. Solve extreme-value problems involving quadratic functions.
4. Solve quadratic inequalities.

9-6   the graph of $y = a(x - h)^2 + k$

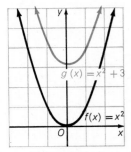

Figure 1

x	$f(x)$
-1	1
0	0
1	1

x	$g(x)$
-1	4
0	3
1	4

A function f with domain $\mathcal{R}$ and values given by a quadratic polynomial, that is,

$$f = \{(x, y): y = ax^2 + bx + c,\ a,\ b,\ c,\ \text{and}\ x \in \mathcal{R},\ a \neq 0\},$$

is called a **quadratic function**, or a *polynomial function of degree two*, over $\mathcal{R}$.

The graphs of two quadratic functions shown in Figure 1,

$$f(x) = x^2 \qquad \text{and} \qquad g(x) = x^2 + 3,$$

are both symmetric with respect to the y-axis. Notice that the *minimum* (lowest) *point* of the graph of g, (0, 3), is 3 units above that of f, (0, 0).

Now compare the graphs of f and g with those of the quadratic functions F and G in Figure 2, where

$$F(x) = -\tfrac{1}{2}x^2 \qquad \text{and} \qquad G(x) = -\tfrac{1}{2}x^2 - 4.$$

Again, both are symmetric with respect to the line $x = 0$ (the y-axis). But in this case, the graph of G has a *maximum* (highest) point, that is, a point with greatest ordinate, which is 4 units below the maximum of F.

In general, the graphs of

$$f(x) = ax^2 \qquad \text{and} \qquad g(x) = ax^2 + k$$

are both symmetric with respect to the line $x = 0$. Moreover, if $k > 0$, each point of the graph of g is k units above the corresponding point of the graph of f; and if $k < 0$, it is $|k|$ units below.

Next let us compare the graph of $\{(x, y): f(x) = ax^2\}$ with those of two other general quadratic functions, of the form

$$p(x) = a(x - h)^2,\ a \neq 0,$$

and

$$q(x) = a(x - h)^2 + k,\ a \neq 0.$$

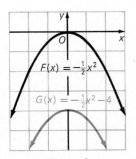

Figure 2

x	$F(x)$
-2	-2
0	0
2	-2

x	$G(x)$
-2	-6
0	-4
2	-6

If we let $a = \frac{1}{2}$, $h = 2$, $k = 3$, we obtain the graphs shown in Figure 3.

x	$f(x)$
-2	2
0	0
2	2

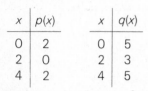

x	$p(x)$		x	$q(x)$
0	2		0	5
2	0		2	3
4	2		4	5

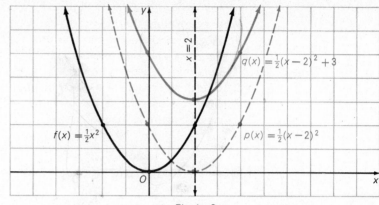

Figure 3

By observing these three graphs, we can summarize the facts concerning the *axis of symmetry* and the *vertex* (the point of the graph that lies on the axis) of the graph of $y = a(x - h)^2 + k$.

> The graph of the function
>
> $$\{(x, y): y = a(x - h)^2 + k, a \neq 0\}$$
>
> over $\mathcal{R}$ has the line $x = h$ as an axis of symmetry and the point (h, k) as vertex. If $a > 0$, (h, k) is a minimum point, and the graph opens upward; if $a < 0$, (h, k) is a maximum point, and the graph opens downward.

ORAL EXERCISES   For the graph of the given function state **(a)** an equation of the axis of symmetry; **(b)** the coordinates of the vertex; **(c)** whether the vertex is a maximum or whether it is a minimum point; **(d)** the corresponding maximum or minimum value of the function.

EXAMPLE $\{(x, y): y = 3(x + 4)^2 - 5\}$

SOLUTION   a. $x = -4$ b. $(-4, -5)$ c. a minimum point   d. -5

1. $\{(x, y): y = -2(x + 6)^2 + 3\}$
2. $\{(x, y): y = 4(x - 3)^2 - 2\}$
3. $\{(x, y): y = \frac{2}{3}(x - 1)^2 - 4\}$
4. $\{(x, y): y = -\frac{1}{2}(x + 2)^2 + 5\}$

5. $f(x) = (x + 1)^2$
6. $g(x) = -x^2 - 4$
7. $P: x \rightarrow -2(x - 1)^2$
8. $Q: x \rightarrow 3x^2$

The given ordered pair belongs to a quadratic function whose graph is symmetric with respect to the line with the given equation. Name another ordered pair that the function must therefore include.

A   1. $(4, 3)$; $x = 0$ 4. $(9, 6)$; $x = -4$

2. $(5, 3)$; $x = 1$ 5. $(m + p, q)$; $x = m$

3. $(-2, -1)$; $x = -3$ 6. (a, b); $x = 2a$

Sketch the two graphs of the two given functions on the same set of axes.

7. $\{(x, y): y = x^2 + 2\}$; $\{(x, y): y = x^2 - 2\}$

8. $\{(x, y): y = 2x^2 - 4\}$; $\{(x, y): y = 2x^2 + 4\}$

9. $\{(x, y): y = 2 - (x - 1)^2\}$; $\{(x, y): y = 2 - (x - 3)^2\}$

10. $\{(x, y): y = 1 - (x - 2)^2\}$; $\{(x, y): y = 1 - (x + 2)^2\}$

11. $F: x \rightarrow \frac{1}{2} + \frac{1}{2}(x + \frac{3}{2})^2$; $G: x \rightarrow \frac{1}{2} + (-\frac{1}{2}(x + \frac{3}{2})^2)$

12. $P: x \rightarrow \frac{1}{4}(x - 4)^2 + 2$; $Q: x \rightarrow -\frac{1}{4}(x - 4)^2 + 2$

In each of Exercises 13–20, one of the constants a, h, or k is undetermined. Find the value(s) of the constant such that the graph of the given equation contains the given point.

13. $y = a(x - 2)^2 + 3$; $(1, 4)$ 16. $y = -2(x + 4)^2 - k$; $(-7, 31)$

14. $y = a(x + 3)^2 + 2$; $(2, -3)$ 17. $y = (x - h)^2 + 1$; $(0, 10)$

15. $y = 3(x - 2)^2 + k$; $(5, 18)$ 18. $y = -2(x - h)^2$; $(-1, -32)$

B   19. $y = (x + h)^2 - 3$; $(-2, 1)$ 20. $y = \frac{1}{3}(x - h)^2 - 4$; $(-2, 71)$

Find values of a and k such that the two given ordered pairs belong to the given function. (*Hint:* Solve a system of two equations in a and k.)

21. $F: x \rightarrow a(x + 4)^2 + k$; $(-1, 4)$, $(2, 31)$

22. $f: x \rightarrow a(x - 2)^2 + k$; $(0, -2)$, $(2, 2)$

23. $\{(x, y): y = a(x + 3)^2 + k\}$; $(1, -9)$, $(-1, -3)$

24. $\{(x, y): y = ax^2 + k\}$; $(1, -6)$, $(2, -24)$

C   25. Can a graph that is symmetric with respect to the x-axis ever represent a function? Explain your answer.

26. Show that if the two points $(r_1, 0)$ and $(r_2, 0)$, $r_1 \neq r_2$, lie on the graph of $y = a(x - h)^2 + k$, then $\dfrac{r_1 + r_2}{2} = h$.

27. Show that the graph of $y = a(x - h)^2 + k$, $a \neq 0$, contains these two points: $\left(h + \dfrac{1}{2a}, k + \dfrac{1}{4a}\right)$ and $\left(h - \dfrac{1}{2a}, k + \dfrac{1}{4a}\right)$

28. Graph the function $\{(x, y): y = |x^2 - 4|\}$.

9–7   *the graph of a quadratic function*

To graph a general quadratic function over $\mathfrak{R}$ of the form

$$\{(x, y): y = ax^2 + bx + c, a \neq 0\}, \qquad (1)$$

it would be helpful if we could express it equivalently in the form described in the preceding section:

$$\{(x, y): y = a(x - h)^2 + k, a \neq 0\}. \qquad (2)$$

We could then specify the vertex, (h, k), and the axis of symmetry, $x = h$, in terms of the coefficients, a, b, c, in (1). Then by locating two or three more points we could draw the graph with reasonable accuracy. First let us consider an example.

EXAMPLE 1   Specify the vertex and the axis of symmetry, and draw the graph, of the function defined by $y = 3x^2 + 6x + 1$.

SOLUTION   1. Rewrite the given equation in the form $\dfrac{y - c}{a} = \dfrac{ax^2 + bx}{a}$.

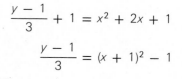

$$y = 3x^2 + 6x + 1$$
$$\frac{y - 1}{3} = \frac{3x^2 + 6x}{3}$$
$$= x^2 + \tfrac{6}{3}x$$

2. Add to both members the number $\dfrac{b^2}{4a^2}$ in order to complete the square in the right-hand member.

$$\frac{y - 1}{3} + 1 = x^2 + 2x + 1$$
$$\frac{y - 1}{3} = (x + 1)^2 - 1$$

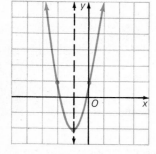

3. Then transform the equation into the desired form (2), above.

$$y = 3[(x + 1)^2 - 1] + 1$$
$$y = 3(x + 1)^2 - 2$$
$$y = 3(x - (-1))^2 + (-2)$$

Thus the axis of symmetry is $x = -1$, and the vertex is $(-1, -2)$. Substituting 0 and -2 for x in the original equation, you find that $(0, 1)$ and $(-2, 1)$ also are on the graph, which is sketched at the left.   **Answer.**

Using the method of Example 1 you can find the vertex and an equation of the axis of symmetry for the general case of the function

$$f = \{(x, y): y = ax^2 + bx + c, a \neq 0\}.$$

First rewrite the equation as

$$\frac{y - c}{a} = \frac{ax^2 + bx}{a} = x^2 + \frac{b}{a}x.$$

Completing the square, you obtain at the top of page 311:

$$\frac{y - c}{a} + \frac{b^2}{4a^2} = x^2 + \frac{b}{a}x + \frac{b^2}{4a^2} = \left(x + \frac{b}{2a}\right)^2$$

$$y - c = a\left[\left(x + \frac{b}{2a}\right)^2 - \frac{b^2}{4a^2}\right]$$

$$y = a\left(x + \frac{b}{2a}\right)^2 - \frac{b^2}{4a} + c$$

$$y = a\left(x - \left(\frac{-b}{2a}\right)\right)^2 + \left(-\frac{b^2 - 4ac}{4a}\right) \qquad (3)$$

Comparing Equation (3) with

$$y = a(x - h)^2 + k,$$

you have for equation $x = h$ of the axis of symmetry: $x = -\dfrac{b}{2a}$; and for coordinates (h, k) of the vertex: $\left(-\dfrac{b}{2a}, -\dfrac{b^2 - 4ac}{4a}\right)$. The vertex is a minimum or a maximum point according as $a > 0$ or $a < 0$.

EXAMPLE 2   **Specify the axis of symmetry and the vertex of $f(x) = 2x^2 - 4x + 1$.**

SOLUTION $a = 2, b = -4, c = 1$. Equation of axis of symmetry:

$$x = -\frac{b}{2a} = \frac{4}{4}, \qquad \text{or} \qquad x = 1.$$

The vertex is $\left(-\dfrac{b}{2a}, -\dfrac{b^2 - 4ac}{4a}\right)$, or $\left(1, -\dfrac{16 - 8}{8}\right) = (1, -1)$.
  Answer.

The fact that the quadratic function $f(x) = ax^2 + bx + c$ has exactly one *extreme value* (minimum for $a > 0$, maximum for $a < 0$) is useful in practical applications. The ordered pair $\left(-\dfrac{b}{2a}, -\dfrac{b^2 - 4ac}{4a}\right)$ specifies the value of $(x, f(x))$ at the extreme point of the graph of f. Thus the ordinate, $-\dfrac{b^2}{4a} + c$, at the extreme point is the extreme value of the function, $f\left(-\dfrac{b}{2a}\right)$.

EXAMPLE 3   **Find two real numbers whose sum is 18 and whose product is as great as possible.**

SOLUTION   Let x be one number, and $18 - x$ the other. We want to find the value of x for which the function specified by the product of x and $18 - x$,

$$f(x) = x(18 - x), \qquad \text{or} \qquad f(x) = -x^2 + 18x,$$

assumes its maximum value. Here $a = -1$ and $b = 18$. The maximum occurs when $x = -\dfrac{b}{2a} = -\dfrac{18}{-2}$, or 9. Then the other number is $18 - x = 18 - 9$, or 9. ∴ the two numbers are 9 and 9. **Answer.**

Identify the axis of symmetry and the vertex of the graph of each function. Sketch the graph.

A
1. $\{(x, y): y = x^2 - 4x\}$
2. $\{(x, y): y = x^2 + 3x\}$
3. $\{(x, y): y = -x^2 + x\}$
4. $\{(x, y): y = -x^2 - 5x\}$
5. $\{(x, y): y = 2x^2 - 3\}$
6. $\{(x, y): y = 5x^2 + 12\}$

7. $P: x \rightarrow x^2 - 3x + 2$
8. $Q: x \rightarrow x^2 + 4x + 5$
9. $f(x) = 3x^2 + 6x + 1$
10. $g(x) = 2x^2 + 4x + 3$
11. $F(x) = 5 - 2x - x^2$
12. $G(x) = 2 + 4x - 4x^2$

Find the quadratic function f containing the given ordered pairs. (*Hint:* Determine a, b, and c so that the given ordered pairs satisfy the equation $y = ax^2 + bx + c$.)

B
13. $(0, 1), (2, -3), (-1, 0)$
14. $(0, 0), (1, 3), (-1, -1)$

15. $(1, -2), (2, 3), (3, 10)$
16. $(1, -3), (-1, -1), (0, -1)$

C
17. Show that $f(x) = ax^2 + bx + c$ is an even function if and only if $b = 0$.
18. Show that there are no odd quadratic functions.

PROBLEMS

A
1. Find two real numbers whose sum is 16 and whose product is as great as possible.
2. Find two real numbers whose difference is 10 and whose product has the least possible value.
3. Find two numbers whose sum is 10 and the sum of whose squares is a minimum.
4. Find the area of the rectangle of maximum area with perimeter 12 centimeters. (*Hint:* Let x denote the length of one side of the rectangle.)

B
5. If an object is thrown upward with an initial velocity of 24.5 meters per second from a height above the ground of 10 meters, its height in meters above the ground after t seconds is given by $h = 10 + 24.5t - 4.9t^2$. What is the maximum height attained by the object?
6. A real-estate operator estimates that the monthly profit p in dollars from a building s stories high is given by $p = -2s^2 + 88s$. In stories, what height building would she consider most profitable?

C
7. A wire 40 centimeters long is cut into two pieces, and each piece is bent into a square. Where should the wire be cut if the total area of the two squares is to be a minimum?

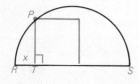

8. From a point P on a semicircle, a perpendicular $\overline{PT}$ is drawn to the diameter, $\overline{RS}$. If the length of $\overline{RT}$ is x and the length of $\overline{RS}$ is 9:

a. Express in terms of x the area of a square of side $\overline{PT}$.
b. Find the maximum area for the square. (*Hint:* $RT:PT = PT:TS$.)

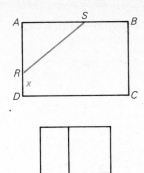

9. From the rectangle *ABCD*, triangle *RAS* is cut. If the length of $\overline{AB}$ is 22, the length of $\overline{BC}$ is 15, and the length of $\overline{DR}$ (denoted by *x*) is half the length of $\overline{SB}$:

a. Express the area *y* of *RSBCD* in terms of *x*.

b. Determine the lengths of $\overline{RA}$ and $\overline{AS}$ so that *y* is maximum.

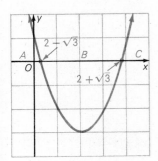

10. Sixty meters of fencing are to be used to enclose a rectangular field and to separate it into two parts by means of a fence parallel to two of the sides. What is the maximum area that can be enclosed?

9–8 *quadratic inequalities*

Figure 4 shows the graph of the function

$$\{(x, y): y = x^2 - 4x + 1\}.$$

From the graph, you can see that the points with coordinates $2 - \sqrt{3}$ and $2 + \sqrt{3}$ (the zeros of the function) separate the other points on the *x*-axis into three sets:

$$A = \{x: x < 2 - \sqrt{3}\}$$
$$B = \{x: 2 - \sqrt{3} < x < 2 + \sqrt{3}\}$$
$$C = \{x: x > 2 + \sqrt{3}\}$$

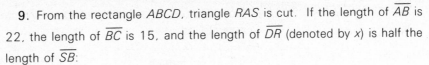

Figure 4

Do you see that over any one of these subsets the value of $x^2 - 4x + 1$ (that is, the value of *y*) is *always positive* (the graph is above the *x*-axis) or *always negative* (the graph is below the *x*-axis)?

$x \in A$	$x \in B$	$x \in C$
$x^2 - 4x + 1 > 0$	$x^2 - 4x + 1 < 0$	$x^2 - 4x + 1 > 0$

Thus, to test whether $x^2 - 4x + 1$ denotes a positive number or whether it denotes a negative number for *every* value of *x* in one of these subsets, you need only determine the sign of $x^2 - 4x + 1$ for *any one* value of *x* in that subset.

EXAMPLE   Find the solution set over $\mathfrak{R}$ of $-x^2 + 3x + 5 > 0$.

SOLUTION   1. Determine the roots of $-x^2 + 3x + 5 = 0$. $a = -1, b = 3, c = 5$.

$$x = \frac{-3 \pm \sqrt{3^2 - 4(-1)(5)}}{2(-1)} = \frac{-3 \pm \sqrt{29}}{-2} = \frac{3}{2} \pm \frac{\sqrt{29}}{2}$$

(Solution continued on page 314.)

2. From each subset into which these numbers separate the set of real numbers, choose a number for which to evaluate $-x^2 + 3x + 5$.

Subset	Particular Number	$-x^2 + 3x + 5$
$x < \dfrac{3}{2} - \dfrac{\sqrt{29}}{2}$	-2	-5, negative
$\dfrac{3}{2} - \dfrac{\sqrt{29}}{2} < x < \dfrac{3}{2} + \dfrac{\sqrt{29}}{2}$	0	5, positive
$x > \dfrac{3}{2} + \dfrac{\sqrt{29}}{2}$	5	-5, negative

$$\{x: -x^2 + 3x + 5 > 0\} = \left\{ x: \dfrac{3}{2} - \dfrac{\sqrt{29}}{2} < x < \dfrac{3}{2} + \dfrac{\sqrt{29}}{2} \right\}. \quad \text{Answer.}$$

WRITTEN EXERCISES

Determine the solution set over $\mathcal{R}$ of the given inequality and show its graph on the number line.

A

1. $x^2 - 4 > 0$
2. $16x^2 - 25 > 0$
3. $2x - x^2 \leq 0$
4. $5x - 3x^2 < 0$
5. $x^2 - 2x \geq 8$

6. $3x^2 + 5x \leq 2$
7. $3 - 3x^2 < -x$
8. $2x^2 + x \geq 1$
9. $x^2 - 2x - 3 < 0$
10. $-x^2 - 6x > 7$

SELF-TEST 2

Give the meaning of each of the following.

1. quadratic function
2. vertex

Objective 1, page 307

3. Find an equation of the line of symmetry and the coordinates of the vertex of the graph of the equation $y = 10 - (x + 2)^2$, and determine whether the vertex is a maximum or a minimum point.

Objective 2, page 307

4. Sketch the graph of $\{(x, y): y = -x^2 + 3x\}$.

Objective 3, page 307

5. Find two numbers whose difference is 16 and whose product has the least possible value.

Objective 4, page 307

6. Determine the solution set over $\mathcal{R}$ of the inequality $2 < -x^2 + 3$ and show its graph on the number line.

Check your answers with those printed at the back of the book.

polynomial functions and equations

After completing the next four sections, you should be able to:
1. Use synthetic substitution to find the value of a given polynomial function at a given domain value.
2. Use synthetic division to find the partial quotient and the remainder when a polynomial is divided by $x - c$, where $c \in \mathcal{C}$.
3. Use synthetic division and depressed equations to factor polynomials and to find rational zeros of polynomial functions.
4. Use the fact that imaginary roots of polynomial equations with real coefficients occur in complex conjugate pairs to solve such equations.
5. Use synthetic substitution and linear interpolation to approximate the real roots of a polynomial equation.

9-9   values of polynomial functions

Functions such as

$$\{(x, y): y = 3x - \sqrt{2}\}, \quad \{(x, y): y = x^2 - 2ix + 3\},$$

or

$$\{(x, y): y = 4x^3 + 2x^2 - 1\},$$

whose values are given by polynomials, are called polynomial functions. You know how to evaluate a polynomial function by direct substitution. For example, if a_0, a_1, a_2, a_3 denote complex numbers and P is the function

$$\{(x, P(x)): P(x) = a_0x^3 + a_1x^2 + a_2x + a_3\},$$

then to evaluate P at 7, you write

$$P(7) = a_0(7^3) + a_1(7^2) + a_2(7) + a_3.$$

To find the value of $P(7)$, you might compute:

(1) 7^2
(2) 7^3
(3) $a_0(7^3)$
(4) $a_1(7^2)$
(5) $a_2(7)$
(6) $a_0(7)^3 + a_1(7^2) + a_2(7) + a_3$

However, this pattern of computation is not the most efficient one to use as a basis for a program for a computer. Each product would have to be stored until needed (using valuable space) and the final addition would have to be performed by taking two addends at a time, making additional steps.

To discover a more efficient way to compute $P(7)$, study the following sequence of operations.

1. Write the coefficients a_0, a_1, a_2, a_3.
2. Multiply a_0 by 7: $\qquad\qquad\qquad$ $a_0 \cdot 7$
3. Add a_1: $\qquad\qquad\qquad\qquad\quad$ $a_0 \cdot 7 + a_1$
4. Multiply the result of Step 3 by 7: $\quad$ $(a_0 \cdot 7 + a_1) \cdot 7$
5. Add a_2: $\qquad\qquad\qquad\qquad\quad$ $(a_0 \cdot 7 + a_1) \cdot 7 + a_2$
6. Multiply the result of Step 5 by 7: $\quad$ $[(a_0 \cdot 7 + a_1) \cdot 7 + a_2] \cdot 7$
7. Add a_3: $\qquad\qquad\qquad\qquad\quad$ $[(a_0 \cdot 7 + a_1) \cdot 7 + a_2] \cdot 7 + a_3$

By simplifying the expression in Step 7, you can verify that

$$[(a_0 \cdot 7 + a_1) \cdot 7 + a_2] \cdot 7 + a_3 = a_0 \cdot 7^3 + a_1 \cdot 7^2 + a_2 \cdot 7 + a_3 = P(7).$$

Notice that in this sequence of steps, each result is computed directly from the preceding result. No values need to be saved or "stored."

You can use this second method even if you do not have a computer. Steps 2–7 can be arranged conveniently as shown below. The circled numerals designate each of the steps.

$$7\rfloor \quad a_0 \qquad a_1 \qquad\qquad a_2 \qquad\qquad\qquad a_3$$
$$\qquad \textcircled{2} \quad a_0 \cdot 7 \quad \textcircled{4}(a_0 \cdot 7 + a_1) \cdot 7 \quad \textcircled{6}[(a_0 \cdot 7 + a_1) \cdot 7 + a_2] \cdot 7$$
$$\overline{\quad a_0 \quad a_0 \cdot 7 + a_1 \quad (a_0 \cdot 7 + a_1) \cdot 7 + a_2 \quad [(a_0 \cdot 7 + a_1) \cdot 7 + a_2] \cdot 7 + a_3}$$
$$\qquad\qquad \textcircled{3} \qquad\qquad\quad \textcircled{5} \qquad\qquad\qquad\quad \textcircled{7}$$

If $P(x) = 5x^3 - 12x^2 - 20x + 1$, you can find $P(7)$ by following Steps 1–7, using 5, -12, -20, and 1 in place of a_0, a_1, a_2, and a_3, respectively:

$$
\begin{array}{r|rrrr}
7\rfloor & 5 & -12 & -20 & 1 \\
 &   & 35 & 161 & 987 \\
\hline
 & 5 & 23 & 141 & 988 \\
 &   &   &   & P(7)
\end{array}
$$

Thus $P(7) = 988$. This process, called synthetic substitution, applies to polynomials of any degree. Notice that $P(x)$ must be written in descending powers of x. Also, if a power is missing, 0 must be written in the corresponding place.

EXAMPLE $\quad$ If $Q(x) = 2x^4 - x^3 + 2x - 1$, find $Q(3)$ and $Q(3i)$.

SOLUTION $\quad$ Write the coefficients of $Q(x)$ in order, using 0 where necessary. Then, use synthetic substitution.

$$
\begin{array}{r|rrrrr}
3\rfloor & 2 & -1 & 0 & 2 & -1 \\
 &   & 6 & 15 & 45 & 141 \\
\hline
 & 2 & 5 & 15 & 47 & 140
\end{array}
$$

$$
\begin{array}{r|rrrrr}
3i\rfloor & 2 & -1 & 0 & 2 & -1 \\
 &   & 0 + 6i & -18 - 3i & 9 - 54i & 162 + 33i \\
\hline
 & 2 & -1 + 6i & -18 - 3i & 11 - 54i & 161 + 33i
\end{array}
$$

$\therefore Q(3) = 140$; $Q(3i) = 161 + 33i$. **Answer.**

In Exercises 1–14 use synthetic substitution to find the indicated values of the given polynomial function. Assume that the domain of the function is $\mathcal{C}$. If the substituted value is a zero of the function, so state.

$$P(x) = x^3 - 2x^2 - 5x + 6$$
$$Q(z) = 2z^4 - z^2 + 2z + 3$$
$$R(x) = x^4 - x^3 - 5x^2 - x - 6$$
$$S(y) = y^3 - (2a + b)y^2 + (a^2 + 2ab)y - a^2b$$

A

1. $P(3)$
2. $P(-4)$
3. $P(-2)$

4. $P(0)$
5. $Q(0)$
6. $Q(3)$

7. $Q(2i)$
8. $Q(-i)$
9. $R(3)$

10. $R(-2)$
11. $R(-3)$
12. $R(2)$

B

13. $S(a)$
14. $S(b)$

15. If $P(x) = 4x^3 - x^2 + 2x + m$, find m so that $P(3) = -1$.
16. If $Q(x) = 3x^3 - 2x^2 + x + 2m$, find m so that $Q(-1) = 3$.
17. If $R(x) = x^4 - 3x^3 + mx - 1$, find m so that $R(2) = 0$.
18. If $S(y) = 2y^3 + ay^2 + 2y - 4$, find a so that $S(4) = 0$.
19. If $T(z) = -z^3 + 3z^2 + az + b$, find a and b so that $T(-3) = 49$ and $T(5) = -39$.
20. If $T(z) = z^4 - z^2 + az + b$, find a and b so that $T(1) = 2$ and $T(2) = 17$.

programming in BASIC

EXERCISE

Write a program that will print out the numbers you obtain by synthetic substitution. For example, the program should give a print-out something like this for $P(x) = 5x^3 - 12x^2 - 20x + 1$ shown on page 316.

```
RUN

DEGREE OF POLYNOMIAL?3
INPUT COEFFICIENTS IN DESCENDING ORDER.
?5
?-12
?-20
?1
INPUT VALUE.
?7
 5   23   141   988 = P( 7)
ANOTHER VALUE (1,YES; 0,NO)?0
```

9-10 *remainder and factor theorems*

By dividing $2x^2 - 4x - 5$, $x^2 - x - 6$, $x^3 - 4x^2 + 5x - 6$, and $x^3 + 2x^2 - 7x - 4$, respectively, by $x - 3$, you obtain the "partial quotients" (Q) and remainders (R) shown in the following chart.

P	Q	R	P(3)
$2x^2 - 4x - 5$	$2x + 2$	1	1
$x^2 - x - 6$	$x + 2$	0	0
$x^3 - 4x^2 + 5x - 6$	$x^2 - x + 2$	0	0
$x^3 + 2x^2 - 7x - 4$	$x^2 + 5x + 8$	20	20

Notice that in every case the remainder R equals $P(3)$. This fact illustrates the following:

Remainder Theorem

For every polynomial $P(x)$ of positive degree n over the set of complex numbers, and for every complex number r, there exists a polynomial $Q(x)$ of degree $n - 1$, such that

$$P(x) = (x - r)Q(x) + P(r).$$

We shall show how the Remainder Theorem is proved by examining a particular case, the polynomial

$$P(x) = a_0x^3 + a_1x^2 + a_2x + a_3,$$

with "7" in place of r.

$$P(7) = a_0(7^3) + a_1(7^2) + a_2(7) + a_3$$

$$P(x) - P(7) = a_0(x^3 - 7^3) + a_1(x^2 - 7^2) + a_2(x - 7) + (a_3 - a_3)$$

$$= a_0(x - 7)(x^2 + 7x + 49)$$

$$+ a_1(x - 7)(x + 7) + a_2(x - 7)$$

$$= (x - 7)[a_0(x^2 + 7x + 49) + a_1(x + 7) + a_2]$$

$$= (x - 7)[a_0x^2 + [a_0(7) + a_1]x + [a_0(7)^2 + a_1(7) + a_2]].$$

Thus, if you let $Q(x) = a_0x^2 + [a_0(7) + a_1]x + [a_0(7^2) + a_1(7) + a_2]$, you have $P(x) = (x - 7)Q(x) + P(7)$.

You can use this argument to prove the Remainder Theorem for any polynomial of any positive degree in x and any divisor $x - r$.

Do you recognize the coefficients of $Q(x)$ in the preceding proof? They are the first three expressions in the last line of the substitution process shown on page 316. Because for any polynomial $P(x)$ you can use the synthetic-substitution process to find the partial quotient $Q(x)$ and the remainder $P(r)$ that is obtained on dividing $P(x)$ by $(x - r)$, synthetic substitution is often called synthetic division.

EXAMPLE 1 Use synthetic division to divide $x^3 - 2x^2 + 3x - 6$ by $x - 2$.

SOLUTION
$$2\rfloor \quad 1 \quad -2 \quad 3 \quad -6$$
$$ \quad 2 \quad 0 \quad 6$$
$$ \quad 1 \quad 0 \quad 3 \quad 0 \qquad Q(x) = x^2 + 3;\ R = 0$$

CHECK $x^3 - 2x^2 + 3x - 6 = (x - 2)(x^2 + 3) + 0\ \checkmark$

$$\therefore \frac{x^3 - 2x^2 + 3x - 6}{x - 2} = x^2 + 3 + \frac{0}{x - 2} = x^2 + 3.\ \text{Answer.}$$

A corollary of the Remainder Theorem is the following:

Factor Theorem

Over the set of complex numbers, $x - r$ is a factor of a polynomial $P(x)$ if and only if r is a root of $P(x) = 0$.

PROOF

If r is a root of $P(x) = 0$, then by the definition of root, $P(r) = 0$. Therefore, by the Remainder Theorem,

$$P(x) = (x - r)Q(x) + P(r) = (x - r)Q(x) + 0 = (x - r)Q(x)$$

and $(x - r)$ is a factor of $P(x)$. Conversely, if $(x - r)$ is a factor of $P(x)$, then

$$P(x) = (x - r)Q(x), \text{ so that } P(r) = (r - r)Q(r) = 0 \cdot Q(r) = 0.$$

This theorem can help you identify factors of polynomials and zeros of polynomial functions.

EXAMPLE 2 Is $x - 5$ a factor of $P(x) = x^4 - 3x^3 - 11x^2 + 3x + 10$?

SOLUTION If $P(5) = 0$, then $x - 5$ is a factor. Use synthetic substitution.

$$5\rfloor \quad 1 \quad -3 \quad -11 \quad 3 \quad 10$$
$$ \quad 5 \quad 10 \quad -5 \quad -10$$
$$ \quad 1 \quad 2 \quad -1 \quad -2 \quad 0$$

$\therefore (x - 5)$ is a factor. **Answer.**

EXAMPLE 3 Find the zeros of the function P, where $P(x) = 2x^3 + x^2 - 6x - 3$.

(Solution on page 320.)

SOLUTION   *Plan:* Solve the equation $P(x) = 0$.

1. Because the coefficients are integers, use the theorem on page 265 to identify possible rational roots, $\dfrac{p}{q}$.

$$2x^3 + x^2 - 6x - 3 = 0$$

$$\frac{p}{q} \in \{\tfrac{1}{2}, -\tfrac{1}{2}, \tfrac{3}{2}, -\tfrac{3}{2}, 1, -1, 3, -3\}$$

2. Use the Factor Theorem and synthetic substitution to test each possibility. By mentally doing the addition steps in the process, you can arrange the work conveniently, as shown.

∴ $P(x) = (x + \tfrac{1}{2})(2x^2 - 6) = 0$.

x				$P(x)$
	2	1	−6	−3
$\tfrac{1}{2}$	2	2	−5	$-\tfrac{11}{2}$
$-\tfrac{1}{2}$	2	0	−6	0

3. Solve the *depressed* equation, $2x^2 - 6 = 0$:

$$x^2 = 3;\ x = \sqrt{3} \text{ or } x = -\sqrt{3}$$

∴ the set of zeros of P is $\{-\tfrac{1}{2}, -\sqrt{3}, \sqrt{3}\}$. **Answer.**

Whenever r is a root of the polynomial equation $P(x) = 0$, you find the remaining roots by solving the depressed equation $P(x) \div (x - r) = 0$.

ORAL EXERCISES   The synthetic division of $P(x) = x^3 - 4x^2 + 5$ by $x - 2$ is shown below. State:

1. The partial quotient
2. The remainder
3. $P(2)$

```
2⌋  1  −4   0    5
        2  −4   −8
    1  −2  −4   −3
```

The synthetic division of $Q(x) = x^4 - 13x^2 - 40$ by $x + 4$ is shown below. State:

4. The partial quotient
5. The remainder
6. $Q(-4)$

```
−4⌋  1   0  −13    0  −40
        −4   16  −12   48
     1  −4    3  −12    8
```

WRITTEN EXERCISES   Use synthetic division to write the given polynomial in the form $P(x) = (x - r)Q(x) + P(r)$ for the given value of r.

A   1. $P(x) = 4x^3 - 5x^2 + 2x + 1;\ r = 2$
2. $P(x) = 6x^3 - 3x^2 + 2x + 4;\ r = 1$
3. $P(x) = x^3 + 4x^2 + 5x + 2;\ r = -3$
4. $P(x) = x^3 + 3x^2 - 3x - 2;\ r = -1$

Use synthetic division to express the given quotient as the sum of a polynomial and a rational expression whose numerator is a constant.

5. $(x^3 + 11x^2 + 11x + 15) \div (x + 4)$

6. $(x^3 - 7x^2 - 17x + 10) \div (x - 3)$

7. $(2x^4 - x^3 + 2x + 4) \div (x - 3i)$

8. $(3x^4 - 3x^2 + 4x + 3) \div (x + 2i)$

Use the Factor Theorem to show that the first polynomial is a factor of the second.

9. $x - 4; 2x^3 - 11x^2 + 10x + 8$

10. $x - 5; x^3 - x^2 - 15x - 25$

11. $x + 2; 6x^3 + 7x^2 - 7x + 6$

12. $x + 3; x^4 + 2x^3 + 8x - 3$

Use the Factor Theorem to show that the equation has the given root.

13. $x^4 - 4x^3 - 3x^2 - 9x - 5 = 0; 5$

14. $x^4 - 5x^3 - 13x^2 - 12x - 5 = 0; -1$

15. $x^3 + 4x^2 + x + 4 = 0; i$

16. $x^3 - x^2 + 9x - 9 = 0; -3i$

Find $Q(x)$ for each equation.

17. $2x^3 - 7x^2 - 10x + 32 = (x - 2)Q(x)$

18. $2x^3 + 3x^2 - 12x - 9 = (x + 3)Q(x)$

19. $2x^3 + 3x^2 - 4x + 64 = (x + 4)Q(x)$

20. $2x^3 - 3x^2 - 4x + 5 = (x - 1)Q(x)$

Find the zeros of the function.

21. $\{(x, P(x)): P(x) = x^3 + x^2 - 14x - 24\}$

22. $\{(x, P(x)): P(x) = x^3 + 3x^2 - 10x - 24\}$

23. $\{(x, P(x)): P(x) = 2x^4 - 7x^3 + 4x^2 + 7x - 6\}$

24. $\{(x, P(x)): P(x) = 6x^4 + 29x^3 + 40x^2 + 7x - 12\}$

B 25. Show that a is a root of $x^3 + (a + 1)x^2 + 2(a - a^2)x = 3a^2$.

26. Show that $2b$ is a root of $x^3 + (1 - b)x^2 - (b + 2b^2)x = 2b^2$.

27. Show that $1 - 2i$ is a root of $x^4 - 2x^3 + 8x^2 - 6x + 15 = 0$.

28. Show that $2 + \sqrt{3}\,i$ is a root of $x^4 - 4x^3 + 4x^2 + 12x - 21 = 0$.

Determine m so that the first polynomial is a factor of the second.

29. $x - 2; x^3 - 2x^2 + 3x + m$

30. $x + 4; 2x^4 - 3x^2 + 2x + m$

31. $x + 1; x^3 - 3x^2 + mx - 4$

32. $x - 3; 2x^3 + 3x^2 - mx + 10$

Given the indicated root(s), find the other roots of the equation.

33. $ix^3 + 2x^2 - 2ix - 1 = 0$; i
34. $x^3 - i = 0$; $-i$
35. $x^4 - x^2 - 6 = 0$; $\sqrt{3}$ and $-\sqrt{3}$
36. $x^4 - x^3 - x - 1 = 0$; i and $-i$

programming in BASIC

EXERCISE

Write a program that will help you find the rational roots of a polynomial equation. Study this print-out for solving $x^3 - 7x - 6 = 0$.

```
RUN

DEGREE OF POLYNOMIAL EQUATION?3
INPUT COEFFICIENTS IN DESCENDING ORDER.
?1
?0
?-7
?-6
TRY FACTORS OF -6 / 1 AS VALUES.
INPUT VALUE (TYPE 9E+10 TO END)?6
   1  6  29  168 = P( 6)
INPUT VALUE (TYPE 9E+10 TO END)?3
   1  3  2  0 = P( 3)
   3 IS A ROOT.
DEPRESSED EQUATION--DEGREE 2:
TRY FACTORS OF 2 / 1 AS VALUES.
INPUT VALUE (TYPE 9E+10 TO END)?2
   1  5  12 = P( 2)
INPUT VALUE (TYPE 9E+10 TO END)?1
   1  4  6 = P( 1)
INPUT VALUE (TYPE 9E+10 TO END)?-1
   1  2  0 = P(-1)
  -1 IS A ROOT.
DEPRESSED EQUATION--DEGREE 1:
TRY FACTORS OF 2 / 1 AS VALUES.
INPUT VALUE (TYPE 9E+10 TO END)?-2
   1  0 = P(-2)
  -2 IS A ROOT.
```

This program ends if n roots are found (n is the degree of the equation). If not all roots are rational, this program can be ended by typing 9E + 10 as indicated.

9-11 *the fundamental theorem of algebra*

Over the set of real numbers a polynomial equation may have no solution. For example, $x^2 + 1 = 0$ has no *real* root. But over the set of complex numbers it has two roots, namely i and $-i$. The German mathematician C. F. Gauss in 1799 first proved that *every polynomial equation with complex coefficients has at least one root*. This result, called the Fundamental Theorem of Algebra, leads to the following assertion, which we will accept without proof.

> **Theorem.** Every polynomial equation with complex coefficients and positive degree n has exactly n complex roots.

In applying this theorem, you may have to count the same number as a root more than once. For example, 5 is a *double* root of the equation $x^2 - 10x + 25 = 0$.

You recall (page 301) that the imaginary roots of a quadratic equation with real coefficients occur in conjugate pairs. Thus, the fact that $2 - 3i$ is a root of $x^2 - 4x + 13 = 0$ implies that $2 + 3i$ is also a root. This property is typical of all polynomial equations with *real* coefficients.

> **Theorem.** If a polynomial equation with real coefficients has $a + bi$ as a root (a and b real, $b \neq 0$), then $a - bi$ is also a root.

The proof of this theorem is indicated in Exercises 15–17, page 324.

If you know that

$$P(x) = x^4 + 4x^3 + 12x^2 + 28x + 35 = 0$$

has the root $-2 + i$, the preceding theorem together with the Factor Theorem enables you to solve the equation. Since the equation has real coefficients, *both* $-2 + i$ *and* $-2 - i$ are roots. Therefore, both $x - (-2 + i)$ and $x - (-2 - i)$ are factors of the left-hand member. Since neither of these polynomials is a factor of the other, their product

$$[(x + 2) - i][(x + 2) + i],$$

or $x^2 + 4x + 5$, must be a factor of $P(x) = 0$. But

$$P(x) \div (x^2 + 4x + 5) = x^2 + 7.$$

The roots of the depressed equation are $i\sqrt{7}$ and $-i\sqrt{7}$; hence, the solution set of $P(x) = 0$ is

$$\{-2 + i, -2 - i, i\sqrt{7}, -i\sqrt{7}\}.$$

A

1. Two roots of $x^3 - 2x^2 + 3x - 6 = 0$ are 2 and $i\sqrt{3}$. What is the other root? Verify your answer by synthetic substitution.

2. Two roots of $x^3 - 5x^2 + 7x + 13 = 0$ are -1 and $3 + 2i$. What is the other root? Verify your answer by synthetic substitution.

3. A cubic equation with real coefficients has roots 7 and $2 - i$. What is the third root? Find the equation.

4. A cubic equation with real coefficients has roots -2 and $1 - 3i$. What is the third root? Find the equation.

5. Given that one root of $x^4 - 3x^3 - 11x^2 + 53x - 60 = 0$ is $2 - i$, find the remaining roots.

6. Given that one root of $x^4 - 7x^3 + 10x^2 + 26x - 60 = 0$ is $3 - i$, find the remaining roots.

Factor each polynomial completely over (a) the real numbers, and (b) the complex numbers.

7. $x^3 + x^2 + 3x + 3$

8. $y^3 + 2y^2 + y + 2$

9. $x^3 - 20x + 25$

10. $x^3 - 15x + 4$

11. $x^3 - 10x + 24$

12. $x^3 - 15x + 50$

B

13. Explain why the complex conjugate of a pure imaginary number is the negative of the number itself.

14. Explain why the complex conjugate of a real number is the number itself.

Let a, b, and c denote real numbers. Prove that each statement is true.

15. For each positive integer k, the conjugate of $c \cdot (a + bi)^k$ is $c \cdot (a - bi)^k$. (Hint: Use Exercise 25, page 300, and Exercise 14 above.)

16. If $P(x) = a_0 x^n + a_1 x^{n-1} + \cdots + a_n$ is a polynomial with *real* coefficients, then the conjugate of $P(a + bi)$ is $P(a - bi)$. (Hint: Use Exercise 24, page 298, and Exercise 15 above.)

17. Show that if $P(x)$ is the polynomial described in Exercise 16, and if $P(a + bi) = 0$, then $P(a - bi) = 0$.

9–12 estimates of real roots

Estimates of the real roots of a polynomial equation (or the real zeros of a polynomial function) can be found by several methods. First, you can consider the graphs of polynomial functions. You have sketched the graphs of many first- and second-degree polynomial functions over $\mathcal{R}$, as well as of some power functions (Section 8–1). The following example suggests how to get some idea of the shape of the graph of a polynomial function of higher degree over $\mathcal{R}$.

EXAMPLE   Graph P if $P(x) = x^3 - 3x^2 + 3$.

x				$P(x)$
0	1	−3	0	3
1	1	−2	−2	1
2	1	−1	−2	−1
3	1	0	0	3
−1	1	−4	4	−1

SOLUTION   Use synthetic substitution to find some values for $P(x)$. When these points are connected by a smooth curve, you obtain the graph shown at the left.

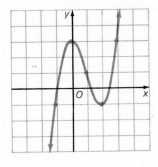

In drawing the graphs of polynomial functions as smooth unbroken curves, you assume the following:

Property of Continuity

If P is a polynomial function with real coefficients, and if m is any number between $P(a)$ and $P(b)$, then there is at least one number c between a and b for which $P(c) = m$.

In other words, P takes on every value between any two of its values.

In the example above, since $P(2) = -1$ and $P(3) = 3$, so that $P(2) < 0 < P(3)$, there must be a value of x between 2 and 3 for which $P(x) = 0$. By inspecting the diagram, you can see that the graph crosses the x-axis at a point whose x-coordinate is approximately 2.5. Thus, an estimate of one root of $P(x) = 0$ is 2.5.

You can also see that since $P(1) = 1$ and $P(2) = -1$, there must be a root between 1 and 2 (approximately 1.4), and since $P(-1) = -1$ and $P(0) = 3$, there must be a root between -1 and 0 (approximately -0.9). Thus, the equation $x^3 - 3x^2 + 3 = 0$ has three real roots.

You can obtain a closer estimate of a root by computation. By direct or synthetic substitution, you can show that

$$P(2.5) = -0.125 < 0 \quad \text{and} \quad P(2.6) = 0.296 > 0,$$

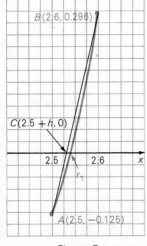

Figure 5

so that $2.5 < r_1 < 2.6$. Now look at Figure 5, which shows the part of the graph of P over the interval $2.5 \le x \le 2.6$. Notice that the line segment joining the points $A(2.5, -0.125)$ and $B(2.6, 0.296)$ of the graph crosses the x-axis at C, which is near the point where the graph itself crosses. This suggests that the x-coordinate of C is a fairly good approximation of r_1. Denoting the coordinates of C by $(2.5 + h, 0)$, you have:

$$\text{slope of } \overline{AC} = \text{slope of } \overline{AB}$$

$$\frac{0.125}{h} \doteq \frac{0.421}{0.1} = 4.21$$

$$\therefore h \doteq \frac{0.125}{4.21} \doteq 0.03.$$

Thus, $r_1 \doteq 2.5 + 0.03$, or 2.53. As a matter of fact, $P(2.53) \doteq -0.008423$, which is fairly close to 0. This process of approximating a value of $P(x)$ by using a line segment is called linear interpolation.

You can check that $P(2.54) \doteq 0.032264$, so that $2.53 < r_1 < 2.54$. To obtain an even better approximation of r_1, you can repeat the interpolation over this shorter interval. The process can be repeated as many times as desired, until you have an approximation of a root to any number of decimal places. Such repetitive procedures can be programmed for a computer.

ORAL EXERCISES

1. If $P(x)$ is a polynomial function satisfying $P(4) = -6$ and $P(7) = 3$, explain why $P(x)$ must have a zero for some value c, $4 < c < 7$.

2. In Exercise 1, might P have more than one zero in the interval $4 < x < 7$?

3. Explain why $P(x) = x^5 - 73x^4 - 32x^3 + x^2 - 2x - 1$ must be negative for negative values of x having very large absolute values, and positive for very large positive values of x, and must therefore have at least one real zero.

4. Can you generalize the result of Exercise 3?

WRITTEN EXERCISES

Graph the given polynomial function, and estimate any real zeros.

A

1. $\{(x, y): y = x^3 - 9x\}$
2. $\{(x, y): y = x^3 + 9x\}$
3. $\{(x, y): y = x^3 - 3x^2\}$
4. $\{(x, y): y = x^3 + 3x^2\}$

5. $\{(x, y): y = x^3 - 5x^2 + 6x\}$
6. $\{(x, y): y = x^3 + x^2 - 8x - 12\}$
7. $\{(x, y): y = x^4 - 5x^2 + 4\}$
8. $\{(x, y): y = x^5 + 2x^4 + x^3 + 1\}$

Find the indicated zero to the nearest hundredth.

9. $y = x^3 - 5x^2 + 6x - 1$, between 0 and 1.

10. $y = x^3 - 2x - 2$, between 1 and 2.

B

11. Observe that if $P(x) = x^2 - x - 10$, then $P(0) = -10$ and $P(5) = 10$. The principle of continuity assures you that there must be a number c between 0 and 5 such that $P(c) = -4$. Find c.

12. In Exercise 11, $P(-5) = 20$ and $P(-1) = -8$. Find a number c, $-5 < c < -1$, such that $P(c) = 10$.

programming in BASIC

EXERCISE

BASIC provides a method of defining special functions. This is done by a statement of the form DEF FNA(X), where A may be replaced by any letter and X is a variable.

1. This is the beginning of a program which uses a defined function in locating integral roots from -10 to 10 of the equation $x^3 - 2x^2 + 4x - 8 = 0$. Complete the program and run it.

```
10   DEF FNA(X) = X↑3 − 2*X↑2 + 4*X − 8
20   FOR X = −10 TO 10
30   IF FNA(X) = 0 THEN 60
```

careers *astronomy*

Astronomers collect and analyze data on the sun, the planets and their moons, stars, and galaxies. They attempt to determine the motions of these bodies, their chemical composition, surface temperatures, sizes, and shapes, as well as their history and probable future. They study the earth—its size and shape, and the characteristics of the upper atmosphere.

In making observations, astronomers use a variety of equipment. Photographic devices are usually attached to telescopes to record observations. Measuring devices are also placed on balloons, rockets, and satellites. Astronomers observe not only the visible light radiated from stars and reflected from planets, but also x-rays, radio waves, and infra-red radiation.

One area of astronomy deals with the motion of the bodies of the solar system. It can be shown that the orbit about the sun of every object in the solar system is a conic section with the sun at one focus. The 17th century astronomer Johannes Kepler deduced that the orbits of all of the planets are ellipses (see Section 10–5).

This scientist (above) is operating a special camera used to photograph objects at great distances. The astronomers below are making adjustments on a telescope.

EXAMPLE How far is Mercury from the sun at perihelion, the point in the orbit of the planet that is nearest the sun?

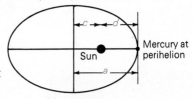

SOLUTION The planet is closest to the sun when it is on the major axis of the ellipse representing the path of its orbit. We are trying to find the distance d in the figure. The data available are: the distance a from the center of the orbit to the planet, which for Mercury is 58×10^6 km, and the *eccentricity* of the orbit, which gives a measure of how the shape of an ellipse differs from that of a circle. The eccentricity is the ratio c/a, and has the value 0.206 for the orbit of Mercury.

$$\text{eccentricity} = \frac{c}{a} = \frac{\text{distance from center of orbit to sun}}{\text{distance from center of orbit to planet}}$$

For Mercury: $0.206 = \dfrac{c}{58 \times 10^6}$

$$c = 0.206 \times (58 \times 10^6) = 12 \times 10^6 \text{ km}$$

From the figure you can see that $d = a - c$:

$$d = (58 \times 10^6) - (12 \times 10^6) = 46 \times 10^6 \text{ km}$$

COMPLEX NUMBERS AND POLYNOMIAL FUNCTIONS **327**

SELF-TEST 3   Give the meaning of each of the following.

1. polynomial function
2. synthetic substitution (synthetic division)
3. partial quotient
4. depressed equation
5. linear interpolation

Objective 1, page 315   6. If $P(x) = x^5 - 2x^3 + 4x^2 + 5x + 4$, use synthetic substitution to find **(a)** $P(-2)$, and **(b)** $P(i)$.

Objective 2, page 315   7. Use synthetic division to find the partial quotient and the remainder when $x^3 - 3x^2 + 2x + 4$ is divided by $x - 6$.

Objective 3, page 315   8. Use synthetic substitution and a depressed equation to solve the equation $3x^3 + x^2 + 6x + 2 = 0$.

Objective 4, page 315   9. Find all zeros of $P(x) = x^3 - 2x + 4$, given that $P(1 - i) = 0$.

Objective 5, page 315   10. Determine the zero of $F(x) = x^3 - 3x + 1$ between 1 and 2 to the nearest hundredth.

Check your answers with those printed at the back of the book.

Leonhard Euler
1707–1783

Leonhard Euler is probably the greatest Swiss scientist in history, and certainly one of the most prolific mathematicians of all times. Euler, who spent most of his lifetime at St. Petersburg Academy in Russia and the Berlin Academy, was one of several great mathematicians who could work almost anywhere under any conditions. He was able to perform long calculations in his head, so that even after he was totally blind, his mathematical output did not stop. His writings included works on calculus, topology, navigation, celestial mechanics, and algebra. In trigonometry Euler extended the sine, cosine, and tangent functions to angles other than those occurring in right triangles.

In addition, many of the mathematical symbols used today are what they are because of Euler. He adopted the symbols

$$i \text{ to represent } \sqrt{-1},$$

$$\Sigma \text{ to indicate summation,}$$

and

$$f(x) \text{ to denote a function of } x.$$

chapter summary

1. A **complex number,** $a + bi$, where a and b are real numbers and i, or $\sqrt{-1}$, is the **imaginary unit,** is a real number if $b = 0$, is an **imaginary number** if $b \neq 0$, and is a **pure imaginary number** if $a = 0$, $b \neq 0$. If a, b, c, and d are real numbers, then $a + bi = c + di$ if and only if $a = c$ and $b = d$.

2. Complex numbers may be added and also multiplied: For all real numbers a, b, c, and d, $(a + bi) + (c + di) = (a + c) + (b + d)i$; and $(a + bi)(c + di) = (ac - bd) + (ad + bc)i$. The closure, associative, commutative, and distributive properties hold for the set $\mathcal{C}$ of complex numbers.

   The **additive identity element** in $\mathcal{C}$ is $0 + 0i$, or 0; for all real numbers c and d, the **additive inverse** of $c + di$ is $-c - di$.

   The **multiplicative identity element** in $\mathcal{C}$ is $1 + 0i$, or 1.

3. From the value of the **discriminant** $b^2 - 4ac$ of a quadratic equation $ax^2 + bx + c = 0$ with real coefficients, $a \neq 0$, you can tell whether its roots are real roots or imaginary, complex conjugate roots and whether its real roots are rational or irrational, and equal or unequal.

4. To solve a **quadratic inequality** such as $ax^2 + bx + c > 0$, $a \neq 0$, you first find roots, r_1 and r_2, $r_1 \leq r_2$, of $ax^2 + bx + c = 0$, and then consider the intervals $x < r_1$, $r_1 < x < r_2$, and $x > r_2$.

5. For any polynomial function P, **synthetic substitution** (or **synthetic division**) may be used in finding values of $P(x)$ for given values of x.

6. The **Remainder Theorem** states that for every polynomial $P(x)$, of degree n $(n \geq 1)$, and every complex number r, there is a polynomial $Q(x)$, of degree $n - 1$, such that $P(x) = (x - r)Q(x) + P(r)$. This leads to the **Factor Theorem,** which states that $x - r$ is a factor of $P(x)$ if and only if r is a root of $P(x) = 0$. The coefficients of $Q(x)$, as well as $P(r)$, can be determined by synthetic division.

7. From the **Fundamental Theorem of Algebra** it can be proved that every polynomial equation of degree n $(n \geq 1)$ with complex coefficients has exactly n complex roots.

   If a polynomial with real coefficients has $a + bi$ as a root (a and b real, $b \neq 0$), then $a - bi$ is also a root.

8. The **Property of Continuity** states that if P is a polynomial function, and if m is any number between $P(a)$ and $P(b)$, then there is a number c between a and b for which $P(c) = m$.

9. If a and b are real numbers and you find $P(a) > 0$ and $P(b) < 0$ or $P(a) < 0$ and $P(b) > 0$, then there is at least one root between a and b.

9-1   **1.** Simplify **(a)** $(-2\sqrt{-3})(4\sqrt{-18})$ and **(b)** $\dfrac{\sqrt{-32}}{\sqrt{-8}}$.

        2. Find all roots of **(a)** $x^2 + 8 = 0$, and **(b)** $x^2 + 36 = 0$.

9-2   **3.** Find **(a)** the sum and **(b)** the difference of $7 - 3i$ and $4 - 5i$.

9-3   **4.** Find **(a)** the product and **(b)** the quotient of $-3 + 4i$ and $-2 + i$.

9-4   **5.** Determine the nature of the roots of **(a)** $x^2 + 2x + 2 = 0$, and **(b)** $3x^2 - 4x + 1 = 0$.

9-5   **6.** Write in simple form the quadratic equation in x whose roots are $7 + \sqrt{3}$ and $7 - \sqrt{3}$.

9-6   **7.** For the graph of $y = 2(x + 3)^2 - 6$ determine **(a)** an equation of the axis of symmetry, **(b)** the coordinates of the vertex, **(c)** whether the vertex is a maximum or a minimum point, and **(d)** the corresponding maximum or minimum value of the function.

9-7   **8.** Draw the graph of $\{(x, y): y = x^2 + 4x + 2\}$ for $-4 \le x \le 0$.

        9. Find the real number for which the product of the number and 12 less than twice the number has the least possible value.

9-8   **10.** Determine the solution set over $\mathcal{R}$ of the inequality $-2x^2 - 5x \le 0$.

9-9   **11.** For $P(x) = x^3 - 4x^2 - 3x + 2$, use synthetic substitution to find **(a)** $P(5)$, and **(b)** $P(3i)$.

9-10   **12.** Use synthetic division to write $P(x) = 2x^3 + 5x^2 - 4x - 3$ in the form $(x - 2)Q(x) + P(2)$.

        13. Find the solution set of $x^3 - 7x^2 + 13x - 15 = 0$.

9-11   **14.** Find all roots of $x^4 - 4x^3 + 10x^2 - 20x + 25$, given that $2 - i$ is one root.

9-12   **15.** Graph $\{(x, y): y = x^3 - 2x^2 - 5x + 6\}$, and estimate any real zeros.

        16. Find the zero of $f: f(x) = x^3 - 4x^2 - 6x + 8$ between 0 and 1 to the nearest hundredth.

cumulative review
chapters 1–9

1. Simplify: $3(2 - 7) - 2(5 + 8) + 3(8 - 10)$.

2. State the axiom justifying $3 \cdot (8 \cdot 2) = (8 \cdot 2) \cdot 3$.

3. Simplify: $(3p^2 + 2p - 4) + (6p^2 - 3p + 5) - (4p^2 - p - 1)$

4. Solve over $\mathcal{R}$: $2r - 3(r + 1) = 5r - 6$

5. Graph over $\mathcal{R}$: $3x - 7 > 2(x + 5)$

6. Simplify: $3(|5 - 9| - 2 \,|\, 3 - 1|)$

7. If $r(x) = \dfrac{x - 3}{2x + 1}$, find (a) $r(0)$, (b) $r(-1)$, and (c) $r(3)$.

8. Find an equation for the line containing $(-7, 2)$ and $(2, 7)$.

9. Solve using Cramer's Rule:
$$\begin{aligned} a - 2b + c &= 3 \\ 2a - b + 3c &= 8 \\ 3a + b + c &= 5 \end{aligned}$$

10. Write in simple form using positive exponents only: $\dfrac{14a^{-4}b^2c^{-3}}{2a^{-2}bc^{-4}}$.

11. Write $(x^3 - 2x^2 + 3x - 1)(x + 2)$ as a polynomial in simple form.

Factor completely.

12. $2x^2 - 6x - 20$

13. $3 - 81y^3$

14. $x^2 + xy - 2x - 2y$

15. $x^4 - 81y^4$

16. Solve $x^2 + 3x = 4$ over $\mathcal{R}$.

Simplify.

17. $\dfrac{8y^2 - 4y^3}{2y - y^2}$

18. $\dfrac{n^2 - 3n}{n^3 - n} \cdot \dfrac{n^2 + 2n - 3}{n^2 + 6n + 9}$

19. $\dfrac{2x - 6}{z + 2x} \div \dfrac{4x - 12}{2x + 4z}$

20. $\dfrac{x}{x^2 - 16} - \dfrac{x + 1}{x^2 - 5x + 4}$

21. In an arithmetic sequence, if $a_1 = 4$ and $d = 6$, find a_{10}.

22. Find the value of the sum S_8 for the arithmetic sequence 9, 6, 3, ...

23. Insert two geometric means between 5 and 135.

24. Find the value of $\displaystyle\sum_{i=1}^{5} (-2^i)$.

25. Write $0.\overline{56}$ as a geometric series and find its value.

26. Solve $z^2 = 0.81$ over $\mathcal{R}$.

Simplify.

27. $4\sqrt{98}$

28. $\dfrac{\sqrt[3]{27x^4}}{3x}$

29. $2\sqrt{27} - 5\sqrt{12} + \sqrt{3}$

30. $(3 + \sqrt{7})(2 - 3\sqrt{7})$

31. Solve $z^2 - 2z - 1 = 0$ by completing the square.

Simplify.

32. $(3\sqrt{-2})(-1\sqrt{-8})$

33. $(5 - 2i) + (7 + 3i)$

34. $(6 - 3i) - (7 + i)$

35. $\dfrac{2 - i}{5 + 3i}$

36. Sketch the graph of $\{(x, y): y = x^2 - 4x + 3\}$ over $-4 \le x \le 4$.

37. Use synthetic substitution to find $P(2i)$ if $P(x) = x^3 - x^2 + 2x + 3$.

38. Graph $\{(x, y): y = x^3 - 3x^2 + 2x + 1\}$ and estimate any real zeros.

This photograph of the stars visible in the southern hemisphere was taken near Sydney, Australia. The circular pattern was created by the earth's rotation about its axis during the 45-minute exposure. A radar antenna used to study radio waves emitted by stars is in the foreground.

10 *quadratic relations and systems*

coordinates and distances in a plane

Objectives

After completing the next two sections, you should be able to:
1. Determine the distance between two points in a plane.
2. Determine an equation of the line perpendicular to a given line and passing through a given point.

10-1 *distance between points*

On page 60, you saw that the distance between the points having coordinates a and b on the number line is $|b - a|$. To determine the distance between *any* two points in a coordinate plane with equal units on both axes, you use the following familiar theorem:

Pythagorean Theorem

In a right triangle, the square of the length c of the hypotenuse is equal to the sum of the squares of the lengths a and b of the other two sides: $c^2 = a^2 + b^2$.

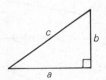

Of course, you should recall that the converse is also true:

Converse of the Pythagorean Theorem

If a, b, and c are the lengths of the sides of a triangle, and if $c^2 = a^2 + b^2$, then the triangle is a right triangle with hypotenuse of length c.

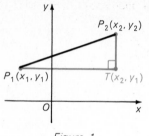

Figure 1

Figure 1 shows two points $P_1(x_1, y_1)$ and $P_2(x_2, y_2)$ in the plane, where segment $\overline{P_1P_2}$ is not parallel to a coordinate axis. Then you can construct a right triangle such as the one shown, where T, the third vertex, has coordinates (x_2, y_1). Since $\overline{P_1T}$ and $\overline{P_2T}$ are parallel to the coordinate axes, their lengths are $|x_2 - x_1|$ and $|y_2 - y_1|$, respectively. Then, by the Pythagorean Theorem, $d(P_1, P_2)$ (read "the distance from P_1 to P_2") satisfies

$$[d(P_1, P_2)]^2 = |x_2 - x_1|^2 + |y_2 - y_1|^2 = (x_2 - x_1)^2 + (y_2 - y_1)^2.$$

Since distance is a nonnegative number, you have the following:

Distance Formula

$$d(P_1, P_2) = \sqrt{(x_2 - x_1)^2 + (y_2 - y_1)^2}$$

EXAMPLE 1   Find the distance between $P_1(-2, 6)$ and $P_2(3, 7)$.

SOLUTION $d(P_1, P_2) = \sqrt{[3 - (-2)]^2 + (7 - 6)^2} = \sqrt{5^2 + 1^2} = \sqrt{26}$. **Answer.**

EXAMPLE 2   Find the perimeter of the triangle whose vertices are $(6, 4)$, $(-3, 1)$, and $(9, -5)$. Determine whether the triangle is isosceles and whether it is a right triangle.

SOLUTION   First, make a sketch showing the triangle. Next, use the distance formula to find the lengths of the sides.

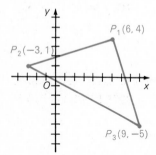

$$d(P_2, P_1) = \sqrt{[6 - (-3)]^2 + (4 - 1)^2}$$
$$= \sqrt{9^2 + 3^2} = \sqrt{90} = 3\sqrt{10}$$

$$d(P_1, P_3) = \sqrt{(9 - 6)^2 + (-5 - 4)^2}$$
$$= \sqrt{3^2 + (-9)^2} = \sqrt{90} = 3\sqrt{10}$$

$$d(P_2, P_3) = \sqrt{[9 - (-3)]^2 + (-5 - 1)^2}$$
$$= \sqrt{12^2 + (-6)^2} = \sqrt{180} = 6\sqrt{5}$$

Then the perimeter is $3\sqrt{10} + 3\sqrt{10} + 6\sqrt{5} = 6\sqrt{10} + 6\sqrt{5}$. Since $d(P_2, P_1) = d(P_1, P_3)$, the triangle is isosceles. Also, since $(3\sqrt{10})^2 + (3\sqrt{10})^2 = (6\sqrt{5})^2$, the converse of the Pythagorean Theorem assures us that the triangle is a right triangle.

$\therefore$ the perimeter is $6\sqrt{10} + 6\sqrt{5}$, and the triangle is an isosceles right triangle. **Answer.**

EXAMPLE 3   Show that $M\left(\dfrac{x_1 + x_2}{2}, \dfrac{y_1 + y_2}{2}\right)$ is the midpoint of the segment with endpoints $P_1(x_1, y_1)$ and $P_2(x_2, y_2)$.

SOLUTION If $d(P_1, M) = d(M, P_2) = \frac{1}{2}d(P_1, P_2)$, then M is the midpoint of $\overline{P_1P_2}$. Using the distance formula you find that:

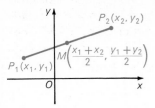

$$d(P_1, M) = \sqrt{\left(\frac{x_1 + x_2}{2} - x_1\right)^2 + \left(\frac{y_1 + y_2}{2} - y_1\right)^2}$$

$$= \sqrt{\left(\frac{x_2 - x_1}{2}\right)^2 + \left(\frac{y_2 - y_1}{2}\right)^2} = \frac{1}{2}\sqrt{(x_2 - x_1)^2 + (y_2 - y_1)^2}$$

$$d(M, P_2) = \sqrt{\left(x_2 - \frac{x_1 + x_2}{2}\right)^2 + \left(y_2 - \frac{y_1 + y_2}{2}\right)^2}$$

$$= \sqrt{\left(\frac{x_2 - x_1}{2}\right)^2 + \left(\frac{y_2 - y_1}{2}\right)^2} = \frac{1}{2}\sqrt{(x_2 - x_1)^2 + (y_2 - y_1)^2}$$

Since $d(P_1, P_2) = \sqrt{(x_2 - x_1)^2 + (y_2 - y_1)^2}$, you have

$$d(P_1, M) = \tfrac{1}{2}d(P_1, P_2), \qquad d(M, P_2) = \tfrac{1}{2}d(P_1, P_2),$$

and M is the midpoint of $\overline{P_1P_2}$. **Answer.**

WRITTEN EXERCISES

Find **(a)** the length of the line segment with endpoints as given, and **(b)** the coordinates of the midpoint of the segment. Express all radicals in simple form.

A

1. $(4, 6), (0, 6)$ 5. $(3, 5), (5, 8)$ 9. $(m, n), (n, m)$
2. $(-5, 1), (7, 1)$ 6. $(1, -1), (-2, 3)$ 10. $(3a, b), (6a, 6b)$
3. $(\frac{1}{2}, 7), (\frac{1}{2}, 5)$ 7. $(1, -3), (2, -5)$
4. $(5, 8), (5, 24)$ 8. $(2\sqrt{5}, 1), (-\sqrt{5}, 3)$

For the triangle whose vertices are given, find **(a)** the perimeter, **(b)** whether or not it is isosceles, and **(c)** whether or not it is a right triangle. If it is a right triangle, find its area.

11. $(0, 0); (4, -4); (3, -1)$ 14. $(2, 7); (-1, 1); (11, -5)$
12. $(7, 5); (-2, 2); (10, -4)$ 15. $(8, -4); (2, 4); (-13, -4)$
13. $(3, -1); (0, 0); (2, 6)$ 16. $(1, 2); (5, -1); (-2, -2)$

Use the distance formula to determine whether or not the given points are the vertices of a parallelogram. Make a sketch.

17. $(-2, 3); (-4, 2); (-2, -2); (0, -1)$
18. $(6, 2); (-1, -1); (-3, -5); (6, -2)$
19. $(6, 3); (5, -4); (-6, -5); (-1, 4)$
20. $(-2, 1); (9, 8); (4, 3); (11, 2)$

Find the coordinates of A if M is the midpoint of $\overline{AB}$.

21. $M(4, 3)$; $B(5, 1)$
22. $M(6, -4)$; $B(4, 3)$
23. $M(-3, 3)$; $B(-6, 0)$
24. $M(1, -6)$; $B(0, 2)$

25. Use the distance formula to find the distance between $P_1(a, 0)$ and $P_2(b, 0)$.
26. Show that the distance r between the origin and the point $Q(a, b)$ is given by the formula $r = \sqrt{a^2 + b^2}$.

B 27. Let $P(x, y)$ be a point equidistant from $P_1(4, 2)$ and $P_2(-3, 3)$. Find a linear equation in x and y whose solution set contains all those and only those points P which meet the given condition.

28. Find all values of y such that the distance between $P_1(4, 1)$ and $P_2(-1, y)$ is 13 units.

29. Find the distance between the midpoints of the segments S and T with endpoints $P_1(3, -1)$, $P_2(-1, 5)$ and $R_1(-2, 7)$, $R_2(4, 3)$, respectively.

30. Find the perimeter of the triangle formed by joining the midpoints of the sides of the triangle whose vertices are $P_1(-3, 2)$, $P_2(3, 6)$, and $P_3(0, 4)$.

C 31. The coordinates of the vertices of a parallelogram are $P_1(0, 0)$, $P_2(a, 0)$, $P_3(b, c)$, and $P_4(a + b, c)$. Show that the diagonals of the parallelogram bisect each other.

32. The coordinates of the vertices of a right triangle are $P_1(0, 0)$, $P_2(a, 0)$, and $P_3(0, b)$. Show that the midpoint of the hypotenuse is equidistant from the three vertices.

10–2 *perpendicular lines*

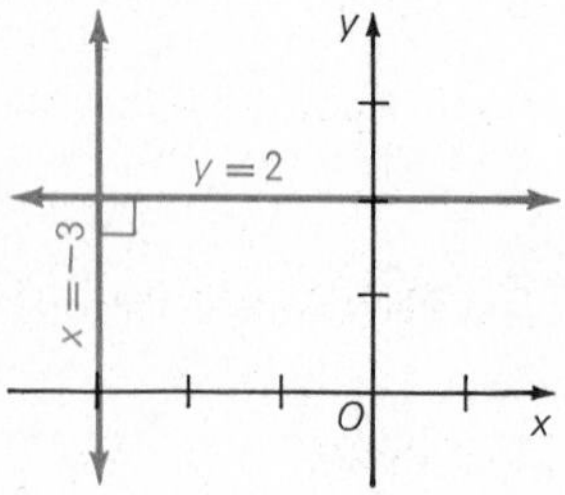

Figure 2

You know, of course, that two lines intersecting at right angles are called perpendicular lines. For example, every horizontal line in a plane, such as the graph of $y = 2$ in Figure 2, is perpendicular to each vertical line, as, for example, the graph of $x = -3$.

If neither of two perpendicular lines is vertical, you can use the Pythagorean Theorem and its converse to establish an interesting relationship between their slopes. Figure 3 on page 337 shows two lines L_1 and L_2, with equations

$$y = m_1x + b_1,$$
$$y = m_2x + b_2,$$

and intersecting at $P(x_1, y_1)$. Since $P(x_1, y_1)$ lies on both lines, the points

and
$$T_1(x_1 + 1, y_1 + m_1)$$
$$T_2(x_1 + 1, y_1 + m_2)$$

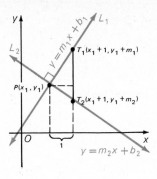

Figure 3

must lie on L_1 and L_2, respectively. The points P, T_1, and T_2 are then the vertices of a triangle. If, now, the lines L_1 and L_2 are perpendicular, triangle PT_1T_2 is a right triangle, with right angle at P. Thus, by the Pythagorean Theorem:

$$[d(T_1, T_2)]^2 = [d(P, T_1)]^2 + [d(P, T_2)]^2$$
$$(m_1 - m_2)^2 = (1 + m_1^2) + (1 + m_2^2)$$
$$m_1^2 - 2m_1m_2 + m_2^2 = 2 + m_1^2 + m_2^2$$
$$-2m_1m_2 = 2$$
$$m_1m_2 = -1$$

Conversely, suppose that, for nonvertical lines L_1 and L_2, the slopes m_1 and m_2 are such that $m_1m_2 = -1$. In this case, L_1 and L_2 cannot be parallel, because for parallel lines, $m_1 = m_2$, and $m_1m_2 = -1$ would imply $m_1^2 = -1$, a statement that is false for every $m_1 \in \mathcal{R}$. Hence, L_1 and L_2 must intersect at some point $P(x_1, y_1)$. If points T_1 and T_2 are now determined as above,

$$[d(T_1, T_2)]^2 = m_1^2 - 2m_1m_2 + m_2^2 = m_1^2 - 2(-1) + m_2^2$$
$$= m_1^2 + 2 + m_2^2 = (1 + m_1^2) + (1 + m_2^2).$$
$$\therefore [d(T_1, T_2)]^2 = [d(P, T_1)]^2 + [d(P, T_2)]^2.$$

By the converse of the Pythagorean Theorem, then, L_1 and L_2 must be perpendicular.

Summarizing the foregoing arguments, you have the following:

> **Theorem.** Two nonvertical lines are perpendicular if and only if the product of their slopes is -1.

Notice that $m_1m_2 = -1$ implies that

$$m_1 = -\frac{1}{m_2} \quad \text{and} \quad m_2 = -\frac{1}{m_1}.$$

Thus, we say that the slopes of perpendicular lines are *negative reciprocals* of each other.

EXAMPLE Find an equation of the line passing through $(-2, 5)$ that is perpendicular to the graph of $x - 3y = 7$.

SOLUTION Transform the given equation to slope-intercept form (page 87),

$$y = \tfrac{1}{3}x - \tfrac{7}{3},$$

from which the slope of its graph is seen to be $\tfrac{1}{3}$. Any line perpendicular to the graph of the given equation will then have slope $-\dfrac{1}{\frac{1}{3}}$, or -3.

(Solution continued on page 338.)

Use the point-slope form $y - y_1 = m(x - x_1)$ with $m = -3$, $x_1 = -2$ and $y_1 = 5$ to obtain the required equation:

$$y - 5 = -3[x - (-2)],$$
$$y - 5 = -3x - 6,$$

or $\qquad\qquad 3x + y = -1.$ Answer.

WRITTEN EXERCISES Find an equation of the line containing P_3, which is perpendicular to the line through points P_1 and P_2.

A

1. $P_1(2, -3)$; $P_2(-2, 1)$; $P_3(1, 1)$
3. $P_1(\frac{1}{2}, \frac{2}{3})$; $P_2(\frac{3}{2}, -\frac{5}{8})$; $P_3(2, 3)$

2. $P_1(-5, 1)$; $P_2(3, -6)$; $P_3(4, 1)$
4. $P_1(-\frac{3}{4}, \frac{2}{3})$; $P_2(\frac{1}{2}, \frac{1}{6})$; $P_3(-2, 3)$

5. $P_1(1.2, 3.1)$; $P_2(1.1, -2.4)$; $P_3(-1, 2)$

6. $P_1(-2.3, 4.4)$; $P_2(5.2, -3.1)$; $P_3(2, -4)$

Find an equation of the line satisfying the given conditions.

7. Containing $(-1, 2)$ and perpendicular to the graph of $3x - y = 4$.

8. Containing $(-3, 2)$ and perpendicular to the graph of $3x + 2y = 10$.

9. Containing $(-1, 6)$ and perpendicular to the x-axis.

10. Containing $(-3, -2)$ and perpendicular to the y-axis.

11. Perpendicular to and bisecting the segment with endpoints $(2, 4)$ and $(3, 8)$.

12. Perpendicular to and bisecting the segment with endpoints $(6, 5)$ and $(5, -7)$.

In Exercises 13–18 use the slope relationship for perpendicular lines to work the exercises.

B

13. Show that the triangle with vertices $(2, 5)$, $(8, -1)$, and $(-2, 1)$ is a right triangle.

14. Show that the triangle with vertices $(2, 1)$, $(3, 3)$, and $(6, -1)$ is a right triangle.

15. Show that the parallelogram with vertices $(-3, 3)$, $(0, 4)$, $(1, 1)$, and $(-2, 0)$ is a rectangle.

16. Show that the parallelogram with vertices $(5, 7)$, $(6, -6)$, $(-7, -7)$, and $(-8, 6)$ is a rectangle.

C

17. Show that the quadrilateral with vertices $(-3c, 0)$, $(0, 4c)$, $(5c, 4c)$, and $(2c, 0)$ is a rhombus, and show that its diagonals are perpendicular to each other.

18. Show that the median of the triangle with vertices $(a, 0)$, $(a + b, 0)$, and $(a + b, b)$, from $(a + b, 0)$ to the opposite side, is perpendicular to that side.

State each of the following.

1. Pythagorean Theorem   2. distance formula

Objective 1, page 333   3. Find the distance between $P_1(3, -1)$ and $P_2(-1, 7)$.

Objective 2, page 333   4. Find an equation of the line containing $(0, 6)$ and perpendicular to the line through the points $(-1, 3)$ and $(5, -1)$.

Check your answers with those printed at the back of the book.

graphing quadratic relations

Objectives

After completing the next five sections, you should be able to:
1. Sketch graphs for second-degree sentences in two variables.
2. Write equations for circles, parabolas, ellipses, and hyperbolas, given appropriate properties of these curves.
3. Find a set of values in an inverse variation, given appropriate information.
4. Apply inverse variations to solve simple word problems.

10–3   *circles*

Can you find an equation for the circle with center at $(3, 2)$ and radius 5? You can if you recall that in a plane, a circle is the set of all points at a given distance, the radius, from a given point, called the center of the circle.

By the distance formula, for each point (x, y) on the circle (Figure 4), you have

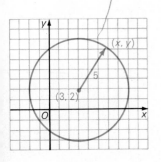

$$\sqrt{(x - 3)^2 + (y - 2)^2} = 5, \tag{1}$$

or

$$(x - 3)^2 + (y - 2)^2 = 25. \tag{2}$$

Conversely, if (2) is satisfied then so is (1), and the distance from $(3, 2)$ to (x, y) is 5. Hence (2) is an equation of the circle.

In general, you have:

Figure 4

An equation of the circle with center (h, k) and radius r is

$$(x - h)^2 + (y - k)^2 = r^2.$$

If the center is the origin, then an equation of the circle is

$$x^2 + y^2 = r^2.$$

Notice that $(x - 3)^2 + (y - 2)^2 = 25$ is equivalent to

$$x^2 + y^2 - 6x - 4y - 12 = 0.$$

This is an example of the fact that $(x - h)^2 + (y - k)^2 = r^2$ is equivalent to an equation of the form

$$x^2 + y^2 + ax + by + c = 0,$$

where a, b, and c are real-number constants. If you are given an equation of a circle in the latter form, you can transform it to an equivalent equation in the form $(x - h)^2 + (y - k)^2 = r^2$ by completing the square (page 284) twice, once for x and once for y.

EXAMPLE   Sketch the graph of $\{(x, y): x^2 + y^2 + 6x - 2y - 6 = 0\}$.

SOLUTION   Add 6 to each member and group the terms involving x and y.

$$(x^2 + 6x \quad) + (y^2 - 2y \quad) = 6$$

Complete the square in x by adding $(\frac{6}{2})^2 = 9$ to each member and the square in y by adding $(-\frac{2}{2})^2 = 1$ to each member.

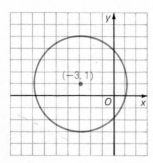

$$\underbrace{(x^2 + 6x + 9)}_{(x + 3)^2} + \underbrace{(y^2 - 2y + 1)}_{(y - 1)^2} = \underbrace{6 + 9 + 1}_{16}$$

From the resulting equation, it is evident by inspection that the graph is a circle with center $(-3, 1)$ and radius 4, as shown at the left. **Answer.**

WRITTEN EXERCISES   Write an equation in the form $x^2 + y^2 + ax + by + c = 0$ for the circle with given center and given radius; then graph the equation.

A   1. $(1, 2)$; 2   3. $(0, 0)$; 6   5. $(\frac{1}{2}, 3\frac{1}{2})$; 1   7. (h, k); r
     2. $(-2, 3)$; 3   4. $(-3, -3)$; 5   6. $(-2, 4)$; $\frac{1}{2}$ 8. $(-h, -k)$; r

Write the defining equation in the form $(x - h)^2 + (y - k)^2 = r^2$; then sketch the graph of the relation.

9. $\{(x, y): x^2 + y^2 = 25\}$
10. $\{(x, y): 3x^2 + 3y^2 = 27\}$
11. $\{(x, y): x^2 + y^2 + 4x = 0\}$
12. $\{(x, y): x^2 + y^2 - 6y = 0\}$
13. $\{(x, y): x^2 + y^2 + 6x - 2y + 1 = 0\}$
14. $\{(x, y): x^2 + y^2 - 8x + 4y - 5 = 0\}$
15. $\{(x, y): 2x^2 + 2y^2 - 12x + 8y - 6 = 0\}$
16. $\{(x, y): 2x^2 + 2y^2 - 3x + 4y + 3 = 0\}$

In Exercises 17–20 sketch the graph of the relation.

EXAMPLE $\{(x, y): x^2 + y^2 - 4x - 12 \geq 0\}$

SOLUTION   Complete the square in x:

$$(x^2 - 4x + 4) + y^2 \geq 12 + 4$$
$$(x - 2)^2 + y^2 \geq 16$$

Because this equation is equivalent to

$$\sqrt{(x - 2)^2 + y^2} \geq 4,$$

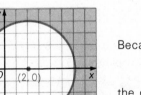

the graph of its solution set is the set of points located a distance of 4 or more units from $(2, 0)$. The graph is then the entire plane on and exterior to the circle with center $(2, 0)$ and radius 4.

B   17. $\{(x, y): x^2 + y^2 \leq 9\}$

18. $\{(x, y): x^2 + y^2 \geq 4\}$

19. $\{(x, y): x^2 + y^2 - 4y > 0\}$

20. $\{(x, y): x^2 + y^2 + 2x - 4y - 4 < 0\}$

Find an equation of the form $x^2 + y^2 + ax + by + c = 0$ for the circle with center C and containing point P.

21. $C(-2, 1)$; $P(3, -2)$ 23. $C(h, k)$; $P(h + 3, k + 4)$

22. $C(3, 4)$; $P(6, 0)$ 24. $C(h, k)$; $P(h - 6, k - 8)$

C   25. Find an equation for the circle with a diameter having endpoints $(-4, 4)$ and $(8, -2)$. Mid pt   dist = $\sqrt{13}$

26. Find an equation for the circle with center at $(-3, 2)$ and tangent to the y-axis. (*Hint:* The tangent line to a circle at a point on the circle is perpendicular to the radius of the circle to the point.)

27. A circle with center at the origin passes through $(2, 3)$. Find an equation of the tangent line to the circle at $(2, 3)$.

28. Prove that if $x^2 + y^2 + ax + by + c = 0$ has a graph in the plane, then $a^2 + b^2 - 4c \geq 0$.

10–4 *parabolas*

In the preceding section, you saw that an equation can be found for the set of points called a *circle*. Equations can be found for other sets of points. Consider, for example, the set consisting of every point P whose distance from a fixed point, called the **focus**, is equal to the perpendicular distance from P to a line, called the **directrix**, that does not contain the focus. A curve consisting of a set of points satisfying these conditions is called a **parabola**.

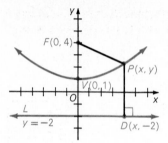

F(0, 4)

P(x, y)

V(0,1)

L

y = −2

D(x, −2)

Figure 5

x	y
−4	$2\frac{1}{3}$
−2	$1\frac{1}{3}$
0	1
2	$1\frac{1}{3}$
4	$2\frac{1}{3}$

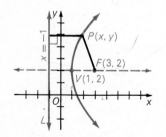

P(x, y)

F(3, 2)

V(1, 2)

Figure 6

x	y
3	6
$1\frac{1}{2}$	4
1	2
$1\frac{1}{2}$	0
3	−2

To find an equation for the parabola with focus $F(0, 4)$ and directrix the line L with equation $y = -2$ (Figure 5), you have

$$d(F, P) = \sqrt{(x - 0)^2 + (y - 4)^2},$$
$$d(P, L) = |y - (-2)|,$$

from which:

$$|y + 2| = \sqrt{x^2 + (y - 4)^2}$$
$$|y + 2|^2 = (\sqrt{x^2 + (y - 4)^2})^2$$
$$(y + 2)^2 = x^2 + (y - 4)^2$$
$$y^2 + 4y + 4 = x^2 + y^2 - 8y + 16$$
$$12y = x^2 + 12$$
$$y = \tfrac{1}{12}x^2 + 1$$

Thus, the set of points described above is the graph of the quadratic function

$$\{(x, y): y = \tfrac{1}{12}x^2 + 1\}.$$

Using the methods of Section 9–6, you can plot its graph as pictured in Figure 5.

The table at the left suggests that the graph is symmetric with respect to the line with equation $x = 0$, that is, the y-axis. In fact, since $(-r, t)$ satisfies the equation of the function whenever (r, t) does (recall page 260), the y-axis is the axis of symmetry, or simply the axis, of this parabola. The point $V(0, 1)$, where the parabola intersects the axis is called the vertex of the parabola.

Similarly, you can show that an equation for the parabola with focus $F(3, 2)$ and directrix the line L with equation $x = -1$ is

$$x = \tfrac{1}{8}(y - 2)^2 + 1,$$

whose graph is shown in Figure 6. The vertex of this parabola is the point $V(1, 2)$, and the axis is the line with equation $y = 2$, as suggested by the table below Figure 6.

From the definition of a parabola and Figures 5 and 6, can you explain why *the vertex is the midpoint of the segment of the axis between the focus and the directrix?*

In general, a parabola whose equation is of the form

$$y = a(x - h)^2 + k \qquad \text{or} \qquad x = a(y - k)^2 + h$$

has vertex $V(h, k)$ and axis of symmetry

$$x = h \qquad \text{or} \qquad y = k,$$

respectively. If $a > 0$, the graph opens upward or to the right; if $a < 0$, the graph opens downward or to the left.

If you are given an equation of the form

$$y = ax^2 + bx + c \qquad \text{or} \qquad x = ay^2 + by + c,$$

you can sketch the curve more readily by completing the square in the squared variable and comparing the resulting equation with the information above.

EXAMPLE Sketch the graph of $\{(x, y): x - 3 = 2y - y^2\}$.

SOLUTION Complete the square in y:

$$x - 3 = -(y^2 - 2y)$$
$$x - 3 - 1 = -(y^2 - 2y + 1)$$
$$x - 4 = -(y - 1)^2$$
$$x = -(y - 1)^2 + 4$$

x	y
0	-1
3	0
4	1
3	2
0	3

Comparing this with relations on page 342, you see that the vertex is $V(4, 1)$, and the axis is the graph of $y = 1$. Since $a = -1$, and $-1 < 0$, the equation has a graph that is a parabola opening to the left.

WRITTEN EXERCISES

Sketch the graph of each relation.

A
1. $\{(x, y): y = 4x^2\}$
2. $\{(x, y): x = -4y^2\}$
3. $\{(x, y): x = y^2 - 4y\}$
4. $\{(x, y): y = 2x^2 - 12x\}$
5. $\{(x, y): y = \frac{1}{4}(x^2 - 4)\}$

6. $\{(x, y): x = \frac{1}{2}(y^2 - 2)\}$
7. $\{(x, y): y = 3x^2 + 6x - 1\}$
8. $\{(x, y): x = 2y^2 + 6y + 1\}$
9. $\{(x, y): 6x = y^2 - 4y - 10\}$
10. $\{(x, y): 4x = y^2 - 8y + 8\}$

B
11. $\{(x, y): y = 3 + \sqrt{x - 2}\}$
12. $\{(x, y): x = -1 + \sqrt{y + 3}\}$

13. $\{(x, y): y \le (x + 1)^2 - 2\}$
14. $\{(x, y): x \ge (y - 3)^2 + 1\}$

Find an equation of the form $y = ax^2 + bx + c$ or $x = ay^2 + by + c$ for the parabola with focus F and directrix the line with the given equation.

15. $F(2, 0); x = -2$
16. $F(-2, 0); x = 0$

17. $F(1, 2); y = -2$
18. $F(2, -1); y = 3$

C
19. Find an equation of the parabola with vertex $(2, 3)$ and focus $(2, 5)$.
20. Find an equation of the parabola with vertex $(2, 3)$ and focus $(6, 3)$.
21. Verify that the parabola with focus $F(0, m)$, $m \ne 0$, and directrix with equation $y = -m$ is the graph of

$$\left\{ (x, y): y = \frac{1}{4m} x^2 \right\}.$$

22. Verify that the parabola with focus $F(m, 0)$, $m \ne 0$, and directrix with equation $x = -m$ is the graph of

$$\left\{ (x, y): x = \frac{1}{4m} y^2 \right\}.$$

23. Verify that the parabola with vertex $V(h, k)$ and the line L with equation $y = k - m$, $m \neq 0$, as directrix is the graph of

$$\left\{(x, y): y - k = \frac{1}{4m}(x - h)^2\right\}.$$

24. Verify that the parabola with vertex $V(h, k)$ and the line L with equation $x = h - m$, $m \neq 0$, as directrix is the graph of

$$\left\{(x, y): x - h = \frac{1}{4m}(y - k)^2\right\}.$$

10–5 *ellipses*

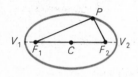

Figure 7

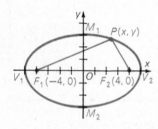

Figure 8

The path traversed by a planet as it revolves about the sun is a plane curve called an *ellipse*, which is defined as follows: In the plane, the set of points for each of which the sum of the distances from two fixed points is a given constant is an **ellipse**. Each of the fixed points is a **focus** (plural: **foci**) of the ellipse, and the distances from these points to a point P on the curve are called **focal radii** of P (Figure 7). The point C bisecting $\overline{F_1F_2}$ is called the **center** of the ellipse. This definition suggests that a sketch of an ellipse may be made by fastening a piece of string at the points F_1 and F_2, stretching it taut with a pencil at point P, and drawing the curve.

To find an equation for an ellipse with foci $F_1(-4, 0)$ and $F_2(4, 0)$ and $d(P, F_1) + d(P, F_2) = 10$ (Figure 8), you have:

$$d(P, F_1) = \sqrt{[x - (-4)]^2 + (y - 0)^2} = \sqrt{(x + 4)^2 + y^2}$$

$$d(P, F_2) = \sqrt{(x - 4)^2 + (y - 0)^2} = \sqrt{(x - 4)^2 + y^2}$$

Since $d(P, F_1) + d(P, F_2) = 10$, it follows that

$$\sqrt{(x + 4)^2 + y^2} + \sqrt{(x - 4)^2 + y^2} = 10,$$

or

$$\sqrt{(x + 4)^2 + y^2} = 10 - \sqrt{(x - 4)^2 + y^2}.$$

Squaring each member and simplifying, you obtain

$$(x + 4)^2 + y^2 = 100 - 20\sqrt{(x - 4)^2 + y^2} + (x - 4)^2 + y^2,$$
$$4x - 25 = -5\sqrt{(x - 4)^2 + y^2}.$$

Again squaring and simplifying, you find that:

$$16x^2 - 200x + 625 = 25[(x - 4)^2 + y^2]$$
$$9x^2 + 25y^2 = 225$$
$$\frac{x^2}{25} + \frac{y^2}{9} = 1$$

Thus, the ellipse described is the graph of the relation

$$\left\{(x, y): \frac{x^2}{25} + \frac{y^2}{9} = 1\right\}.$$

You can verify that the equation is satisfied by the coordinates of these points shown in Figure 8: $V_1(-5, 0)$, $V_2(5, 0)$, $M_1(0, 3)$, $M_2(0, -3)$. Thus,

the x-intercepts are -5 *and* 5;

the y-intercepts are 3 *and* -3.

Also, since $(r, -t)$ and $(-r, t)$ satisfy the equation whenever (r, t) does,

the curve is symmetric with respect to both coordinate axes.

x	y
3	$\pm\frac{12}{5}$
4	$\pm\frac{9}{5}$
-3	$\pm\frac{12}{5}$
-4	$\pm\frac{9}{5}$

The graph of $\frac{x^2}{25} + \frac{y^2}{9} = 1$ can be sketched by plotting the intercepts and a few additional points obtained from $y = \pm\frac{3}{5}\sqrt{25 - x^2}$, as shown in the adjoining table. The graph is pictured in Figure 8.

Do you see that the curve contains only points for which $|x| \leq 5$ and $|y| \leq 3$?

In general, you can show (Exercise 17, page 347) that:

The ellipse with center at the origin, foci $(c, 0)$ and $(-c, 0)$, and the sum of the focal radii for each of its points the constant $2a$, where $a > c$, is the graph of the relation

$$\left\{(x, y): \frac{x^2}{a^2} + \frac{y^2}{b^2} = 1\right\}, \qquad (1)$$

where $b^2 = a^2 - c^2$. It has x-intercepts a and $-a$ and y-intercepts b and $-b$.

If the foci are on the y-axis, you can verify (Exercise 18, page 347) the following.

The ellipse with center at the origin, foci $(0, c)$ and $(0, -c)$, and the sum of the focal radii for each of its points the constant $2a$, where $a > c$, is the graph of the relation

$$\left\{(x, y): \frac{x^2}{b^2} + \frac{y^2}{a^2} = 1\right\}, \qquad (2)$$

where again $b^2 = a^2 - c^2$. Here the x-intercepts are b and $-b$, and the y-intercepts are a and $-a$.

In each case, the ellipse is symmetric with respect to both the x-axis and the y-axis. Notice also that $a > b$.

As you can verify, for an ellipse with an equation of either form (1) or form (2) above, $2a$ and $2b$ represent the distances between intercepts. The segments of length $2a$ and $2b$ cut off on the axes by the ellipse are called the major axis and minor axis of the ellipse, respectively. In Figure 8, the major axis is $\overline{V_1 V_2}$, and the minor axis is $\overline{M_1 M_2}$.

EXAMPLE **Sketch the graph of $\{(x, y): x^2 + 9y^2 = 36\}$.**

SOLUTION Divide both members of $x^2 + 9y^2 = 36$ by 36 to obtain

$$\frac{x^2}{36} + \frac{y^2}{4} = 1.$$

Since $36 > 4$, this is of the form (1). Then, by inspection, the graph is an ellipse, and:

1. It is symmetric with respect to both axes.
2. The x-intercepts are 6 and -6.
3. The y-intercepts are 2 and -2.

x	y
0	2
2	$\dfrac{4\sqrt{2}}{3}$
4	$\dfrac{2\sqrt{5}}{3}$
6	0

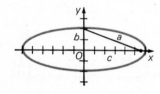

From $y = \frac{1}{3}\sqrt{36 - x^2}$, you can find the first-quadrant points shown in the table. By symmetry, you can find corresponding points in the other quadrants and sketch the graph as shown.

In the preceding Example, the foci are on the x-axis. Since you know that $c^2 = a^2 - b^2 = 36 - 4 = 32$, it follows that $c = \sqrt{32} = 4\sqrt{2}$, and the foci are $(4\sqrt{2}, 0)$ and $(-4\sqrt{2}, 0)$. The foci are not used in sketching the graph. A right triangle with sides a, b, and c is shown in the figure for the example above.

WRITTEN EXERCISES Graph each relation.

A 1. $\left\{(x, y): \dfrac{x^2}{4} + \dfrac{y^2}{9} = 1\right\}$

2. $\left\{(x, y): \dfrac{x^2}{9} + \dfrac{y^2}{4} = 1\right\}$

3. $\left\{(x, y): \dfrac{x^2}{4} + y^2 = 1\right\}$

4. $\left\{(x, y): x^2 + \dfrac{y^2}{9} = 1\right\}$

5. $\left\{(x, y): \dfrac{x^2}{100} + \dfrac{y^2}{36} = 1\right\}$

6. $\left\{(x, y): \dfrac{x^2}{9} + \dfrac{y^2}{25} = 1\right\}$

7. $\{(x, y): 4x^2 + y^2 = 100\}$

8. $\{(x, y): 4x^2 + 16y^2 = 64\}$

9. $\{(x, y): 25x^2 + 9y^2 \leq 225\}$

10. $\{(x, y): 16x^2 + 25y^2 \geq 400\}$

In Exercises 11–16 find an equation for the ellipse with axes on the coordinate axes and with the given characteristics.

EXAMPLE   Major axis of length 8; y-intercepts 3 and -3.

SOLUTION   Since the major axis has length $2a$, you have $2a = 8$, or $a = 4$. The y-intercept 3 is then equal to b.

$$\therefore \frac{x^2}{16} + \frac{y^2}{9} = 1. \quad \text{Answer.}$$

B   11. Distance between y-intercepts, 4; major axis of length 6; center of ellipse is the origin.

12. Major axis of length 8; x-intercepts 2 and -2.

13. Minor axis of length 4; foci at $(0, 3)$ and $(0, -3)$.

14. y-intercepts 4 and -4; minor axis of length 4.

15. y-intercepts 4 and -4; sum of focal radii 10.

16. Sum of focal radii 8; x-intercepts 2 and -2.

C   17. Use the methods of the example in the text on page 344 to derive an equation for the ellipse with foci $(c, 0)$ and $(-c, 0)$ and sum of focal radii $2a$.

18. Repeat Exercise 17 for the ellipse with foci $(0, c)$ and $(0, -c)$ with sum of focal radii $2a$.

Graph each of the following.

19. $\{(x, y): 0 \leq y \leq 2\sqrt{9 - x^2}\}$

20. $\{(x, y): 0 \geq y \geq -\frac{2}{3}\sqrt{9 - x^2}\}$

21. $\left\{(x, y): \dfrac{(x - 2)^2}{9} + \dfrac{(y - 2)^2}{4} = 1\right\}$

22. $\left\{(x, y): \dfrac{(x - 3)^2}{4} + \dfrac{(y + 2)^2}{16} = 1\right\}$

10–6 *hyperbolas*

Just as in Section 10–5 you used the sum of distances between points to define an ellipse, so do you use the *difference* of such distances to define another curve. Consider the set of points in the plane such that for each point, the absolute value of the difference of its distances, called the focal radii, from two fixed points, called the foci, is a constant. Such a set of points is a two-branched curve called a hyperbola.

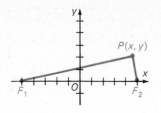

Figure 9

To obtain an equation for the hyperbola with foci at $F_1(-5, 0)$ and $F_2(5, 0)$ and with focal radii differing by 8 (Figure 9), you can begin by expressing the fact that for any point $P(x, y)$ on the hyperbola, either

$$\sqrt{[x-(-5)]^2 + y^2} - \sqrt{(x-5)^2 + y^2} = 8$$

or

$$\sqrt{[x-(-5)]^2 + y^2} - \sqrt{(x-5)^2 + y^2} = -8.$$

In either case, the squaring process you used to obtain the equation for an ellipse (page 344) can be applied to obtain

$$\frac{x^2}{16} - \frac{y^2}{9} = 1.$$

By inspection, you can see that the graph of this equation:

(1) Is symmetric with respect to both axes.
(2) Has x-intercepts 4 and -4.

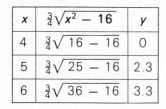

x	$\frac{3}{4}\sqrt{x^2-16}$	y
4	$\frac{3}{4}\sqrt{16-16}$	0
5	$\frac{3}{4}\sqrt{25-16}$	2.3
6	$\frac{3}{4}\sqrt{36-16}$	3.3

It has no y-intercepts, since if you solve the equation for y in terms of x, you obtain

$$y = \pm\frac{3}{4}\sqrt{x^2-16},$$

from which it is evident that the curve has no points for which $|x| < 4$.

Using the foregoing facts, and constructing the brief table of first-quadrant values shown, you can sketch the hyperbola in Figure 10.

As you can see in Figure 10, the graph lies entirely within two of the regions determined by the diagonals of the rectangle that is bounded by segments of the lines with equations

$$x = -4, \qquad x = 4, \qquad y = 3, \qquad \text{and} \qquad y = -3.$$

These diagonals are called **asymptotes** of the hyperbola and have equations

$$y = \tfrac{3}{4}x \qquad \text{and} \qquad y = -\tfrac{3}{4}x.$$

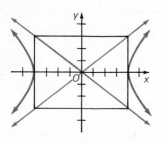

Figure 10

For a given value, $x_1 > 0$, of x, the difference between the ordinate of a point on the asymptote in Quadrant I and the ordinate of the corresponding point on the curve is given by

$$\tfrac{3}{4}x_1 - \tfrac{3}{4}\sqrt{x_1^2-16} = \frac{(\tfrac{3}{4}x_1 - \tfrac{3}{4}\sqrt{x_1^2-16})(\tfrac{3}{4}x_1 + \tfrac{3}{4}\sqrt{x_1^2-16})}{\tfrac{3}{4}x_1 + \tfrac{3}{4}\sqrt{x_1^2-16}}$$

$$= \frac{36}{3x_1 + 3\sqrt{x_1^2-16}}.$$

As you can see, the greater x_1, the less the difference in ordinates, and for increasing values of x_1, the curve approaches closer and closer to the asymptote. By symmetry you can see that the corresponding situation holds in each of the remaining quadrants.

In general, you can show (Exercise 17, page 352) that:

If $(-c, 0)$ and $(c, 0)$ are foci of the hyperbola for which the absolute value of the difference of the focal radii is the constant $2a > 0$, then the hyperbola is the graph of the relation

$$\left\{ (x, y): \frac{x^2}{a^2} - \frac{y^2}{b^2} = 1 \right\}, \tag{1}$$

where $b^2 = c^2 - a^2$. The equations for the asymptotes are

$$y = \frac{b}{a}x \quad \text{and} \quad y = -\frac{b}{a}x.$$

Similarly, you can show (Exercise 18, page 352) that:

If $(0, -c)$ and $(0, c)$ are foci of the hyperbola for which the absolute value of the difference of the focal radii is the constant $2a > 0$, then the hyperbola is the graph of the relation

$$\left\{ (x, y): \frac{y^2}{a^2} - \frac{x^2}{b^2} = 1 \right\}, \tag{2}$$

where $b^2 = c^2 - a^2$. The equations for the asymptotes are

$$y = \frac{a}{b}x \quad \text{and} \quad y = -\frac{a}{b}x.$$

EXAMPLE   Sketch the graph of $\{(x, y): x^2 - 4y^2 = 36\}$.

SOLUTION   Divide each member by 36 to obtain $\dfrac{x^2}{36} - \dfrac{y^2}{9} = 1$.

Comparing this with Equation (1) above, you see that $a = 6$ and $b = 3$. Then, by inspection, you can determine that:

(1) The graph is symmetric with respect to both axes.
(2) The x-intercepts are 6 and -6. There are no y-intercepts.
(3) The asymptotes are the graphs of $y = \frac{1}{2}x$ and $y = -\frac{1}{2}x$.

First sketching the asymptotes and identifying the intercepts, you have the graph shown at the right. A right triangle with sides measuring a, b, and c is also shown in the figure.

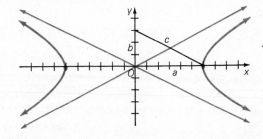

For hyperbolas with equations of the form (1) or (2) above, the origin is called the center of the hyperbola, the points of intersection of the branches of the curve with a coordinate axis are the vertices, the segment of length $2a$ of a coordinate axis between the intercepts is the transverse axis, and the segment of length $2b$ of the remaining coordinate axis with each endpoint a distance b from the origin is the conjugate axis (Figure 11).

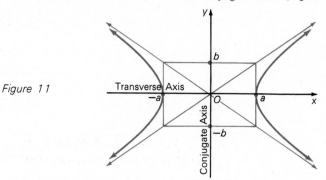

Figure 11

The circle, ellipse, parabola, and hyperbola are called conic sections because each can be formed as the intersection of a plane with a *conical surface of two nappes* (see Figure 12). (It is assumed that such a conical surface extends indefinitely.) A point, a line, and a pair of intersecting lines are sometimes called degenerate conic sections.

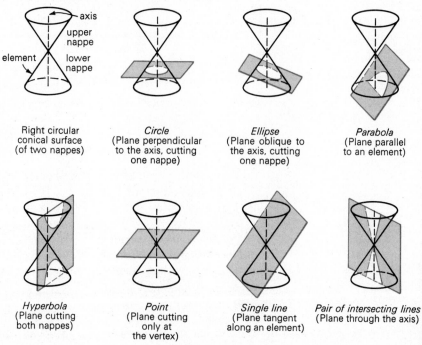

Right circular conical surface (of two nappes)

Circle (Plane perpendicular to the axis, cutting one nappe)

Ellipse (Plane oblique to the axis, cutting one nappe)

Parabola (Plane parallel to an element)

Hyperbola (Plane cutting both nappes)

Point (Plane cutting only at the vertex)

Single line (Plane tangent along an element)

Pair of intersecting lines (Plane through the axis)

Figure 12

WRITTEN EXERCISES Graph each relation.

A 1. $\left\{(x, y): \dfrac{x^2}{4} - \dfrac{y^2}{25} = 1\right\}$

6. $\left\{(x, y): \dfrac{y^2}{25} - x^2 = 1\right\}$

2. $\left\{(x, y): \dfrac{x^2}{9} - \dfrac{y^2}{64} = 1\right\}$

7. $\{(x, y): 2x^2 - 2y^2 = 8\}$

3. $\left\{(x, y): \dfrac{y^2}{9} - \dfrac{x^2}{16} = 1\right\}$

8. $\{(x, y): 3y^2 - 3x^2 = 48\}$

4. $\left\{(x, y): \dfrac{y^2}{25} - \dfrac{x^2}{4} = 1\right\}$

9. $\{(x, y): 5x^2 - 20y^2 = 100\}$

5. $\left\{(x, y): \dfrac{x^2}{16} - y^2 = 1\right\}$

10. $\{(x, y): 3y^2 - 75x^2 = 225\}$

In Exercises 11–16 find an equation for a hyperbola with axes on the coordinate axes and with the given characteristics.

EXAMPLE Foci at (4, 0) and (−4, 0); slope of asymptotes, 3 and −3.

SOLUTION Since the foci are located on the x-axis at $(c, 0)$ and $(-c, 0)$, you seek an equation of the form (1) with $c = 4$. Since the slope of one asymptote is $\dfrac{b}{a} = 3$, you have $b = 3a$. Substituting into $b^2 = c^2 - a^2$, you have

$$(3a)^2 = 4^2 - a^2,$$

$$10a^2 = 16,$$

$$a^2 = \frac{16}{10} = \frac{8}{5}.$$

Since $b = 3a$,

$$b^2 = 9a^2 = \frac{72}{5},$$

and an equation for the hyperbola is

$$\frac{x^2}{\frac{8}{5}} - \frac{y^2}{\frac{72}{5}} = 1, \quad \frac{5x^2}{8} - \frac{5y^2}{72} = 1, \text{ or } 45x^2 - 5y^2 = 72. \textbf{ Answer.}$$

B 11. Intercepts at (0, 4) and (0, −4); foci at (0, 5) and (0, −5).

12. Transversal axis of length 4; one focus at (−3, 0).

13. Foci at (0, 4) and (0, −4); one vertex at (0, 3).

14. Length of conjugate axis 3; one intercept at (0, 5).

15. Foci at (5, 0) and (−5, 0); absolute value of difference of focal radii 7.

16. Foci at (0, 6) and (0, −6); absolute value of the difference of focal radii 8.

C **17.** Use the methods of the example in the text on page 348 to derive an equation for a hyperbola with foci $(c, 0)$ and $(-c, 0)$ and absolute value of difference of focal radii $2a > 0$ where $a < c$.

18. Repeat Exercise 17 for the hyperbola with foci $(0, c)$ and $(0, -c)$ and absolute value of the difference of focal radii $2a > 0$, where $a < c$.

Graph each relation.

19. $\{(x, y): 0 \le y \le \sqrt{x^2 - 9}\}$

20. $\{(x, y): -\sqrt{y^2 - 16} \le x \le \sqrt{y^2 - 16}\}$

21. $\left\{(x, y): \dfrac{(x - 2)^2}{4} - \dfrac{(y + 3)^2}{9} = 1\right\}$

22. $\left\{(x, y): \dfrac{(y + 2)^2}{16} - \dfrac{(x - 1)^2}{9} = 1\right\}$

10–7 *inverse and other kinds of variation*

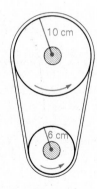

Figure 13

When two pulleys are connected (Figure 13), the one with smaller diameter revolves more rapidly. If d_1 represents the diameter of one pulley and n_1 the number of revolutions per minute (rpm) of the pulley, and if d_2 and n_2 represent the corresponding numbers for the other pulley, then

$$d_1 n_1 = d_2 n_2, \quad \text{or} \quad \frac{d_1}{d_2} = \frac{n_2}{n_1}.$$

In the pulleys shown in Figure 13, $d_1 = 6$ centimeters and $d_2 = 10$ centimeters. If the smaller pulley revolves at 120 rpm, you can compute the rpm of the other pulley:

$$\frac{6}{10} = \frac{n_2}{120}$$

$$n_2 = 72$$

For this set of pulleys, $dn = 720$. Because this implies that

$$n = \frac{720}{d} \quad \text{or} \quad d = \frac{720}{n},$$

you say that n and d vary *inversely* as each other, or are *inversely proportional* to each other.

In general, any function defined by an equation of the form

$$xy = k,$$

where k is a nonzero constant, is called an *inverse variation*, and k is the constant of variation. The graph of such a function is of the form shown

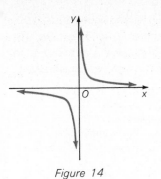

Figure 14

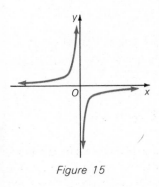

Figure 15

in Figure 14 if $k > 0$, and of the form shown in Figure 15 if $k < 0$. It can be shown (compare Exercises 21–22, page 352) that these graphs are hyperbolas, with foci on the lines with equations $y = x$ and $y = -x$, respectively, and with the coordinate axes as asymptotes. Ordinarily, in practical situations, you have $x > 0$, $y > 0$, and $k > 0$, and the graph is limited to one such as the first-quadrant branch of Figure 14.

As with direct variation (recall page 91), there is an important relationship among the coordinates of two ordered pairs (x_1, y_1) and (x_2, y_2) of the inverse variation specified by the equation $xy = k$, $k \neq 0$. You have

$$x_1 y_1 = k \quad \text{and} \quad x_2 y_2 = k, \quad \text{and so} \quad x_1 y_1 = x_2 y_2.$$

Hence, $x_1 \neq 0$, $x_2 \neq 0$, $y_1 \neq 0$, and $y_2 \neq 0$, and you have

$$\frac{x_1}{x_2} = \frac{y_2}{y_1}.$$

We state this result as a theorem.

Theorem. For all real numbers x_1, y_1, x_2, y_2 ($x_1 \neq 0, x_2 \neq 0, y_1 \neq 0$, and $y_2 \neq 0$), if (x_1, y_1) and (x_2, y_2) are ordered pairs of an inverse variation, then

$$\frac{x_1}{x_2} = \frac{y_2}{y_1}.$$

Everyday examples of inverse variation are:

1. For a fixed distance, the greater the speed, the proportionately less the time needed to cover it (and vice versa): $rt = D$
2. For a stated income, the greater the rate of interest, the proportionately less the amount of principal needed: $pr = I$
3. For a given area, the greater the length of a rectangle, the proportionately less the width: $bh = A$
4. Boyle's Law in physics. If the temperature is kept constant, the greater the pressure on a gas, the proportionately less the volume: $pv = K$

In Section 8–1, the idea of direct variation was extended to include variation defined by $y = ax^2$, that is, "y varies directly as x^2." (The graph of that variation is a parabola.) Similarly, the idea of inverse variation is extended to include variation defined, for example, by

$$y = \frac{k}{x^2},$$

that is, y varies inversely as x^2. (The graph of such a variation is not a curve with which we are familiar.) Corresponding extensions involving other powers may also be made.

Still another form of variation is typified by the relationship between the electrical resistance of a wire and the length and diameter of the wire. The electrical resistance R of a wire varies *directly* as the length l of the wire and *inversely* as the square of its diameter d. An equation expressing this fact is

$$R = \frac{kl}{d^2}.$$

You call such a variation a combined variation. If y varies directly as x and also directly as z, then the equation relating these variables is of the form

$$y = kxz,$$

and you say y varies jointly as x and z.

EXAMPLE   If 20 meters of wire of diameter 1.5 millimeters has a resistance of 12 ohms, what is the resistance of 20 meters of the same type of wire if the diameter is increased to 2 millimeters?

SOLUTION   You have a combined variation

$$R = \frac{kl}{d^2}.$$

Since $R = 12$ when $l = 20$ and $d = 1.5$,

$$12 = \frac{k(20)}{(1.5)^2}, \quad \text{or} \quad k = 1.35.$$

$$\therefore R = \frac{1.35l}{d^2}.$$

Replacing l with "20" with d with "2," you have

$$R = \frac{1.35(20)}{(2)^2} = 6.75.$$

$\therefore$ the resistance is 6.75 ohms.   **Answer.**

WRITTEN EXERCISES   Determine c so that both ordered pairs are members of the same inverse variation.

A   1. $(2, \frac{3}{2})$; $(6, c)$

2. $(-4, -2)$; $(c, 4)$

3. $(10, \frac{1}{2})$; $(c, -5)$

4. $(5, 10)$; $(4, c)$

5. $(-1, -\frac{1}{3})$; $(c, 15)$

6. $(1, -3)$; $(-\frac{1}{2}, c)$

7. $(-2, -8)$; (c, c)

8. $(4, 1)$; (c, c)

In Exercises 9–12 determine c so that the given statement is true.

9. $\{(-3, 3), (9, c)\} \subset \{(x, y): y \text{ varies inversely as } x^2\}$.

10. $\{(4, \frac{1}{32}), (c, \frac{1}{4})\} \subset \{(x, y): y \text{ varies inversely as } x^3\}$.

11. $\{(9, 1), (16, c)\} \subset \{(x, y): y \text{ varies inversely as } \sqrt{x}\}$.

12. $\{(8, \frac{1}{4}), (c, \frac{1}{6})\} \subset \{(x, y): y \text{ varies inversely as } \sqrt[3]{x}\}$.

13. If z varies jointly as x and y, and $z = 8$ when $x = 2$ and $y = 2$, find z, when $x = 6$ and $y = 4$.

14. If z varies jointly as x and y, and $z = 5$ when $x = 2$ and $y = 7$, find z when $x = 4$ and $y = 3$.

B 15. If z varies directly as the square of x and inversely as the cube of y, and $z = 4$, when $x = 3$ and $y = 2$, find z when $x = 4$ and $y = 3$.

16. If z varies directly as x and inversely as y, and if $z = 40$ when $x = 300$ and $y = 30$, find z when $x = 324$ and $y = 24$.

17. If y varies jointly as x and z and inversely as u, and if $y = 6$ when $x = 2$, $z = 3$, and $u = 4$, find y when $x = 4$, $z = 3$, and $u = 8$.

18. If y varies jointly as x and z^2 and inversely as u^2, and if $y = 8$ when $x = 6$, $z = 2$, and $u = 3$, find y when $x = 8$, $z = 4$, and $u = 8$.

19. If y varies inversely as x, find the resulting change in y if x is doubled.

20. If y varies inversely as x^2, find the resulting change in y if x is doubled.

C 21. Use the definition on page 349 to find an equation for the hyperbola with foci at $(2, 2)$ and $(-2, -2)$ and with difference of focal radii 4.

22. Repeat Exercise 21 for the hyperbola with foci at $(-1, 1)$ and $(1, -1)$ and with difference of focal radii 2.

PROBLEMS

A   1. The volume V that a gas occupies varies directly as the temperature T (in degrees Kelvin, °K) of the gas and inversely as the pressure P. What volume will a gas occupying 20 cubic meters at a temperature of 300°K and a pressure of 30 kilograms per square meter have if the temperature is raised to 320°K and the pressure is decreased to 20 kilograms per square meter?

2. The frequency f of a radio wave is inversely proportional to the wave length L. If the frequency is 100 megacycles per second for a wave 3 meters long, what is the frequency for a wave 5 meters long?

3. In planting corn in rows, the number n of plants per hectare will vary inversely as the square of the distance d between the plants in each direction. If plants are separated by a distance of 62 centimeters in each direction, there will be approximately 27250 plants per hectare. About how many plants per hectare will there be under a separation of 70 centimeters in each direction?

4. The amount A of a substance digested in n grams of pepsin in one hour varies inversely as $\sqrt{n}$. If 7 grams of a substance are digested in 100 grams of pepsin, how many grams of the same substance will be digested in an hour in 196 grams of pepsin?

5. In a railroad-track curve, the elevation E of the outer rail over the inner rail varies inversely as the radius r of the curve of the inner track. If the elevation of the outer rail is 5 centimeters when the radius of the curve of the inner rail is 1000 meters, what is the elevation of the outer rail when the radius of the curve of the inner rail is 1200 meters?

6. The force F with which two spheres containing certain electrical charges attract each other is inversely proportional to the distance d between their centers. If two spheres whose centers are 2 centimeters apart attract each other with a force of 5 dynes, how far apart must the centers of the spheres be if the force of attraction between them is to be only $1\frac{1}{2}$ dynes?

B

7. The crushing load of a square wooden post varies directly as the fourth power of its thickness and inversely as the square of its length. If a post 10 centimeters thick and 2 meters high is crushed by a load of 90 tonnes, what is the crushing load of a post 5 centimeters thick and 3 meters high?

8. The time in hours it takes a satellite to complete a circular orbit about the earth varies directly as the radius (from center of earth) of the orbit and inversely as the orbital velocity. If a satellite completes an orbit 800 kilometers above the earth in 100 minutes at a velocity of 30,000 kilometers per hour, how long would it take a satellite to complete an orbit if it is circling 1700 kilometers above the earth at 25,000 kilometers per hour? Assume that the radius of the earth is 6400 km.

SELF-TEST 2   Give the meaning of each of the following.

1. parabola
2. focus of a parabola
3. directrix of a parabola

4. ellipse
5. hyperbola
6. inverse variation

Sketch the graph of each relation.

Objective 1, page 339   **7.** $\{(x, y): 4x = y^2 - 16\}$ **8.** $\{(x, y): x^2 - 4y^2 = 4\}$

Objective 2, page 339   **9.** Find an equation of the form $x^2 + y^2 + ax + by + c = 0$ for the circle with center $(-2, 4)$ and radius 3.

10. Find an equation of the form $y = ax^2 + bx + c$ for the parabola with focus $(3, -5)$ and directrix the line with equation $y = 4$.

Objective 3, page 339   **11.** If y varies jointly as x and z, and $y = 6$ when $x = 3$ and $z = 5$, find y when $x = 6$ and $z = 4$.

Objective 4, page 339   **12.** Near the surface of a planet, the weight of an object varies inversely as the square of the distance from the center of the planet. Find the ratio of the weight of an object at the surface of a planet of radius 8000 km to the weight of the object at a height of 4000 km.

Check your answers with those printed at the back of the book.

solving quadratic systems

Objectives | After completing the next three sections, you should be able to:
1. Solve simple quadratic systems graphically.
2. Solve simple quadratic systems by substitution.

10–8 *graphic solutions of systems*

Graphical methods can be used to determine or to estimate real-number solutions of systems of equations in two variables in which one or both of the equations are quadratic.

EXAMPLE   Find the solution set of the system over $\mathcal{R}$: $4x^2 + y^2 = 25$
$$x^2 - y^2 = -5.$$

SOLUTION   Graph both equations on the same coordinate plane and determine any points of intersection.

$$\{(2, 3), (-2, 3), (-2, -3), (2, -3)\}. \text{ Answer.}$$

CHECK $4(2)^2 + (3)^2 \stackrel{?}{=} 25$ $(2)^2 - (3)^2 \stackrel{?}{=} -5$
$16 + 9 = 25 \checkmark$ $4 - 9 = -5 \checkmark$

Clearly, because $(-2)^2 = 2^2$ and $(-3)^2 = 3^2$, all values will check in a similar way.

In solving graphically systems containing one or more quadratic equations, you will discover that:

(1) A system consisting of a linear equation and a quadratic equation may have no real solutions or as many as two.
(2) A system consisting of two quadratic equations may have no real solutions or as many as four.

WRITTEN EXERCISES   Solve each system over $\mathcal{R}$ by graphing. Where necessary, estimate components of solutions to the nearest $\frac{1}{2}$ unit.

A
1. $y = x^2 - 5$
   $y = 4x$

2. $y = x^2 - 2$
   $y = -x$

3. $y = x^2 - 2x + 1$
   $x + y = 3$

4. $y = x^2 + 2x + 1$
   $x - y = -3$

5. $x^2 + y^2 = 10$
   $9x^2 + y^2 = 18$

6. $x^2 + 4y^2 = 17$
   $3x^2 - y^2 = -1$

7. $9x^2 + 16y^2 = 100$
   $x^2 + y^2 = 8$

8. $x^2 + 4y^2 = 25$
   $4x^2 + y^2 = 25$

B 9. $xy = 4$
      $x^2 + y^2 = 8$

   10. $x^2 - y^2 = 35$
       $xy = 6$

   11. $2x - y = 9$
       $xy = -4$

   12. $x + y = 1$
       $xy = -12$

Graph the solution set of each system over $\mathfrak{R}$.

C 13. $x^2 + y^2 \leq 9$
       $y \leq x$

   14. $y \geq x^2 - 1$
       $y \leq 1$

   15. $4x^2 + 9y^2 \leq 36$
       $y \geq x^2 + 1$

   16. $x^2 + y^2 \geq 4$
       $x^2 + 9y^2 \leq 9$

10-9 *linear-quadratic systems: substitution*

If a system of equations involves a linear equation and a quadratic equation, you can solve the system by substitution. In this process the quadratic equation is replaced by one involving a single variable.

EXAMPLE 1   Find the solution set of the system:

$$x^2 + 9y^2 = 37$$
$$x - 2y = -3$$

SOLUTION   1. Transform the *linear equation* to express x in terms of y.

$$x - 2y = -3$$
$$x = 2y - 3$$

2. Replace the given quadratic equation with the equation obtained from it by replacing x with "$2y - 3$."

$$x^2 + 9y^2 = 37$$
$$(2y - 3)^2 + 9y^2 = 37$$
$$4y^2 - 12y + 9 + 9y^2 = 37$$

3. Solve the new quadratic equation.

$$13y^2 - 12y - 28 = 0$$
$$(13y + 14)(y - 2) = 0$$
$$y = -\tfrac{14}{13},\ y = 2$$

4. Solve two linear systems:

$x = 2y - 3$	$x = 2y - 3$
$y = -\tfrac{14}{13}$	$y = 2$
$x = 2(-\tfrac{14}{13}) - 3$	$x = 2(2) - 3$
$x = -\tfrac{67}{13}$	$x = 1$

Thus, the solutions are $(-\tfrac{67}{13}, -\tfrac{14}{13})$ and $(1, 2)$.

5. Check each ordered pair in both equations.

$$(-\tfrac{67}{13})^2 + 9(-\tfrac{14}{13})^2 \overset{?}{=} 37 \qquad \Big| \qquad (1)^2 + 9(2)^2 \overset{?}{=} 37$$

$$\tfrac{4489}{169} + \tfrac{1764}{169} \overset{?}{=} 37 \qquad\qquad 1 + 36 \overset{?}{=} 37$$

$$\tfrac{6253}{169} \overset{?}{=} 37 \qquad\qquad\qquad 37 = 37\ \checkmark$$

$$37 = 37\ \checkmark$$

$\therefore$ the solution set is $\{(-\tfrac{67}{13}, -\tfrac{14}{13}), (1, 2)\}$. **Answer.**

Figure 16 depicts the graphical situation in the foregoing example. Figure 16a shows the graph of the original system of equations, while Figure 16b shows the result after Step 3, when the ellipse has been replaced with the two horizontal lines with equations $y = 2$ and $y = -\tfrac{14}{13}$.

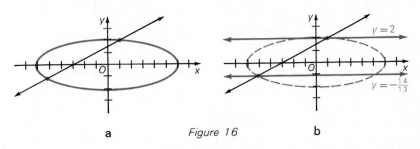

a   *Figure 16*   b

Notice also, in Example 1, that the linear equation was transformed to express x in terms of y rather than y in terms of x because in this case the computation was simpler.

It is important to be aware of the fact that systems of equations involving one or more quadratic equations may have complex as well as real solutions. While graphing may be used to identify such real solutions as exist, substitution will yield complex as well as real solutions.

EXAMPLE 2   **Find the solution set of the system:**

$$x^2 - 2y^2 = 3$$
$$x - y = 1$$

SOLUTION   Solve the linear equation for y in terms of x:

$$y = x - 1$$

Substitute $x - 1$ for y in the quadratic equation and simplify:

$$x^2 - 2(x - 1)^2 = 3$$
$$x^2 - 2x^2 + 4x - 2 = 3$$
$$x^2 - 4x + 5 = 0$$

(*Solution continued on page 360.*)

Solve for x using the quadratic formula:

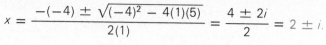

$$x = \frac{-(-4) \pm \sqrt{(-4)^2 - 4(1)(5)}}{2(1)} = \frac{4 \pm 2i}{2} = 2 \pm i.$$

Then since $y = x - 1$, you have

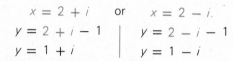

$$x = 2 + i \quad \text{or} \quad x = 2 - i.$$
$$y = 2 + i - 1 \quad \mid \quad y = 2 - i - 1$$
$$y = 1 + i \quad \mid \quad y = 1 - i$$

∴ the solution set is $\{(2 + i, 1 + i), (2 - i, 1 - i)\}$. **Answer.**

Note that, as in Example 2, when a system has no real solutions, the graphs of the equations do not intersect.

WRITTEN EXERCISES   Find the solution set of each system over $\mathcal{C}$.

A   1. $y = x^2 - 5$
        $y = 4x$

6. $x^2 + y^2 = 9$
    $y = 2$

2. $x^2 - y^2 = -15$
    $x - 4y = 0$

7. $x^2 + 2y^2 = 12$
    $2x - y = 4$

3. $x^2 + y^2 = 13$
    $x + y = 5$

8. $x^2 + y^2 = 5$
    $3x + y = 1$

4. $x^2 + y^2 = 6$
    $x + y = 6$

9. $x^2 + y^2 = 9$
    $y = 4$

5. $x^2 + y^2 = 20$
    $x + y = 6$

10. $x^2 + y^2 = 26$
    $x + y = 8$

B   11. $xy = -12$
            $x + y = 1$

15. $2x^2 - 5xy + 2y^2 = 5$
    $2x - y = 1$

12. $xy = -4$
        $2x - y = 9$

16. $2x^2 + xy + y^2 = 9$
    $-x + 2y = 1$

13. $x^2 - xy - 2y^2 = 4$
            $x - y = 2$

17. $\dfrac{2}{x} + \dfrac{4}{y} = 1$
    $4x - y = 0$

14. $x^2 - 2x + y^2 = 3$
            $2x + y = 4$

18. $\dfrac{2}{x} - \dfrac{2}{y} = 1$
    $x + y = 0$

Solve for x and y in terms of a and b.

C   19. $\dfrac{x^2}{a^2} + \dfrac{y^2}{b^2} = \dfrac{a^2 + b^2}{a^2 b^2}$ 20. $a^2 x^2 + y^2 = b^2$

$\dfrac{x}{a} + \dfrac{y}{b} = \dfrac{a + b}{ab}$ $ax - y = -b$

PROBLEMS

A   **1.** The sum of the squares of two positive integers is 13. The sum of the greater integer and twice the lesser is 7. Find the integers.

2. The sum of two positive real numbers is 6, and their product is $8\frac{3}{4}$. Find the numbers.

3. A rectangle with an area of 12 square meters has a perimeter of 26 meters. Find the dimensions of the rectangle.

4. A rectangle has a perimeter of 18 centimeters. If the width is increased by 12 centimeters and the length is decreased by 5 centimeters, the area of the new rectangle is twice that of the original rectangle. Find the dimensions of the original rectangle.

B   **5.** Find two positive integers whose sum is 14 and the sum of whose reciprocals is $\frac{7}{24}$.

6. Find two positive real numbers whose sum is $1\frac{3}{8}$ and whose product is $\frac{15}{32}$.

7. The difference of the areas of two squares is 45. The length of a side of one square is 3 less than twice the length of a side of the other square. Find the length of a side of each square.

8. A rectangular lot with one side along a straight river contains 2100 square meters. To fence the three sides of the lot not on the river requires 130 meters of fence. What are the dimensions of the lot?

Isaac Newton
1642–1727

Isaac Newton was born in England, almost a year after the death of Galileo. He had no equal when it came to insight into physical problems and the ability to treat them mathematically.

Newton's greatest contributions in the fields of astronomy, optics, mathematics and mechanics were conceived by the time he was 24. Observations of the motions of the planets led him to his great discoveries of the laws of motion and gravitation and showed them to be universal throughout the solar system. In his three-volume work, generally known as the *Principia*, published in 1687, the laws are stated as a fundamental basis for all mechanics. Thus, Newton succeeded, for the first time in the history of mankind, in unifying most of the known facts concerning the physical behavior of our universe with some basic principles.

10–10 *quadratic-quadratic systems*

Substitution often provides a means of solving systems of two quadratic equations in two variables.

EXAMPLE 1 **Find the solution set of the system:** $x^2 + 4y^2 = 17$
$$3x^2 - y^2 = -1$$

SOLUTION   1. Solve the second equation for y^2 in terms of x.

$$3x^2 - y^2 = -1$$
$$y^2 = 3x^2 + 1$$

2. Replace y^2 in the first equation with "$3x^2 + 1$."

$$x^2 + 4(3x^2 + 1) = 17$$
$$x^2 + 12x^2 + 4 = 17$$
$$13x^2 = 13$$
$$x^2 = 1$$

3. Solve the resulting equation.

$$x = 1 \text{ or } x = -1$$

4. Solve two simple systems.

$y^2 = 3x^2 + 1$	$y^2 = 3x^2 + 1$
$x = 1$	$x = -1$
$y^2 = 3(1)^2 + 1$	$y^2 = 3(-1)^2 + 1$
$y^2 = 4$	$y^2 = 4$
$y = 2 \text{ or } y = -2$	$y = 2 \text{ or } y = -2$
$\{(1, 2), (1, -2)\}$	$\{(-1, 2), (-1, -2)\}$

5. Checking the solutions in the original system is left to you.

$\therefore$ the solution set is $\{(1, 2), (1, -2), (-1, 2), (-1, -2)\}$. **Answer.**

Figure 17 shows that the result of Step 3 is the replacement of the ellipse having equation $x^2 + 4y^2 = 17$ with the two straight lines having equations $x = 1$ and $x = -1$.

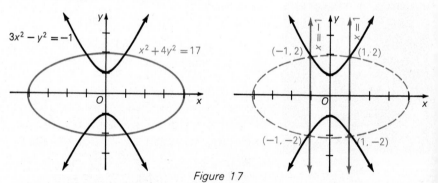

Figure 17

Linear combinations (Section 4–2) of quadratic equations can also be used to find solution sets of systems of such equations.

EXAMPLE 2   Find the solution set of the system: $x^2 + y^2 = 10$
$9x^2 + y^2 = 18$

SOLUTION   Subtracting the first equation from the second produces the linear combination

$$8x^2 = 8 \quad \text{or} \quad x^2 = 1,$$

which can be used together with equation 1 to form the equivalent system:

$$x^2 + y^2 = 10 \quad \text{or} \quad x^2 + y^2 = 10$$
$$x = 1 \quad\qquad\qquad x = -1$$

Substituting 1 and -1 for x in turn in the first equation then produces values for y. You have:

$$
\begin{array}{c|c}
1^2 + y^2 = 10 & (-1)^2 + y^2 = 10 \\
y^2 = 9 & y^2 = 9 \\
y = 3 \text{ or } y = -3 & y = 3 \text{ or } y = -3 \\
\{(1, 3), (1, -3)\} & \{(-1, 3), (-1, -3)\}
\end{array}
$$

Checking the solutions in both equations is left to you.

$\therefore$ the solution set is $\{(1, 3), (1, -3), (-1, 3), (-1, -3)\}$. **Answer.**

WRITTEN EXERCISES   Find the solution set over $\mathcal{C}$.

A
1. $x^2 + 4y^2 = 52$
$x^2 + y^2 = 25$

2. $9x^2 + 16y^2 = 100$
$x^2 + y^2 = 8$

3. $x^2 - y^2 = 7$
$2x^2 + 3y^2 = 24$

4. $3x^2 + 4y^2 = 16$
$x^2 - y^2 = 3$

5. $4x^2 + 3y^2 = 12$
$x^2 + 3y^2 = 12$

6. $x^2 + 4y^2 = 25$
$4x^2 + y^2 = 25$

7. $4x^2 - 9y^2 = -132$
$x^2 + 4y^2 = 67$

8. $5x^2 + 16y^2 = 26$
$-4x^2 + 25y^2 = 17$

9. $4x^2 - y^2 = 0$
$x^2 + 2y^2 = 81$

10. $x^2 - y^2 = -35$
$x^2 + y^2 = 37$

B
11. $9x^2 + 4y^2 = 36$
$x^2 + y^2 = 81$

12. $9x^2 + 25y^2 = 225$
$x^2 + y^2 = 4$

13. $x^2 - y^2 = 3$
$xy = 2$

14. $x^2 + 3xy = 10$
$xy = 3$

15. $(x - 1)(y + 1) = 12$
$xy = 12$

16. $(x - 5)(y + 1) = 100$
$xy = 100$

Find solutions in terms of a and b.

C
17. $x^2 + y^2 = 2a^2 - 2ab + b^2$
$2x^2 - y^2 = a^2 + 2ab - b^2$

18. $x^2 + y^2 = 10a^2$
$xy = 3a^2$

PROBLEMS

A

1. Find two positive integers such that the sum of their squares is 41, and the square of the greater is 9 more than the square of the lesser.

2. Find two positive integers such that the difference of their squares is 40 and the square of the greater is 4 more than 5 times the square of the lesser.

3. If the width of a rectangular flower bed is increased by 2 meters, the area of the bed is then 140 square meters. On the other hand, if the length of the flower bed is increased by 1 meter, the area is only 120 square meters. Find the dimensions of the flower bed.

4. A rectangular photograph that measures 15 centimeters along a diagonal has an area of 108 square centimeters. What are the dimensions of the photograph?

5. How many electric drills did a hardware dealer buy if she paid $360 for the drills, sold all but 1 drill at an increase of $14 per drill, and received $432?

6. Driving along a straight seacoast, Mr. Evans covered 150 kilometers in 2 hours less time than Mrs. Evans, who made the trip by boat. Find Mr. Evans' rate if he averaged 20 kilometers per hour more than the rate of the boat.

B

7. The product of the positive intercepts of an ellipse with center at the origin is 18. Given that $\left(1, \dfrac{4\sqrt{2}}{3}\right)$ is a point on the ellipse, find its equation.

8. A hyperbola with equation of the form $\dfrac{x^2}{a^2} - \dfrac{y^2}{b^2} = 1$ contains the points $\left(3, \dfrac{3\sqrt{5}}{2}\right)$ and $\left(\dfrac{5}{2}, \dfrac{9}{4}\right)$. Find a^2 and b^2.

SELF-TEST 3

Give the meaning of each of the following.

1. linear-quadratic system

2. quadratic-quadratic system

Objective 1, page 357

3. Solve the system over $\mathcal{R}$ by graphing:

$$x^2 + 4y^2 = 16$$
$$x + 2y = 4$$

Solve each system over $\mathcal{C}$.

Objective 2, page 357

4. $x^2 + 4y^2 = 25$
$x - 2y = -1$

5. $4x^2 + y^2 = 13$
$4x^2 - y = 7$

Check your answers with those printed at the back of the book.

1. The distance from point $P_1(x_1, y_1)$ to point $P_2(x_2, y_2)$ is given by the formula

$$d(P_1, P_2) = \sqrt{(x_2 - x_1)^2 + (y_2 - y_1)^2}.$$

2. If m_1 and m_2 are the slopes of nonvertical lines L_1 and L_2, respectively, then L_1 and L_2 are perpendicular if and only if

$$m_1 m_2 = -1.$$

3. Given certain properties, you can find equations for circles, parabolas, ellipses, and hyperbolas.

4. A function specified by an equation of the form $xy = k$, $k \neq 0$, is called an **inverse variation**. You say that x and y **vary inversely** as each other or are **inversely proportional** to each other.

5. The points of intersection of the graphs of the equations of a system represent the real solutions of the system. A linear-quadratic system may have as many as 2 real solutions; a quadratic-quadratic system may have as many as 4 real solutions.

chapter test and review

10-1   1. Find the distance between $(-3, 1)$ and $(5, 7)$.

10-2   2. Find an equation in the form $ax + by = c$ of the line passing through $(-2, 5)$ and perpendicular to the graph of $3x - 2y = 6$.

10-3   3. Transform the equation $x^2 + y^2 - 4x + 2y - 4 = 0$ into the form $(x - h)^2 + (y - k)^2 = r^2$ and state the coordinates of the center and the radius of its graph.

10-4   4. Sketch the graph of $\{(x, y): y = x^2 - 2x - 3\}$.

10-5   5. Sketch the graph of $\{(x, y): x^2 + 25y^2 = 25\}$.

10-6   6. Sketch the graph of $\{(x, y): x^2 - 9y^2 = 36\}$.

10-7   7. If y varies directly as x and inversely as z, and $y = 4$ when $x = 8$ and $z = 6$, find y when $x = 4$ and $z = 2$.

10-8   8. Solve the system by graphing: $y = x^2$
$$y = -x$$

10-9   9. Solve the system over $\mathcal{C}$: $x^2 - 2y^2 = 7$
$$x - 2y = 1$$

10-10   10. Solve the system over $\mathcal{C}$: $4x^2 + y^2 = 25$
$$x^2 - y^2 = -5$$

. . . a single crystal hemisphere of platinum. The photograph was made by directing X-ray beams through the crystals onto the film. It was taken through a microscope and enlarged to 500,000 times the actual size.

exponents and logarithms

extending the laws of exponents

Objectives | After completing the next two sections, you should be able to:
1. Simplify expressions involving rational and real-number exponents.
2. Solve simple exponential equations.

11–1 rational exponents

In Section 6–1 you saw that, by suitable definitions, the laws of exponents can be extended to apply to powers with any integer as an exponent. Thus,

$$4^{-1} \cdot 4^2 = 4^{-1+2} = 4^1 = 4, \qquad \text{and} \qquad 3^{-2} \cdot 3^0 = 3^{-2+0} = 3^{-2} = \tfrac{1}{9}.$$

Can we now use these laws to help define powers so that any rational number can be used as an exponent? Let us look first at a special case, say $3^{\frac{1}{2}}$. For $3^{\frac{1}{2}}$ to have a meaning consistent with the familiar laws of exponents (page 174), it should be true that

$$(3^{\frac{1}{2}})^2 = 3^{(\frac{1}{2} \cdot 2)} = 3^1 = 3.$$

Since $3^{\frac{1}{2}}$ is to denote a number whose square is 3, we define it to be $\sqrt{3}$ (rather than $-\sqrt{3}$) so that the inequality

$$3^0 < 3^{\frac{1}{2}} < 3^1$$

is true. Thus, $3^{\frac{1}{2}}$ represents the positive square root of the positive number 3. Similar reasoning requires that

$$3^{\frac{5}{2}} = (3^{\frac{1}{2}})^5 = (\sqrt{3})^5 \qquad \text{and} \qquad 3^{-\frac{5}{2}} = (3^{\frac{1}{2}})^{-5} = (\sqrt{3})^{-5}.$$

These observations suggest the following definition.

If p denotes an *integer*, r a *positive integer*, and b a *positive real number*, then

$$b^{\frac{p}{r}} = \left(\sqrt[r]{b}\right)^p.$$

In particular, if $p = 1$,

$$b^{\frac{1}{r}} = \sqrt[r]{b}.$$

Moreover, if p *as well as* r is a positive integer, we define

$$0^{\frac{p}{r}} = 0.$$

The fact (page 276) that $\sqrt[r]{b^p} = \left(\sqrt[r]{b}\right)^p$ implies that

$$\left(b^p\right)^{\frac{1}{r}} = \left(b^{\frac{1}{r}}\right)^p,$$

and either member of this latter equation is thus equal to $b^{\frac{p}{r}}$.

Using powers with rational exponents, you can write radical expressions in exponential form, that is, as powers or products of powers. Then, because the laws of exponents apply to these powers (Exercises 59–62, page 370), you can use the laws to simplify the exponential expressions.

EXAMPLE 1 $2\sqrt[3]{8x^7y^{-3}z} = 2(8)^{\frac{1}{3}}(x^7)^{\frac{1}{3}}(y^{-3})^{\frac{1}{3}}(z)^{\frac{1}{3}}$

$$= 2(2)(x^{\frac{6}{3}} \cdot x^{\frac{1}{3}})(y^{-\frac{3}{3}})(z^{\frac{1}{3}})$$

$$= 4x^2y^{-1}x^{\frac{1}{3}}z^{\frac{1}{3}} = \frac{4x^2}{y}\sqrt[3]{xz} \quad (y \neq 0). \textbf{ Answer.}$$

EXAMPLE 2 $\sqrt{x}\sqrt[3]{x^2} = x^{\frac{1}{2}} \cdot x^{\frac{2}{3}} = x^{\frac{1}{2}+\frac{2}{3}} = x^{\frac{7}{6}} = x^{\frac{6}{6}} \cdot x^{\frac{1}{6}} = x\sqrt[6]{x}. \textbf{ Answer.}$

EXAMPLE 3 $\left(\dfrac{1}{64}\right)^{-\frac{5}{6}} = (64)^{\frac{5}{6}} = [(64)^{\frac{1}{6}}]^5 = 2^5 = 32. \textbf{ Answer.}$

The laws of exponents can be used to develop another useful fact about radical expressions. Thus the laws of integral exponents permit you to write for any integer s,

$$\left(b^{\frac{p}{r}}\right)^{rs} = \left[\left(b^{\frac{p}{r}}\right)^r\right]^s$$

$$= [b^p]^s$$

$$= b^{ps}$$

Because $b^{ps} = \left(b^{\frac{p}{r}}\right)^{rs}$, $r > 0$, and $b > 0$, if $s > 0$, you have $rs > 0$ and so you can assert that $b^{\frac{ps}{rs}} = b^{\frac{p}{r}}$, or

$$\sqrt[rs]{b^{ps}} = \sqrt[r]{b^p}.$$

For example,

$$\sqrt[12]{81x^8} = \sqrt[3 \cdot 4]{3^{1 \cdot 4}x^{2 \cdot 4}} = \sqrt[3]{3x^2}.$$

Note that in extending powers to include all rational exponents, we have restricted the base b to be a *positive* real number. Without that restriction, we could not always define b^r to be a real number. For example, $(-2)^{\frac{1}{2}}$ could not represent a real number, since there is no real number whose square is negative.

ORAL EXERCISES In this exercise set, assume that all variables denote positive real numbers.

State an equivalent exponential form for each radical expression.

1. $\sqrt{7}$ 3. $\sqrt[4]{t^3}$ 5. $\sqrt[3]{3t^2}$ 7. $\sqrt[7]{a+b}$

2. $\sqrt[3]{11}$ 4. $\sqrt[5]{n^2}$ 6. $\sqrt[4]{(2y)^3}$ 8. $\sqrt[10]{x+y}$

State an equivalent radical expression for each of the following.

9. $3^{\frac{1}{2}}$ 11. $10^{\frac{3}{4}}$ 13. $3^{\frac{1}{2}}x^{\frac{1}{2}}$ 15. $(x+4)^{\frac{3}{7}}$

10. $8^{\frac{1}{5}}$ 12. $15^{\frac{2}{5}}$ 14. $4^{\frac{1}{3}}y^{\frac{2}{3}}$ 16. $(t+5)^{\frac{5}{12}}$

WRITTEN EXERCISES In this exercise set, assume that all variables denote positive real numbers.

Write in exponential form using positive exponents only.

A   1. $\sqrt{23}$ 4. $\sqrt[3]{x^2}$ 7. $\sqrt[4]{a^3b}$ 10. $\sqrt[5]{\dfrac{x^2}{y^3}}$

2. $\sqrt{5x}$ 5. $\sqrt[5]{x^{-1}}$ 8. $\sqrt[5]{2t^4}$ 11. $\sqrt[3]{a+b^2}$

3. $\sqrt[3]{11}$ 6. $\sqrt[7]{x^{-3}}$ 9. $\sqrt[3]{\dfrac{3}{t}}$ 12. $\sqrt[5]{t^2+3}$

Write in radical form.

13. $3^{\frac{2}{5}}$ 16. $(5x)^{\frac{1}{6}}$ 19. $(x^{\frac{2}{7}})^2$ 22. $(x^3y)^{\frac{1}{4}}$

14. $5^{\frac{4}{9}}$ 17. $r^{\frac{2}{3}}t^{\frac{1}{3}}$ 20. $(y^{\frac{3}{11}})^3$ 23. $(y^2+4)^{\frac{3}{5}}$

15. $(3t)^{\frac{2}{3}}$ 18. $4^{\frac{2}{5}}n^{\frac{3}{5}}$ 21. $(m^2n^5)^{\frac{2}{11}}$ 24. $(2x^2+5)^{\frac{1}{3}}$

Evaluate.

25. $27^{\frac{1}{3}}$ 27. $25^{-\frac{1}{2}}$ 29. $32^{\frac{7}{5}}$ 31. $0.027^{\frac{1}{3}}$

26. $144^{\frac{1}{2}}$ 28. $125^{\frac{2}{3}}$ 30. $16^{-\frac{3}{4}}$ 32. $0.0016^{\frac{5}{4}}$

Express in simplest (page 276) radical form.

33. $\sqrt[3]{9}\ \sqrt[6]{9}$ 35. $\sqrt[3]{3}\ \sqrt{27}$ 37. $\sqrt[6]{32}\div\sqrt{32}$ 39. $\sqrt[6]{8}\div\sqrt[3]{64}$

34. $\sqrt[3]{8}\ \sqrt[6]{16}$ 36. $\sqrt{27}\ \sqrt[3]{81}$ 38. $\sqrt[6]{27}\div\sqrt[3]{9}$ 40. $\sqrt[4]{9}\div\sqrt[8]{81}$

Express in simplest radical form.

B 41. $\sqrt{\sqrt{16}}$ 43. $\sqrt[3]{\sqrt{32y^6}}$ 45. $\sqrt{\sqrt{\sqrt{n^{16}}}}$

42. $\sqrt{\sqrt{81}}$ 44. $\sqrt{\sqrt[3]{x^{12}}}$ 46. $\sqrt[3]{\sqrt[3]{\sqrt[3]{r^{54}}}}$

Simplify. Assume that all bases are positive.

47. $(n - 2\sqrt{n} + 1)^{\frac{1}{2}}$ 50. $(x^{\frac{1}{2}} - y^{\frac{1}{2}})(x^{\frac{1}{2}} + y^{\frac{1}{2}})$

48. $(4r - 4\sqrt{rs} + s)^{\frac{1}{2}}$ 51. $(c^{\frac{5}{3}} - d^{\frac{3}{2}})(c^{\frac{5}{3}} + d^{\frac{3}{2}})$

49. $(t^{\frac{1}{2}} - 1)(t^{\frac{1}{2}} + 1)$ 52. $(a^{\frac{7}{2}} + 1)(a^{\frac{7}{2}} - 1)$

Solve over $\mathcal{R}$. Assume that all bases are positive.

53. $r^{-\frac{3}{4}} = \frac{8}{27}$ 55. $(z + 2)^{\frac{2}{3}} = 16$ 57. $z - 2\sqrt{z} + 1 = 0$

54. $t^{-\frac{5}{6}} = 32$ 56. $(v - 3)^{\frac{2}{5}} = 9$ 58. $r + 4\sqrt{r} + 4 = 0$

Let a and b denote positive real numbers, r and s positive integers, and p and q integers. Prove each statement.

C 59. $b^{\frac{p}{r}} \cdot b^{\frac{q}{s}} = b^{\frac{ps+rq}{rs}}$ 60. $(b^{\frac{p}{r}})^{\frac{q}{s}} = b^{\frac{pq}{rs}}$

Hint: Raise each member of the equation to the rsth power.

61. $a^{\frac{p}{r}} \cdot b^{\frac{p}{r}} = (ab)^{\frac{p}{r}}$ 62. $\dfrac{a^{\frac{p}{r}}}{b^{\frac{p}{r}}} = \left(\dfrac{a}{b}\right)^{\frac{p}{r}}$

11-2 *real-number exponents*

In Chapter 1 we defined powers with natural-number exponents, in Chapter 6 we extended this definition to integral powers, and then in Section 11-1 we extended it to powers with rational-number exponents. Thus, we have defined such powers as

$$2^3 = 2 \cdot 2 \cdot 2 = 8, \quad 2^0 = 1, \quad 2^{-3} = \frac{1}{2^3} = \frac{1}{8}, \quad \text{and} \quad 2^{\frac{1}{2}} = \sqrt{2}.$$

Also,

$$2^{\frac{3}{2}} = \sqrt{2^3} \quad \text{and} \quad 2^{1.7} = 2^{\frac{17}{10}} = \sqrt[10]{2^{17}}.$$

Can we now define powers such as $2^{\sqrt{3}}$, which have irrational numbers as exponents, to have a meaning consistent with the familiar laws of exponents? The answer to the question is "Yes," as the following discussion shows.

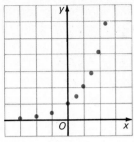

Figure 1

You can construct a table of coordinates of points of the graph of the function $\{(x, y): y = 2^x\}$ for selected rational values of x (these are graphed in Figure 1 at the left):

x	$y = 2^x$
-3	$\frac{1}{8}$
-2	$\frac{1}{4}$
-1	$\frac{1}{2}$
0	1

x	$y = 2^x$
$\frac{1}{2}$	$1.4 \ldots$
1	2
$\frac{3}{2}$	$2.8 \ldots$
2	4
$\frac{5}{2}$	$5.6 \ldots$

In order for the graph to be represented by a smooth unbroken curve (Figure 2), it must be true that powers such as $2^{\sqrt{3}}$, in which the exponents are irrational, exist. You can see that since

$$1.5 < \sqrt{3} < 2,$$

you have

$$2^{\frac{3}{2}} < 2^{\sqrt{3}} < 2^2,$$

or

$$2.8 < 2^{\sqrt{3}} < 4.$$

The power $2^{\sqrt{3}}$ can be approximated by the successive powers

$$2^1,\ 2^{1.7},\ 2^{1.73},\ 2^{1.732},\ \ldots$$

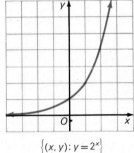

$\{(x, y): y = 2^x\}$

Figure 2

in which the exponents are rational numbers represented by taking more and more places in the decimal representing $\sqrt{3}$. Since these powers steadily increase but remain less than 2^2, it follows from the Axiom of Completeness (page 246) that they converge to a certain positive real number, which we call $2^{\sqrt{3}}$. As a matter of fact, to four decimal places $2^{\sqrt{3}} \doteq 3.3220$.

Similar reasoning leads to the definition of b^x where b is any *positive* real number and x any irrational number. Furthermore, it can be proved that the laws of exponents continue to hold for these powers. For example,

$$(3^{\sqrt{2}})^{\sqrt{2}} = 3^{\sqrt{2}\cdot\sqrt{2}} = 3^2 = 9; \qquad 2^{1-\pi} \cdot 2^\pi = 2^{(1-\pi)+\pi} = 2^1 = 2.$$

The curve shown in Figure 2 continuously rises with increasing abscissa and is typical of the graph of every function of the form

$$\{(x, y): y = b^x, b > 1\}.$$

On the other hand, the graph of

$$\{(x, y): y = b^x, 0 < b < 1\}$$

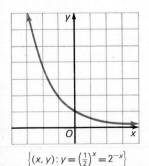

$\{(x, y): y = \left(\frac{1}{2}\right)^x = 2^{-x}\}$

Figure 3

falls with increasing abscissa, as illustrated by the graph of the function $\{(x, y): y = \left(\frac{1}{2}\right)^x\}$, shown in Figure 3. Notice that this can also be described by $\{(x, y): y = 2^{-x}\}$.

In either Figure 2 or Figure 3 on page 371, any vertical line and any horizontal line above the x-axis intersects the graph in just one point. In general, you have:

> For $b > 0$, $b \neq 1$, $b^{x_1} = b^{x_2}$ if and only if $x_1 = x_2$.

EXAMPLE   Solve $8^{2r+1} = (\frac{1}{2})^{r-4}$ over $\mathcal{R}$.

SOLUTION 1. First express each member as a power of $8^{2r+1} = (\frac{1}{2})^{r-4}$
the same base, 2. $(2^3)^{2r+1} = (2^{-1})^{r-4}$

2. Simplify each member. $2^{6r+3} = 2^{-r+4}$

3. Equate exponents and $6r + 3 = -r + 4$
solve for r. $7r = 1$

4. The check is left for you. $r = \frac{1}{7}$

∴ the solution set is $\{\frac{1}{7}\}$. **Answer.**

WRITTEN EXERCISES   **Simplify.**

A   1. $(3^{\sqrt{2}})^{2\sqrt{2}}$ 3. $2(4^{\sqrt{2}})(2^{2\sqrt{2}})$ 5. $5^{\sqrt{2}+3} \div 5^{\sqrt{2}}$ 7. $2^{\sqrt{5}} \div 2^{3+\sqrt{5}}$

2. $(2^{\sqrt{3}})^{\frac{3}{\sqrt{3}}}$ 4. $3(2^{\pi})(2^{\frac{3}{\pi}})$ 6. $3^{4-\sqrt{3}} \div 3^{\sqrt{3}}$ 8. $6^{\sqrt{5}} \div 6^{\sqrt{5}-2}$

Solve over $\mathcal{R}$.

9. $3^3 = 3^{2x-1}$ 13. $8^{3-r} = 4^{r+3}$

10. $4^{y-2} = 2^{2y+3}$ 14. $(\frac{1}{9})^{n+4} = 3^{3n-2}$

11. $25^{z+4} = 5^{3z-4}$ 15. $(\frac{1}{5})^{2x} = 25^{3x+1}$

12. $7^{3+t} = 49^{t+4}$ 16. $(\frac{2}{3})^{4t} = (\frac{9}{4})^{t+6}$

Determine an integer n such that $n < y < n + 1$.

B   17. $3^y = 18.7$ 18. $5^y = 327$ 19. $2^y = 150$ 20. $4^y = 172$

Graph each set.

21. $\{(x, y): y = 3^x\}$ 23. $\{(x, y): y = 4^{-x}\}$
22. $\{(x, y): y = (\frac{1}{3})^x\}$ 24. $\{(x, y): y = 4^x\}$

Solve each system graphically, approximating solutions to the nearest half unit.

C   25. $y = 2^x$; $y = 2x$ 26. $y = 3^x$; $y = x + 1$

Simplify.

Objective 1, page 367   **1.** $\sqrt[3]{16} \ \sqrt[5]{16}$ **2.** $\sqrt[4]{9} \ \sqrt{27}$ **3.** $[(2)^{\sqrt{2}}]^{3\sqrt{2}}$ **4.** $6^{3+\pi} \div 6^{\pi-1}$

Solve over $\mathcal{R}$.

Objective 2, page 367   **5.** $5^{x-2} = 25^{x-4}$ **7.** $4^{y-1} = 8^{y}$

6. $(\frac{1}{3})^{2z} = (\frac{1}{9})^{4-z}$ **8.** $9^{3z} = 27^{z-2}$

Check your answers with those printed at the back of the book.

from exponents to logarithms

Objectives | After completing the next two sections, you should be able to:
1. Identify inverses of functions.
2. Convert sentences from exponential to logarithmic form and vice versa.
3. Identify integral logarithms to various bases.

11–3   *the inverse of a relation*

In Section 3–2, you saw that any set of ordered pairs is a relation. If, now, in a relation R, the components of each of the pairs are interchanged, the result is another set of ordered pairs, and, hence, another relation. We denote this latter relation by R^{-1} (read "R inverse" or "the inverse of R"), and say that R and R^{-1} are inverses of each other. For example, if

$$R = \{(3,\ 4),\ (4,\ 5),\ (5,\ 6)\},$$

then

$$R^{-1} = \{(4,\ 3),\ (5,\ 4),\ (6,\ 5)\}.$$

Clearly, the domain and range of R^{-1} are the range and domain of R, respectively. Given an equation of the form $y = R(x)$ defining a relation R, you can obtain an equation defining its inverse simply by interchanging the variables. Thus, $x = R(y)$ defines the inverse of R. For example, the inverse of the relation defined by

$$y = 3x - 2$$

is defined by

$$x = 3y - 2,$$

or, when solved for y in terms of x,

$$y = \tfrac{1}{3}(x + 2).$$

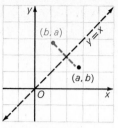

Figure 4

Because for every ordered pair (a, b) in a relation R, the ordered pair (b, a) is in R^{-1}, the graphs of R and R^{-1} are related in an interesting and useful way, as we shall now show.

Figure 4 illustrates the fact that when the same scale is used on both axes, (a, b) and (b, a) are always located symmetrically with respect to the graph of $y = x$. That is, the graph of $y = x$ is the perpendicular bisector of the segment with endpoints (a, b) and (b, a). Therefore:

the graphs of R and R^{-1} are always the reflections of each other in the line with equation $y = x$.

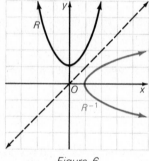

Figure 5

Figure 5 shows the graphs of

$$R = \{(x, y): y = 3x - 2\}$$

and

$$R^{-1} = \{(x, y): y = \tfrac{1}{3}(x + 2)\},$$

together with the line having equation $y = x$.

Since every function is a relation, every function has an inverse, but the inverse of a function is not always a function. Figure 6 shows the graph of

$$R = \{(x, y): y = x^2 + 1\}$$

and that of its inverse

$$R^{-1} = \{(x, y): x = y^2 + 1\}.$$

Figure 6

Clearly, R^{-1} is not a function, because for many values of x, there are two values of y. If a function f is to have an inverse f^{-1} that is a function, then not only must each element in the domain of f be paired with exactly one element in the range, but also each element in the range must be paired with exactly one element in the domain. Such a function is called a one-to-one function. If this is the case, then if f maps x_1 onto y_1, f^{-1} will map y_1 onto x_1, and it must be true that for every x in the domain of f,

$$f^{-1}[f(x)] = x,$$

and for every x in the domain of f^{-1},

$$f[f^{-1}(x)] = x.$$

For the example shown in Figure 5, you have

$$f(x) = 3x - 2$$

and

$$f^{-1}(x) = \tfrac{1}{3}(x + 2),$$

and you can verify that

$$f^{-1}[f(x)] = \tfrac{1}{3}[(3x - 2) + 2] = x$$

and

$$f[f^{-1}(x)] = 3[\tfrac{1}{3}(x + 2)] - 2 = x.$$

In Exercises 1–14 write the equation defining F^{-1}, graph F and F^{-1}, and state whether or not F and F^{-1} are functions.

A

1. $\{(x, y)\colon y = x - 3\}$

2. $\{(x, y)\colon y = 2x + 2\}$

3. $\{(x, y)\colon y = x^2\}$

4. $\{(x, y)\colon y = 1 - x^2\}$

5. $\{(x, y)\colon y = 3\}$

6. $\{(x, y)\colon y = -2\}$

7. $\{(x, y)\colon y = -x\}$

8. $\left\{(x, y)\colon y = \dfrac{1}{x}\right\}$

9. $\{(x, y)\colon y = |x|\}$

10. $\{(x, y)\colon y = \sqrt{x}\}$

11. $\{(x, y)\colon y = \sqrt{4 - x^2}\}$

12. $\{(x, y)\colon y = \sqrt{x^2 + 9}\}$

B

13. $\{(x, y)\colon y = 3^x\}$

14. $\{(x, y)\colon y = 10^x\}$

15. Show that $y = \dfrac{1}{1 - x}$ and $y = 1 - \dfrac{1}{x}$ define inverse relations. State the domain and range of each relation, and state whether or not each is a function.

16. Find a function that is its own inverse and has $\mathcal{R}$ as domain.

11–4   *the logarithmic function*

A function defined by an equation of the form

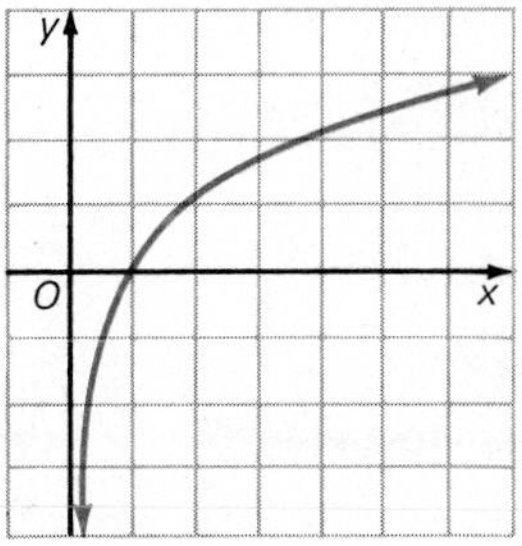

$$y = b^x \qquad (b > 0,\ b \neq 1)$$

is called an exponential function with base b. Its domain is $\mathcal{R}$ while its range is $\{y\colon y > 0\}$.

   For example, the graph of

$$R = \{(x, y)\colon y = 2^x\}$$

is pictured in Figure 7. Do you see that as x increases, y increases, and so this function is one-to-one? It therefore has an inverse that is a function, namely,

$$R^{-1} = \{(x, y)\colon x = 2^y\}.$$

Because the domain and range of R^{-1} are the range and domain, respectively, of R, R^{-1} has $\{x\colon x > 0\}$ as domain and $\mathcal{R}$ as range. Its graph is shown in Figure 8.

   In the equation

$$x = 2^y,$$

the exponent y is called "the logarithm of x to the base 2." This is written

$$y = \log_2 x.$$

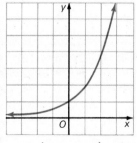

$\{(x, y)\colon y = 2^x\}$

Figure 7

$\{(x, y)\colon x = 2^y\}$

Figure 8

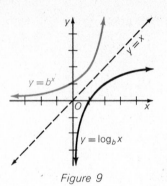

Figure 9

More generally, the function defined by an equation of the form

$$x = b^y \quad \text{or} \quad y = \log_b x \quad (b > 0,\ b \neq 1,\ x > 0)$$

is called the logarithmic function with base b. Since such a function is the inverse of an exponential function with base b, the graphs of the two are reflections of each other in the graph of $y = x$, as shown in Figure 9.

It should be emphasized that

$$\boxed{y = \log_b x \text{ if and only if } x = b^y.}$$

That is, these two equations are equivalent. By definition, then, since $b^0 = 1$, $\log_b 1 = 0$ for all permissible numbers b.

Either the logarithmic form or the exponential form should be used as is most convenient. Thus, you can say that the following are true:

$$2^5 = 32 \quad \text{is equivalent to} \quad \log_2 32 = 5.$$
$$4^{-2} = \tfrac{1}{16} \quad \text{is equivalent to} \quad \log_4 \tfrac{1}{16} = -2.$$
$$\log_{10} 1000 = 3 \quad \text{is equivalent to} \quad 10^3 = 1000.$$
$$\log_{100} 10 = \tfrac{1}{2} \quad \text{is equivalent to} \quad 100^{\frac{1}{2}} = 10.$$

The close relationship between exponential and logarithmic functions produces two additional useful facts about the latter functions. You saw on page 372 that for $b > 0$, $b \neq 1$, $b^{y_1} = b^{y_2}$ if and only if $y_1 = y_2$. It follows that:

$$\boxed{\text{For } b > 0,\ b \neq 1,\ \log_b x_1 = \log_b x_2 \text{ if and only if } x_1 = x_2\ (x_1,\ x_2 > 0).}$$

Next, since exponential and logarithmic functions are inverses, the fact that, for inverses, $f^{-1}[f(x)] = x$ and $f[f^{-1}(x)] = x$ implies that:

$$\boxed{\begin{aligned} b^{\log_b x} &= x \quad (b > 0,\ b \neq 1,\ x > 0), \\ \log_b b^x &= x \quad (b > 0,\ b \neq 1). \end{aligned}}$$

ORAL EXERCISES Express each of the following in logarithmic form.

EXAMPLE 1 $81 = 3^4$ SOLUTION $\log_3 81 = 4$. **Answer.**

1. $3^2 = 9$ 3. $(\tfrac{1}{4})^{\frac{1}{2}} = \tfrac{1}{2}$ 5. $3^{-2} = \tfrac{1}{9}$ 7. $100^{-\frac{1}{2}} = 0.1$

2. $5^3 = 125$ 4. $(16)^{\frac{1}{4}} = 2$ 6. $10^{-2} = 0.01$ 8. $(\tfrac{1}{2})^3 = \tfrac{1}{8}$

Express each of the following in exponential form.

EXAMPLE 2 $\log_3 9 = 2$ SOLUTION $3^2 = 9$. Answer.

9. $\log_4 64 = 3$ 11. $\log_{10} 0.0001 = -4$ 13. $\log_3 1 = 0$
10. $\log_{\frac{1}{2}} 4 = -2$ 12. $\log_2 64 = 6$ 14. $\log_{\sqrt{2}} 2 = 2$

WRITTEN EXERCISES Find each logarithm.

A
1. $\log_3 27$ 4. $\log_5 125$ 7. $\log_5 1$ 10. $\log_5 5$
2. $\log_6 36$ 5. $\log_{\frac{1}{3}} \frac{1}{27}$ 8. $\log_{\frac{1}{2}} 1$ 11. $\log_{\sqrt{5}} \sqrt{5}$
3. $\log_2 64$ 6. $\log_{\frac{1}{2}} \frac{1}{16}$ 9. $\log_{\sqrt{3}} 9$ 12. $\log_{\sqrt{5}} 5\sqrt{5}$

Find the real number x for which each sentence becomes a true statement.

EXAMPLE 1 a. $\log_x 3 = \frac{1}{2}$ b. $\log_5 x = -1$ c. $\log_7 \frac{1}{49} = x$

SOLUTION
a. $\log_x 3 = \frac{1}{2}$ b. $\log_5 x = -1$ c. $\log_7 \frac{1}{49} = x$

$\therefore x^{\frac{1}{2}} = 3$ $\therefore 5^{-1} = x$ $\therefore 7^x = \frac{1}{49}$

or $x = 9$.   or $x = \frac{1}{5}$.   or $x = -2$.

Answer.   Answer.   Answer.

13. $\log_4 4 = x$ 17. $\log_4 x = 3$ 21. $\log_2 1 = x$
14. $\log_x 625 = 4$ 18. $\log_7 7 = x$ 22. $\log_{16} 8 = x$
15. $\log_{\frac{1}{2}} x = -5$ 19. $\log_x 10 = \frac{1}{2}$ 23. $\log_9 x = \frac{3}{2}$
16. $\log_2 \frac{1}{64} = x$ 20. $\log_3 x = 1$ 24. $\log_4 8 = x$

EXAMPLE 2 $\log_{10} (x^2 + 9x) = 1$

SOLUTION $\log_{10} (x^2 + 9x) = 1$ $\rightarrow x^2 + 9x - 10 = 0$
$10^1 = x^2 + 9x$ $\longrightarrow$ $(x + 10)(x - 1) = 0$
$x = -10$ or $x = 1$

CHECK $\log_{10} [(-10)^2 + 9(-10)] \overset{?}{=} 1$ $\log_{10} [1^2 + 9(1)] \overset{?}{=} 1$
$\log_{10} (100 - 90) \overset{?}{=} 1$ $\log_{10} (1 + 9) \overset{?}{=} 1$
$\log_{10} 10 = 1$ ✓ $\log_{10} 10 = 1$ ✓

$\therefore$ the solution set is $\{-10, 1\}$. Answer.

B
25. $\log_{10} 2x = 3$ 28. $\log_{10} \dfrac{x - 3}{x + 1} = 1$

26. $\log_{10} (x^2 + 21x) = 2$ 29. $\log_{10} \dfrac{x - 1}{4} = 2$

27. $\log_{10} (x^2 + 3x) = 1$ 30. $\log_{10} (x - 1)^2 = -2$

Show that each statement is true.

31. $\log_3 27 = \frac{3}{2}\log_9 81$ 34. $\log_3 9 \cdot \log_9 3 = 1$
32. $\log_4 64 = 3 \log_2 2$ 35. $\log_5 25 \cdot \log_{25} 5 = 1$
33. $\log_5 25 = \frac{1}{2}\log_3 81$ 36. $\log_4 4 \cdot \log_3 3 = \log_2 2$

C 37. $\log_2 (\log_4 16) = \log_7 7$ 40. $\log_{10} [\log_2 (\log_3 9)] = 0$
38. $\log_5 (\log_5 5) = \log_3 1$ 41. For $x > 0$, $\log_x x^x = x$.
39. $\log_{10} [\log_3 (\log_5 125)] = 0$ 42. For $x > 0$, $\log_x x = 1$.

SELF-TEST 2 Give the meaning of each of the following.

1. inverse relations   3. exponential function
2. one-to-one function   4. logarithmic function

Objective 1, page 373 5. Write an equation defining the inverse of $\{(x, y): y = 2x - 5\}$.
6. State whether or not the inverse of $\{(x, y): y = \sqrt{x}\}$ is a function. Give a reason for your answer.

Objective 2, page 373 7. Write $12^2 = 144$ in logarithmic form.
8. Write $\log_{\frac{1}{2}} 8 = -3$ in exponential form.

Objective 3, page 373 Find the real number x for which each sentence becomes a true statement.

9. $\log_7 1 = x$ 10. $\log_x 2 = 1$

Check your answers with those printed at the back of the book.

Carl Friedrich Gauss
1777–1855

It was Carl Friedrich Gauss, born six years before Euler's death, who paved the way for many of the scientific discoveries of this century. Born in Germany, the son of a bricklayer, at age three he corrected his father's figuring of the weekly payroll. At ten he discovered the formula for the sum of an arithmetic progression. For his doctoral dissertation, he gave the first correct proof of the Fundamental Theorem of Algebra (see page 323).

Gauss's genius became even more evident in subsequent years. His discoveries dealt not only with pure mathematics but also with applied mathematics. His work with the geometry of curved surfaces provided the foundation for Einstein's work in relativity, and, amazingly, such fields as electronics and aerodynamics rely heavily on the results of Gauss's work with functions of a complex variable.

using logarithms

Objectives

After completing the next six sections, you should be able to:
1. Find the logarithm of a given number and the antilogarithm of a given logarithm.
2. Determine the precision and accuracy of a measurement.
3. Use logarithms to make calculations.
4. Use logarithms to solve exponential equations.

11–5 *logarithms and computation*

People have always been looking for shorter, easier methods of computation. One method, developed originally to aid astronomers in their complicated and tedious calculations, uses logarithms. Because logarithms are exponents, you can find products (or quotients) of positive numbers by first adding (or subtracting) their logarithms and then finding the number that has the result as its logarithm. This process is justified by the following theorem which gives the product and quotient properties of logarithms.

If x_1 and x_2 are positive real numbers, then

1. $\log_b x_1 x_2 = \log_b x_1 + \log_b x_2$.

2. $\log_b \dfrac{x_1}{x_2} = \log_b x_1 - \log_b x_2$.

To prove the first property, you start with the fact (page 376) that

$$x_1 = b^{\log_b x_1} \quad \text{and} \quad x_2 = b^{\log_b x_2}.$$

Then

$$x_1 x_2 = b^{\log_b x_1} \cdot b^{\log_b x_2}$$

or

$$x_1 x_2 = b^{\log_b x_1 + \log_b x_2}$$

or

$$\log_b x_1 x_2 = \log_b x_1 + \log_b x_2.$$

Property 2 can be established in a similar way (Exercise 13, page 381).

EXAMPLE 1 Express $\log_b \dfrac{xy}{z}$ without using multiplication or division.

SOLUTION By the quotient property of logarithms: $\log_b \dfrac{xy}{z} = \log_b xy - \log_b z$.

Then, by the product property:

$$\log_b xy - \log_b z = \log_b x + \log_b y - \log_b z. \quad \textbf{Answer.}$$

It is easy to find logarithms of integral powers of a base. For example, since $2^3 = 8$, $\log_2 8 = 3$. Logarithms of nonintegral powers of a base can be computed by methods of advanced mathematics to any desired number of decimal places. Some of these values are shown in the following tables:

$b = 2$	$b = 10$
$\log_2 1 = 0$	$\log_{10} 1 = 0$
$\log_2 2 = 1$	$\log_{10} 2 \doteq 0.301030$
$\log_2 3 \doteq 1.58496$	$\log_{10} 3 \doteq 0.477121$
$\log_2 4 = 2$	$\log_{10} 4 \doteq 0.602060$
$\log_2 5 \doteq 2.32193$	$\log_{10} 5 \doteq 0.698970$
$\log_2 6 \doteq 2.58496$	$\log_{10} 6 \doteq 0.778151$
$\log_2 7 \doteq 2.80736$	$\log_{10} 7 \doteq 0.845098$
$\log_2 8 = 3$	$\log_{10} 8 \doteq 0.903090$
$\log_2 9 \doteq 3.16993$	$\log_{10} 9 \doteq 0.954242$
$\log_2 10 \doteq 3.32193$	$\log_{10} 10 = 1$

Notice in both tables the following illustrations of the product property of logarithms:

$$\log_b (2 \times 3) = \log_b 2 + \log_b 3 = \log_b 6$$
$$\log_b (2 \times 4) = \log_b 2 + \log_b 4 = \log_b 8$$
$$\log_b (2 \times 5) = \log_b 2 + \log_b 5 = \log_b 10$$

Because our numeration system has the base 10, it is convenient to use logarithms to the base 10, which are called common logarithms. In this usage, it is customary to omit writing the base 10, and we agree that log x will mean $\log_{10} x$.

Some other logarithms can be computed easily. For example, since $30 = 3 \times 10$:

$$\log 30 = \log 3 + \log 10$$
$$= \log 3 + 1$$

In general, each time you multiply a number by 10, you add 1 to its common logarithm. Thus:

$$\log 3 \doteq 0.477121$$
$$\log 30 \doteq 1.477121$$
$$\log 300 \doteq 2.477121$$
$$\log 3000 \doteq 3.477121$$
and so on

However, in order to use logarithms in computation, it is necessary to be able to find the approximate logarithm for any positive real number. You will learn how to do that in succeeding sections.

Now you can use the product and quotient properties of logarithms to solve certain logarithmic equations.

EXAMPLE 2   Solve $\log_7 (x + 1) + \log_7 (x - 5) = 1$ over $\mathcal{R}$.

SOLUTION

1. Use the product property.
2. Write the equation in exponential form.
3. Solve for x.

$$\log_7 (x + 1) + \log_7 (x - 5) = 1$$
$$\log_7 (x + 1)(x - 5) = 1$$
$$(x + 1)(x - 5) = 7^1$$
$$x^2 - 4x - 5 = 7$$
$$x^2 - 4x - 12 = 0$$
$$(x - 6)(x + 2) = 0$$
$$x = 6 \text{ or } x = -2$$

4. Check.

$x = 6$
$\log_7 (6 + 1) + \log_7 (6 - 5) \overset{?}{=} 1$
$\log_7 7 + \log_7 1 \overset{?}{=} 1$
$1 + 0 \overset{?}{=} 1$
$1 = 1$

$x = -2$
$\log_7 (-2 + 1) + \log_7 (-2 - 5) \overset{?}{=} 1$
$\log_7 (-1) + \log_7 (-7) \overset{?}{=} 1$
No, because logarithms of negative numbers are not defined.

$\therefore$ the solution set is $\{6\}$. **Answer.**

ORAL EXERCISES   Using the table of logarithms to base 10 on page 380, state the following:

1. log 20
2. log 50
3. log 700
4. log 300
5. log 1000
6. log 9000

WRITTEN EXERCISES   Use the product and quotient properties of logarithms to solve the given equation over $\mathcal{R}$.

A
1. $\log x + \log 8 = 2$
2. $\log z - \log 3 = 1$
3. $\log_5 x^4 - \log_5 x^2 = 2$
4. $\log_3 y + \log_3 4y = 4$
5. $\log_7 z + \log_7 (z - 1) = \log_7 12$
6. $\log_4 t - \log_4 (t - 2) = \log_4 2$

B
7. $\log x + \log (x + 21) = \log_3 9$
8. $\log (z + 2) + \log (z - 1) = \log_7 7$
9. $\log (x - 3) - \log (x + 1) = \log_8 8$
10. $\log (r - 1) - \log (r + 2) = \log_2 4$
11. $\log_2 (9z + 5) - \log_2 (z^2 - 1) = \log 100$
12. $\log_3 (n^2 + 4n + 4) - \log_3 (2n - 5) = \log_5 25$

C
13. Prove that for positive numbers x_1 and x_2, $\log_b \dfrac{x_1}{x_2} = \log_b x_1 - \log_b x_2$.

14. When you multiply a number by 2, how much do you add to its logarithm base 2? Check your answer by referring to the table on page 380.

11–6   *using a table of common logarithms*

Tables of logarithms have been computed to various numbers of decimal places, but we shall use a table (Table 5 in the Appendix) that gives the first four decimal places of common logarithms.

There is a traditional arrangement of logarithmic tables, which you have to learn to read. The first few lines of Table 5 are:

x	0	1	2	3	4	5	6	7	8	9
10	0000	0043	0086	0128	0170	0212	0253	0294	0334	0374
11	0414	0453	0492	0531	0569	0607	0645	0682	0719	0755
12	0792	0828	0864	0899	0934	0969	1004	1038	1072	1106
13	1139	1173	1206	1239	1271	1303	1335	1367	1399	1430
14	1461	1492	1523	1553	1584	1614	1644	1673	1703	1732

Notice that no decimal points are given. You read the digits from the table, but you have to put the decimal points in the correct places yourself.

For example, to find an approximate value for log 1.24, you find "12" in the column under "x." You then move along row "12" to the column headed "4," where you find "0934." This means that

$$\log 1.24 \doteq 0.0934.$$

From this, you see that, since $12.4 = 1.24 \times 10$, you have by the product property of logarithms (page 379), log 12.4 = log 1.24 + log 10, or

$$\log 12.4 \doteq 1.0934.$$

Here are four more examples:

$$124 = 1.24 \times 10^2; \qquad \log 124 \doteq 2.0934$$
$$12400 = 1.24 \times 10^4; \qquad \log 12400 \doteq 4.0934$$
$$0.0124 = 1.24 \times 10^{-2}; \qquad \log 0.0124 \doteq -2 + 0.0934$$
$$0.000124 = 1.24 \times 10^{-4}; \qquad \log 0.000124 \doteq -4 + 0.0934$$

Notice that the logarithm of a number is the sum of two parts:

(1) a part between 0 and 1, called the mantissa, which is nonnegative and is found from Table 5, and
(2) an integral part, called the characteristic, which is the exponent of 10 when the number is expressed in scientific notation.

To maintain this pattern, we usually do not simplify sums involving negative characteristics. That is, we do not change $-2 + 0.0934$ to obtain log 0.0124 $\doteq -1.9066$. Instead, we write "$-2 = 8.0000 - 10$," giving us

$$\log 0.0124 \doteq 8.0934 - 10.$$

Similarly,

$$\log 0.000124 \doteq 6.0934 - 10.$$

Usually the difference with "−10" is used, although occasionally it is helpful to use some other difference, for example, $18.0000 - 20$ instead of $8.0000 - 10$.

In general, one may say that Table 5 gives approximate values of the *logarithms* of numbers from 1.000 to 9.999, or of the *mantissas* of other numbers.

EXAMPLE 1 **Find log 1470.**

SOLUTION We first write

$$1470 = 1.47 \times 10^3.$$

So the characteristic is 3.

Next, we examine the left-hand column for "14" and the top row for "7," and find that the mantissa is 0.1673.

∴ $\log 1470 \doteq 3 + 0.1673 = 3.1673$. **Answer.**

You can reverse the foregoing procedure to find an approximation for a number with a given logarithm. If $\log x = a$, then x is called the antilogarithm of a, abbreviated "antilog a."

EXAMPLE 2 **Find antilog 9.1523 − 10.**

SOLUTION First find the mantissa, 0.1523, in the body of the table. Then read the first two digits, "14," directly across in the left-hand column. Going directly up from 0.1523, you find the third digit, "2," in the top row. Since the characteristic is −1, you have

$$\text{antilog } 9.1523 - 10 \doteq 1.42 \times 10^{-1} = 0.142. \textbf{Answer.}$$

ORAL EXERCISES **State the characteristic of each logarithm.**

1. log 51
2. log 378
3. log 7.5
4. log 0.52
5. log 0.0079
6. log 34,700
7. $\log (1.03 \times 10^2)$
8. $\log (3.98 \times 10^{-3})$
9. log 0.000037
10. log 0.0888
11. log 800,000
12. log 0.00081

Find each logarithm or antilogarithm. Use Table 5.

A 1–12. Oral Exercises 1–12 above.

13. antilog 1.2253

14. antilog 3.6335

15. antilog (9.9047 − 10)

16. antilog (7.3927 − 10)

17. antilog 0.5302

18. antilog 2.9284

19. antilog (19.9590 − 20)

20. antilog (8.0969 − 10)

21. antilog (6.3598 − 8)

22. antilog (4.7101 − 7)

23. antilog 0.7404

24. antilog 2.9425

Use Table 5 to find the value of each power.

B 25. $10^{1.4362}$

26. $10^{0.8401}$

27. $10^{4.5911}$

28. $10^{0.9782} \times 10^{-2}$

29. $10^{0.0253} \times 10^{-1}$

30. $10^{0.7388}$

Solve each inequality.

C 31. $\dfrac{(x - 2)\log x}{x^2} > 0$

32. $\dfrac{\log (x - 1)}{x + 3} \leq 0$

11–7 *interpolation*

Table 5 gives direct readings for the logarithms of numbers with numerals having *at most three* significant digits (page 177). A method of estimating logarithms for numbers with four significant digits is given in the following example.

EXAMPLE 1 Find log 1.374.

SOLUTION You can find entries for log 1.370 and log 1.380 but not for log 1.374. However,

$$\log 1.370 < \log 1.374 < \log 1.380;$$

that is,

$$0.1367 < \log 1.374 < 0.1399.$$

If the graph of this logarithmic function were a straight line ($\overleftrightarrow{PR}$ in Figure 10), you could find log 1.374 by using a proportion. However, the graph is close enough to a straight line over much of its range for us to make the assumption that

the ordinate *h* of point *C′*

on the line is an acceptable approximation of

log 1.374,

the ordinate of point *C* on the curve.

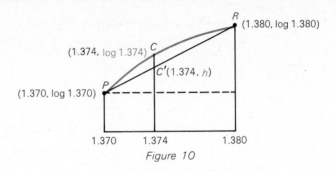

Figure 10

Because *P, C',* and *R* are collinear,

$$\underbrace{\text{the slope of segment } PC'}_{} = \underbrace{\text{the slope of segment } PR}_{}$$

$$\frac{h - \log 1.370}{1.374 - 1.370} = \frac{\log 1.380 - \log 1.370}{1.380 - 1.370}$$

$$\frac{h - \log 1.370}{0.004} = \frac{\log 1.380 - \log 1.370}{0.010}$$

$$\therefore h \doteq \log 1.370 + \tfrac{4}{10}(\log 1.380 - \log 1.370).$$

This means that we assume that because

1.374 is $\tfrac{4}{10}$ of the way from 1.370 to 1.380,
log 1.374 is $\tfrac{4}{10}$ of the way from log 1.370 to log 1.380.

Letting $d = \log 1.374 - \log 1.370 = \tfrac{4}{10}(\log 1.380 - \log 1.370)$, you can arrange the work as follows:

	x	log x	
	1.380	0.1399	
0.010 [0.004 [	1.374	log 1.374] d] 0.0032	
	1.370	0.1367	

$d \doteq \tfrac{4}{10} \times 0.0032 \doteq 0.0013$ (rounded to four places because mantissas in Table 5 are reliable only to four places).

$\therefore \log 1.374 \doteq 0.1367 + 0.0013$, or $\log 1.374 \doteq 0.1380$. **Answer.**

The process just described is *linear interpolation* (page 326). It enables you to use a four-place table of logarithms to approximate the logarithm of a number whose decimal numeral is known to four significant digits, with the result usually correct to four decimal places. To approximate the logarithm of a number whose numeral is known to more than four digits, you first round the numeral for the given number to four digits (page 178), and then find the logarithm of the result.

You can also interpolate in reverse to find antilog x if log x is known and its mantissa is not an entry in the table.

EXAMPLE 2   **Find antilog 2.3176.**

SOLUTION   Ignore the characteristic for now, and locate 0.3176 between entries in Table 5. You find that 0.3160 and 0.3181 are table entries, with antilogarithms 2.07 and 2.08, respectively. Then arrange these facts as shown below:

$$\begin{array}{c|c} x & \log x \\ \hline \end{array}$$

$$0.010 \left[\; d'\left[\begin{array}{c} 2.080 \\ \text{antilog } 0.3176 \\ 2.070 \end{array}\right.\right. \left|\begin{array}{c} 0.3181 \\ \left.\begin{array}{c} 0.3176 \\ 0.3160 \end{array}\right] 0.0016 \end{array}\right] 0.0021$$

$$\frac{d'}{0.010} = \frac{0.0016}{0.0021} = \frac{16}{21} \quad \text{or} \quad d' = 0.010 \cdot \left(\frac{16}{21}\right) \doteq 0.008.$$

$$\therefore \text{ antilog } 0.3176 \doteq 2.070 + 0.008 = 2.078.$$

Next, note that the characteristic of the given logarithm is 2. Hence,

$$\text{antilog } 2.3176 \doteq 207.8. \quad \textbf{Answer.}$$

Notice that the numeral for the value of d' was rounded to one significant digit because reverse interpolation in a four-place table yields at most four significant digits for the numeral for the antilogarithm.

WRITTEN EXERCISES   Find log x.

A   1. $x = 1522$ 5. $x = 203.4$ 9. $x = 0.01451$
    2. $x = 4.213$ 6. $x = 72.36$ 10. $x = 0.3741$
    3. $x = 0.8676$ 7. $x = 0.01257$ 11. $x = 1.031$
    4. $x = 0.09142$ 8. $x = 0.008351$ 12. $x = 37,110$

Find antilog y.

13. $y = 1.5085$ 17. $y = 9.7055 - 10$ 21. $y = 3.8257$
14. $y = 3.2620$ 18. $y = 8.9979 - 10$ 22. $y = 0.5555$
15. $y = 1.8087$ 19. $y = 7.6660 - 10$ 23. $y = 1.0759$
16. $y = 4.0220$ 20. $y = 6.2210 - 10$ 24. $y = 2.9431$

B   25. In interpolating for logarithms, is the interpolated value ordinarily too great or too small? Why?

26. In interpolating for antilogarithms, is the interpolated value ordinarily too great or too small? Why?

11–8 *computing products and quotients*

In computing with four-place logarithms, results can be given to at most four significant digits. If, moreover, the numbers involved in the computation are approximations, the accuracy of the result may be further restricted.

Measurements always produce approximations. A measurement is made by comparing some quantity with a measuring device which has a numerical scale. The measurement may be read as a number of the smallest units on the scale.

The precision of a measurement is defined to be the *unit* used in making it. For example, an atomic physicist reporting the weight of a sample of uranium to be 0.0304 grams *precise to the nearest ten-thousandth of a gram* means that the true weight w satisfies the inequality

$$0.03035 \leq w < 0.03045.$$

The unit (precision) of this measurement is

$$0.0001 \text{ gram,}$$

and the *maximum possible error* is half that unit, or

$$0.00005 \text{ gram.}$$

On the other hand, a rancher may list the weight of a steer as 355 kilograms, *to the nearest kilogram*. In this measurement the precision is

$$1 \text{ kilogram,}$$

and the maximum possible error is

$$0.5 \text{ kilogram.}$$

We define the accuracy of a measurement to be the *relative error*, that is, the ratio of the maximum possible error in the measurement to the measurement itself. Thus, the accuracy of the physicist's measurement is

$$\frac{0.00005}{0.0304} = \frac{5}{3040} \doteq 0.002, \quad \text{or} \quad 0.2\%.$$

The relative error of the rancher's measurement, however, is

$$\frac{0.5}{355} = \frac{5}{3550} \doteq 0.0014 \quad \text{or} \quad 0.14\%.$$

Thus, the rancher has made the "more accurate" measurement!

The following measurements are all reported by numerals having three significant digits:

327 meters, 32.7 meters, 3.27 meters, 0.327 meters, 0.0327 meters.

You can verify that the accuracy of these measurements is the same, but the last one, 0.0327 meters, is the most precise.

It is easy to tell the number of significant digits if a measurement is given in standard (scientific) notation (Section 6–2). For example, instead of 200 meters, you would write

$$2 \times 10^2, \qquad 2.0 \times 10^2, \qquad \text{or} \qquad 2.00 \times 10^2,$$

according as the measurement is precise to the nearest hundred meters, the nearest ten meters, or the nearest meter.

For computations in general, we use the following working rules:

To Round the Numerals for Results:

1. Give products, quotients, and powers to the same number of *significant digits* as appear in the *least accurate* approximation involved.

2. Give sums and differences to the same number of decimal places as appear in the approximation with the *least number* of decimal places (the least *precise* measurement).

Since there may be some doubt about the fourth digit obtained by using four-place logarithms, we shall usually round the result to three significant digits.

To guard against errors in computation, you should adopt two practices as a matter of routine.

First, make an estimate of the result. This guards against such gross errors as misplacing a decimal point.

Second, plan and arrange your work systematically and neatly. This makes it easier to check for errors. A good rule to follow is always to write numerals for numbers that must be added or subtracted in vertical columns, aligning equality signs vertically and keeping decimal points directly under one another. You can indicate the operations (+) or (−) and put in the characteristics in advance. Also, label the steps of your computation, so that if you have to check back, you will know what you are checking.

EXAMPLE 1 Compute $\dfrac{438 \times 0.410}{2.32}$.

SOLUTION Let $N = \dfrac{438 \times 0.410}{2.32}$.

1. Estimate N.

$$N \doteq \frac{400 \times 0.4}{2} = \frac{4 \times 10^2 \times 4 \times 10^{-1}}{2} = \frac{160}{2} = 80.$$

2. Write an equation showing the plan of work.

$$\log N = \log 438 + \log 0.41 - \log 2.32$$

3. Find log N.

$$\begin{array}{rl}
\log 438 \doteq & 2.6415 \\
\log 0.410 \doteq & 9.6128 - 10 \quad (+) \\
\hline
& 12.2543 - 10 \\
\log 2.32 \doteq & 0.3655 \qquad (-) \\
\hline
\log N \doteq & 11.8888 - 10
\end{array}$$

4. Find N. $N \doteq$ antilog $11.8888 - 10 =$ antilog $1.8888 \doteq 77.42$.

Note that the value arrived at is in reasonable accord with your estimate. ∴ to three significant digits, the result is 77.4. **Answer.**

Because logarithms are defined only for positive numbers, if negative numbers are involved in a calculation, you simply first determine by inspection whether the result is a positive or a negative number, and then perform the calculation using absolute values.

EXAMPLE 2   Compute $\dfrac{7.08}{-15.9}$.

SOLUTION   Let $N = \dfrac{7.08}{-15.9}$ and note that N is negative.

1. Estimate N. $\dfrac{7.08}{-15.9} \doteq -\dfrac{7}{16} \doteq -0.5$

2. Use $\log |N| = \log 7.08 - \log 15.9$.

3. $\log 7.08 \doteq 0.8500$
    $\log 15.9 \doteq 1.2014 \quad (-)$

Since $1.2014 > 0.8500$, to avoid a negative mantissa we replace 0.8500 with $10.8500 - 10$.

$$\begin{array}{rl}
\log 7.08 \doteq & 10.8500 - 10 \\
\log 15.9 \doteq & 1.2014 \qquad (-) \\
\hline
& 9.6486 - 10 \\
\therefore \log |N| \doteq & 9.6486 - 10
\end{array}$$

4. $|N| \doteq$ antilog $9.6486 - 10 \doteq 0.4452$ and $N \doteq -0.4452$. Note that the result is in reasonable accord with the estimate.

∴ to three significant digits, $\dfrac{7.08}{-15.9} \doteq -0.445$. **Answer.**

ORAL EXERCISES   Assume that each of the following represents in scientific notation a measurement in meters. For each, state **(a)** the precision; **(b)** the maximum possible error; and **(c)** the relative error.

1. 7×10^2 3. 5.7×10^1 5. 4.45×10^5

2. 2.3×10^{-2} 4. 3.81×10^0 6. 9.32×10^{-6}

State the logarithmic equation you would use to compute each of the following.

7. $(7.12)(18.1)$

8. $(63.2)(104)$

9. $(0.078)(-32.4)$

10. $(-0.00451)(-5620)$

11. $\dfrac{385}{22.3}$

12. $\dfrac{41.5}{10.6}$

13. $\dfrac{-3.88}{15.7}$

14. $\dfrac{-26.8}{-28.2}$

15. $\dfrac{0.782}{1.63}$

16. $\dfrac{0.0254}{0.888}$

WRITTEN EXERCISES   Compute each of the following.

A   **1–10.** The product or quotient in Oral Exercises 7–16.

11. $\dfrac{(82.3)(15.9)}{124}$

12. $\dfrac{(2.38)(165)}{0.895}$

13. $\dfrac{(-7.82)}{(6.13)(0.95)}$

14. $\dfrac{(42.6)}{(-8.02)(2.31)}$

15. $(2.19)(38.6)(0.0895)$

16. $(-46.8)(-0.732)(1.07)$

17. $\dfrac{(24.53)}{(7.026)}$

18. $(15.35)(7.084)$

19. $(2317)(0.8102)$

20. $\dfrac{(0.7186)}{(0.9325)}$

B   **21.** Observe that $\log_a b^2 = \log_a (b \cdot b) = \log_a b + \log_a b = 2\log_a b$. Express $\log_a b^3$ in terms of $\log_a b$.

22. Use the results of Problem 21 to infer an expression for $\log_a b^n$ in terms of $\log_a b$.

using computing devices

The computations in the preceding section can be done on such digital computers as a desk calculator or an electronic computer. These may give results to more digits than you have obtained by logarithms, but the results should agree to three significant digits.

There is another device that can be used to estimate products and quotients to about three significant digits. That is a slide rule made up of two logarithmic scales. A logarithmic scale is constructed by marking off lengths in proportion to the logarithms of numbers:

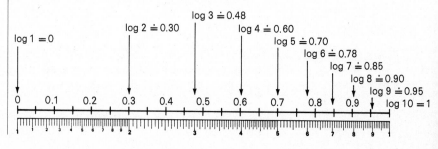

In Chapter 1, you represented addition of numbers by "adding" lengths on a number line. A slide rule provides a means for adding (or subtracting) logarithms of numbers, and hence for finding products (or quotients).

The diagram below shows how to multiply 1.5 by various numbers.

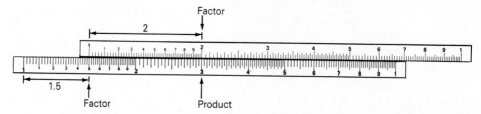

For example, you can read from the diagram that $1.5 \times 2 = 3$. The same setting could mean $15 \times 20 = 300$ or $.15 \times 20 = 3$. You have to place the decimal point yourself.

To use a slide rule for division, you reverse the process. For example, the diagram above can be read as $3 \div 2 = 1.5$.

To estimate the result of Example 1 on page 388, set the slide rule for $438 \div 2.32$ and then read off the product of that result times 0.410:

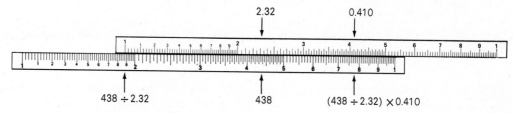

The result is a little more than 0.77.

The slide rule is an example of an analog computer. An analog computer is not a digital computer; rather it uses measurements (in this case, lengths) to obtain results.

EXERCISES

Read off the following products from the diagram at the top of the page.

1. $1.5 \times 3 = $ __?__   3. $15 \times 5 = $ __?__   5. $15 \times 15 = $ __?__

2. $1.5 \times 4 = $ __?__   4. $15 \times 6 = $ __?__   6. $1.5 \times 2.5 = $ __?__

Read off the following quotients from the diagram at the top of the page.

7. $300 \div 200 = $ __?__   9. $0.6 \div 0.4 = $ __?__   11. $9 \div 0.6 = $ __?__

8. $4.5 \div 3 = $ __?__   10. $7.5 \div 5 = $ __?__   12. $24 \div 16 = $ __?__

Use a calculator or a computer to check your work in the Exercises on page 390.

careers

biomedical engineering

What is biomedical engineering? It is one of the most exciting new professions, combining the techniques of engineering and the field of medical research. The biomedical engineer works in a variety of areas. He may work on developing artificial organs, improving patient-monitoring systems, adapting computers for medical use, or designing new instruments and equipment. To do this, he must be able to design a workable model of his idea, and test the model in a controlled situation.

The biomedical engineer may also work in medical research, seeking completely new techniques of treatment or trying to understand how the human body works. In order to study such complicated systems as the nervous system or the circulatory system, he must know mathematics, as well as physiology, chemistry, physics, and electronics. In addition, the biomedical engineer should know how to program a computer to do the lengthy calculations needed to predict results of his experiments and how to analyze data.

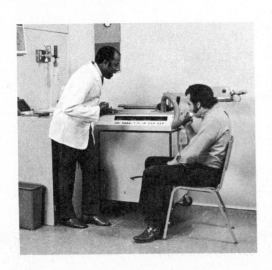

Biomedical engineers may design equipment, such as that above, for use in medical laboratories.

Below are two examples of the kinds of equipment developed by biomedical engineers: a machine used to detect problems in the respiratory system (left), and a device which records a patient's heartbeat (right).

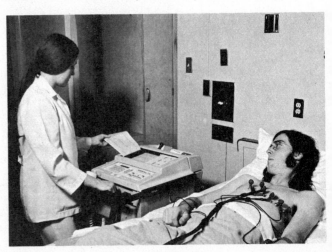

11-9 *computing powers and roots*

To discover another very useful property of logarithms, recall that

$$x = b^{\log_b x}$$

so that

$$x^n = (b^{\log_b x})^n = b^{n \log_b x}$$

Writing this latter exponential equation in logarithmic form produces the power property of logarithms.

If $x > 0$ and $n \in \mathcal{R}$, then $\log_b x^n = n \log_b x$.

To illustrate this property, look at these tables:

$b = 2$	$b = 10$
$\log_2 1 = 0$	$\log_{10} 1 = 0$
$\log_2 2 = 1$	$\log_{10} 2 \doteq 0.301030$
$\log_2 3 \doteq 1.58496$	$\log_{10} 3 \doteq 0.477121$
$\log_2 4 = 2$	$\log_{10} 4 \doteq 0.602060$
$\log_2 5 \doteq 2.32193$	$\log_{10} 5 \doteq 0.698970$
$\log_2 6 \doteq 2.58496$	$\log_{10} 6 \doteq 0.778151$
$\log_2 7 \doteq 2.80736$	$\log_{10} 7 \doteq 0.845098$
$\log_2 8 = 3$	$\log_{10} 8 \doteq 0.903090$
$\log_2 9 \doteq 3.16993$	$\log_{10} 9 \doteq 0.954242$
$\log_2 10 \doteq 3.32193$	$\log_{10} 10 = 1$

Notice that in either table:

$$\log_b 2^2 = 2 \log_b 2 = \log_b 4$$

$$\log_b 2^3 = 3 \log_b 2 = \log_b 8$$

$$\log_b 3^2 = 2 \log_b 3 = \log_b 9$$

This property of logarithms is a very powerful aid in estimating values that cannot be computed by an ordinary desk calculator.

EXAMPLE 1   Find $\sqrt[12]{2}$.

SOLUTION   Let $N = \sqrt[12]{2}$.

1. Use: $\log N = \frac{1}{12} \log 2$

2. Compute: $\log 2 \doteq 0.3010$

$$\frac{12}{\log N \doteq 0.0251} \quad (\div)$$

3. $N = $ antilog $0.0251 \doteq 1.060$

$\therefore$ to three significant digits, $\sqrt[12]{2} \doteq 1.06$. **Answer.**

To find a root of a number between 0 and 1, you must adjust the negative portion of the logarithm to fit the division, as in the following example.

EXAMPLE 2   Find $\sqrt[3]{0.83}$.

SOLUTION   Let $N = \sqrt[3]{0.83}$

1. Estimate N. $\sqrt[3]{0.83} \doteq \sqrt[3]{0.729} = 0.9$
2. Use: $\log N = \frac{1}{3} \log 0.83 = \frac{1}{3}(9.9191 - 10)$
   Here 10 is not a multiple of 3, so use

$$\tfrac{1}{3}(8.9191 - 9) \text{ or } \tfrac{1}{3}(29.9191 - 30)$$

(or some other equivalent form). Thus,

$$\log N = 2.9730 - 3, \text{ or } 9.9730 - 10.$$

In either case, the mantissa is 0.9730 and the characteristic is -1.
3. N = antilog $(2.9730 - 3) = 0.9398$. This result is in reasonable agreement with the estimate.
$\therefore$ to three significant digits, $\sqrt[3]{0.83} \doteq 0.940$. **Answer.**

EXAMPLE 3   Compute $\sqrt[3]{(0.831)^2}$.

SOLUTION   Let $N = \sqrt[3]{(0.831)^2}$.

1. Estimate N. $\sqrt[3]{(0.8)^2} = \sqrt[3]{0.64} = \sqrt[3]{640 \times 10^{-3}} \doteq \sqrt[3]{9^3 \times 10^{-3}} = 9 \times 10^{-1} = 0.9$

2. Use: $\log N = \log (0.831)^{\frac{2}{3}} = \frac{2}{3} \log (0.831)$
3. Compute: $\log (0.831) \doteq$ $8.9196 - 9$

$$\frac{2 \quad (\times)}{17.8392 - 18}$$

$$\frac{3 \quad (\div)}{5.9464 - 6}$$

$\therefore \log N \doteq 5.9464 - 6$
4. $N \doteq$ antilog $(5.9464 - 6) \doteq 0.8839$. This result is in reasonable agreement with the estimate.
$\therefore$ to three significant digits, $\sqrt[3]{(0.831)^2} \doteq 0.884$. **Answer.**

EXAMPLE 4   If $1000 is deposited in a savings account paying 6% interest compounded quarterly, what will the account amount to in 10 years if no deposits or withdrawals are made? Use the compound interest formula

$$A = P\left(1 + \frac{r}{n}\right)^{nt},$$

where P represents the principal invested at $100r$ percent annual interest (expressed as a decimal), n represents the number of times the interest is compounded during a year, and A represents the amount accumulated after t years.

SOLUTION
$$A = P\left(1 + \frac{r}{n}\right)^{nt}$$

$P = 1000$, $r = 0.06$, $n = 4$, and $t = 10$

$$\therefore A = 1000\left(1 + \frac{0.06}{4}\right)^{4(10)}$$

$$A = 1000(1.015)^{40}$$

$\log A = \log 1000 + 40 \log 1.015$

$$\begin{aligned} \log 1.015 &\doteq 0.0065 \\ &\underline{40} \quad (\times) \\ &.2600 \end{aligned}$$

$$\log 1000 = \underline{3.0000} \quad (+)$$
$$3.2600$$

$\therefore \log N \doteq 3.2600$ and $N \doteq$ antilog $3.2600 \doteq 1820$.
$\therefore$ there will be approximately $\$1800$ in the account after 10 years. **Answer.**

Note: A more accurate result can be obtained if log 1.015 can be found to more places, since any "error" is multiplied by 40. A more extensive table of logarithms gives log 1.015 $\doteq$ 0.006466, that is, with four significant digits. Using this value, you can find that the result is approximately $\$1814$.

WRITTEN EXERCISES   Compute. Round results to three significant digits.

A

1. $(7.21)^3$
2. $(5.37)^6$
3. $(18.5)^{\frac{1}{3}}$
4. $(400)^{\frac{1}{5}}$

5. $\sqrt[4]{3850}$
6. $\sqrt[6]{28000}$
7. $\sqrt{0.851}$
8. $\sqrt[3]{0.935}$

9. $\sqrt[6]{0.0342}$
10. $\sqrt[4]{0.0153}$
11. $\sqrt[3]{(2.5)^2}$
12. $\sqrt[4]{(31.2)^3}$

13. $\sqrt[10]{7455}$
14. $\sqrt[8]{0.1781}$
15. $(6.382)^{-2}$
16. $(5.318)^{-3}$

17. $(31.8)^2(-6.23)$

18. $(-0.942)^3(17.8)$

19. $\dfrac{(4.32)^2}{\sqrt{27.3}}$

20. $\dfrac{\sqrt[3]{187}}{0.832}$

21. $\dfrac{(5.81)^2(7.09)}{\sqrt{183}}$

22. $\dfrac{27.8\sqrt[3]{504}}{(0.812)^2}$

23. $\sqrt[3]{\dfrac{(5.92)(0.00483)}{(0.873)^2}}$

24. $\sqrt[5]{\dfrac{(23.9)^2\sqrt{2400}}{(0.08)^2}}$

Solve over $\mathcal{R}$. Express results to three significant digits.

B

25. $t^3 = 348$
26. $x^5 - 123.2 = 0$
27. $5 \log y = 3 \log 18$

28. $\log x^2 = (\log x)^2$
29. $\sqrt[3]{\log x} = 3 \log \sqrt[3]{2}$
30. $\sqrt{\log y} = 4 \log \sqrt{2}$

Solve each of the following equations without using a table of logarithms.

C 31. $\log x = \frac{1}{3}[2 \log 8 - 6 \log 3] - 2 \log 2 + \log 3$

32. $\log x = \frac{1}{2}[\log 2 - \log 5] + \frac{1}{2}[\log 20 - \log 2]$

33. $\log x = \frac{1}{2}[\log 6 + \log 4 - \log 13 + \log 2] + \frac{1}{2} \log 5$

34. $\log x = \frac{3}{8} \log \sqrt{2} + \frac{1}{8} \log 2 - \frac{1}{4} \log \sqrt[4]{2} + \frac{1}{8} \log 8 - \frac{1}{4} \log \frac{1}{\sqrt{2}}$

35. Show that $\log \dfrac{x + \sqrt{x^2 - 1}}{x - \sqrt{x^2 - 1}} = 2 \log (x + \sqrt{x^2 - 1})$.

36. Show that $\dfrac{\log (x + h) - \log x}{h} = \log \left(1 + \dfrac{h}{x}\right)^{\frac{1}{h}}$.

37. Show that $\log \dfrac{y}{a + \sqrt{a^2 + y^2}} = \log \dfrac{\sqrt{a^2 + y^2} - a}{y}$.

38. Solve for x: $\log_4 |2x + 2| - \log_4 |3x + 1| = \frac{1}{2}$.

39. Show that the logarithms of the terms in a geometric progression of positive terms form an arithmetic progression.

PROBLEMS

A 1. Find the amount after 10 years in an account in which $6000 is invested at a rate of 6% compounded semiannually.

2. What amount would a building-and-loan association account contain after 8 years if $4000 were deposited at $5\frac{1}{2}$% interest compounded quarterly?

3. At an altitude of n km above the surface of the earth, the atmospheric pressure P in mm of mercury is given approximately by

$$P = 760(10)^{-0.054n}.$$

What is the atmospheric pressure at sea level? At an altitude of 4 km above the surface of the earth?

4. The period T of a simple pendulum is given by

$$T = 2\pi \sqrt{\frac{L}{g}},$$

where T is in seconds, L is the length of the pendulum arm in meters, and g is approximately equal to 10 meters-per-second-per-second. What is the period of a pendulum 3 meters long? (Use 3.14 for π.)

5. The volume of a sphere is given by

$$V = \frac{4}{3}\pi r^3,$$

where r is the radius of the sphere. What is the volume of a sphere with a radius of 3.76 meters? (Use 3.14 for π.)

6. The amount of a certain radioactive element present at a time t in seconds after an initial time is given by

$$A = A_0(2.72)^{-0.4t},$$

where A_0 is the amount present at the initial time. How much of the element will remain after 4 seconds if 90 grams is present initially?

programming in BASIC

In the BASIC language, you can use exponents written in fractional or decimal form. For example:

```
10   PRINT 2↑(1/2);2↑.5;2↑1.567
20   END
RUN

    1.41421   1.41421   2.96288
END
```

Notice that a fractional exponent must be enclosed in parentheses because of the order of operations described on page 101.

EXERCISES

1. Use the computer to find $2^{\frac{1}{12}}$, $0.83^{\frac{1}{3}}$, and $0.831^{\frac{2}{3}}$. Compare the results with those of Examples 1–3 (pages 393–394).

2. $\log_{10} 2 = .301030$ means $10↑.301030 = 2$. Test this by having the computer find $10↑.301030$.

3. Test $2↑3.32193$.

4. Check the results of Exercises 2 and 3 with the tables on page 393.

5. Check the value of $2^{\sqrt{3}}$ given on page 371.

6. Write a program that will find the value of

$$A = P*(1 + R/N)↑(N*T)$$

when you input values of P, R, T, N. Compare the values of A for the following input values:

P	R	T	N	
1000	.06	10	1	
1000	.06	10	2	
1000	.06	10	4	(Compare this with Example 4.)
1000	.06	10	12	
1000	.06	10	365	

Use a computer to check your work in the Exercises on pages 395–396.

11-10 *solving equations using logarithms*

You can use logarithms to find approximate solutions for some exponential equations over $\mathcal{R}$.

EXAMPLE 1   Solve $x^{\frac{3}{7}} = 4.63$ over $\mathcal{R}$ and express the solution to three significant digits.

SOLUTION   1. Raise both sides $\qquad\qquad\qquad$ $x^{\frac{3}{7}} = 4.63$
to $\frac{7}{3}$ power. $\qquad\qquad\qquad\qquad$ $x = (4.63)^{\frac{7}{3}}$

2. Use one of the properties on page $\qquad$ $\log x = \log (4.63)^{\frac{7}{3}}$
376 to equate common
logarithms.

3. Apply the power property $\qquad\qquad$ $\log x = \frac{7}{3} \log 4.63$
of logarithms to simplify $\qquad\qquad$ $\log x \doteq \frac{7}{3}(0.6656)$
the right member and solve $\qquad\qquad$ $\log x \doteq 1.5530$
for $\log x$.

4. Find x. $\qquad\qquad\qquad\qquad\qquad$ $x \doteq$ antilog $1.5530 \doteq 35.73$

∴ the solution set is $\{35.7\}$. **Answer.**

EXAMPLE 2   A culture of bacteria contains N bacteria after t hours according to

$$N = N_0(2.72)^{0.04t}$$

where N_0 is the number present originally. How long will it take for 10,000 bacteria to multiply to 30,000?

SOLUTION   Substitute 30,000 for N and 10,000 for N_0.

$$30{,}000 = 10{,}000(2.72)^{0.04t}$$

Divide each member by 10,000.

$$3 = (2.72)^{0.04t}$$

Equate common logarithms.

$$\log 3 = \log (2.72)^{0.04t}$$

Apply the power property of logarithms and solve for t.

$$\log 3 = 0.04t \log (2.72)$$

$$t = \frac{\log 3}{(0.04)(\log 2.72)}$$

$$t \doteq \frac{0.4771}{(0.04)(0.4346)}$$

$\log t \doteq \log 0.4771 - \log 0.04 - \log 0.4346$

$$\log 0.4771 \doteq \quad 9.6786 - 10$$
$$\log 0.04 \doteq \quad \underline{8.6021 - 10} \quad (-)$$
$$1.0765$$
$$\text{Change to} \quad 11.0765 - 10$$
$$\log 0.4346 \doteq \quad \underline{9.6381 - 10} \quad (-)$$
$$1.4384$$

$$\log t \doteq 1.4384$$
$$t \doteq \text{antilog } 1.4384 \doteq 27.4$$

∴ it would take approximately 27.4 hours for the number of bacteria to multiply from 10,000 to 30,000. **Answer.**

EXAMPLE 3   **Express $\log_5 11$ in terms of common logarithms.**

SOLUTION   Let $N = \log_5 11$.

1. Write in exponential form. $5^N = 11$

2. Equate common logarithms. $\log 5^N = \log 11$

3. Apply the power property of logarithms and solve for N. $N \log 5 = \log 11$
$$N = \frac{\log 11}{\log 5}$$

$$\therefore \log_5 11 = \frac{\log 11}{\log 5}. \quad \textbf{Answer.}$$

The result of Example 3 suggests the following:

Relationship Between the Logarithms of a Number n to Two Different Bases a and b

$$\log_b n = \frac{\log_a n}{\log_a b} \quad (n > 0, \; a > 0, \; a \neq 1, \; b > 0, \; b \neq 1).$$

Can you justify the steps in the following proof of this relationship?

$$\text{Let } x = \log_b n.$$
$$b^x = n$$
$$\log_a b^x = \log_a n$$
$$x \log_a b = \log_a n$$
$$x = \frac{\log_a n}{\log_a b}$$
$$\text{or } \log_b n = \frac{\log_a n}{\log_a b}.$$

In particular, if $n = a$ in the preceding equation, you obtain, since $\log_a a = 1$:

$$\log_b a = \frac{1}{\log_a b}, \ (a > 0, a \neq 1, b > 0, b \neq 1).$$

For example, using the values in the tables on page 393, you can write

$$\log_2 6 = \frac{\log_{10} 6}{\log_{10} 2}$$

$$= \frac{0.778151}{0.301030}$$

A little arithmetic will verify that

$$\frac{0.778151}{0.301030} \doteq 2.58496.$$

Another very important base for logarithms is the irrational number e ($e \doteq 2.7182818$) which arises naturally in many practical situations and is used a great deal in more advanced mathematics. To find $\log_e x$ given a table of common logarithms, you simply use

$$\log_e x = \frac{\log_{10} x}{\log_{10} e}.$$

Since $\log_{10} e \doteq 0.4343$, you have

$$\log_e x = \frac{\log_{10} x}{0.4343}$$

$$= 2.303 \log_{10} x.$$

WRITTEN EXERCISES Solve over $\Re$. Use Table 5 as needed and express each solution to three significant figures.

A

1. $6^x = 12$ 3. $3^z = 25$ 5. $n^{\frac{3}{5}} = 12$ 7. $3k^{\frac{7}{5}} = 171$

2. $7.2^y = 4$ 4. $13^t = 4.6$ 6. $2z^{\frac{2}{3}} = 4.24$ 8. $x^{2.5} = 0.881$

Approximate each logarithm to three significant digits.

9. $\log_3 8$ 12. $\log_3 1.38$ 15. $\log_{1.5} 8$ 18. $\log_{0.15} 17$

10. $\log_5 38$ 13. $\log_e 15$ 16. $\log_{3.21} 3.21$ 19. $\log_{104} 90$

11. $\log_7 0.81$ 14. $\log_e 321$ 17. $\log_{0.7} 2$ 20. $\log_{215} 175$

Solve over $\mathfrak{R}$. Use Table 5 as needed and express each root to three significant digits.

B   **21.** $10^{x-5} = 17.8$ **23.** $3^{4-2x} = 8.1$ **25.** $25^{2x+1} = 150$

22. $10^{2x+3} = 6.91$ **24.** $5^{2-z} = 1.41$ **26.** $18^{3x-5} = 7.12$

Without using a table of logarithms, show that each of the following is a true statement.

C   **27.** $\log_4 3 = \frac{1}{2} \log_2 3$ *Hint:* $\log_4 3 = \dfrac{1}{\log_3 4}$, and $4 = 2^2$.

28. $\log_{27} 6 = \frac{1}{3} \log_3 6$

29. $\log_b x = 2 \log_{b^2} x$

30. $\log_b x = n \log_{b^n} x$

31. $(\log_{10} 4 - \log_{10} 8) \log_2 10 = -1$

32. $(\log_9 2 - \log_9 4) \log_2 3 = -\frac{1}{2}$

33. Given $\pi \doteq 3.142$ and $e \doteq 2.718$, determine which statement is true,

$$\pi^e > e^\pi \qquad \text{or} \qquad \pi^e < e^\pi.$$

PROBLEMS

A   **1.** Approximately how long will it take a principal of $\$2000$ invested at 5% interest compounded quarterly to amount to $\$3000$?

2. If you wish to have $\$2000$ in a savings account 5 years from now, approximately how much should you invest now at 4% compounded quarterly?

3. If the atmospheric pressure P mm of mercury at a point n km over the surface of the earth is given by

$$P = 760(10)^{-0.054n},$$

at what altitude will the pressure be approximately 380 mm of mercury?

4. Approximately how many hours will it take a culture of 10,000 bacteria to grow to 20,000 bacteria if the culture grows according to

$$N = N_0 e^{0.04t}$$

where N is the number present t hours after N_0 are present in the culture? (Use $e \doteq 2.72$.)

5. The intensity I in lumens of a light beam passing through a thickness t in centimeters of a certain substance is given by

$$I = 900\, e^{-0.12t}.$$

How thick should the substance be to reduce the illumination to 700 lumens?

6. In Problem 5, how thick should the substance be to reduce the illumination by 50%?

careers *microbiology*

Working under the auspices of the Food and Agriculture Administration of the United Nations, this specialist is testing food quality.

A microbiologist examines samples of bacteria.

Biology is the study of living beings—their structure, evolutionary development, behavior, and life processes. Microbiologists restrict their study to microscopic and submicroscopic organisms, such as bacteria, viruses, protozoa, algae, and fungi.

The field of microbiology has a wide range of applications. In medicine, the study of bacteria and viruses has led to the control of many diseases and to the discovery of antibiotics. Since microorganisms have a vital part in the cycle of matter in the soil, agriculture has benefited from greater knowledge about their function. The food industry is concerned with organisms that cause spoilage. Knowledge of bacterial growth is also important in sanitation and water pollution control.

EXAMPLE   Under certain conditions, bacterial growth can be represented by $N \doteq N_0(2.72)^{kt}$, where N_0 is the number of bacteria originally, N is the number after t hours and k is a constant depending on the type of bacteria and the conditions (see Example 2, section 10–11). A biologist has a culture of bacteria, whose growth is described by $N = N_0(2.72)^{0.03t}$. When there are about 10^5 of these bacteria, a mutation occurs in one of them. The mutants can make better use of some of the chemicals being supplied to the culture, and therefore their growth is described by $M = M_0(2.72)^{0.07t}$. How long after the mutation occurs (assuming there are no other mutations), will the number of mutants, M, equal the number of original type bacteria, N?

SOLUTION   We want to find t such that $M = N$. That is,

$$M_0(2.72)^{0.07t} = N_0(2.72)^{0.03t}$$

Since when the mutation occurred, there were 10^5 of the original type of bacteria, and 1 mutant, we must solve

$$1(2.72)^{0.07t} = 10^5(2.72)^{0.03t}$$

Taking the log of each member:

$$0.07t \log (2.72) = \log 10^5 + 0.03t \log (2.72)$$
$$0.04t \log (2.72) = 5$$
$$0.04t (0.4346) = 5$$
$$t \doteq 288 \text{ hours, or 12 days.}$$

Give the meaning of each of the following.

1. common logarithm
2. antilogarithm
3. mantissa
4. characteristic

5. linear interpolation
6. precision
7. accuracy

Objective 1, page 379

8. Use Table 5 to find log 32.15.
9. Use Table 5 to find antilog $(8.3172 - 10)$.

Objective 2, page 379

The length of a living room is given as 7.8 meters.

10. What is the unit of measure? The precision?
11. What is the maximum possible error?
12. What is the relative error? The accuracy?

Objective 3, page 379

Use logarithms to compute each of the following.

13. $\dfrac{25.7}{0.813}$

14. $\dfrac{\sqrt[3]{82.1}}{0.0814}$

Objective 4, page 379

Solve over $\Re$, **giving results to three significant digits.**

15. $6^x = 18$

16. $2x^{\frac{3}{4}} = 124$

Check your answers with those printed at the back of the book.

programming in BASIC

The BASIC language has a built-in function LOG(X). However, the base of this function is e (see page 400). To find logarithms to another base, b, use the formula on page 399:

$$\log_b n = \text{LOG(N)} \ / \ \text{LOG(B)} \quad (b > 0, b \neq 1, n > 0).$$

EXERCISES

1. Use the computer to check Example 1, page 398. (That is, compute $4.63\uparrow(7/3)$.)

2. Use the computer to check Example 2, page 398, by finding

$$\text{LOG(3)} \ / \ (0.04*\text{LOG(2.72)}).$$

3. Prove that

$$\frac{\log_a m}{\log_a n} = \frac{\log_b m}{\log_b n}$$

$$(m > 0, n > 0, n \neq 1, a > 0, a \neq 1, b > 0, b \neq 1).$$

4. Write a program that will print out common logarithms of the positive integers 20 through 40.

5. The value of e can be found to any desired number of decimal places by using the series

$$e = 1 + \frac{1}{1} + \frac{1}{1 \cdot 2} + \frac{1}{1 \cdot 2 \cdot 3} + \frac{1}{1 \cdot 2 \cdot 3 \cdot 4} + \cdots$$

to as many terms as needed. Write a program to find the value of e, stopping when you reach a term that is less than 0.000005. Print each term and the accumulated sum.

6. It can be proved by advanced methods that

$$\log_e (1 + x) = x - \tfrac{1}{2}x^2 + \tfrac{1}{3}x^3 - \tfrac{1}{4}x^4 + \cdots$$

for $-1 < x \leq 1$. The general term is

$$(-1)^{n+1} x^n / n.$$

Write a program to find $\log_e (1 + x)$ when you input x. Print each term and the accumulated sum, and end the program when the absolute value of the term is less than $5E - 08$. For comparison print out the value of LOG $(1 + x)$. Try $x = 0.1, 0.3, 0.5$.

Use a computer to check your work in some of the Exercises on pages 400–401.

chapter summary

1. Radical expressions may be written equivalently in **exponential form**: $(\sqrt[r]{b})^p = b^{\frac{p}{r}}$, provided $\sqrt[r]{b}$ and p are real numbers.

2. The laws of exponents apply to real-number exponents for positive bases.

3. Relations in which reversing the components of the ordered pairs of each produces the other are called **inverses** of each other. The inverse of a one-to-one function is a function. If f^{-1} is the inverse of a one-to-one function f, then $f^{-1}[f(x)] = x$ for each x in the domain of f, and $f[f^{-1}(x)] = x$ for each x in the domain of f^{-1}.

4. The inverse of the **exponential function**

$$\{(x, y): y = b^x, b > 0, b \neq 1\}$$

is the **logarithmic function**

$$\{(x, y): y = \log_b x, b > 0, b \neq 1, x > 0\}.$$

If $x \in \mathcal{R}$, $x > 0$, $b > 0$, $b \neq 1$, then $b^{\log_b x} = x$; if $x \in \mathcal{R}$, $b > 0$, $b \neq 1$, then $\log_b b^x = x$.

5. The **precision** of a measurement is defined to be the unit of measure. The **accuracy** of a measurement is defined to be the *relative error,* that is, the *maximum possible error* divided by the measurement itself.

6. The **characteristic** of the common logarithm of a number may be found by inspection of the number in scientific notation; the **mantissa** is determined from the table.

7. In using **linear interpolation,** you assume that small portions of the graph of $y = \log x$ are straight line segments.

8. The laws of exponents are the basis for the laws of logarithms:

$$\log (x_1 x_2) = \log x_1 + \log x_2; \quad \log \frac{x_1}{x_2} = \log x_1 - \log x_2;$$

$$\log x_1{}^n = n \log x_1.$$

9. To find the logarithm of a number to another base, you use the relationship:

$$\log_b n = \frac{\log_a n}{\log_a b}.$$

chapter test and review

11–1
1. Evaluate $81^{\frac{3}{4}}$.
2. Simplify $\sqrt{8} \cdot \sqrt[4]{32}$.

11–2
3. Solve $4^{x-1} = 8^x$ over $\mathcal{R}$.

11–3
4. Give the equation defining the inverse of $\{(x, y): y = 3 - 4x\}$.

11–4
5. Write $\log_3 27 = 3$ in exponential form.
6. Solve $\log_4 x = -3$ over $\mathcal{R}$.

11–5
7. Solve $\log_2 x + \log_2 (x - 1) = 1$ over $\mathcal{R}$.

For Items 8–15, use Table 5. Evaluate each of the following.

11–6
8. log 0.783

9. antilog 4.5911

11–7
10. log 0.7023

11. antilog $(8.5410 - 10)$

11–8
12. $\dfrac{(3.12)(17.6)}{125}$

11–9
13. $(4.2)^3 \sqrt[3]{10.8}$

11–10
14. $\log_3 29$

15. Solve $2.72^{0.5x} = 25$ over $\mathcal{R}$.

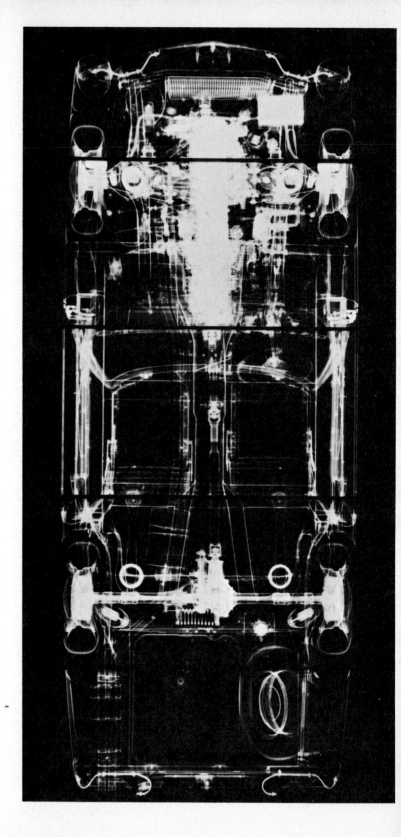

Photographic plates were placed under this car, which was then exposed to X-rays for fifty hours. The resulting picture, called a radiograph, was used to check the strength of the metal and the structural soundness of the car.

12 *permutations, combinations, and probability*

permutations

12-1 *two fundamental counting principles*

Can you find the number of elements in the union of two finite sets if you know the number of elements in each of the sets? Consider the following examples:

(1) $A = \{1, 2, 3, 4\}$, $B = \{5, 6\}$, $A \cup B = \{1, 2, 3, 4, 5, 6\}$
(2) $A = \{1, 2, 3, 4\}$, $C = \{2, 4, 6\}$, $A \cup C = \{1, 2, 3, 4, 6\}$

In (1), the number of elements in the union is just the sum of the numbers of elements in the given sets: $6 = 4 + 2$. In (2), however, the union has only 5 elements, instead of $4 + 3 = 7$, since the elements "2" and "4" belong to both A and C. In set notation, $\{2, 4\} = A \cap C$.

Thus to find the number of elements in the union of two sets, you must also know the number of elements in their intersection.

> If a finite set A contains r elements, a finite set B contains s elements, and their intersection ($A \cap B$) contains t elements, then the union of A and B ($A \cup B$) contains $r + s - t$ elements.

If $A \cap B = \emptyset$, as in case (1) above, then $t = 0$ and $A \cup B = r + s$.

EXAMPLE 1   The Mathematics Club at East High School has 34 members, the Spanish Club has 28 members, and 8 students are members of both organizations. If all members attended, what would be the attendance at a joint meeting of the two clubs?

SOLUTION   You want to determine the number N of members in the union of two sets whose intersection contains 8 members. You have:

$$N = 34 + 28 - 8 = 54$$

∴ the attendance at the joint meeting would be 54. **Answer.**

To discover a second counting principle, consider this problem: If A is the set of *two* integers $\{1, 2\}$ and B is the set of *three* integers $\{4, 5, 6\}$, how many different ordered pairs (a, b) are there with $a \in A$ and $b \in B$?

For each of the *two* ways that you can choose the first entry, a, there are *three* ways you can choose the second entry, b. Thus the set of all such ordered pairs (a, b) is

$$\{(1, 4), (1, 5), (1, 6), (2, 4), (2, 5), (2, 6)\},$$

which contains $2 \cdot 3 = 6$ elements. This set of ordered pairs is called the Cartesian product of A and B and is denoted by $A \times B$.

The result in this example can be generalized as follows:

> If a finite set A contains r elements and a finite set B contains s elements, then there are rs different ordered pairs (a, b) with $a \in A$ and $b \in B$ (that is, $A \times B$ contains rs elements).

This principle can be extended to any number of sets and applied in many counting situations.

EXAMPLE 2   How many four-digit numerals for even numbers can be formed using the digits 0, 1, 2, 3, 4, 5, 6?

SOLUTION   To help you think through such problems, it is useful to employ a diagram such as this: ☐☐☐☐ or this: ___ ___ ___ ___ .

For the thousands digit, you can use any of the six digits 1, 2, 3, 4, 5, or 6, but not 0. Therefore, you write 6 in the first space: [6]☐☐☐

For the hundreds and tens digits you can use any one of the given seven digits, so you write 7 in each of these places: | 6 | 7 | 7 | |

In the units place, you can use any one of the four digits 0, 2, 4, or 6, but not 1, 3, or 5. Therefore, you write 4 in the units place: | 6 | 7 | 7 | 4 |

The second counting principle tells you that there are $6 \times 7 \times 7 \times 4$, or 1176, ways of forming the required even numerals. **Answer.**

ORAL EXERCISES

If A and B are as given, state the number of elements in $A \cap B$, $A \cup B$, and $A \times B$.

1. $A = \{3, 5, 7\}$, $B = \{5, 7, 9\}$
2. $A = \{1\}$, $B = \{1, 2, 3, 4, 5\}$
3. $A = B = \{1, 2, 3, 4\}$
4. $A = \{1, 3, 5\}$, $B = \{2, 4, 6\}$
5. $A = \{1\}$, $B = \{2\}$
6. $A = \{1, 2, 3, 4\}$, $B = \emptyset$
7. $A = \{1, 2, 3, 4\}$, $B = \{2, 3\}$
8. $A = \{1, 2, 3, 4, 5, 6\}$, $B = \{7, 8\}$

WRITTEN EXERCISES

A

1. How many two-digit numerals can be formed from the digits 1, 2, 3, 4, 5?

2. How many three-letter sequences can you form from the letters a, e, i, o, u, y?

3. In a combined charity drive, 430 persons donated to the Red Cross and the Salvation Army. If 330 persons donated to the Red Cross and 310 to the Salvation Army, how many donated to both?

4. The day faculty and night faculty of State College held a joint meeting. In attendance were 130 members of the day staff and 92 members of the night staff. If 31 persons were members of both staffs, how many persons attended the joint meeting?

5. A tourist can go from Central City to Travis by plane, train, or car, and from Travis to Southern Island by plane or boat. In how many ways can a tourist go from Central City to Southern Island if he travels one day from Central City to Travis, and the next day from Travis to Southern Island?

6. Montauk's Department Store has six entrances. In how many ways can a person enter and leave the store? How many ways can a person enter and leave the store if the same entrance is not used both ways?

7. How many 6-symbol license plates containing three letters of the alphabet and three digits can be made if the first 3 symbols are letters and the last 3 are digits?

8. In Exercise 7 how many license plates can be made if the letters *Y* and *Z* cannot be used and if the digits cannot all be 0?

9. An election ballot contains the names of 4 candidates for president, 5 for vice-president, and 3 for secretary. How many ways can a ballot be marked if 1 vote must be cast for each office?

10. In Exercise 9 how many ways can a ballot be marked if no more than 1 vote for each office may be cast (and at least 1 vote for some office is cast)?

B **11.** How many numerals for positive odd integers less than 6000 can be formed using the digits 0, 1, 4, 5?

12. How many numerals for positive even integers less than 10,000 can be formed using the digits 0, 3, 6, 9?

13. How many different three-digit numerals for whole-number multiples of 5 can be formed from the digits 0, 1, 2, 3, 4, 5, 6?

14. In Exercise 13 how many of the numerals formed will name odd numbers?

12-2 *linear and circular permutations*

You can list the members of the set $\{a, b, c\}$ in six different orders:

abc *acb* *bac* *bca* *cab* *cba*

Each ordering, or arrangement, of the letters is called a (*linear*) *permutation* of the set $\{a, b, c\}$. A permutation is any arrangement of the elements of a set in a definite order.

Notice that the first letter listed can be any member of $\{a, b, c\}$. This means there are 3 choices for first place, so we write 3 in the first space of a diagram: $\boxed{3\ |\ \ \ |\ \ \ }$. *After a letter has been selected for first place,* the choice for second place is made from the set of 2 letters remaining. Therefore, we write 2 in the second space: $\boxed{3\ |\ 2\ |\ \ \ }$. *After letters have been assigned to both the first and the second places,* there is only 1 choice for third place; so we write 1 in the third space: $\boxed{3\ |\ 2\ |\ 1}$. Thus, the number of permutations of the elements of $\{a, b, c\}$ is

$$3 \times 2 \times 1.$$

The product $3 \times 2 \times 1$ can be written in brief factorial notation as 3! (read "three factorial" or "factorial three"). Thus, factorial five is

$$5! = 5 \cdot 4 \cdot 3 \cdot 2 \cdot 1 = 120,$$

and in general,

$$n! = n \cdot (n - 1) \cdot \ \cdots \ \cdot 3 \cdot 2 \cdot 1, \text{ where } n \text{ is any natural number.}$$

The preceding example illustrates the following fact:

> The number of permutations of the members of a set containing n different elements is $n!$.

EXAMPLE 1   How many different signals can be made using the four flags pictured at the right if all the flags must be used in each signal?

SOLUTION   You want to determine the number of permutations of 4 things:

$$4! = 4 \cdot 3 \cdot 2 \cdot 1 = 24$$

$\therefore$ 24 signals can be made using the four flags. **Answer.**

Now suppose you are asked to find the number of permutations of five letters taken three at a time. In the diagram ☐☐☐ , the first space could be filled in five ways, the second in four ways, and the last in three. Thus $\boxed{5\,|\,4\,|\,3}$ would represent the situation. From the fundamental counting principle there are $5 \cdot 4 \cdot 3$, or 60, ways in which the letters could be arranged.

In a set, the number of permutations of n different elements taken r at a time is denoted by $_nP_r$. Other representations are $P(n, r)$ and P_r^n. To obtain a formula for $_nP_r$, notice that the diagram representing the situation contains r spaces to be filled as shown:

$$\boxed{n\,|\,n-1\,|\,n-2\,|\,\cdots\,|\,n-(r-1)}$$

Thus, you have the following result:

> The number of permutations of r members of a set containing n different elements is
> $$_nP_r = n(n-1)(n-2) \cdots (n-r+1).$$

Note that if $r = n$ then $_nP_n = n!$.

EXAMPLE 2   How many different three-letter sequences can you form from the letters of the alphabet if no two letters in a sequence are the same?

SOLUTION   You want to determine the number of permutations of 3 elements from a set of 26 elements:

$$_{26}P_3 = 26 \cdot 25 \cdot 24 = 15{,}600$$

$\therefore$ you can form 15,600 different three-letter sequences. **Answer.**

There is a special type of permutation, called a circular permutation, which is an arrangement of objects in a circular pattern. A common example is the seating of people around a circular table. In such an arrangement there is no first place, so that if each person shifts his position one place counter-clockwise (or clockwise) the relative positions are not changed. In fact, if there are n people at the table, each person can shift position n times and return to his original position without disturbing the arrangement. Therefore, if you use the formula for a linear permutation to find the number of possible arrangements, you will have counted each different arrangement n times. Thus, there are

$$\frac{n!}{n} = \frac{n \cdot (n-1) \cdot \ldots \cdot 3 \cdot 2 \cdot 1}{n} = (n-1)!$$

distinguishable permutations.

The diagram below shows the $(3-1)!$, or 2, circular permutations of the 3-element set $\{a, b, c\}$ and the corresponding $3!$, or 6, linear permutations.

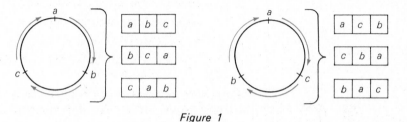

Figure 1

EXAMPLE 3 **In how many ways can six persons be seated around a circular table?**

SOLUTION Since this is a circular permutation of 6 things, there are $(6-1)!$, or 120, possible different seating arrangements.

You may think of this in a slightly different manner: Since a rotation of any permutation does not produce a new permutation, one of the positions can be considered fixed, and $\boxed{1\ |\ 5\ |\ 4\ |\ 3\ |\ 2\ |\ 1}$ describes the situation. We see again that there are 120 different arrangements. **Answer.**

The analysis of problems involving circular permutations of objects which do not have a definite top or bottom, such as bracelets or key rings, is somewhat different. In these cases it seems reasonable to consider that flipping an arrangement over does not change the arrangement. Thus, since flipping over the first arrangement in Figure 1 above yields the second arrangement, and vice versa, there is only $\dfrac{(3-1)!}{2}$, or 1, permutation of 3 objects about a key ring or bracelet. In general, for n objects, there are $\dfrac{(n-1)!}{2}$ such permutations, provided $n > 2$.

EXAMPLE 4   In how many ways can 5 keys be arranged on a key ring?

SOLUTION   You have

$$\frac{(n-1)!}{2} = \frac{4!}{2} = \frac{4 \cdot 3 \cdot 2 \cdot 1}{2} = 12. \text{ Answer.}$$

WRITTEN EXERCISES

A   1. In how many ways can 8 students be seated in a row?

2. In how many ways can 6 books be arranged side by side on a shelf?

3. In how many ways can 11 players be assigned to positions on a soccer team?

4. How many permutations are there for the letters in the word INQUEST?

5. How many different signals can be given by flying 5 different signal flags on a vertical staff?

6. In how many ways can six cars be assigned to six parking places?

7. How many permutations of the letters in the word ASTEROID can be made that end in vowels?

8. How many permutations of the letters in the word CONVERT can be made that end in consonants?

9. How many numerals for numbers divisible by 5 can be formed from the digits 0, 1, 2, 3, 4, 5, 6 if no digit may be used more than once?

10. In how many ways can 5 horses be placed in 10 stalls?

11. In how many ways can 7 persons be seated around a circular table?

12. In how many ways can 8 life guards be positioned around a circular swimming pool?

B   13. In how many ways can 5 persons be seated around a circular table if two particular persons must be seated side by side?

14. In how many ways can 3 men and 3 women be seated around a circular table if men and women must occupy alternate seats?

15. In how many different ways can 6 keys be arranged on a key ring?

16. In how many different ways can 8 charms be hung on a charm bracelet?

17. Show that $_6P_4 = 6(_5P_3)$.   19. Show that $_5P_r = 5(_4P_{r-1})$.

18. Show that $_nP_4 = n(_{n-1}P_3)$.   20. Show that $_5P_3 - _5P_2 = 2(_5P_2)$.

C   21. Show that $_nP_4 - _nP_3 = (n-4)(_nP_3)$.

22. Show that $_nP_r - _nP_{r-1} = (n-r)(_nP_{r-1})$.

23. Solve for n: $_nP_3 = 3(_{n-1}P_2)$ 26. Solve for n: $_nP_r = k(_{n-1}P_{r-1})$

24. Solve for n: $_nP_4 = 8(_{n-1}P_3)$

25. Solve for n: $_nP_4 = 4(_nP_3)$ 27. Show that $_nP_r = \dfrac{n!}{(n-r)!}$.

12-3 permutations of elements not all different

Finding the number of distinguishable permutations of a set of elements that are not all different involves an extension of the method used in Section 12–2. For example, to find the number of distinguishable permutations of the letters in the word

reverse,

we must consider the fact that the letter *e* occurs three times and the letter *r* twice in the word, and that simply interchanging any of the three *e*'s or the two *r*'s with each other does not produce a distinguishable permutation. To analyze the situation in detail, let us label the *r*'s and *e*'s with subscripts:

$$r_1 \quad e_1 \quad v \quad e_2 \quad r_2 \quad s \quad e_3$$

There are, of course, $_7P_7 = 7!$ permutations of these 7 letters. If we let P denote the number of *distinguishable* permutations, then for each of these P permutations, there are $3!$ permutations of the *e*'s (e_1, e_2, and e_3) and $2!$ permutations of the *r*'s (r_1 and r_2). It follows that

$$2! \cdot 3!P = _7P_7 = 7!,$$

so that

$$P = \frac{7!}{2! \cdot 3!} = 420.$$

Using similar reasoning, we can assert that, in general:

The number of distinguishable permutations of *n* elements taken *n* at a time, with n_1 elements alike, n_2 of another kind alike, and so on, is

$$\frac{n!}{n_1!n_2!\cdots}.$$

WRITTEN EXERCISES Find the number of distinguishable permutations of all the letters in the given word.

A
1. Sweden
2. Canada
3. Madagascar
4. Guatemala

5. Jamaica
6. Ethiopia
7. Russia
8. Tanzania

9. Morocco
10. Shanghai
11. Shenandoah
12. Mediterranean

13. How many signals can be made by displaying 6 flags all at one time on a vertical flagpole if the flags differ only in color, 3 of them being red, 2 white, and 1 green?

14. In Exercise 13 how many signals can be made with 9 flags, 4 of which are red, 3 green, and 2 white?

B 15. How many distinguishable circular permutations can be formed with the letters in the word LIMIT?

16. How many distinguishable circular permutations can be formed with the letters in the word CIRCLE?

SELF-TEST 1 Give the meaning of each of the following.

1. Cartesian product   2. permutation   3. factorial notation

Objective 1, page 407   4. How many three-digit numerals can be written using the digits 7, 8, and 9?

Objective 2, page 407   5. In how many ways may a milliner arrange six different flowers on a hat brim?

Objective 3, page 407   6. How many three-letter arrangements can be made using the letters in CHANGES if any letter may be repeated at most twice?

7. How many four-letter radio station call letters can be made if the first letter must be W or K and no letter may be repeated?

Objective 4, page 407   8. How many distinguishable permutations are there of the letters in the word DIFFERENCE?

Check your answers with those printed at the back of the book.

combinations

After completing the next two sections, you should be able to:

Objectives
1. **Find the number of combinations of *n* elements taken *r* at a time.**
2. **Find the number of ways in which specified subsets can be selected from two or more given sets.**

12-4   *counting subsets*

Can you list the three-element subsets of the set T, where $T = \{a, b, c, d\}$? To obtain any of these subsets, all you have to do is remove one of the members of the original set. Thus the three-element subsets are:

$$\{a, b, c\} \quad \{a, b, d\} \quad \{a, c, d\} \quad \{b, c, d\}$$

Hence, denoting the number of three-element subsets of a four-element set by $_4C_3$, you have $_4C_3 = 4$.

You can classify the *permutations* of T's elements *taken three at a time* according to the three-element subset involved in each permutation. For example, the $3!$, or 6, arrangements

$$\begin{array}{ccc} abd & bad & dab \\ adb & bda & dba \end{array}$$

are the permutations of the subset $\{a, b, d\}$. Similarly, each of the other three-element subsets yields $3!$ other permutations of the letters a, b, c, and d taken three at a time. Thus, you have

$$_4C_3 \times 3! = {_4P_3} \qquad \text{or} \qquad _4C_3 = \frac{_4P_3}{3!}.$$

This formula is consistent with our observation that $_4C_3 = 4$, since

$$\frac{_4P_3}{3!} = \frac{4 \cdot 3 \cdot 2}{1 \cdot 2 \cdot 3} = 4.$$

Moreover, the formula suggests the general relationship between $_nC_r$, the number of r-element subsets of a set with n elements, and $_nP_r$, the number of permutations of the n elements taken r at a time for $0 < r < n$:

$$_nC_r = \frac{_nP_r}{r!}.$$

Since $_nP_r = n(n - 1)(n - 2) \cdots (n - r + 1)$, you have:

The number of r-element subsets of a set containing n elements is

$$_nC_r = \frac{n(n - 1)(n - 2) \cdots (n - r + 1)}{r!}.$$

Note that the numerator and the denominator of the expression on the right are both products of r factors.

An r-element subset of a set with n elements is often called a **combination** of n elements taken r at a time. Thus, $_nC_r$, also denoted by $\binom{n}{r}$, $C(n, r)$, or C_r^n, is the number of combinations of n elements taken r at a time.

EXAMPLE   How many 5-card hands can be dealt from a standard 52-card bridge deck?

SOLUTION   You are asked for the number of 5-card subsets of a 52-card set. Letting $r = 5$ and $n = 52$, you can begin by noting that the denominator of

$$_{52}C_5 = \frac{}{5!}$$

contains 5 factors. Therefore, the required numerator contains 5 descending factors starting with 52. Thus

$$_{52}C_5 = \frac{52 \cdot 51 \cdot 50 \cdot 49 \cdot 48}{1 \cdot 2 \cdot 3 \cdot 4 \cdot 5} = 2,598,960.$$

∴ there are 2,598,960 possible 5-card hands in a 52-card deck. **Answer.**

If you multiply the numerator and denominator of the expression for $_nC_r$ by $(n - r)!$, you obtain the equivalent expression:

$$_nC_r = \frac{n(n - 1)(n - 2) \ldots (n - r + 1)(n - r)(n - r - 1) \ldots 3 \cdot 2 \cdot 1}{r!(n - r)!}$$

or

$$_nC_r = \frac{n!}{r!(n - r)!}$$

The symbol $_nC_0$ denotes the number of subsets with no elements in a set having n elements. Since there is just one such subset, namely the empty set $\emptyset$, $_nC_0 = 1$. Thus, you have:

$$_nC_0 = \frac{n!}{0!n!} = \frac{1}{0!}, \quad \text{or} \quad 1 = \frac{1}{0!}$$

Therefore, for the formula to hold when r is a whole number, we must *define* 0! to be 1. Now, you should verify that this definition also makes the formula for $_nC_r$ valid in the case $r = n$.

You can discover a useful fact about $_nC_r$ by noticing that whenever r elements are selected from a set of n elements, $n - r$ elements are left behind. Therefore, the combinations of r elements selected, and the combinations of $n - r$ elements left, are paired one-to-one and are consequently the same in number; that is,

$$_nC_r = {_nC_{n-r}}.$$

You can use this fact to simplify computations; for example,

$$_{50}C_{48} = {_{50}C_2} = \frac{50 \cdot 49}{1 \cdot 2} = 1225.$$

WRITTEN EXERCISES

A

1. In how many ways can a 4-member committee be appointed from a club with 12 members?

2. How many different samples of 3 transistors can be taken from a stock of 60 transistors?

3. How many different withdrawals of 2 microfilms can be made from a library containing 2000 microfilms?

4. How many straight lines are determined by 6 points, no 3 of which lie on the same line?

5. How many chords can be drawn joining pairs of points, given 7 fixed points on a circle?

6. In how many ways can you draw 3 marbles from a pouch containing 12 marbles?

7. How many diagonals does a regular octagon (8-sided figure) have?

8. A slate of 14 persons is running for the school board in Central City. In how many ways can 3 of the persons be elected?

B   9. In how many ways can 8 articles be divided into two equal groups?

10. In how many ways can you divide 12 articles into two equal groups?

11. Six points lie on the circumference of a circle. How many inscribed triangles can be drawn having these points as vertices?

12. Eleven points lie on the circumference of a circle. How many inscribed hexagons can be drawn having these points as vertices?

13. Find n, given $_nC_2 = {_{100}}C_{98}$.

14. Find n if $_nC_5 = {_n}C_3$.

C   15. Prove $_nC_r = {_n}C_{n-r}$ by using the formula $_nC_r = \dfrac{n!}{(n-r)!r!}$.

16. Show that the total number of subsets of a set with n elements is 2^n. *Hint:* Each member of the set either is or is not selected in forming a subset.

12–5   *combinations and products*

You can use the second fundamental principle of counting (page 408) to help determine the number of ways specified subsets can be selected from two or more given sets.

EXAMPLE   In how many ways can 3 white and 2 red marbles be chosen from an urn containing 12 white and 8 red marbles?

SOLUTION   For the white marbles, you compute

$$_{12}C_3 = \frac{12 \cdot 11 \cdot 10}{1 \cdot 2 \cdot 3} = 220.$$

For the red marbles, you compute

$$_8C_2 = \frac{8 \cdot 7}{1 \cdot 2} = 28.$$

Then, by the second counting principle, the number of ways both selections can be made is just

$$28 \times 220 = 6160. \quad \textbf{Answer.}$$

A

1. In how many ways can you select 4 white and 3 black marbles from a bag containing 10 white and 8 black marbles?

2. In how many ways can you select 3 red, 2 green, and 4 white marbles from an urn containing 5 red, 5 green, and 7 white marbles?

3. In how many ways can you select 3 hearts and 2 spades from a standard 52-card bridge deck?

4. A golf bag contains 4 woods and 10 irons, one iron being a putter. In how many ways can you select 2 woods and 5 irons from the set if one of the irons must be the putter?

5. An examination contains two parts. If Part A contains 10 questions and Part B, 6 questions, in how many ways can you select 5 questions from Part A and 3 from Part B?

6. A book club offers a subscriber a choice of any 2 out of 5 biographies and any 3 out of 7 novels. In how many ways can a subscriber make a choice?

B

7. In how many ways can you select 3 face cards (king, queen, jack) and 2 aces from a standard 52-card bridge deck?

8. In how many ways can you select 3 black cards and 2 hearts from a standard 52-card bridge deck?

In Exercises 9–15 first find the number of combinations, and then find the number of permutations of each combination.

9. How many five-letter arrangements of the letters in MIRACLE are possible if 3 consonants and 2 vowels are used and no letter is repeated?

10. How many 4-letter arrangements of the letters in the word COMPARE have 3 consonants and 1 vowel if no letter is repeated?

C

11. How many arrangements of 5 different letters are possible using 3 letters from SPOON and 2 letters from DIVIDE?

12. How many arrangements of 4 different letters are possible using 2 letters from MULTIPLY and 2 letters from SEED?

13. How many numerals having five different digits can be formed from the digits 1, 2, 3, 4, 5, 6, 7, 8, 9, if each numeral is to be written with 3 odd digits and 2 even digits?

14. How many 5-letter arrangements can be formed using the letters in the word CREATION if each arrangement has 3 vowels and 2 consonants and if no letter is repeated?

15. If there are 12 desks in the front row of a classroom, in how many ways can 3 students be seated at the desks? In how many ways can they be seated next to each other at the desks?

1. Give the meaning of "combination."

Objective 1, page 415 **2.** In how many ways can 2 marbles be drawn from an urn containing 11 marbles?

3. In how many ways can a committee of 4 persons be chosen from a group of 14?

Objective 2, page 415 **4.** In how many ways can you select 4 white marbles and 3 red marbles from an urn containing 6 white and 6 red marbles?

5. A department-store window designer has 8 spring dresses, 4 pantsuits, and 7 bathing suits from which to choose 3 dresses, 2 pantsuits, and 2 bathing suits. In how many ways can she arrange these on 7 mannequins?

Check your answers with those printed at the back of the book.

binomial expansions

Objectives

After completing the next two sections, you should be able to:
1. Expand a binomial.
2. Use Pascal's triangle to expand a binomial.
3. Find a given term in a binomial expansion.

12–6 *the binomial theorem*

When you expand natural-number powers of binomials, you discover an interesting pattern:

$$(a + b)^1 = a + b$$
$$(a + b)^2 = a^2 + 2ab + b^2$$
$$(a + b)^3 = a^3 + 3a^2b + 3ab^2 + b^3$$
$$(a + b)^4 = a^4 + 4a^3b + 6a^2b^2 + 4ab^3 + b^4$$

$$(a - b)^1 = a - b$$
$$(a - b)^2 = a^2 - 2ab + b^2$$
$$(a - b)^3 = a^3 - 3a^2b + 3ab^2 - b^3$$
$$(a - b)^4 = a^4 - 4a^3b + 6a^2b^2 - 4ab^3 + b^4$$

These examples suggest:

1. The number of terms in the expansion of $(a \pm b)^n$ is $n + 1$.

2. If the binomial is a sum, all terms in the expansion are added; if the binomial is a difference, the terms are alternately added and subtracted, the even-numbered terms being subtracted.

3. The coefficient of the first term is 1.

4. The coefficient of any other term is the product of the coefficient of the preceding term and the exponent of *a* in the preceding term divided by the number of the preceding term.

5. The exponent of *a* in any term after the first is one less than the exponent of *a* in the preceding term.

6. The exponent of *b* in any term after the first is one greater than the exponent of *b* in the preceding term.

7. The sum of the exponents of *a* and *b* in each term is *n*.

EXAMPLE 1 **Expand $(3n - 2)^5$.**

SOLUTION

$$\overset{\overset{5 \cdot 1}{1}}{} \quad \overset{\overset{4 \cdot 5}{2}}{} \quad \overset{\overset{3 \cdot 10}{3}}{} \quad \overset{\overset{2 \cdot 10}{4}}{} \quad \overset{1 \cdot 5}{5}$$

$$1 \cdot (3n)^5 - 5(3n)^4(2) + 10(3n)^3(2)^2 - 10(3n)^2(2)^3 + 5(3n)(2)^4 - 2^5$$

Term Number   1   2   3   4   5   6

The arrows show how the numerical coefficients of the first four terms are computed. (Explain the last two terms.) In simplified form,

$$(3n - 2)^5 = 243n^5 - 810n^4 + 1080n^3 - 720n^2 + 240n - 32.$$
Answer.

The pattern displayed by the expansion of binomials suggests the *Binomial Theorem*, which states that for any positive integer *n* the expansion of $(a + b)^n$ is:

$$a^n + \frac{n}{1} a^{n-1}b^1 + \frac{n}{1} \cdot \frac{n-1}{2} a^{n-2}b^2 + \frac{n}{1} \cdot \frac{n-1}{2} \cdot \frac{n-2}{3} a^{n-3}b^3 + \cdots$$

$$+ \frac{n}{1} \cdot \frac{n-1}{2} \cdot \frac{n-2}{3} \cdots \frac{n-(r-2)}{r-1} a^{n-(r-1)}b^{r-1} + \cdots + b^n.$$

The *r*th term is

$$\frac{n(n-1)(n-2) \dots (n-r+2)}{(r-1)!} a^{n-r+1}b^{r-1}, \qquad r > 1.$$

Observe that in the *r*th term, the exponent of *b* is $r - 1$, the exponent of *a* is $n - r + 1$, the denominator of the coefficient is $(r - 1)!$, and the numerator of the coefficient is $n(n - 1) \dots (n - r + 2)$, which consists of $r - 1$ consecutive integers decreasing from *n*. Thus, the numerator and denominator of the coefficient contain the same number of factors.

EXAMPLE 2 Find the fifth term in the expansion of $(2x + y)^{10}$.

SOLUTION You have $n = 10$ and $r = 5$.

1. Find the exponent of b (in this case, y). It is $5 - 1$, or 4. $\quad y^4$

2. The exponent of a (in this case, $2x$) is then $10 - 4$, or 6. $\quad (2x)^6 y^4$

3. The denominator of the coefficient is then $(5 - 1)!$, or $4 \cdot 3 \cdot 2 \cdot 1$. $\quad \dfrac{}{4 \cdot 3 \cdot 2 \cdot 1} (2x)^6 y^4$

4. The numerator of the coefficient contains 4 factors starting with 10. $\quad \dfrac{10 \cdot 9 \cdot 8 \cdot 7}{4 \cdot 3 \cdot 2 \cdot 1} (2x)^6 y^4$

Simplifying, you have, $210(2)^6 x^6 y^4$ or $13{,}440 x^6 y^4$. **Answer.**

WRITTEN EXERCISES Expand each binomial and express the result in simplest form.

A

1. $(x + 2)^4$
2. $(x - 2y)^5$
3. $(y - 3)^6$
4. $(2a + b)^6$

5. $(2x - \frac{1}{2})^4$
6. $(3x + \frac{1}{3})^5$
7. $\left(4 + \dfrac{z}{2}\right)^5$
8. $\left(\dfrac{t}{3} - 3\right)^5$

9. $(n^2 - 2)^4$
10. $(k^2 + 3)^5$
11. $(p^2 - q^2)^6$
12. $(r^2 + s^2)^6$

Find and simplify the specified term in each expression.

13. Fifth: $(a - b)^{12}$
14. Sixth: $(r + 2t)^{10}$
15. Seventh: $(n^2 - 1)^{15}$

16. Eighth: $(a^3 + 1)^9$
17. Third: $(t + 1)^{16}$
18. Fourth: $(2 - 3y)^{15}$

B Use the first three terms of a binomial expansion to compute an approximation of the given power.

19. $(1.01)^7$ *Hint:* $(1.01) = (1 + 0.01)$
20. $(0.99)^6$

21. $(1.02)^{10}$
22. $(0.98)^{12}$

12–7   *Pascal's triangle*

You can look at the expansion of a positive integral power of a binomial from the point of view of combinations of terms selected from each of the binomial factors. Consider the following expansion:

$$(a + b)^3 = (a + b)(a + b)(a + b)$$
$$= aaa + baa + aab + aba + bba + bab + abb + bbb$$

You obtain each product shown in the expansion by multiplying three variables, one from each of the binomial factors of $(a + b)^3$. The term *baa*, for example, is the result of choosing *b* from the first binomial factor, *a* from the second, and *a* from the third. If you combine similar terms in the expansion to obtain

$$(a + b)^3 = a^3 + 3a^2b + 3ab^2 + b^3,$$

then 3, the coefficient of a^2b, is the number of ways of selecting one *b* from the three factors, that is $_3C_1$. Similarly, because you obtain a^3 by choosing no *b* from the three factors, the coefficient of a^3 is 1, or $_3C_0$. In fact, you can rewrite the expansion as follows:

$$(a + b)^3 = {}_3C_0a^3 + {}_3C_1a^2b + {}_3C_2ab^2 + {}_3C_3b^3$$

The reasoning used in determining the coefficients in the expansion of $(a + b)^3$ can be extended to determining the coefficients in the expansion of $(a + b)^n$. Thus,

$$(a + b)^n = {}_nC_0a^n + {}_nC_1a^{n-1}b + {}_nC_2a^{n-2}b^2 + \cdots + {}_nC_nb^n,$$

where the *r*th term is $_nC_{r-1}a^{n-(r-1)}b^{r-1}$.

If you write the expansions of $(a + b)^n$ for successive values of *n* in the form of a triangle, you have

$$(a + b)^0 = \qquad\qquad 1$$
$$(a + b)^1 = \qquad\qquad a + b$$
$$(a + b)^2 = \qquad\quad a^2 + 2ab + b^2$$
$$(a + b)^3 = \qquad a^3 + 3a^2b + 3ab^2 + b^3$$
$$(a + b)^4 = a^4 + 4a^3b + 6a^2b^2 + 4ab^3 + b^4$$

Now, looking only at the coefficients, you see the triangle:

$$
\begin{array}{ccccccccc}
 & & & & 1 & & & & \\
 & & & 1 & & 1 & & & \\
 & & 1 & & 2 & & 1 & & \\
 & 1 & & 3 & & 3 & & 1 & \\
1 & & 4 & & 6 & & 4 & & 1
\end{array}
$$

Notice that each term other than 1 is the sum of the term to the right and the term to the left of it in the row directly above. Thus, the next row is:

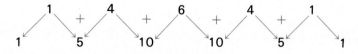

This array is known as Pascal's triangle, named after the French mathematician and philosopher Blaise Pascal.

EXAMPLE 1 Use Pascal's triangle to expand $(2m - 1)^6$.

SOLUTION You use the seventh row of this triangle:

Sixth Row: 1   5   10   10   5   1
Seventh Row: 1   6   15   20   15   6   1

$$\therefore (2m - 1)^6 = 1(2m)^6 - 6(2m)^5 + 15(2m)^4 - 20(2m)^3 + 15(2m)^2$$
$$- 6(2m) + 1$$
$$= 64m^6 - 192m^5 + 240m^4 - 160m^3 + 60m^2$$
$$- 12m + 1. \text{ Answer.}$$

EXAMPLE 2 Find the seventh term in the expansion of $(t + 2)^{10}$.

SOLUTION The rth term is given by $_nC_{r-1}(t)^{n-r+1}(2)^{r-1}$.

The seventh term is $_{10}C_6 t^{10-7+1}(2)^{7-1}$.

Since $_{10}C_6 = _{10}C_4 = \dfrac{10 \cdot 9 \cdot 8 \cdot 7}{1 \cdot 2 \cdot 3 \cdot 4} = 210$, the seventh term is

$$210t^4(2)^6 = 210(64)t^4 = 13,440t^4. \text{ Answer.}$$

WRITTEN EXERCISES Use Pascal's triangle to expand each binomial.

A   1. $(r + 1)^7$ 3. $(2t + 3)^4$ 5. $(1 + 0.1)^5$ 7. $\left(\dfrac{x}{2} - 1\right)^6$

2. $(x - 1)^6$ 4. $(z - \frac{1}{2})^4$ 6. $(1 - 0.1)^5$ 8. $\left(\dfrac{x}{3} + 3\right)^5$

Find the given term in each expansion.

B   9. Seventh: $(x - 2)^9$ 11. Fifth: $(2r + 1)^7$ 13. Third: $\left(\dfrac{y}{2} + 2\right)^{15}$

10. Sixth: $(r + 2)^8$ 12. Eighth: $\left(\dfrac{x}{2} - 1\right)^{10}$ 14. Fourth: $\left(\dfrac{m}{2} - 2\right)^{16}$

C   15. Prove: $_nC_2 = _{n-1}C_1 + _{n-1}C_2$, if $n \geq 3$.

16. Prove: $_nC_r = _{n-1}C_{r-1} + _{n-1}C_r$, if $n \geq r + 1$.

SELF-TEST 3 Give the meaning of each of the following.

1. binomial expansion   2. Pascal's triangle

Objective 1, page 420   3. Expand $(t - 5)^4$.

Objective 2, page 420   4. Expand $\left(\dfrac{t}{2} - 1\right)^5$ using Pascal's triangle.

Objective 3, page 420   5. Find the sixth term in the expansion of $(1 - 2x)^8$.

Check your answers with those printed at the back of the book.

careers *actuarial science*

An actuary collects and analyzes statistical data relating to insurance. Actuaries must apply their knowledge of mathematics and statistics, as well as principles of business and finance. Some of the typical problems an actuary solves are: determining mortality, accident, sickness, disability, and retirement rates; finding the probability of fires, natural disasters, and unemployment; designing insurance and pension plans; calculating premiums; and determining the amount of money an insurance company needs to cover payment of its benefits.

Most actuaries are employed by private insurance companies. They may also serve as consultants for large corporations, where they advise on insurance and pension plans for the employees. The government also employs actuaries who may be involved in the regulation of insurance companies or in social security programs.

Actuarial workers rely on statistical information in their calculations.

EXAMPLE In calculating the premium for a one-year term life insurance policy, an actuarial worker has the following information. Out of a given number of people alive at a given age at the beginning of a year, a certain number will be likely to die during that year. Under the terms of the policy, the beneficiary is to receive $1000 in the event of the death of the policyholder. The problem is to determine the amount of the premium to be charged in order to cover payments to the beneficiaries.

SOLUTION The premium for persons of a given age is calculated by the following formula:

$$\text{Premium} = \frac{\left(\begin{array}{c}\text{am't. pd. to}\\ \text{ea. beneficiary}\end{array}\right) \cdot \dfrac{100}{103} \cdot \left(\begin{array}{c}\text{number likely to}\\ \text{die during year}\end{array}\right)}{\text{number living at beginning of year}}$$

The factor $\frac{100}{103}$ takes into account the interest the collected premiums will earn before any benefits are paid. For age 35, probability tables show that of 9374 people alive at the beginning of a year, 24 will die during the year.

$$\text{Premium} = \frac{1000 \cdot \frac{100}{103} \cdot 24}{9374}$$

$$= \$2.49 \quad \begin{array}{l}\text{(for \$1000 life insurance}\\ \text{for 1 year, at age 35)}\end{array}$$

probability

Objectives

After completing the next four sections, you should be able to:
1. List a sample space for an experiment, and identify an event.
2. Find the probability of an event and of its complement.
3. Find the probability of mutually exclusive events.
4. Find the probability of the occurrence of a second event given the occurrence of a first event.

12–8 *sample spaces and events*

Suppose you conduct an experiment by tossing three coins—a dime, a nickel, and a quarter. If h represents heads and t tails, any possible outcome of the experiment is an element of

$$\{(h, h, h), (h, h, t), (h, t, h), (h, t, t), (t, h, h), (t, h, t), (t, t, h), (t, t, t)\},$$

where the components of the ordered triples represent in order the result of tossing the dime, the nickel, and the quarter. This set is called a *sample space* or *universe* of the experiment. A sample space is a set S of elements that correspond one-to-one with the outcomes of an experiment. Each of the elements corresponding to an outcome is called a sample point.

EXAMPLE 1 A die is rolled and the number of spots on its top face when it comes to rest is observed. List a sample space for the experiment.

SOLUTION $\{1, 2, 3, 4, 5, 6\}$. Answer.

Now suppose you are interested in whether the number of spots observed in Example 1 is an even number. You can call the result of an even number an *event*, and, in this case, the event is the occurrence of any of the outcomes 2, 4, or 6. The set $\{2, 4, 6\}$ can be seen to be a subset of the sample space. An event is any subset of a sample space.

EXAMPLE 2 Two dice are cast. List a sample space for this experiment and then list the event that both dice show the same number of spots.

SOLUTION We can use ordered pairs to list the outcomes. Thus, we have the set of thirty-six sample points shown at the right.

$\{(1, 1), (1, 2), (1, 3), (1, 4), (1, 5), (1, 6),$
$(2, 1), (2, 2), (2, 3), (2, 4), (2, 5), (2, 6),$
$(3, 1), (3, 2), (3, 3), (3, 4), (3, 5), (3, 6),$
$(4, 1), (4, 2), (4, 3), (4, 4), (4, 5), (4, 6),$
$(5, 1), (5, 2), (5, 3), (5, 4), (5, 5), (5, 6),$
$(6, 1), (6, 2), (6, 3), (6, 4), (6, 5), (6, 6)\}$

The event that both dice show the same number of spots is then
$\{(1, 1), (2, 2), (3, 3), (4, 4), (5, 5), (6, 6)\}$. Answer.

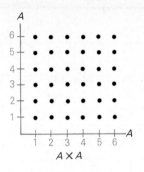

Figure 2

The list of outcomes in the same space in Example 2 suggests that it would be useful to discuss such sample spaces in terms of Cartesian products. Thus, the sample space for the first die is

$$A = \{1, 2, 3, 4, 5, 6\}$$

and that for the second die is the same. Then the sample space for the experiment is just $A \times A$. A lattice which portrays this sample space is shown in Figure 2. Experiments such as tossing coins or dice, in which the outcome is purely a matter of chance, are said to have *random* outcomes.

EXAMPLE 2   A letter is selected at random from those in the word HEART.
a. List the sample space.
b. List the event that the letter selected is a vowel.

SOLUTION   **a.** $\{$H, E, A, R, T$\}$. **Answer.**   **b.** $\{$E, A$\}$. **Answer.**

WRITTEN EXERCISES

A   1. A digit is chosen at random from those in the numeral "813567." **(a)** List a sample space; and **(b)** list the event that the digit names an odd number.

2. A marble is drawn at random from a paper bag containing yellow, white, and green marbles, and the color of the marble is observed. **(a)** List a sample space; and **(b)** list the event that the marble is not white.

3. A letter is selected at random from those in the word KILOGRAM. **(a)** List a sample space; and **(b)** list the event that the letter selected is a vowel.

4. An integer is selected from those between −3 and 2, inclusive. **(a)** List a sample space; and **(b)** list the event that the integer selected is non-positive.

5. Two marbles are drawn successively from an urn containing red, white, and blue marbles, and their colors observed. **(a)** List a sample space; and **(b)** list the event that the marbles are not the same color.

6. In Exercise 5 **(a)** list the event that neither marble is blue; and **(b)** list the event that at least one marble is white.

B   7. One bill is drawn from a box containing $5 and $10 bills, then another bill is drawn from a different box containing $1 and $10 bills. **(a)** List a sample space; and **(b)** list the event that at least one of the bills is a $10 bill.

8. In Exercise 7 **(a)** list the event that only one $10 bill is drawn; and **(b)** list the event that the bills drawn are of different denominations.

9. Two numbers are chosen at random from among the integers from −2 to 2, inclusive. **(a)** List a sample space; and **(b)** list the event that the sum of the numbers is 0.

12-9 *mathematical probability*

Consider the following experiment: From a bag containing 5 blue and 12 white marbles, draw one marble, record its color, then replace it.

If the experiment is designed so that each marble is just as likely to be drawn as any other, we say that the experiment has 17 *equally likely* outcomes. The event that a white marble is drawn consists of 12 outcomes. Therefore, if you repeat the experiment many times, it seems reasonable to expect that about $\frac{12}{17}$ of the time you will find that you have drawn a white marble. This ratio, $\frac{12}{17}$, is called the *probability* that the outcome of any single trial of the experiment will be the drawing of a white marble. This example suggests the following definition:

> Let S be a sample space of an experiment in which there are n possible outcomes, each equally likely. If an event A is a subset of S such that A contains h elements, then the probability of the event A, denoted by $P(A)$, is given by $P(A) = \dfrac{h}{n}$.

EXAMPLE 1   If two cards are drawn at random from a standard 52-card bridge deck, what is the probability that both cards are hearts?

SOLUTION   Since there are 13 hearts in the deck, there are $_{13}C_2$ ways in which two of them can be drawn. There are 52 cards altogether, so there are $_{52}C_2$ possible ways in which two of them can be drawn. If A represents drawing 2 hearts, then

$$P(A) = \frac{_{13}C_2}{_{52}C_2} = \frac{\dfrac{13 \cdot 12}{1 \cdot 2}}{\dfrac{52 \cdot 51}{1 \cdot 2}} = \frac{78}{1326} = \frac{1}{17}. \quad \text{Answer.}$$

In the foregoing example, the answer $\frac{1}{17}$ does not tell you anything *certain* about what is going to happen. It does not, for example, tell you that you will get exactly one pair of hearts out of 17 draws. You might get one such draw, or you might get none, or you might even get 17. However, if you perform the experiment a very large number of times, the ratio of the number of times you draw 2 hearts to the total number of draws will probably come close to $\frac{1}{17}$.

An event A in the sample space S is called *certain* if $A = S$; it is called *impossible* if $A = \emptyset$. Since $P(S) = \dfrac{n}{n} = 1$, while $P(\emptyset) = \dfrac{0}{n} = 0$, the probability is 1 for a certain event and 0 for an impossible one. Do you see that the probability of an event which is neither certain nor impossible is a number between 0 and 1?

By the symbol $\bar{A}$ (read "the complement of A"), we mean the set of the elements of S that are *not* members of A. If A has h members, then $\bar{A}$ contains $n - h$ elements. Therefore, $P(\bar{A})$ is the probability that A does *not* occur, and

$$P(\bar{A}) = \frac{n - h}{n} = 1 - \frac{h}{n} = 1 - P(A).$$

The **odds** that the event A will occur are given by

$$\frac{P(A)}{P(\bar{A})}, \quad \text{or} \quad \frac{h}{n - h}, \quad \text{or} \quad h \text{ to } n - h.$$

Thus, in the original experiment the odds are *12 to 5 in favor of* drawing a white marble or *5 to 12 against* drawing a white marble.

EXAMPLE 2   Two marbles are drawn at random from an urn containing 14 red and 12 blue marbles.
a. What is the probability that at least one marble is blue?
b. What are the odds that at least one marble is blue?

SOLUTION   **a.** The probability that at least one marble is blue, is just the probability that *not both* marbles are *red*. Let A represent the event that both *are* red. Then

$$P(A) = \frac{_{14}C_2}{_{26}C_2} = \frac{14 \cdot 13}{26 \cdot 25} = \frac{7}{25},$$

and the probability that at least one marble is blue is just

$$P(\bar{A}) = 1 - \tfrac{7}{25} = \tfrac{18}{25}. \quad \textbf{Answer.}$$

b. The odds that at least one marble is blue are

$$\frac{18}{25 - 18}, \text{ or 18 to 7.} \quad \textbf{Answer.}$$

WRITTEN EXERCISES

A   1. A card is drawn at random from a standard bridge deck of 52 cards. What is the probability that the card is:

   a. a spade?   **d.** a face card (jack, queen, king)?
   b. a king?   **e.** not a face card?
   c. black?   **f.** the ten of diamonds?

2. In Exercise 1, what are the odds in each case?

3. Two marbles are drawn at random from an urn containing 8 white, 4 blue, and 3 red marbles. What is the probability that:

   a. both are white?   **d.** one is white and one is blue?
   b. both are red?   **e.** neither is red?
   c. neither is blue?   **f.** both are blue?

4. An integer from 1 to 20, inclusive, is selected at random. What is the probability that the integer is:
   a. even?   c. divisible by 5?   e. prime?
   b. odd?   d. less than 5?   f. divisible by 3?

5. In Exercise 4, what are the odds in each case?

6. One letter is drawn at random from the letters in the word LOBSTER and another from the letters in the word SCARLET. What is the probability that:
   a. both are vowels?   b. both are the same?
   c. the first is a vowel and the second is a consonant?
   d. the first is a consonant and the second is a vowel?

7. One letter is drawn at random from the letters in the word SEASIDE and another from the letters in the word SURF. What is the probability that:
   a. both are vowels?   b. both are the same?
   c. the first is a vowel and the second a consonant?
   d. the first is a consonant and the second a vowel?

8. Each item on a multiple-choice test has four responses, only one of which is correct. On a test containing 5 items:
   a. How many correct choices are there?
   b. How many incorrect choices are there?
   c. If random choices of responses are made, what is the probability of getting exactly 2 items correct?
   d. What is the probability of getting exactly 3 items correct?

B 9. Two letters are chosen at random from the English alphabet. If y is considered to be a consonant, what is the probability that:
   a. both are vowels?   b. both are consonants?

10. Of the 500,000 income-tax returns that come into a branch of a state tax bureau, 500,000 returns are checked for arithmetic and 50,000 returns are analyzed thoroughly. If Mr. Bell's return is at this branch:
   a. What is the probability that it will be inspected for arithmetic?
   b. What is the probability that it will both be inspected for arithmetic and be thoroughly analyzed?
   c. What is the probability that it will not be analyzed thoroughly?

11. Ten cards, the 2 through the 6 of spades and the 2 through the 6 of diamonds, are shuffled thoroughly and then taken one by one from the top of the deck and placed in a row from left to right on a table. How many arrangements are possible? What is the probability that each card is next to a card bearing the same numeral?

12. If the letters of the word ALGEBRA are placed at random in a row, what is the probability that two successive letters will be A?

13. If the letters of the word ABOUT are placed at random in a row, what is the probability that three successive letters will be vowels?

14. In an extrasensory perception experiment, a blindfolded subject has two rows of blocks before him. Each row has blocks numbered 1 to 10 arranged in random order. The subject is to place one hand on a block in the first row and then try to place his other hand on the block having the same numeral in the second row. If the subject has no ESP, what is the probability of his making a match on the first try?

C 15. Mr. and Mrs. Evans have two children, one of whom is a girl. What is the probability that both are girls?

16. Mr. and Mrs. Evans have two children, the older of whom is a girl. What is the probability that both are girls? (Compare your answer with the answer to Exercise 15.)

12–10 *mutually exclusive events*

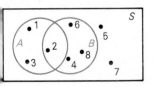

Figure 3

The diagram* in Figure 3 shows the sample space S for the experiment of drawing a number from $\{1, 2, 3, 4, 5, 6, 7, 8\}$. The diagram also shows two events A and B in S. A corresponds to the drawing of a number less than 4, so that $A = \{1, 2, 3\}$. B corresponds to the drawing of an even number; that is, $B = \{2, 4, 6, 8\}$. Therefore,

$$P(A) = \tfrac{3}{8} \text{ and } P(B) = \tfrac{4}{8} = \tfrac{1}{2}.$$

What is the probability that either A or B (or both) will occur? This amounts to asking for $P(A \cup B)$. Since $A \cup B = \{1, 2, 3, 4, 6, 8\}$, $P(A \cup B) = \tfrac{6}{8} = \tfrac{3}{4}$. To see the relationship between $P(A \cup B)$, $P(A)$, and $P(B)$, notice that the intersection of A and B ($A \cap B$) is $\{2\}$. Also, $P(\{2\}) = \tfrac{1}{8}$ and

$$P(A \cup B) = \frac{6}{8} = \frac{3 + 4 - 1}{8} = \frac{3}{8} + \frac{4}{8} - \frac{1}{8}.$$

$$P(A \cup B) = P(A) + P(B) - P(A \cap B).$$

You can prove that this relationship holds for any two events A and B in a sample space. If the events have no outcome in common, that is, $A \cap B = \emptyset$, we say that the events are mutually exclusive. In this case, $P(A \cap B) = P(\emptyset) = 0$. Thus:

If A and B are mutually exclusive events,

$$P(A \cup B) = P(A) + P(B).$$

---

*Such diagrams are used to picture set relationships and are called *Venn diagrams* in honor of the English mathematician John Venn (1834–1923).

EXAMPLE   Three marbles are drawn at random from an urn containing 4 white, 3 red
and 5 blue marbles. What is the probability that at least one of them is red?

SOLUTION   The desired probability is the sum of the probabilities that *exactly* one marble
is red (A), that *exactly* two marbles are red (B), or that *exactly* three marbles
are red (C).

$$P(A) = \frac{{}_3C_1 \times {}_9C_2}{{}_{12}C_3} = \frac{3 \times 36}{220} = \frac{108}{220}$$

$$P(B) = \frac{{}_3C_2 \times {}_9C_1}{{}_{12}C_3} = \frac{3 \times 9}{220} = \frac{27}{220}$$

$$P(C) = \frac{{}_3C_3}{{}_{12}C_3} = \frac{1}{220}$$

∴ the required probability is $\frac{108}{220} + \frac{27}{220} + \frac{1}{220} = \frac{136}{220} = \frac{34}{55}$. Answer.

WRITTEN EXERCISES

A   1. Two marbles are drawn at random from an urn containing 4 white, 6
red, and 5 blue marbles. What is the probability that: (a) Both marbles
are the same color? (b) The marbles are not the same color? (c) At
least one marble is white? (d) At least one marble is red?

2. Two cards are selected at random from a standard 52-card bridge deck.
What is the probability that: (a) One is red and one is black? (b) One
is red and the other is a black ten? (c) One is a four and the other a
face card? (d) One is a black queen and the other a six?

3. In a game of backgammon, Jack can take one man out if he throws
a three using two dice and another man out if he throws a ten. What
is the probability that he can take a man out on his next throw?

4. In a game, Janet will have to pay rent if she throws a 5, 7, or 10 on
her next throw of two dice, and otherwise will not have to pay. What
is the probability that she will have to pay rent on her next throw?

5. Two dice are thrown. What is the probability that: (a) The sum of the
numbers is 6? (b) The sum of the numbers is 6 or 11? (c) Either the
sum of the numbers is 5 or exactly one of the dice shows a 5? (d) Either
the sum of the numbers is less than 3 or else it is greater than 10?

6. Two cards are drawn from a standard 52-card bridge deck. What is the
probability that: (a) Both cards are 4's or both cards are 5's? (b) One
card is a spade and the other a heart? (c) One card is a face card and
the other the ace of spades? (d) One card is a face card and the other
a red ten?

B   7. One bag contains 3 red, 2 orange, and 2 white tennis balls. Another
bag contains 1 red, 1 orange, and 3 white tennis balls. If a ball is drawn
at random from each bag, find the probability that either both are orange
or neither is orange.

8. If the volumes in a 5-volume set of books are randomly placed side by side on a shelf, what is the probability that they will be arranged in either normal or reverse order?

C 9. Ten green gumdrops and ten yellow gumdrops are to be distributed between two identical candy bags, and a gumdrop is to be randomly drawn from a randomly chosen bag. How would you distribute the gumdrops to ensure the greatest probability that the gumdrop drawn will be green?

10. What is the probability that the gumdrop will be green with your distribution in Exercise 9?

12–11 *independent and dependent events*

Suppose two balls are drawn at random from a bag containing 4 red and 3 black balls. What is the probability that both balls drawn are red?

Let A be the event of drawing a red ball the first time, and B, the event of drawing a red ball the second time. The sample space S of the experiment depends on whether or not the first ball drawn is returned to the bag before the second ball is chosen. The question amounts to asking for $P(A \cap B)$.

Case I. The first ball is replaced before the second is drawn.

The sample space S consists of all ordered pairs (x, y) where both x and y denote elements of a set of 7 outcomes (4 red, 3 black).

Figure 4 shows the sample space containing 7×7 or 49 sample points. We use r_i and b_i to designate the drawing of red and black balls, respectively. The colored dashed rectangle outlines all possible experiment outcomes in which the first ball is red, and the colored solid rectangle outlines all possible outcomes in which the second ball is red. Since $A \cap B$ consists of the ordered pairs of the form (red, red), there are $4 \times 4 = 16$ elements in $A \cap B$. Therefore,

$$P(A \cap B) = \tfrac{16}{49} = \tfrac{4}{7} \cdot \tfrac{4}{7}.$$

Note:
$$P(A \cap B) = P(A) \cdot P(B).$$

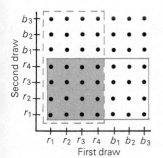

b_3
b_2
b_1
r_4
r_3
r_2
r_1

Second draw

r_1 r_2 r_3 r_4 b_1 b_2 b_3
First draw

Figure 4

The outcomes in $A \cap B$ are in the colored shaded region in Figure 4.

Case II. The first ball is not replaced before the second is drawn.

Any one of the 7 balls may be selected on the first draw, but since this ball will not be replaced, there remain only 6 balls for the second draw. All ordered pairs with equal components must be deleted from the sample space. Note in Figure 5 that one diagonal will not be in the new sample space. Therefore, there are 7×6, or 42, ordered pairs possible. The number of these that are of the form (red, red) is 4×3, or 12, because any of the 4 red balls can be the first, but there are only 3 choices for the second red ball. Thus,

$$P(A \cap B) = \tfrac{12}{42} = \tfrac{2}{7}.$$

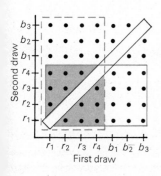

b_3
b_2
b_1
r_4
r_3
r_2
r_1

Second draw

r_1 r_2 r_3 r_4 b_1 b_2 b_3
First draw

Figure 5

Analyzing this result as

$$P(A \cap B) = \tfrac{12}{42} = \tfrac{4}{7} \cdot \tfrac{3}{6},$$

you can see that $\tfrac{4}{7} = P(A)$. We can interpret the second factor, $\tfrac{3}{6}$, as the *probability that the second ball drawn is red under the condition that the first ball drawn was red;* we shall denote this probability by $P(B|A)$.

This example suggests a general law for a conditional probability.

Let $P(A)$ denote the probability of an event A, and $P(B|A)$ denote the conditional probability of an event B given that event A has occurred. If $P(A \cap B)$ is the probability that A and B occur, then:

$$P(A \cap B) = P(A) \cdot P(B|A).$$

If $P(B|A) = P(B)$, we say that events A and B are *independent*. This means that the probability of one does not depend on the occurrence of the other. For example, in Case I where the balls are drawn *with replacement,* the events A and B are independent because the outcome on the first draw does not affect the outcome on the second draw. Thus, two events A and B are independent if and only if

$$P(A \cap B) = P(A) \cdot P(B).$$

Two events that are not independent are said to be dependent.

EXAMPLE 1   **A red die and a green die are thrown. What is the probability that the sum of the numbers shown is 6 and that the green die shows a number 3 or less? Are these events independent?**

SOLUTION   Graph the sample space. Let A be the event that the sum of the numbers is 6. This is shown by the solid rectangle.

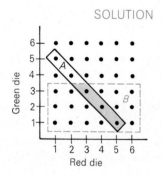

Let B be the event that the green die shows a number 3 or less. This is shown by the dashed colored rectangle.

Then $A \cap B$ is shown by the shaded region. You have

$$P(A) = \tfrac{5}{36}, \; P(B) = \tfrac{18}{36} = \tfrac{1}{2}, \; P(A \cap B) = \tfrac{3}{36} = \tfrac{1}{12}. \;\; \textbf{Answer.}$$

Since $\tfrac{1}{12} \neq \tfrac{5}{36} \cdot \tfrac{1}{2}$, $P(A \cap B) \neq P(A) \cdot P(B)$. Hence, A and B are dependent events. **Answer.**

In many cases, rather than use the relationship

$$P(A \cap B) = P(A) \cdot P(B)$$

to determine the independence of events A and B, you use the fact that A and B are obviously independent events and employ the relationship to find $P(A \cap B)$.

EXAMPLE 2   A die is thrown and a coin is tossed. What is the probability that the die shows a 2 or a 3 and the coin shows a head?

SOLUTION   Let A be the event that the die shows a 2 or a 3, and B be the event that the coin shows a head. These events are clearly independent. Hence, knowing that $P(A) = \frac{2}{6} = \frac{1}{3}$, and $P(B) = \frac{1}{2}$, you have

$$P(A \cap B) = \frac{1}{3} \cdot \frac{1}{2} = \frac{1}{6}. \text{ Answer.}$$

WRITTEN EXERCISES
A

1. Two marbles are drawn from an urn containing 4 white, 3 blue, and 6 red marbles, with the first marble not being replaced before the second is drawn. What is the probability that: **(a)** Both marbles are red? **(b)** One is red and one is blue? **(c)** One is white and the other is not white? **(d)** One is red and the other is not blue?

2. A bag contains 5 silver and 7 red jacks. If two jacks are drawn from the bag and replaced, and then two more jacks are drawn from the bag, what is the probability that: **(a)** Exactly two red and two silver jacks are drawn? **(b)** At most two silver jacks are drawn? **(c)** At most three silver jacks are drawn? **(d)** Exactly three silver jacks are drawn?

3. A red and a green die are thrown. Let A be the event that the sum of the numbers thrown is 8, and B be the event that at least one die shows 3. Find: **(a)** $P(A)$; **(b)** $P(B)$; **(c)** $P(A|B)$; and **(d)** $P(B|A)$.

4. In Exercise 3, let C be the event that neither die shows less than 3, and D be the event that the dice do not show the same number. Find: **(a)** $P(C)$; **(b)** $P(D)$; and **(c)** $P(C|D)$. **(d)** Are C and D independent?

5. Two cards are drawn from a standard 52-card bridge deck. After replacing the cards and shuffling the deck, two more cards are drawn. What is the probability that: **(a)** All are spades? **(b)** All are face cards? **(c)** The first two are diamonds and the second two are face cards? **(d)** None are face cards?

6. A die is rolled and a coin is tossed. What is the probability that: **(a)** The die shows a six and the coin shows a tail? **(b)** The die shows a number greater than 2 and the coin shows a tail? **(c)** The die does not show a 2 or a 3 and the coin shows a head? **(d)** The die shows an even number and the coin shows a head?

7. The probability that Mary will pass her algebra course is $\frac{5}{6}$, that Janet will pass is $\frac{3}{4}$, and that Sally will pass is $\frac{2}{3}$. What is the probability that: **(a)** At least one of the girls will pass? **(b)** At least Mary and Sally will pass? **(c)** Mary and Sally will pass but Janet will not? **(d)** At least two of the three will pass?

8. Jack has two dimes in his pocket, one of which is a trick coin with 2 heads. If he removes a coin at random from his pocket, flips it, and obtains a head, what is the probability that he flipped the trick coin?

B   9. One box contains 8 lemon and 3 grape lollipops and a second, identical box contains 12 grape lollipops. If a lollipop is drawn at random from a box and found to be grape, what is the probability that it was drawn from the second box?

10. Two cards are drawn at random from a standard 52-card bridge deck. What is the probability that: (a) Both cards are hearts, and one card is an ace? (b) Both cards are black, and at least one card is an ace? (c) Are the events in (a) independent? (d) Are the events in (b) independent?

11. There are twelve people present at a business conference of a company. Seven of them are executives, three are salespersons, and two are secretaries. Three of the executives and one salesperson are stockholders in the company. A fly in the room lands at random on the hand of one of the persons present. (a) What is the probability that the fly lands on an executive? (b) What is the probability that the fly lands on a stockholder? (c) Are these events independent?

12. Explain why two mutually exclusive events with nonzero probabilities cannot be independent events.

SELF-TEST 4   Give the meaning of each of the following.

1. probability   3. odds   5. independent events
2. complement   4. mutually exclusive events   6. dependent events

Objective 1, page 426   7. A letter is selected at random from those in the word JUPITER. List a sample space for this experiment and also list the event that the letter selected is a vowel.

Objective 2, page 426   8. An integer from 1 to 8 inclusive is selected at random. What is the probability that the integer is greater than 5?

Objective 3, page 426   9. In Exercise 8, what is the probability that either the integer is greater than 5 or else it is 2 or 4?

Objective 4, page 426   10. Two dice are thrown. Let A be the event that the sum of the numbers shown is 5. Let B be the event that one die shows a 4. Are these events independent? Why or why not?

Check your answers with those printed at the back of the book.

chapter summary   1. If finite sets A, B, and $A \cap B$ contain r, s, and t elements, respectively, then $A \cup B$ contains $r + s - t$ elements and $A \times B$ contains rs elements. From the fundamental counting principles you can derive a formula for the number of **permutations** of n elements, r at a time.

$$_nP_r = n(n - 1)(n - 2) \ldots (n - (r - 1)).$$

2. The number of **combinations** of n things, r at a time, is given by $_nC_r = \dfrac{_nP_r}{r!}$.
   Also, $_nC_r = {}_nC_{n-r}$. The **coefficients of the expansion** $(a + b)^n$ can be expressed as numbers of combinations.

3. If there are h ways in which an event A can occur, in n possible outcomes, $0 \le h \le n$, then the **probability** of A is $P(A) = \dfrac{h}{n}$, and if $h < n$, the *odds* in favor of A are $\dfrac{h}{n - h}$. Probabilities may be discussed in terms of **sample spaces** and **events**, and their graphs.

4. The probability that at least *one* of the events A and B will occur is given by $P(A \cup B) = P(A) + P(B) - P(A \cap B)$. When A and B are **mutually exclusive**, $P(A \cap B) = 0$.

5. The probability that *two* events A and B will occur is given by $P(A \cap B)$ where $P(A \cap B) = P(A) \cdot P(B|A)$. $P(B|A)$ is the **conditional probability** that B will occur given that A has occurred.

chapter test and review

12–1 1. How many four-digit numerals for odd numbers can be formed using 0, 1, 2, 3, 4, 5, 6, 7?

12–2 2. How many permutations of the letters in the word ANSWER end in a consonant?

12–3 3. How many distinguishable permutations are there of the letters in the word PROGRESSION?

12–4 4. In how many ways can a three-member committee be appointed from the twelve-member executive board of a company?

12–5 5. In how many ways can you select 2 white and 3 red marbles from an urn containing 5 white and 4 red marbles?

12–6 6. Expand $(2 - m)^4$.

12–7 7. The fifth row of Pascal's triangle is __?__ .

12–8 8. List a sample space for rolling a die and tossing a coin.

12–9 9. What is the probability that Mary and John will be chosen in a random selection of two students from a class of 28 students?

12–10 10. If a red and a green die are thrown, what is the probability that the red die will show an even number of spots or the green die will show fewer than 3 spots?

12–11 11. If a marble is selected at random from an urn containing 8 white and 4 blue marbles, and, without replacement, a second marble is selected at random, what is the probability that both are blue?

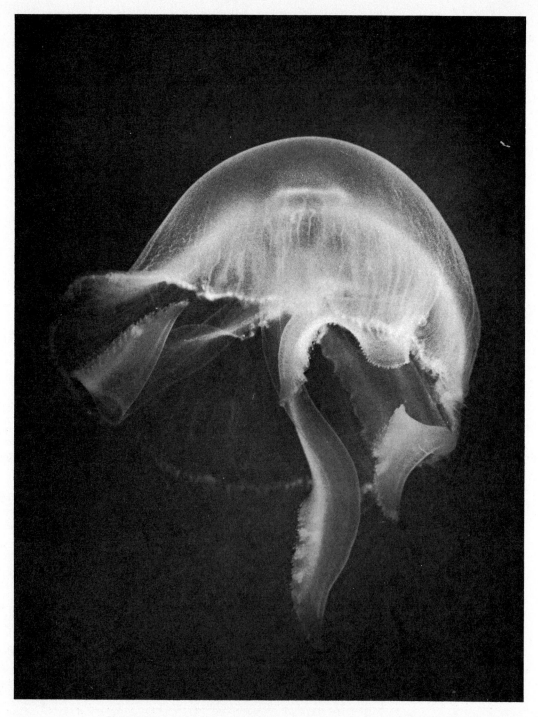

The jellyfish is one of the oldest forms of life on earth, known to have existed for at least 600,000,000 years. Marine biologists refer to this type as a medusa, named for the monster of Greek mythology with snakes for hair.

13 *matrices*

basic properties of matrices

Objectives

After completing the next five sections, you should be able to:
1. Find sums and differences of matrices.
2. Find the product of a scalar and a matrix.
3. Solve certain matrix equations.
4. Find the product of two matrices.

13–1 *matrices and their sums*

In Chapter 4 you saw that it is sometimes convenient to name a number by means of a square array of numerals. Thus the *determinant* $\begin{vmatrix} a & b \\ c & d \end{vmatrix}$ names the number $ad - bc$:

$$\begin{vmatrix} a & b \\ c & d \end{vmatrix} = ad - bc$$

The array $\begin{bmatrix} a & b \\ c & d \end{bmatrix}$ itself is called a *matrix*. Notice that brackets [ ] are used to distinguish the matrix from the determinant. In general, a rectangular array of numerals such as that shown in red at the left is a matrix (plural, matrices).

Each numeral in the array is an entry of the matrix. The number of (horizontal) rows and the number of (vertical) columns of entries in the matrix are its dimensions. For example, the matrix displayed has three rows and two columns and is called a

$$\text{column}$$
$$\begin{array}{c} \\ \text{row } 1 \\ 2 \\ 3 \end{array} \begin{array}{cc} 1 & 2 \\ \left[\begin{array}{cc} 2 & 1 \\ -3 & 0 \\ 5 & 2 \end{array}\right] \end{array}$$

3 × 2 (read ''three by two'') matrix.

Notice that the number of rows is given first and then the number of columns. In this book, we shall use only real numbers for entries of a matrix. An entry of a matrix is referred to by giving its row and column numbers. In the matrix shown at the left, the entry in the second row and first column is -3.

Capital letters, such as A, B, C, are used to denote matrices, and sometimes subscripts, as in $A_{3 \times 2}$, are used to represent the dimensions of a matrix. Thus, for

$$A = \begin{bmatrix} 4 & 1 & 7 \\ 2 & 0 & 6 \\ 5 & 3 & 2 \end{bmatrix}, \quad B = [1 \quad 5], \quad \text{and} \quad C = \begin{bmatrix} -1 \\ 7 \\ 8 \end{bmatrix},$$

you might write $A_{3 \times 3}$, $B_{1 \times 2}$, and $C_{3 \times 1}$. Matrices, such as B and C, which have only one row or one column are called row matrices and column matrices (or row vectors and column vectors), respectively. Since the matrix $A_{3 \times 3}$ has 3 rows and 3 columns, it is said to be a square matrix of order 3. Similarly, we have square matrices of order 2, square matrices of order 4, and so on.

For two matrices of the same dimensions, the entries in the same row and same column are said to be corresponding entries.

Two matrices are equal if and only if they have the same dimensions and all their corresponding entries are equal. Notice that matrices of different dimensions are never said to be equal, even if corresponding entries, as far as they extend, are equal. For instance,

$$[4 \quad 5] \neq \begin{bmatrix} 4 \\ 5 \end{bmatrix} \quad \text{and} \quad \begin{bmatrix} 0 & 0 \\ 0 & 0 \end{bmatrix} \neq \begin{bmatrix} 0 & 0 & 0 \\ 0 & 0 & 0 \end{bmatrix}.$$

EXAMPLE   Find values of x, y, and z so that

$$\begin{bmatrix} x - 2 & y + 5 \\ z + 3 & 2 \end{bmatrix} = \begin{bmatrix} 4 & 5 \\ 0 & 2 \end{bmatrix}.$$

SOLUTION   By the definition of equal matrices, this matrix equation is true if and only if

$$x - 2 = 4, \quad y + 5 = 5, \quad \text{and} \quad z + 3 = 0,$$

or

$$x = 6, \quad y = 0, \quad \text{and} \quad z = -3.$$

$\therefore$ the value for x is 6, for y is 0, and for z is -3.   **Answer.**

If two matrices A and B have the same dimensions, then their sum, denoted by

$$A + B,$$

is a matrix of the same dimensions, whose entries are the sums of the corresponding entries of A and B. For example,

$$[2 \quad -3] + [-5 \quad 4] = [2 + (-5) \quad -3 + 4] = [-3 \quad 1]$$

and

$$\begin{bmatrix} 1 & 4 \\ -3 & 2 \end{bmatrix} + \begin{bmatrix} -6 & 2 \\ -5 & 7 \end{bmatrix} = \begin{bmatrix} 1 + (-6) & 4 + 2 \\ -3 + (-5) & 2 + 7 \end{bmatrix} = \begin{bmatrix} -5 & 6 \\ -8 & 9 \end{bmatrix}.$$

For any given natural numbers m and n, in the set $\mathcal{S}_{m\times n}$ of $m \times n$ matrices with real number entries, the zero matrix, denoted by

$$O_{m\times n} \text{ (or simply } O),$$

is the $m \times n$ matrix each of whose entries is 0. For example, some zero matrices are:

$$O_{2\times 2} = \begin{bmatrix} 0 & 0 \\ 0 & 0 \end{bmatrix}, \quad O_{2\times 3} = \begin{bmatrix} 0 & 0 & 0 \\ 0 & 0 & 0 \end{bmatrix}, \quad \text{and} \quad O_{3\times 3} = \begin{bmatrix} 0 & 0 & 0 \\ 0 & 0 & 0 \\ 0 & 0 & 0 \end{bmatrix}$$

Because the sum of the zero matrix $O_{m\times n}$ and any other matrix $A_{m\times n}$ is $A_{m\times n}$, the zero matrix $O_{m\times n}$ is also called the identity matrix for addition in the set $\mathcal{S}_{m\times n}$. For example,

$$[a \quad b] + [0 \quad 0] = [a + 0 \quad b + 0] = [a \quad b].$$

The negative of the $m \times n$ matrix A, denoted by

$$-A \text{ (read ''the negative of } A\text{''}),$$

is the $m \times n$ matrix whose entries are the negatives of the corresponding entries in A. For example, if

$$A = \begin{bmatrix} 1 \\ -3 \end{bmatrix}, \quad \text{then} \quad -A = \begin{bmatrix} -1 \\ 3 \end{bmatrix},$$

and if

$$B = \begin{bmatrix} 3 & -7 \\ -4 & 2 \end{bmatrix}, \quad \text{then} \quad -B = \begin{bmatrix} -3 & 7 \\ 4 & -2 \end{bmatrix}.$$

Because the sum of $A_{m\times n}$ and $-A_{m\times n}$ is $O_{m\times n}$, we call $-A_{m\times n}$ the additive inverse of $A_{m\times n}$. For example, if

$$A = \begin{bmatrix} a & b \\ c & d \end{bmatrix}, \quad \text{then} \quad -A = \begin{bmatrix} -a & -b \\ -c & -d \end{bmatrix},$$

and

$$A + (-A) = \begin{bmatrix} a - a & b - b \\ c - c & d - d \end{bmatrix} = \begin{bmatrix} 0 & 0 \\ 0 & 0 \end{bmatrix}.$$

If two matrices have the same dimensions, then they have a difference, denoted by

$$A - B,$$

which is defined to be the sum $A + (-B)$ and is therefore a matrix. Thus, to obtain the difference of two matrices of the same dimensions, you simply subtract their corresponding entries. For example,

$$\begin{bmatrix} 2 & 8 \\ -1 & 4 \end{bmatrix} - \begin{bmatrix} -3 & 2 \\ -5 & -1 \end{bmatrix} = \begin{bmatrix} 2 - (-3) & 8 - 2 \\ -1 - (-5) & 4 - (-1) \end{bmatrix} = \begin{bmatrix} 5 & 6 \\ 4 & 5 \end{bmatrix}.$$

Exercises 1–6 refer to the matrix: $\begin{bmatrix} 3 & -1 & 2 \\ 0 & 14 & 3 \\ 1 & -5 & 2 \end{bmatrix}$

In Exercises 1–4 state the entry in the given row and column.

1. First row, second column

3. Second row, second column

2. Third row, first column

4. Second row, first column

5. State the location of the other entry that is equal to the entry in the first row and first column.

6. State the location of the other entry that is equal to the entry in the third row and third column.

State the value of the given variable so that

$$\begin{bmatrix} x & y-3 \\ z+1 & 5 \end{bmatrix} = \begin{bmatrix} 2 & 3 \\ 7 & w+x \end{bmatrix}.$$

7. x 8. y 9. z 10. w

State the value of the given variable so that

$$\begin{bmatrix} a & 2 \\ 4 & b \end{bmatrix} + \begin{bmatrix} 5 & c \\ 3 & -4 \end{bmatrix} = \begin{bmatrix} 7 & -1 \\ d & 2 \end{bmatrix}.$$

11. a 12. b 13. c 14. d

State the value of the given variable so that

$$\begin{bmatrix} x & y & z+1 \\ 5 & 3 & 7 \end{bmatrix} - \begin{bmatrix} 3 & -2 & 4 \\ u & 2 & -1 \end{bmatrix} = \begin{bmatrix} 1 & 0 & 2 \\ 0 & v & w+5 \end{bmatrix}.$$

15. x 16. y 17. z 18. u 19. v 20. w

In Exercises 21–24 state the dimensions of the matrices for the given exercises.

21. Exercises 1–6

23. Exercises 11–14

22. Exercises 7–10

24. Exercises 15–20

Find the values of the variables for which the given statement is true.

A   1. $[x \quad -4] = [3 \quad y]$ 2. $\begin{bmatrix} 5 \\ x \end{bmatrix} = \begin{bmatrix} y \\ -1 \end{bmatrix}$ 3. $\begin{bmatrix} -2 & x \\ y & 5 \end{bmatrix} = \begin{bmatrix} z & 1 \\ 0 & 5 \end{bmatrix}$

4. $\begin{bmatrix} x & 2 \\ 4 & z \end{bmatrix} = \begin{bmatrix} 0 & y \\ 4 & -1 \end{bmatrix}$ 5. $\begin{bmatrix} 4 & x+1 & 2 \\ z & 1 & 7 \end{bmatrix} = \begin{bmatrix} 4 & -4 & 2 \\ 0 & 1 & 2y-3 \end{bmatrix}$

Express the indicated sum of matrices as a single matrix.

6. $[5 \quad -2] + [6 \quad 1]$

9. $\begin{bmatrix} 2 & 1 \\ 0 & -5 \end{bmatrix} + \begin{bmatrix} -3 & 0 \\ -2 & -1 \end{bmatrix}$

7. $\begin{bmatrix} -3 \\ 4 \end{bmatrix} + \begin{bmatrix} 7 \\ 2 \end{bmatrix}$

10. $\begin{bmatrix} 6 & -4 & 1 \\ -2 & -3 & -1 \end{bmatrix} + \begin{bmatrix} 1 & 3 & 2 \\ 2 & 1 & 4 \end{bmatrix}$

8. $\begin{bmatrix} 6 & -2 \\ 3 & -8 \end{bmatrix} + \begin{bmatrix} -4 & 5 \\ 2 & -7 \end{bmatrix}$

11. $\begin{bmatrix} -3 & -4 & 2 \\ 12 & -6 & 8 \end{bmatrix} + \begin{bmatrix} 10 & 3 & 0 \\ 14 & 6 & 7 \end{bmatrix}$

12–17. For the matrices in Exercises 6–11, express as a single matrix the difference when the second matrix is subtracted from the first.

Find the values of the variables so that the given statement is true.

18. $[x \quad 2] + [-1 \quad z] = [3 \quad 7]$ 19. $\begin{bmatrix} 4 \\ -x \end{bmatrix} + \begin{bmatrix} 2y \\ 3 \end{bmatrix} = \begin{bmatrix} 8 \\ 5 \end{bmatrix}$

20. $\begin{bmatrix} 2 & 3x \\ 4y & 5 \end{bmatrix} + \begin{bmatrix} 3 & -x \\ 16 & z \end{bmatrix} = \begin{bmatrix} 5 & 6 \\ 4x & 9 \end{bmatrix}$

21. $\begin{bmatrix} 3x & 5 & z \\ 5 & -2 & u \end{bmatrix} - \begin{bmatrix} 2 & 3y & x-y \\ -4 & 3 & -3 \end{bmatrix} = \begin{bmatrix} 4 & 2 & 3 \\ 9 & -5 & x+y-z \end{bmatrix}$

13–2   *properties of matrix addition*

With the definitions of the equality and the sum of two matrices (page 440), for any given natural numbers m and n we can state some addition properties of the set $\mathcal{S}_{m \times n}$ of all $m \times n$ matrices with real-number entries as follows:

Theorem. For any given natural numbers m and n, let A, B, and C be members of the set $\mathcal{S}_{m \times n}$ of all $m \times n$ matrices with real-number entries. Then:

  I. $A + B \in \mathcal{S}_{m \times n}$.   Closure Property

  II. $A + B = B + A$.   Commutative Property

  III. $(A + B) + C = A + (B + C)$.   Associative Property

  IV. There exists in $\mathcal{S}_{m \times n}$ a unique element   Additive-Identity Property
      O such that for each $A \in \mathcal{S}_{m \times n}$,
      $O + A = A$ and $A + O = A$.

  V. For each $A \in \mathcal{S}_{m \times n}$ there exists a   Additive-Inverse Property
      unique element $-A$ in $\mathcal{S}_{m \times n}$ such that

      $A + (-A) = O$ and $(-A) + A = O$.

Compare the properties listed in the preceding theorem with the axioms of addition in $\Re$ that are listed on page 29. We shall consider the proofs of these various properties only for the representative case $m = 2, n = 2$. All the properties are direct applications of the definitions that we made for the equality and the sum of two matrices together with the corresponding properties of real numbers.

PROOF OF PART I FOR $\mathcal{S}_{2 \times 2}$

By definition, the entries of $A + B$ are the sums of the corresponding entries in A and B. Since the sum of two real numbers is a real number, the entries of $A + B$ are real numbers, and therefore $A + B$ is a member of $\mathcal{S}_{2 \times 2}$.

PROOF OF PART II FOR $\mathcal{S}_{2 \times 2}$

Let $A = \begin{bmatrix} a_1 & b_1 \\ a_2 & b_2 \end{bmatrix}$ and $B = \begin{bmatrix} c_1 & d_1 \\ c_2 & d_2 \end{bmatrix}$. Then

$$A + B = \begin{bmatrix} a_1 + c_1 & b_1 + d_1 \\ a_2 + c_2 & b_2 + d_2 \end{bmatrix} \quad \text{and} \quad B + A = \begin{bmatrix} c_1 + a_1 & d_1 + b_1 \\ c_2 + a_2 & d_2 + b_2 \end{bmatrix}.$$

But by the commutative property of addition for real numbers,

$$a_1 + c_1 = c_1 + a_1, \qquad b_1 + d_1 = d_1 + b_1,$$
$$a_2 + c_2 = c_2 + a_2, \qquad b_2 + d_2 = d_2 + b_2.$$

Since each entry of the matrix $A + B$ is equal to the corresponding entry of the matrix $B + A$, by the definition of equality for matrices you have $A + B = B + A$.

Proofs of Parts III, IV, and V, for the representative case $m = 2, n = 2$, are similar and are left as exercises (Exercises 10–12, page 446). By using Part II, you need to establish only one of the equations in IV and one in V.

By using the substitution principle and the properties of equality (pages 29–30), you can also solve certain matrix equations.

EXAMPLE   Solve $X + \begin{bmatrix} 4 & 2 & 0 \\ 3 & -1 & 7 \end{bmatrix} = \begin{bmatrix} -3 & 6 & 2 \\ -1 & 5 & 4 \end{bmatrix}$ over $\mathcal{S}_{2 \times 3}$.

SOLUTION   Assume that there is a matrix $X \in \mathcal{S}_{2 \times 3}$ such that

$$X + \begin{bmatrix} 4 & 2 & 0 \\ 3 & -1 & 7 \end{bmatrix} = \begin{bmatrix} -3 & 6 & 2 \\ -1 & 5 & 4 \end{bmatrix}.$$

Then by the substitution principle, you have

$$\left(X + \begin{bmatrix} 4 & 2 & 0 \\ 3 & -1 & 7 \end{bmatrix} \right) + \begin{bmatrix} -4 & -2 & 0 \\ -3 & 1 & -7 \end{bmatrix}$$

$$= \begin{bmatrix} -3 & 6 & 2 \\ -1 & 5 & 4 \end{bmatrix} + \begin{bmatrix} -4 & -2 & 0 \\ -3 & 1 & -7 \end{bmatrix}$$

By Parts III and IV of the theorem on page 443:

$$X + \left(\begin{bmatrix} 4 & 2 & 0 \\ 3 & -1 & 7 \end{bmatrix} + \begin{bmatrix} -4 & -2 & 0 \\ -3 & 1 & -7 \end{bmatrix}\right)$$

$$= \begin{bmatrix} -3 & 6 & 2 \\ -1 & 5 & 4 \end{bmatrix} + \begin{bmatrix} -4 & -2 & 0 \\ -3 & 1 & -7 \end{bmatrix}$$

$$X + \begin{bmatrix} 0 & 0 & 0 \\ 0 & 0 & 0 \end{bmatrix} = \begin{bmatrix} -7 & 4 & 2 \\ -4 & 6 & -3 \end{bmatrix}$$

$$X = \begin{bmatrix} -7 & 4 & 2 \\ -4 & 6 & -3 \end{bmatrix}$$

CHECK Replacing X with $\begin{bmatrix} -7 & 4 & 2 \\ -4 & 6 & -3 \end{bmatrix}$ in the original equation, you get

$$\begin{bmatrix} -7 & 4 & 2 \\ -4 & 6 & -3 \end{bmatrix} + \begin{bmatrix} 4 & 2 & 0 \\ 3 & -1 & 7 \end{bmatrix} = \begin{bmatrix} -7+4 & 4+2 & 2+0 \\ -4+3 & 6-1 & -3+7 \end{bmatrix}$$

$$= \begin{bmatrix} -3 & 6 & 2 \\ -1 & 5 & 4 \end{bmatrix} \checkmark$$

$\therefore$ the solution set is $\left\{\begin{bmatrix} -7 & 4 & 2 \\ -4 & 6 & -3 \end{bmatrix}\right\}$. Answer.

ORAL EXERCISES Give a reason for each statement.

1. $([a \quad b] + [c \quad d]) + [-a \quad -b] = [a \quad b] + ([c \quad d] + [-a \quad -b])$
2. $[a \quad b] + ([c \quad d] + [-a \quad -b]) = [a \quad b] + ([-a \quad -b] + [c \quad d])$
3. $[a \quad b] + ([-a \quad -b] + [c \quad d]) = ([a \quad b] + [-a \quad -b]) + [c \quad d]$
4. $[0 \quad 0] + [c \quad d] = [c \quad d]$
5. $([a \quad b] + [c \quad d]) + [-a \quad -b] = [c \quad d]$

State the sum or difference as a single matrix.

6. $([2 \quad 3] + [5 \quad -1]) + ([-5 \quad 1] + [-2 \quad -3])$
7. $([2 \quad 5] + [2 \quad 5]) + ([2 \quad 5] + [2 \quad 5]) + [2 \quad 5]$
8. $\left(\begin{bmatrix} a & b \\ c & d \end{bmatrix} + \begin{bmatrix} e & f \\ g & h \end{bmatrix}\right) - \begin{bmatrix} a & b \\ c & d \end{bmatrix}$

WRITTEN EXERCISES Solve for the matrix X of the appropriate dimensions.

A 1. $X + \begin{bmatrix} 4 & 2 \\ 0 & -7 \end{bmatrix} = \begin{bmatrix} 9 & 3 \\ 6 & 1 \end{bmatrix}$ 3. $X - \begin{bmatrix} 2 & -1 \\ 6 & 5 \end{bmatrix} = \begin{bmatrix} -2 & -1 \\ 3 & 0 \end{bmatrix}$

2. $X + \begin{bmatrix} -1 & 3 \\ 2 & 0 \end{bmatrix} = \begin{bmatrix} 5 & 1 \\ 4 & -3 \end{bmatrix}$ 4. $X - \begin{bmatrix} 1 & 3 \\ 2 & 5 \end{bmatrix} = \begin{bmatrix} 2 & 3 \\ 1 & 5 \end{bmatrix}$

5. $X + \begin{bmatrix} 4 & 1 & 5 \\ 7 & 0 & 2 \end{bmatrix} = \begin{bmatrix} 1 & -1 & 2 \\ 3 & 0 & 6 \end{bmatrix}$ 7. $X + \begin{bmatrix} -1 & 3 & 9 \\ 2 & 6 & 5 \\ 3 & 1 & 7 \end{bmatrix} = \begin{bmatrix} 5 & 2 & 1 \\ 2 & 3 & 1 \\ 4 & 5 & 5 \end{bmatrix}$

6. $X + \begin{bmatrix} 7 & 0 & 1 \\ 2 & -4 & 3 \end{bmatrix} = \begin{bmatrix} 3 & 9 & 0 \\ 7 & 2 & 1 \end{bmatrix}$ 8. $X - \begin{bmatrix} 3 & 1 & 6 \\ 2 & 1 & 6 \\ 4 & 3 & 8 \end{bmatrix} = -\begin{bmatrix} 7 & 3 & 1 \\ 6 & 5 & 8 \\ 2 & 1 & 7 \end{bmatrix}$

B 9. If $A = [a \quad b]$, $B = [c \quad d]$, $C = [e \quad f]$, prove that $(A + B) + C = A + (B + C)$.

In Exercises 10–12 prove the given statement for the matrices:

$$A = \begin{bmatrix} a_1 & b_1 \\ a_2 & b_2 \end{bmatrix}, B = \begin{bmatrix} c_1 & d_1 \\ c_2 & d_2 \end{bmatrix}, C = \begin{bmatrix} e_1 & f_1 \\ e_2 & f_2 \end{bmatrix}.$$

10. $(A + B) + C = A + (B + C)$

11. $A + O = A$

12. $A + (-A) = O$

13–3 *product of a scalar and a matrix*

In dealing with matrices, we often refer to real numbers as scalars. We define the product of a scalar c and a matrix A, denoted by

$$cA,$$

as the matrix of the same dimensions as A whose entries are the products of c and the corresponding entries of A. For example, if $A = \begin{bmatrix} 2 & 3 \\ 1 & 0 \\ -4 & 7 \end{bmatrix}$ then

$$5A = 5\begin{bmatrix} 2 & 3 \\ 1 & 0 \\ -4 & 7 \end{bmatrix} = \begin{bmatrix} 5(2) & 5(3) \\ 5(1) & 5(0) \\ 5(-4) & 5(7) \end{bmatrix} = \begin{bmatrix} 10 & 15 \\ 5 & 0 \\ -20 & 35 \end{bmatrix}$$

and

$$-2A = -2\begin{bmatrix} 2 & 3 \\ 1 & 0 \\ -4 & 7 \end{bmatrix} = \begin{bmatrix} -2(2) & -2(3) \\ -2(1) & -2(0) \\ -2(-4) & -2(7) \end{bmatrix} = \begin{bmatrix} -4 & -6 \\ -2 & 0 \\ 8 & -14 \end{bmatrix}$$

Notice that the product of a *scalar* and a *matrix* is a *matrix*.

Products of scalars and matrices have a number of basic properties which follow from the definition above and the properties of real numbers. These basic properties are given in the following theorem.

Theorem. If $A \in \mathcal{S}_{m \times n}$ and $B \in \mathcal{S}_{m \times n}$, where m and n are any given natural numbers, and if $c \in \mathcal{R}$ and $d \in \mathcal{R}$, then:

I. $cA \in \mathcal{S}_{m \times n}$

II. $c(dA) = (cd)A$

III. $(c + d)A = cA + dA$

IV. $c(A + B) = cA + cB$

V. $1 \cdot A = A$

VI. $(-1)A = -A$

VII. $0 \cdot A = 0$

VIII. $cO = O$

As in Section 13–2, we shall consider proofs only for the representative case $m = 2$, $n = 2$. For the following sample proof we let

$$A = \begin{bmatrix} a_1 & b_1 \\ a_2 & b_2 \end{bmatrix}.$$

PROOF OF PART VI FOR $\mathcal{S}_{2 \times 2}$

$$(-1)A = (-1)\begin{bmatrix} a_1 & b_1 \\ a_2 & b_2 \end{bmatrix}$$

$$= \begin{bmatrix} (-1)a_1 & (-1)b_1 \\ (-1)a_2 & (-1)b_2 \end{bmatrix}$$

$$= \begin{bmatrix} -a_1 & -b_1 \\ -a_2 & -b_2 \end{bmatrix} = -A.$$

You should be able to supply a reason for each step given above.

Proofs of the remaining parts of this theorem for the representative case $m = 2$, $n = 2$ are similar to the one we have given. Writing them is left to you (Exercises 19–24 on page 449).

You can use parts of the foregoing theorem to help you solve some equations involving matrices.

EXAMPLE Solve over $\mathcal{S}_{3 \times 2}$: $5X - 3\begin{bmatrix} 0 & -2 \\ 1 & 2 \\ -4 & 7 \end{bmatrix} = 2\begin{bmatrix} 5 & -7 \\ 1 & -3 \\ -9 & 2 \end{bmatrix}$

SOLUTION Assuming that there is a 3×2 matrix X satisfying the equation, you first simplify the products; thus,

$$5X - \begin{bmatrix} 0 & -6 \\ 3 & 6 \\ -12 & 21 \end{bmatrix} = \begin{bmatrix} 10 & -14 \\ 2 & -6 \\ -18 & 4 \end{bmatrix}.$$

Then you add $\begin{bmatrix} 0 & -6 \\ 3 & 6 \\ -12 & 21 \end{bmatrix}$ to each member, as shown on page 448.

$$5X - \begin{bmatrix} 0 & -6 \\ 3 & 6 \\ -12 & 21 \end{bmatrix} + \begin{bmatrix} 0 & -6 \\ 3 & 6 \\ -12 & 21 \end{bmatrix} = \begin{bmatrix} 10 & -14 \\ 2 & -6 \\ -18 & 4 \end{bmatrix} + \begin{bmatrix} 0 & -6 \\ 3 & 6 \\ -12 & 21 \end{bmatrix}$$

$$5X + O = \begin{bmatrix} 10 & -20 \\ 5 & 0 \\ -30 & 25 \end{bmatrix}$$

$$X = \frac{1}{5} \begin{bmatrix} 10 & -20 \\ 5 & 0 \\ -30 & 25 \end{bmatrix} = \begin{bmatrix} 2 & -4 \\ 1 & 0 \\ -6 & 5 \end{bmatrix}$$

CHECK Replacing X with $\begin{bmatrix} 2 & -4 \\ 1 & 0 \\ -6 & 5 \end{bmatrix}$ in the original equation, you get

$$5 \begin{bmatrix} 2 & -4 \\ 1 & 0 \\ -6 & 5 \end{bmatrix} - 3 \begin{bmatrix} 0 & -2 \\ 1 & 2 \\ -4 & 7 \end{bmatrix} = \begin{bmatrix} 10 & -20 \\ 5 & 0 \\ -30 & 25 \end{bmatrix} - \begin{bmatrix} 0 & -6 \\ 3 & 6 \\ -12 & 21 \end{bmatrix}$$

$$= \begin{bmatrix} 10 & -14 \\ 2 & -6 \\ -18 & 4 \end{bmatrix} = 2 \begin{bmatrix} 5 & -7 \\ 1 & -3 \\ -9 & 2 \end{bmatrix} \quad \checkmark$$

$\therefore$ the solution set is $\left\{ \begin{bmatrix} 2 & -4 \\ 1 & 0 \\ -6 & 5 \end{bmatrix} \right\}$ Answer.

ORAL EXERCISES State the value of the given variable so that $3 \begin{bmatrix} 2 & 3 \\ 4 & x \end{bmatrix} = \begin{bmatrix} y & z \\ w & 15 \end{bmatrix}$.

1. x 2. y 3. z 4. w

State the value of the given variable so that

$$2 \begin{bmatrix} 1 & 4 \\ 3 & 0 \\ 2 & 7 \end{bmatrix} + \begin{bmatrix} x & 3 \\ y & -2 \\ 1 & -1 \end{bmatrix} = \begin{bmatrix} 3 & u \\ 5 & v \\ z & w \end{bmatrix}.$$

5. x 6. y 7. z 8. u 9. v 10. w

WRITTEN EXERCISES In Exercises 1–12 let $A = \begin{bmatrix} 3 & -2 & 0 \\ 2 & 3 & 1 \end{bmatrix}$ and $B = \begin{bmatrix} 1 & 0 & -2 \\ -3 & 4 & 6 \end{bmatrix}$. Find a 2 × 3 matrix equal to the given expression.

A   1. $4A$ 4. $7B$ 7. $4A + 3B$ 10. $A - 10B$

      2. $-3A$ 5. $3A + B$ 8. $2A + 4B$ 11. $9B - 6A$

      3. $-5B$ 6. $A + 2B$ 9. $3A - B$ 12. $8B - 7A$

In Exercises 13–18 let $A = \begin{bmatrix} 1 & 3 \\ 0 & -2 \end{bmatrix}$ and $B = \begin{bmatrix} 1 & -3 \\ 2 & -4 \end{bmatrix}$. Solve the given equation over $S_{2\times2}$.

B   13. $X + A = 2B$

      14. $X - A = 3B$

      15. $3X - 2A - B = 0$

      16. $2X + 5B - A = 0$

      17. $2X + A = X - B$

      18. $3X - 2A = B + X$

In Exercises 19–24 prove the statement for

$$A = \begin{bmatrix} a_1 & b_1 \\ a_2 & b_2 \end{bmatrix}, \; B = \begin{bmatrix} c_1 & d_1 \\ c_2 & d_2 \end{bmatrix}, \; c \in \mathcal{R}, \text{ and } d \in \mathcal{R}.$$

19. $cA \in S_{2\times2}$

20. $c(dA) = (cd)A$

21. $(c + d)A = cA + dA$

22. $c(A + B) = cA + cB$

23. $1 \cdot A = A$

24. $0 \cdot A = O$ and $c \cdot O = O$

programming in BASIC

Earlier we used variables with single subscripts in handling lists. BASIC also provides variables with two subscripts for use in handling tables. Try this program:

```
10  FOR R=1 TO 3
20  FOR C=1 TO 4
30  READ A(R,C)
40  PRINT A(R,C);
50  NEXT C
60  PRINT
70  NEXT R
80  DATA 10,11,12,13,14,15,16,17,18,19,20,21
90  END
```

(DIMension statements are needed if the table is to be more than 10 by 10.) Insert these lines in the preceding program

```
84  PRINT
85  PRINT ''A(2,3) ='';A(2,3)
86  PRINT ''A(3,2) ='';A(3,2)
```

and run it again.

Change the following lines in the program and run it again.

```
10  FOR R=1 TO 4
20  FOR C=1 TO 3
```

When a table, or array, is used as a matrix, BASIC provides several special statements that save a great deal of time. However, when the MATrix statements are used on some systems, there must be a DIMension statement for every matrix that appears in the program, no matter what size.

In the preceding program, make the changes

```
10   DIM A(3,4)
20   MAT READ A
30   MAT PRINT A;
40
50
60
70
```

and run it again. The semicolon in line 30 will make the entries of the matrix print close together. If the semicolon is omitted, the entries will print in the five regular zones. (Lines 40, 50, 60, 70 are deleted by typing only the line number followed by RETURN.) Notice that DATA for a matrix is listed row by row.

To illustrate multiplication of a matrix by a scalar, delete lines 84, 85, 86 and make these changes:

```
10   DIM A(3,4),P(3,4)
40   PRINT ''    4*A''
50   MAT P=(4)*A
60   MAT PRINT P;
```

(Note that the scalar in line 50 must be in parentheses.)

To illustrate addition and subtraction of two matrices, try this program:

```
10    DIM A(3,4),B(3,4),C(3,4)
20    MAT READ A,B
30    PRINT ''    A''
40    MAT PRINT A;
50    PRINT ''    B''
60    MAT PRINT B;
70    MAT C=A+B
80    PRINT ''    A+B''
90    MAT PRINT C;
100   MAT C=A−B
110   PRINT ''    A−B''
120   MAT PRINT C;
130   DATA 21,20,19,18,17,16,15,14,13,12,11,10
140   DATA 10,11,12,13,14,15,16,17,18,19,20,21
150   END
```

EXERCISES

1. Find the sum and the difference of each pair of matrices given in Exercises 6–11 on page 443.

2. Find the additive inverse of matrix A given above, and verify that $A + (-A) = 0$.

3. Use the computer to check your solutions of Exercises 1–12 on page 448.

13-4 *product of two matrices*

Before introducing the definition of the product of two matrices in general, let us consider the two matrices

$$A_{1\times3} = [a \quad b \quad c] \quad \text{and} \quad B_{3\times2} = \begin{bmatrix} x_1 & x_2 \\ y_1 & y_2 \\ z_1 & z_2 \end{bmatrix}.$$

Suppose that the numbers a, b, and c represent the price per package of frozen strawberries, peaches, and apricots charged by a supermarket, while x_1, y_1, and z_1 represent the number of packages of each sold the first week, respectively, and x_2, y_2, z_2 the numbers sold the second week. How much money would the supermarket collect for these items? For the first week, the total amount collected for the strawberries is $a \cdot x_1$, for the peaches $b \cdot y_1$, and for the apricots $c \cdot z_1$. By adding these products, you obtain the total amount collected, $ax_1 + by_1 + cz_1$. Similarly, for the second week, you have a total collection of $ax_2 + by_2 + cz_2$.

The process of adding the products obtained by multiplying the elements of a row in one matrix by the corresponding elements of a column in another matrix suggests a fruitful way of defining the product of two matrices. We may say that the product of $A_{1\times3}$ and $B_{3\times2}$ shown above is

$$C_{1\times2} = [ax_1 + by_1 + cz_1 \quad ax_2 + by_2 + cz_2].$$

The product of two 2×2 matrices A and B, denoted by

$$A \times B \quad \text{or} \quad A \cdot B \quad \text{or} \quad AB,$$

is defined as follows:

If $A = \begin{bmatrix} a_1 & b_1 \\ a_2 & b_2 \end{bmatrix}$ and $B = \begin{bmatrix} c_1 & d_1 \\ c_2 & d_2 \end{bmatrix}$, then:

$$A \times B = AB = \begin{bmatrix} a_1 & b_1 \\ a_2 & b_2 \end{bmatrix} \times \begin{bmatrix} c_1 & d_1 \\ c_2 & d_2 \end{bmatrix}$$

$$= \begin{bmatrix} a_1c_1 + b_1c_2 & a_1d_1 + b_1d_2 \\ a_2c_1 + b_2c_2 & a_2d_1 + b_2d_2 \end{bmatrix}.$$

Notice that the entries of a given row of A, say the ith row, are multiplied by the entries of a given column of B, say the jth column, in order, and these products are then added to obtain the entry in the ith row and jth column of $A \times B$. Thus, the multiplication of two matrices can be described as ''row by column'' multiplication.

As an example, let us find (at the top of page 452)

$$\begin{bmatrix} 3 & 2 \\ 5 & 4 \end{bmatrix} \times \begin{bmatrix} -2 & 3 \\ 1 & 6 \end{bmatrix}$$

by displaying the computation of each entry in the product, one at a time, in red. Notice that we may omit the times sign between the matrices.

1. First row, first column:

$$\begin{bmatrix} 3 & 2 \end{bmatrix}\begin{bmatrix} -2 \\ 1 \end{bmatrix} = \begin{bmatrix} 3 \times (-2) + 2 \times 1 \end{bmatrix} = \begin{bmatrix} -6 + 2 \end{bmatrix} = \begin{bmatrix} -4 \end{bmatrix}$$

2. First row, second column:

$$\begin{bmatrix} 3 & 2 \end{bmatrix}\begin{bmatrix} 3 \\ 6 \end{bmatrix} = \begin{bmatrix} -4 & 3 \times 3 + 2 \times 6 \end{bmatrix} = \begin{bmatrix} -4 & 9 + 12 \end{bmatrix} = \begin{bmatrix} -4 & 21 \end{bmatrix}$$

3. Second row, first column:

$$\begin{bmatrix} 5 & 4 \end{bmatrix}\begin{bmatrix} -2 \\ 1 \end{bmatrix} = \begin{bmatrix} -4 & & 21 \\ 5 \times (-2) + 4 \times 1 \end{bmatrix} = \begin{bmatrix} -4 & 21 \\ -10 + 4 \end{bmatrix} = \begin{bmatrix} -4 & 21 \\ -6 \end{bmatrix}$$

4. Second row, second column:

$$\begin{bmatrix} 5 & 4 \end{bmatrix}\begin{bmatrix} 3 \\ 6 \end{bmatrix} = \begin{bmatrix} -4 & 21 \\ -6 & 5 \times 3 + 4 \times 6 \end{bmatrix} = \begin{bmatrix} -4 & 21 \\ -6 & 15 + 24 \end{bmatrix} = \begin{bmatrix} -4 & 21 \\ -6 & 39 \end{bmatrix}$$

Putting Steps 1–4 together, we have

$$\begin{bmatrix} 3 & 2 \\ 5 & 4 \end{bmatrix}\begin{bmatrix} -2 & 3 \\ 1 & 6 \end{bmatrix} = \begin{bmatrix} -4 & 21 \\ -6 & 39 \end{bmatrix}.$$

Ordinarily, of course, the steps are not all shown in detail.

In general, the product AB of any two matrices A and B, where A has the same number of *columns* as B has *rows*, can be defined through "row by column" multiplication. The number of rows in the product matrix AB will be the same as the number of rows in A, and the number of columns in AB will be the same as the number of columns in B. Thus,

$$A_{m \times p} \times B_{p \times n} = C_{m \times n}.$$

If the number of *columns* in A is not equal to the number of *rows* in B, then the product of A and B is not defined. Notice that $B_{p \times n} \times A_{m \times p}$ is not defined unless $n = m$.

In particular, the product of a 2×2 and a 2×1 matrix is defined as follows:

If $A = \begin{bmatrix} a_1 & b_1 \\ a_2 & b_2 \end{bmatrix}$ and $B = \begin{bmatrix} x \\ y \end{bmatrix}$, then

$$AB = \begin{bmatrix} a_1 & b_1 \\ a_2 & b_2 \end{bmatrix}\begin{bmatrix} x \\ y \end{bmatrix} = \begin{bmatrix} a_1 x + b_1 y \\ a_2 x + b_2 y \end{bmatrix}.$$

As you can see, the product of a 2 × 2 matrix and a 2 × 1 matrix is a 2 × 1 matrix. Later in this chapter, we shall use products of 2 × 2 and 2 × 1 matrices in connection with systems of equations.

As with numbers, for square matrices A we use the symbol A^2 to mean $A \times A$.

ORAL EXERCISES   In the product

$$\begin{bmatrix} 1 & -3 \\ 5 & 2 \end{bmatrix} \begin{bmatrix} 4 & 2 \\ -1 & 6 \end{bmatrix} = \begin{bmatrix} 1 \times x + y \times (-1) & z \times 2 + (-3) \times w \\ 5 \times 4 + u \times v & a \times b + c \times d \end{bmatrix},$$

state the value you would substitute for the given letter.

1. x	3. z	5. u	7. a	9. c
2. y	4. w	6. v	8. b	10. d

WRITTEN EXERCISES   For $A = \begin{bmatrix} 4 & -3 \\ 2 & 1 \end{bmatrix}$, $B = \begin{bmatrix} 1 & -2 \\ 2 & -1 \end{bmatrix}$, and $C = \begin{bmatrix} 2 & 3 \\ -1 & 2 \end{bmatrix}$, find a 2 × 2 matrix equal to the given product.

A
1. AB	4. CA	7. A^2	10. $C(A + B)$
2. BA	5. BC	8. B^2	11. $(A + B)^2$
3. AC	6. CB	9. $(A + B)C$	12. $(C - A)^2$

In Exercises 13–18 determine whether or not the matrix given in red is a solution of the given matrix equation.

EXAMPLE $\begin{bmatrix} 2 & -1 \\ 1 & 2 \end{bmatrix} \begin{bmatrix} x \\ y \end{bmatrix} = \begin{bmatrix} 0 \\ 5 \end{bmatrix}$; $\begin{bmatrix} 1 \\ 2 \end{bmatrix}$

SOLUTION   Replace $\begin{bmatrix} x \\ y \end{bmatrix}$ with $\begin{bmatrix} 1 \\ 2 \end{bmatrix}$ and simplify the left-hand member.

$$\begin{bmatrix} 2 & -1 \\ 1 & 2 \end{bmatrix} \begin{bmatrix} 1 \\ 2 \end{bmatrix} = \begin{bmatrix} 2 \times 1 + (-1) \times 2 \\ 1 \times 1 + 2 \times 2 \end{bmatrix} = \begin{bmatrix} 0 \\ 5 \end{bmatrix}.$$

CHECK $\begin{bmatrix} 0 \\ 5 \end{bmatrix} \overset{?}{=} \begin{bmatrix} 0 \\ 5 \end{bmatrix}$. ✓   The given matrix is a solution. **Answer.**

13. $\begin{bmatrix} 3 & 4 \\ 2 & -2 \end{bmatrix} \begin{bmatrix} x \\ y \end{bmatrix} = \begin{bmatrix} -6 \\ 6 \end{bmatrix}$; $\begin{bmatrix} 2 \\ -1 \end{bmatrix}$ 15. $\begin{bmatrix} 1 & 1 \\ -2 & 3 \end{bmatrix} \begin{bmatrix} x \\ y \end{bmatrix} = \begin{bmatrix} -3 \\ 12 \end{bmatrix}$; $\begin{bmatrix} -3 \\ 2 \end{bmatrix}$

14. $\begin{bmatrix} 3 & 1 \\ 4 & 2 \end{bmatrix} \begin{bmatrix} x \\ y \end{bmatrix} = \begin{bmatrix} 6 \\ 8 \end{bmatrix}$; $\begin{bmatrix} 2 \\ 0 \end{bmatrix}$ 16. $\begin{bmatrix} 2 & -1 \\ 1 & 3 \end{bmatrix} \begin{bmatrix} x \\ y \end{bmatrix} = \begin{bmatrix} 8 \\ 1 \end{bmatrix}$; $\begin{bmatrix} 3 \\ -2 \end{bmatrix}$

B   17. $X^2 - X = 0$; $\begin{bmatrix} 0 & 1 \\ 1 & 0 \end{bmatrix}$ 18. $X^2 + X - \begin{bmatrix} 2 & 0 \\ 1 & 0 \end{bmatrix} = 0$; $\begin{bmatrix} 1 & 0 \\ 1 & -1 \end{bmatrix}$

Simplify each product.

19. $\begin{bmatrix} 3 & 0 & 2 \\ 1 & -4 & 0 \end{bmatrix} \begin{bmatrix} 2 & 0 \\ 2 & -3 \\ -1 & 1 \end{bmatrix}$ 20. $\begin{bmatrix} 1 & 2 & 4 \end{bmatrix} \begin{bmatrix} 3 \\ 2 \\ 1 \end{bmatrix}$ 21. $\begin{bmatrix} 3 \\ 2 \\ 1 \end{bmatrix} \begin{bmatrix} 1 & 2 & 4 \end{bmatrix}$

22. Show that for any real x and y, you have

$$\begin{bmatrix} 1 & 0 \\ 0 & 1 \end{bmatrix} \begin{bmatrix} x \\ y \end{bmatrix} = \begin{bmatrix} x \\ y \end{bmatrix} \text{ and } \begin{bmatrix} x & y \end{bmatrix} \begin{bmatrix} 1 & 0 \\ 0 & 1 \end{bmatrix} = \begin{bmatrix} x & y \end{bmatrix}.$$

23. Let the matrix $A = \begin{bmatrix} 17 & 19 \\ 2 & 3 \end{bmatrix}$ represent the fact that wristwatch Model I has 17 jewels and 2 straps, while Model II has 19 jewels and 3 straps. Let the matrix $B = \begin{bmatrix} 30 & 40 & 50 \\ 20 & 15 & 10 \end{bmatrix}$ represent the fact that a factory produced 30 Model I wristwatches on Monday, 40 on Tuesday, and 50 on Wednesday, and on the same days produced 20, 15, and 10 sets of the Model II wristwatch, respectively. Simplify the product AB and tell what its entries represent.

13–5 *properties of matrix multiplication*

Although multiplication of matrices with real-number entries has some of the properties of multiplication of real numbers, there are some important differences. We shall illustrate these by considering multiplication in the set $\mathcal{S}_{2\times2}$.

EXAMPLE 1   For $A = \begin{bmatrix} 2 & 1 \\ -4 & -2 \end{bmatrix}$ and $B = \begin{bmatrix} -1 & -3 \\ 2 & 6 \end{bmatrix}$, find **(a)** AB, and **(b)** BA.

SOLUTION   **a.** $AB = \begin{bmatrix} 2 & 1 \\ -4 & -2 \end{bmatrix} \begin{bmatrix} -1 & -3 \\ 2 & 6 \end{bmatrix} = \begin{bmatrix} -2+2 & -6+6 \\ 4-4 & 12-12 \end{bmatrix} = \begin{bmatrix} 0 & 0 \\ 0 & 0 \end{bmatrix}.$

Answer.

b. $BA = \begin{bmatrix} -1 & -3 \\ 2 & 6 \end{bmatrix} \begin{bmatrix} 2 & 1 \\ -4 & -2 \end{bmatrix} = \begin{bmatrix} -2+12 & -1+6 \\ 4-24 & 2-12 \end{bmatrix}$

$= \begin{bmatrix} 10 & 5 \\ -20 & -10 \end{bmatrix}.$ Answer.

Notice in Example 1 that $A \neq O$ and $B \neq O$ but $AB = O$. Thus, in $\mathcal{S}_{2\times2}$ the product of two matrices can be the zero matrix without either factor being the zero matrix!

Notice also in Example 1 that $BA \neq AB$. Therefore, multiplication in $\mathcal{S}_{2\times2}$ *is not commutative.* For this reason, you must be careful to specify the order of the factors in matrix multiplication. To specify the product AB, for example, you say that you right-multiply A by B or that you left-multiply B by A. Some special matrix products, however, do not depend on the order of the factors.

EXAMPLE 2   If $I_{2\times2} = \begin{bmatrix} 1 & 0 \\ 0 & 1 \end{bmatrix}$ and $A = \begin{bmatrix} a_1 & b_1 \\ a_2 & b_2 \end{bmatrix}$, simplify **(a)** $I_{2\times2}A$, and **(b)** $AI_{2\times2}$.

SOLUTION   **a.** $I_{2\times2}A = \begin{bmatrix} 1 & 0 \\ 0 & 1 \end{bmatrix}\begin{bmatrix} a_1 & b_1 \\ a_2 & b_2 \end{bmatrix} = \begin{bmatrix} a_1 + 0 & b_1 + 0 \\ 0 + a_2 & 0 + b_2 \end{bmatrix} = \begin{bmatrix} a_1 & b_1 \\ a_2 & b_2 \end{bmatrix}$.   Answer.

b. $AI_{2\times2} = \begin{bmatrix} a_1 & b_1 \\ a_2 & b_2 \end{bmatrix}\begin{bmatrix} 1 & 0 \\ 0 & 1 \end{bmatrix} = \begin{bmatrix} a_1 + 0 & 0 + b_1 \\ a_2 + 0 & 0 + b_2 \end{bmatrix} = \begin{bmatrix} a_1 & b_1 \\ a_2 & b_2 \end{bmatrix}$.   Answer.

As Example 2 demonstrates, not only do the products of *some* matrices AB in $\mathcal{S}_{2\times2}$ commute, but also the product of any 2×2 matrix A and

$$I_{2\times2} = \begin{bmatrix} 1 & 0 \\ 0 & 1 \end{bmatrix}$$

always is the matrix A. Thus, $I_{2\times2}$ is an identity matrix for multiplication in $\mathcal{S}_{2\times2}$:

$$I_{2\times2}A = AI_{2\times2} = A$$

This property and some other properties of multiplication of 2×2 matrices are listed in the following theorem.

Theorem. If $A \in \mathcal{S}_{2\times2}$, $B \in \mathcal{S}_{2\times2}$, $C \in \mathcal{S}_{2\times2}$, and $a \in \mathcal{R}$, then:

I. $AB \in \mathcal{S}_{2\times2}$
II. $(AB)C = A(BC)$
III. $A(B + C) = AB + AC$
IV. $(B + C)A = BA + CA$

V. $I_{2\times2}A = AI_{2\times2} = A$
VI. $a(AB) = (aA)B = A(aB)$
VII. $O_{2\times2}A = AO_{2\times2} = O_{2\times2}$

EXAMPLE 3   Show that if $A = \begin{bmatrix} 2 & 1 \\ -4 & -2 \end{bmatrix}$ and $B = \begin{bmatrix} -1 & -3 \\ 2 & 6 \end{bmatrix}$, then

(a) $(A + B)(A - B) \neq A^2 - B^2$, but
(b) $(A + B)(A - B) = A^2 - AB + BA - B^2$.

SOLUTION   **a.** First: $A + B = \begin{bmatrix} 2 & 1 \\ -4 & -2 \end{bmatrix} + \begin{bmatrix} -1 & -3 \\ 2 & 6 \end{bmatrix} = \begin{bmatrix} 1 & -2 \\ -2 & 4 \end{bmatrix}$

$A - B = \begin{bmatrix} 2 & 1 \\ -4 & -2 \end{bmatrix} - \begin{bmatrix} -1 & -3 \\ 2 & 6 \end{bmatrix} = \begin{bmatrix} 3 & 4 \\ -6 & -8 \end{bmatrix}$

$(A + B)(A - B) = \begin{bmatrix} 1 & -2 \\ -2 & 4 \end{bmatrix}\begin{bmatrix} 3 & 4 \\ -6 & -8 \end{bmatrix} = \begin{bmatrix} 15 & 20 \\ -30 & -40 \end{bmatrix}$

Next: $A^2 = \begin{bmatrix} 2 & 1 \\ -4 & -2 \end{bmatrix}\begin{bmatrix} 2 & 1 \\ -4 & -2 \end{bmatrix} = \begin{bmatrix} 0 & 0 \\ 0 & 0 \end{bmatrix}$

$B^2 = \begin{bmatrix} -1 & -3 \\ 2 & 6 \end{bmatrix}\begin{bmatrix} -1 & -3 \\ 2 & 6 \end{bmatrix} = \begin{bmatrix} -5 & -15 \\ 10 & 30 \end{bmatrix}$

(Solution continued on page 456.)

$$A^2 - B^2 = \begin{bmatrix} 0 & 0 \\ 0 & 0 \end{bmatrix} - \begin{bmatrix} -5 & -15 \\ 10 & 30 \end{bmatrix} = \begin{bmatrix} 5 & 15 \\ -10 & -30 \end{bmatrix}$$

Since $\begin{bmatrix} 15 & 30 \\ -30 & -40 \end{bmatrix} \neq \begin{bmatrix} 5 & 15 \\ -10 & -30 \end{bmatrix}$, you have

$$(A + B)(A - B) \neq A^2 - B^2. \quad \textbf{Answer.}$$

b. From Example 1 on page 454 you have

$$-AB + BA = -\begin{bmatrix} 0 & 0 \\ 0 & 0 \end{bmatrix} + \begin{bmatrix} 10 & 5 \\ -20 & -10 \end{bmatrix} = \begin{bmatrix} 10 & 5 \\ -20 & -10 \end{bmatrix},$$

so that $A^2 - AB + BA - B^2 = A^2 - B^2 - AB + BA$

$$= \begin{bmatrix} 5 & 15 \\ -10 & -30 \end{bmatrix} + \begin{bmatrix} 10 & 5 \\ -20 & -10 \end{bmatrix} = \begin{bmatrix} 15 & 20 \\ -30 & -40 \end{bmatrix}.$$

Also since $(A + B)(A - B) = \begin{bmatrix} 15 & 20 \\ -30 & -40 \end{bmatrix}$, you have

$$(A + B)(A - B) = A^2 - AB + BA - B^2. \quad \textbf{Answer.}$$

To understand the results in Example 3, notice that by the distributive property you have

$$(A + B)(A - B) = A(A - B) + B(A - B) = A^2 - AB + BA - B^2.$$

WRITTEN EXERCISES   In Exercises 1–20 let

$$A = \begin{bmatrix} 1 & 3 \\ 2 & 6 \end{bmatrix}, \quad B = \begin{bmatrix} -1 & 2 \\ 1 & -2 \end{bmatrix}, \quad \text{and} \quad C = \begin{bmatrix} -2 & -1 \\ -1 & -2 \end{bmatrix}.$$

By computing each expression, determine whether or not the given statement is true for the given matrices.

A   1. $(AB)C = A(BC)$

2. $AC = O$

3. $BC = O$

4. $CB = O$

5. $AC = CA$

6. $AB = BA$

7. $BC = CB$

8. $A(B + C) = (B + C)A$

9. $(2A)C = A(2C)$

10. $(-A)C = A(-C)$

11. $A(C + B) = A(B + C)$

12. $A(C + B) = AC + AB$

13. $(A + B)C = AC + BC$

14. $B^2 = (-B)^2$

15. $B^2 + B = B(B + I)$

16. $AC + C^2 = (A + C)C$

B 17. $(A - B)^2 = A^2 - 2AB + B^2$ 19. $(A + B)(A - B) = A^2 - B^2$

18. $(A - C)^2 = A^2 - 2AC + C^2$ 20. $(B + C)^2 = B^2 + 2BC + C^2$

By letting $A = \begin{bmatrix} a_1 & b_1 \\ a_2 & b_2 \end{bmatrix}$, $B = \begin{bmatrix} c_1 & d_1 \\ c_2 & d_2 \end{bmatrix}$, and $C = \begin{bmatrix} e_1 & f_1 \\ e_2 & f_2 \end{bmatrix}$, prove each statement for all matrices in $S_{2 \times 2}$ and $a \in \mathcal{R}$.

21. $AB \in S_{2 \times 2}$

22. $(AB)C = A(BC)$

23. $A(B + C) = AB + AC$

24. $(B + C)A = BA + CA$

25. $a(AB) = (aA)B$

26. $a(AB) = A(aB)$

27. $AO_{2 \times 2} = O_{2 \times 2}$

28. $O_{2 \times 2}A = O_{2 \times 2}$

SELF-TEST 1   Give the meaning of each of the following.

1. matrix

2. scalar

3. dimensions of a matrix

4. negative of a matrix

Objective 1, page 439   Simplify:

5. $\begin{bmatrix} 2 & 1 & 3 \\ -1 & -4 & 5 \end{bmatrix} + \begin{bmatrix} 0 & 2 & -1 \\ 2 & 4 & -3 \end{bmatrix}$ 6. $\begin{bmatrix} 1 & 5 \\ -3 & 0 \\ 2 & -4 \end{bmatrix} - \begin{bmatrix} -2 & 0 \\ -4 & 2 \\ 1 & 3 \end{bmatrix}$

Objective 2, page 439   7. If $A = \begin{bmatrix} 2 & 1 \\ 4 & -3 \end{bmatrix}$ and $B = \begin{bmatrix} -5 & -2 \\ 0 & 2 \end{bmatrix}$, find a 2 × 2 matrix equal to $2A + 3B$.

Objective 3, page 439   Solve over $S_{2 \times 2}$:

8. $X + \begin{bmatrix} 3 & -1 \\ 2 & 4 \end{bmatrix} = \begin{bmatrix} 4 & 0 \\ 3 & -7 \end{bmatrix}$ 9. $2X + 5 \begin{bmatrix} 1 & 0 \\ 3 & 6 \end{bmatrix} = 5X - 3 \begin{bmatrix} 2 & 1 \\ 0 & 1 \end{bmatrix}$

Objective 4, page 439   10. Simplify: $\begin{bmatrix} 2 & 4 \\ -1 & -5 \end{bmatrix} \begin{bmatrix} x \\ y \end{bmatrix}$

Check your answers with those printed at the back of the book.

programming in BASIC

BASIC also provides for multiplication of matrices. Study this program:

```
10   DIM  A(3,3),B(3,3),P(3,3)
20   MAT READ A,B
30   PRINT "    A"
40   MAT PRINT A;
50   PRINT "    B"
60   MAT PRINT B;
70   MAT P=A*B
```

(Program continued on page 458.)

```
80   PRINT "   A*B"
90   MAT PRINT P;
100  MAT P=B*A
110  PRINT "   B*A"
120  MAT PRINT P;
130  DATA 11,12,13,14,15,16,17,18,19
140  DATA 39,38,37,36,35,34,33,32,31
150  END
```

1. Rewrite the given program to find the products of two 4 × 4 matrices. Supply thirty-two two-digit numbers as DATA.

2. Matrices can also be input. Try this program:

```
10   DIM A(3,4)
20   MAT INPUT A
30   MAT PRINT A;
25   PRINT
40   END
```

The computer will print only one question mark, but you are to respond by typing in 12 numbers for the 3 × 4 matrix.

3. Rewrite the text program so that you can INPUT the two matrices to be multiplied.

4. Use the computer to check your answers to Exercises 1–12 on page 453.

matrices and linear systems

After completing the next section, you should be able to:
1. Determine the inverse of a nonsingular square matrix of order 2.
2. Use the inverse of a matrix to solve a matrix equation.
3. Write a linear system of equations in matrix form.
4. Use a matrix equation to solve a linear system.

13–6   *matrix solution of a linear system*

Every nonzero real number r has a multiplicative inverse. That is, for each $r \in \mathcal{R}$, $r \neq 0$, there is a number $r^{-1} \in \mathcal{R}$ for which

$$rr^{-1} = 1 \quad \text{and} \quad r^{-1}r = 1.$$

Does every nonzero 2 × 2 matrix A with real-number entries also have a multiplicative inverse? That is, for each $A \in \mathcal{S}_{2\times 2}$, $A \neq O$, is there a matrix $A^{-1} \in \mathcal{S}_{2\times 2}$ for which

$$AA^{-1} = I \quad \text{and} \quad A^{-1}A = I?$$

You can readily see, for example, that the matrix $A = \begin{bmatrix} 3 & 0 \\ 0 & 3 \end{bmatrix}$ has a multiplicative inverse $A^{-1} = \begin{bmatrix} \frac{1}{3} & 0 \\ 0 & \frac{1}{3} \end{bmatrix}$, since

$$\begin{bmatrix} 3 & 0 \\ 0 & 3 \end{bmatrix} \begin{bmatrix} \frac{1}{3} & 0 \\ 0 & \frac{1}{3} \end{bmatrix} = \begin{bmatrix} 1 & 0 \\ 0 & 1 \end{bmatrix} \quad \text{and} \quad \begin{bmatrix} \frac{1}{3} & 0 \\ 0 & \frac{1}{3} \end{bmatrix} \begin{bmatrix} 3 & 0 \\ 0 & 3 \end{bmatrix} = \begin{bmatrix} 1 & 0 \\ 0 & 1 \end{bmatrix}$$

In general, for 2 × 2 matrices, given $A = \begin{bmatrix} a_1 & b_1 \\ a_2 & b_2 \end{bmatrix}$, let us try to find $A^{-1} = \begin{bmatrix} x_1 & y_1 \\ x_2 & y_2 \end{bmatrix}$ such that

$$\begin{aligned} AA^{-1} &= \begin{bmatrix} a_1 & b_1 \\ a_2 & b_2 \end{bmatrix} \begin{bmatrix} x_1 & y_1 \\ x_2 & y_2 \end{bmatrix} \\ &= \begin{bmatrix} a_1 x_1 + b_1 x_2 & a_1 y_1 + b_1 y_2 \\ a_2 x_1 + b_2 x_2 & a_2 y_1 + b_2 y_2 \end{bmatrix} = I_{2 \times 2} = \begin{bmatrix} 1 & 0 \\ 0 & 1 \end{bmatrix}. \end{aligned}$$

This is true if and only if

$$a_1 x_1 + b_1 x_2 = 1, \quad a_1 y_1 + b_1 y_2 = 0,$$
$$a_2 x_1 + b_2 x_2 = 0, \quad a_2 y_1 + b_2 y_2 = 1.$$

Recall that, in Chapter 4, we used determinants to solve systems of equations. If the determinant of coefficients in this system, $\begin{vmatrix} a_1 & b_1 \\ a_2 & b_2 \end{vmatrix}$ is not equal to zero, that is, if $a_1 b_2 - a_2 b_1 \neq 0$, then these equations can be solved for x_1, x_2, y_1, and y_2 to produce

$$x_1 = \frac{b_2}{a_1 b_2 - a_2 b_1}, \quad y_1 = \frac{-b_1}{a_1 b_2 - a_2 b_1},$$

$$x_2 = \frac{-a_2}{a_1 b_2 - a_2 b_1}, \quad y_2 = \frac{a_1}{a_1 b_2 - a_2 b_1}.$$

You can check that with these values for x_1, x_2, y_1, and y_2, not only do you have $AA^{-1} = I_{2 \times 2}$, but also (somewhat surprisingly, since products AB of matrices do not ordinarily commute) you have $A^{-1}A = I_{2 \times 2}$. (See Exercises 16 and 17, page 462.)

With each square matrix $\begin{bmatrix} a_1 & b_1 \\ a_2 & b_2 \end{bmatrix}$ we associate a particular real number, namely, the determinant $\begin{vmatrix} a_1 & b_1 \\ a_2 & b_2 \end{vmatrix}$, and we write

$$\det \begin{bmatrix} a_1 & b_1 \\ a_2 & b_2 \end{bmatrix} = \begin{vmatrix} a_1 & b_1 \\ a_2 & b_2 \end{vmatrix} = a_1 b_2 - a_2 b_1.$$

The pairing of each square matrix with its determinant constitutes a function, since associated with each such matrix is one and only one real number. The symbol "det A" (read "determinant of A") represents the element in the range of the function det associated with the matrix A in its domain.

Because each denominator in the preceding equations for x_1, x_2, y_1, and y_2 is det A, you can see that

$$A^{-1} = \frac{1}{\det A} \begin{bmatrix} b_2 & -b_1 \\ -a_2 & a_1 \end{bmatrix}.$$

If det $A = 0$, then the equations for x_1, x_2, y_1, and y_2 have no solution (see Exercise 19, page 462) and so such a matrix A (called a singular matrix) has no inverse. If det $A \neq 0$, then A is said to be nonsingular or invertible.

Notice that, to find A^{-1} from A, you interchange a_1 and b_2, replace a_2 and b_1 with their negatives, and multiply by the reciprocal of det A.

EXAMPLE 1   If $A = \begin{bmatrix} 3 & 6 \\ 2 & 5 \end{bmatrix}$, find A^{-1}.

SOLUTION   Note first that det $A = 3 \times 5 - 2 \times 6 = 15 - 12 = 3$, so that det $A \neq 0$. Then

$$A^{-1} = \tfrac{1}{3} \begin{bmatrix} 5 & -6 \\ -2 & 3 \end{bmatrix} = \begin{bmatrix} \frac{5}{3} & -2 \\ -\frac{2}{3} & 1 \end{bmatrix}.$$

CHECK $\begin{bmatrix} 3 & 6 \\ 2 & 5 \end{bmatrix} \begin{bmatrix} \frac{5}{3} & -2 \\ -\frac{2}{3} & 1 \end{bmatrix} = \begin{bmatrix} 5 - 4 & -6 + 6 \\ \frac{10}{3} - \frac{10}{3} & -4 + 5 \end{bmatrix} = \begin{bmatrix} 1 & 0 \\ 0 & 1 \end{bmatrix}$ ✓

$\therefore A^{-1} = \begin{bmatrix} \frac{5}{3} & -2 \\ -\frac{2}{3} & 1 \end{bmatrix}$.   Answer.

Matrix equations in the form $AX = B$ may be solved using inverse matrices in the following way:

$$AX = B, \quad A^{-1}AX = A^{-1}B, \quad IX = A^{-1}B, \quad X = A^{-1}B.$$

EXAMPLE 2   Solve the following equation for the matrix X.

$$\begin{bmatrix} 2 & -3 \\ 4 & -5 \end{bmatrix} X = \begin{bmatrix} 8 & -6 \\ 14 & -8 \end{bmatrix}$$

SOLUTION   1. First, to find the inverse of $\begin{bmatrix} 2 & -3 \\ 4 & -5 \end{bmatrix}$, note that its determinant is $-10 + 12$, or 2. Then

$$\begin{bmatrix} 2 & -3 \\ 4 & -5 \end{bmatrix}^{-1} = \tfrac{1}{2} \begin{bmatrix} -5 & 3 \\ -4 & 2 \end{bmatrix} = \begin{bmatrix} -\frac{5}{2} & \frac{3}{2} \\ -2 & 1 \end{bmatrix}.$$

2. Next, left-multiply each member of the given equation by this inverse.

$$\begin{bmatrix} -\frac{5}{2} & \frac{3}{2} \\ -2 & 1 \end{bmatrix} \begin{bmatrix} 2 & -3 \\ 4 & -5 \end{bmatrix} X = \begin{bmatrix} -\frac{5}{2} & \frac{3}{2} \\ -2 & 1 \end{bmatrix} \begin{bmatrix} 8 & -6 \\ 14 & -8 \end{bmatrix}$$

$$\begin{bmatrix} 1 & 0 \\ 0 & 1 \end{bmatrix} X = \begin{bmatrix} 1 & 3 \\ -2 & 4 \end{bmatrix}$$

$$X = \begin{bmatrix} 1 & 3 \\ -2 & 4 \end{bmatrix}$$

CHECK $\begin{bmatrix} 2 & -3 \\ 4 & -5 \end{bmatrix}\begin{bmatrix} 1 & 3 \\ -2 & 4 \end{bmatrix} = \begin{bmatrix} 2+6 & 6-12 \\ 4+10 & 12-20 \end{bmatrix} = \begin{bmatrix} 8 & -6 \\ 14 & -8 \end{bmatrix}$ ✓

$\therefore X = \begin{bmatrix} 1 & 3 \\ -2 & 4 \end{bmatrix}$. Answer.

We shall now consider a method of solving the system

$$a_1 x + b_1 y = c_1$$
$$a_2 x + b_2 y = c_2$$

by using matrices. By the definition of matrix equality, this system may be written in matrix notation as

$$\begin{bmatrix} a_1 x + b_1 y \\ a_2 x + b_2 y \end{bmatrix} = \begin{bmatrix} c_1 \\ c_2 \end{bmatrix}.$$

You saw on page 452 that

$$\begin{bmatrix} a_1 x + b_1 y \\ a_2 x + b_2 y \end{bmatrix} = \begin{bmatrix} a_1 & b_1 \\ a_2 & b_2 \end{bmatrix}\begin{bmatrix} x \\ y \end{bmatrix}.$$

Therefore, you can rewrite the matrix equation as

$$\begin{bmatrix} a_1 & b_1 \\ a_2 & b_2 \end{bmatrix}\begin{bmatrix} x \\ y \end{bmatrix} = \begin{bmatrix} c_1 \\ c_2 \end{bmatrix},$$

which represents the linear system in the simple matrix form

$$AX = B,$$

where $A = \begin{bmatrix} a_1 & b_1 \\ a_2 & b_2 \end{bmatrix}$ is called the coefficient matrix, and X and B are 2×1 matrices.

If the coefficient matrix is invertible, the components of the single member of the solution set are the entries in $A^{-1}B$; if it is not invertible, the equations in the system are either dependent or inconsistent.

Cramer's Rule for solving equations using determinants which was presented in Chapter 5 may be derived from this method.

EXAMPLE 3 Use matrices to find the solution set of the system: $\begin{aligned} -x + 2y &= -6 \\ 3x + 4y &= 8 \end{aligned}$

SOLUTION 1. First, write the matrix equation:

$$\begin{bmatrix} -1 & 2 \\ 3 & 4 \end{bmatrix}\begin{bmatrix} x \\ y \end{bmatrix} = \begin{bmatrix} -6 \\ 8 \end{bmatrix}$$

2. Next, find the inverse of the coefficient matrix:

$$\begin{bmatrix} -1 & 2 \\ 3 & 4 \end{bmatrix}^{-1} = -\tfrac{1}{10}\begin{bmatrix} 4 & -2 \\ -3 & -1 \end{bmatrix} = \begin{bmatrix} -\frac{4}{10} & \frac{2}{10} \\ \frac{3}{10} & \frac{1}{10} \end{bmatrix}$$

3. Then: $$\begin{bmatrix} x \\ y \end{bmatrix} = \begin{bmatrix} -\frac{4}{10} & \frac{2}{10} \\ \frac{3}{10} & \frac{1}{10} \end{bmatrix} \begin{bmatrix} -6 \\ 8 \end{bmatrix} = \begin{bmatrix} 4 \\ -1 \end{bmatrix}$$

Checking, you find that the values $x = 4$, $y = -1$ satisfy the given equations. ∴ the solution set is $\{(4, -1)\}$. **Answer.**

Systems of three linear equations in three variables, and also larger systems, can similarly be represented in the simple matrix form $AX = B$, with the unique solution $X = A^{-1}B$ in the case A is nonsingular.

WRITTEN EXERCISES   If the given matrix is nonsingular, find its inverse. If the matrix is singular, so state.

A 1. $A = \begin{bmatrix} 4 & 5 \\ 3 & 4 \end{bmatrix}$ 3. $A = \begin{bmatrix} 8 & 6 \\ 4 & 3 \end{bmatrix}$ 5. $A = \begin{bmatrix} 3 & 5 \\ 2 & 4 \end{bmatrix}$ 7. $A = \begin{bmatrix} 0 & 1 \\ 1 & 0 \end{bmatrix}$

2. $A = \begin{bmatrix} 4 & 6 \\ 6 & 9 \end{bmatrix}$ 4. $A = \begin{bmatrix} 6 & -9 \\ 2 & -3 \end{bmatrix}$ 6. $A = \begin{bmatrix} 5 & 1 \\ 6 & 2 \end{bmatrix}$ 8. $A = \begin{bmatrix} -3 & 1 \\ -5 & 2 \end{bmatrix}$

Solve the given equation for the matrix X.

B 9. $\begin{bmatrix} -3 & 5 \\ 1 & -2 \end{bmatrix} X = \begin{bmatrix} -9 & 14 \\ 3 & -6 \end{bmatrix}$ 11. $\begin{bmatrix} 0 & -3 \\ 2 & 4 \end{bmatrix} X = \begin{bmatrix} 0 & -18 \\ 10 & 28 \end{bmatrix}$

10. $\begin{bmatrix} 1 & -3 \\ -2 & 5 \end{bmatrix} X = \begin{bmatrix} -10 & -3 \\ 3 & 4 \end{bmatrix}$ 12. $\begin{bmatrix} 5 & -2 \\ 3 & 0 \end{bmatrix} X = \begin{bmatrix} 12 & 4 \\ 6 & 6 \end{bmatrix}$

Find the solution set of the given system by using a matrix equation.

C 13. $2x - y = 5$ 14. $5x - 2y = 4$ 15. $2x - 5y = 12$
$3x + 2y = 11$ $10x - 3y = 11$ $3x + y = 1$

For $A = \begin{bmatrix} a_1 & b_1 \\ a_2 & b_2 \end{bmatrix}$ and $B = \begin{bmatrix} c_1 & d_1 \\ c_2 & d_2 \end{bmatrix}$ prove the given statement.

16. $A \cdot \dfrac{1}{\det A} \begin{bmatrix} b_2 & -b_1 \\ -a_2 & a_1 \end{bmatrix} = \begin{bmatrix} 1 & 0 \\ 0 & 1 \end{bmatrix}$

17. $\dfrac{1}{\det A} \begin{bmatrix} b_2 & -b_1 \\ -a_2 & a_1 \end{bmatrix} \cdot A = \begin{bmatrix} 1 & 0 \\ 0 & 1 \end{bmatrix}$ 18. $\det AB = (\det A)(\det B)$

19. Use the result of Exercise 18 and the fact that $AA^{-1} = I$ to show that if $\det A = 0$, then A has no inverse.

SELF-TEST 2   Give the meaning of each of the following.

1. determinant of a square matrix   3. invertible matrix
2. singular matrix

Objective 1, page 458   4. Determine the multiplicative inverse of the matrix $A = \begin{bmatrix} 6 & -5 \\ 9 & -7 \end{bmatrix}$.

Objective 2, page 458 5. Use the inverse of a matrix to solve the matrix equation: $\begin{bmatrix} 5 & 10 \\ 2 & 3 \end{bmatrix} X = \begin{bmatrix} 25 & 50 \\ 7 & 15 \end{bmatrix}$

Objective 3, page 458 6. Write in the matrix form $AX = B$:
$$\begin{aligned} 4x + 3y &= 7 \\ 2x - y &= 10 \end{aligned}$$

Objective 4, page 458 7. Use a matrix equation to solve the system:
$$\begin{aligned} 12x - 5y &= -23 \\ -3x + 2y &= 2 \end{aligned}$$

Check your answers with those printed at the back of the book.

programming in BASIC

It has been shown in the text that a system of linear equations can be expressed in matrix form as $AX = B$. If A is invertible, then the solution can be expressed as $X = A^{-1}B$. In BASIC the inverse of a matrix is found by a statement such as:

MAT V = INV(A)

The program below finds the solution of the system:

$$\begin{aligned} x + y + 2z &= 1 \\ 2x + y - z &= 5 \\ x + 2y + z &= 4 \end{aligned}$$

The solution is printed as $\begin{matrix} 1 \\ 2 \\ -1 \end{matrix}$ which may be interpreted as:

$$x = 1, y = 2, z = -1$$

Notice that B(3) and X(3) in line 10 are dimension matrices with 3 rows and 1 column.

```
10   DIM A(3,3),B(3),V(3,3),X(3)        80   MAT PRINT X
20   MAT READ A,B                       90   DATA 1,1,2
30   MAT PRINT A;B                       100  DATA 2,1,-1
40   PRINT                              110  DATA 1,2,1
50   PRINT                              120  DATA 1,5,4
60   MAT V=INV(A)                       130  END
70   MAT X=V*B
```

If A is singular, the computer will report that. To see what happens, try the program with these DATA changes:

```
100 DATA 2,2,-1
110 DATA 2,2,1
```

EXERCISES

1. Rewrite the text program so that you can INPUT the matrices.

2. Use the computer to check your answers to Exercises 7–12 on page 159.

careers *broadcast engineer*

Broadcast engineers monitor sound equipment at radio stations.

The engineering department of a radio station operates the equipment that converts sound into the electromagnetic impulses transmitted to radios. Some of the broadcast engineer's tasks are: positioning microphones, adjusting sound, making sure that the transmitters operate properly, and installing and repairing the electrical equipment. The networks employ development engineers, who design new electronics equipment.

Technical training in electronics is necessary for jobs in a radio station engineering department. Anyone operating or adjusting a broadcast transmitter must be licensed by the Federal Communications Commission, which administers a series of examinations before granting a license.

EXAMPLE   Each radio station broadcasts a carrier wave at a frequency assigned by the FCC. A carrier wave is a high frequency electromagnetic wave which can be broadcast over long distances. It produces no sound in a receiver, and must be modulated to carry programs. There are two methods of altering a carrier wave to produce sound: amplitude modulation (AM) and frequency modulation (FM).

The equation for the potential energy difference E of a carrier wave is $E(t) = A \sin 2\pi vt$, where v is the frequency of the transmitter. Its graph is a sine wave (Section 14–8). In AM, the amplitude A of the carrier wave is a function of the frequency of the tone being transmitted: $A = A_0 + A_1 \sin 2\pi nt$, where n is the frequency of the tone. The modulated wave now has the equation $E(t) = (A_0 + A_1 \sin 2\pi nt) \sin 2\pi vt$.

In FM, the amplitude A of the carrier wave remains constant. The frequency v varies according to the equation $v(t) = v_0 + v_1 \sin 2\pi nt$, where n is the frequency of the tone being transmitted. In this case the modulated wave has the equation $E(t) = A \sin 2\pi(v_0 + v_1 \sin 2\pi nt)t$. The graphs show how the carrier wave is modulated.

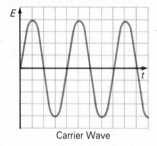

Carrier Wave

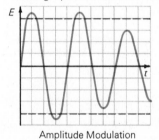

Amplitude Modulation

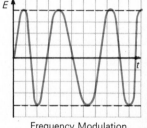

Frequency Modulation

transformations of the plane

Objectives

After completing the next two sections, you should be able to:
1. Determine an equation of a translation of the plane when the image of one point under the translation is given.
2. Find the coordinates of the image of a point, and also the coordinates of the preimage of a point, under a given translation of the plane.
3. Find the coordinates of the image of a point under a given linear transformation of the plane.
4. Find the coordinates of the preimage of a point under a given nonsingular transformation of the plane.

13-7 transformations by matrix addition

Imagine a triangular piece of cardboard resting on a coordinate plane and having vertices at $A(-4, -3)$, $B(3, -1)$, and $C(2, 3)$, as shown in Figure 1. You can think of sliding the cardboard 2 units in the x-direction and 1 unit in the y-direction to the position shown in Figure 2. In their new positions, the vertices will be at $A'(-4 + 2, -3 + 1)$, $B'(3 + 2, -1 + 1)$, and $C'(2 + 2, 3 + 1)$, or $A'(-2, -2)$, $B'(5, 0)$, and $C'(4, 4)$. By such a sliding, you can think of each point $P(x, y)$ of the plane as being *mapped* on a corresponding point $P'(x + 2, y + 1)$.

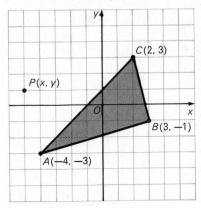

Figure 1

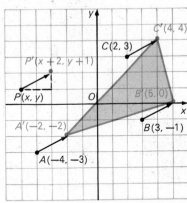

Figure 2

The sliding described above is an example of a transformation, or mapping, of the plane called a translation. In the translation of amount h in the x-direction and k in the y-direction, the point $P(x, y)$ is mapped on the point $P'(x', y')$, where

$$x' = x + h \quad \text{and} \quad y' = y + k.$$

We say that P' is the image of P, and that P is the preimage of P', under the mapping.

It is convenient to use matrices in working with transformations of the plane and to designate the coordinates (x, y) by the matrix $\begin{bmatrix} x \\ y \end{bmatrix}$. Thus the translation given above is written simply as

$$\begin{bmatrix} x' \\ y' \end{bmatrix} = \begin{bmatrix} x \\ y \end{bmatrix} + \begin{bmatrix} h \\ k \end{bmatrix}. \qquad (1)$$

If h and k are given, then Equation (1) can be considered as defining a function,

$$\begin{bmatrix} x \\ y \end{bmatrix} \rightarrow \begin{bmatrix} x' \\ y' \end{bmatrix}$$

with domain the set of 2×1 matrices $\begin{bmatrix} x \\ y \end{bmatrix}$, where $x, y \in \mathcal{R}$, and range the set of corresponding matrices $\begin{bmatrix} x' \\ y' \end{bmatrix}$.

Of course, the function

$$(x, y) \rightarrow (x', y'),$$

whose domain and range are sets of ordered pairs, describes the same transformation. Matrices are used because they are very convenient in studying linear transformations (Section 13-8).

EXAMPLE   In a translation of the plane, the image of $P(5, 4)$ is $P'(8, -2)$.
a. Find a matrix equation of the transformation.
b. Find the image of $Q(-4, 0)$ under the transformation.
c. Find the preimage of $R'(3, 2)$ under the transformation.

SOLUTION   **a.** The matrix equation of the translation,

$$\begin{bmatrix} x' \\ y' \end{bmatrix} = \begin{bmatrix} x \\ y \end{bmatrix} + \begin{bmatrix} h \\ k \end{bmatrix}$$

is satisfied by

$$\begin{bmatrix} x \\ y \end{bmatrix} = \begin{bmatrix} 5 \\ 4 \end{bmatrix}, \begin{bmatrix} x' \\ y' \end{bmatrix} = \begin{bmatrix} 8 \\ -2 \end{bmatrix}.$$

Hence:

$$\begin{bmatrix} 8 \\ -2 \end{bmatrix} = \begin{bmatrix} 5 \\ 4 \end{bmatrix} + \begin{bmatrix} h \\ k \end{bmatrix}$$

$$\begin{bmatrix} 8 \\ -2 \end{bmatrix} - \begin{bmatrix} 5 \\ 4 \end{bmatrix} = \begin{bmatrix} 5 \\ 4 \end{bmatrix} + \begin{bmatrix} h \\ k \end{bmatrix} - \begin{bmatrix} 5 \\ 4 \end{bmatrix} = \begin{bmatrix} h \\ k \end{bmatrix}$$

$$\begin{bmatrix} h \\ k \end{bmatrix} = \begin{bmatrix} 8 - 5 \\ -2 - 4 \end{bmatrix} = \begin{bmatrix} 3 \\ -6 \end{bmatrix}$$

$\therefore$ the transformation is given by $\begin{bmatrix} x' \\ y' \end{bmatrix} = \begin{bmatrix} x \\ y \end{bmatrix} + \begin{bmatrix} 3 \\ -6 \end{bmatrix}$. **Answer.**

b. To find the image of $Q(-4, 0)$, you substitute $\begin{bmatrix} -4 \\ 0 \end{bmatrix}$ for $\begin{bmatrix} x \\ y \end{bmatrix}$ in the equation of the transformation:

$$\begin{bmatrix} x' \\ y' \end{bmatrix} = \begin{bmatrix} -4 \\ 0 \end{bmatrix} + \begin{bmatrix} 3 \\ -6 \end{bmatrix} = \begin{bmatrix} -1 \\ -6 \end{bmatrix}$$

$\therefore$ the image of $Q(-4, 0)$ under the transformation is $Q'(-1, -6)$. **Answer.**

c. To find the preimage of $R'(3, 2)$ you substitute $\begin{bmatrix} 3 \\ 2 \end{bmatrix}$ for $\begin{bmatrix} x' \\ y' \end{bmatrix}$ in the equation of the transformation:

$$\begin{bmatrix} 3 \\ 2 \end{bmatrix} = \begin{bmatrix} x \\ y \end{bmatrix} + \begin{bmatrix} 3 \\ -6 \end{bmatrix}$$

$$\begin{bmatrix} 3 \\ 2 \end{bmatrix} - \begin{bmatrix} 3 \\ -6 \end{bmatrix} = \begin{bmatrix} x \\ y \end{bmatrix} + \begin{bmatrix} 3 \\ -6 \end{bmatrix} - \begin{bmatrix} 3 \\ -6 \end{bmatrix} = \begin{bmatrix} x \\ y \end{bmatrix}$$

$$\begin{bmatrix} x \\ y \end{bmatrix} = \begin{bmatrix} 3 - 3 \\ 2 - (-6) \end{bmatrix} = \begin{bmatrix} 0 \\ 8 \end{bmatrix}$$

$\therefore$ the preimage of $R'(3, 2)$ under the transformation is $R(0, 8)$. **Answer.**

Parts **(b)** and **(c)** of the Example illustrate the fact that under a translation every point of the plane has a unique image, and also every point has a unique preimage. Therefore such a transformation is a one-to-one mapping of the entire plane onto itself.

WRITTEN EXERCISES Find the coordinates of the image P' of the given point P under the given translation of the plane.

A

1. $P(4, -7)$; $\begin{bmatrix} x' \\ y' \end{bmatrix} = \begin{bmatrix} x \\ y \end{bmatrix} + \begin{bmatrix} -2 \\ 5 \end{bmatrix}$ 3. $P(2, -3)$; $\begin{bmatrix} x' \\ y' \end{bmatrix} = \begin{bmatrix} x \\ y \end{bmatrix} + \begin{bmatrix} -4 \\ -3 \end{bmatrix}$

2. $P(0, 3)$; $\begin{bmatrix} x' \\ y' \end{bmatrix} = \begin{bmatrix} x \\ y \end{bmatrix} + \begin{bmatrix} -1 \\ 0 \end{bmatrix}$ 4. $P(-5, 1)$; $\begin{bmatrix} x' \\ y' \end{bmatrix} = \begin{bmatrix} x \\ y \end{bmatrix} + \begin{bmatrix} 5 \\ -1 \end{bmatrix}$

Find the coordinates of the preimage P of the given point P' under the given translation of the plane.

5. $P'(-4, 7)$; $\begin{bmatrix} x' \\ y' \end{bmatrix} = \begin{bmatrix} x \\ y \end{bmatrix} + \begin{bmatrix} -2 \\ 5 \end{bmatrix}$

6. $P'(0, 0)$; $\begin{bmatrix} x' \\ y' \end{bmatrix} = \begin{bmatrix} x \\ y \end{bmatrix} + \begin{bmatrix} 0.6 \\ -0.7 \end{bmatrix}$

7. $P'(-2, -1)$; $\begin{bmatrix} x' \\ y' \end{bmatrix} = \begin{bmatrix} x \\ y \end{bmatrix} + \begin{bmatrix} -2 \\ -1 \end{bmatrix}$

8. $P'(a, b)$; $\begin{bmatrix} x' \\ y' \end{bmatrix} = \begin{bmatrix} x \\ y \end{bmatrix} + \begin{bmatrix} c \\ d \end{bmatrix}$

Find an equation of the translation of the plane for which the image o
the given point P is the given point P'.

9. $P(1, 4)$; $P'(3, 8)$ 12. $P(-1, -3)$; $P'(2, 5)$
10. $P(2, 1)$; $P'(3, 6)$ 13. $P(-4, -3)$; $P'(-5, -2)$
11. $P(-5, -2)$; $P'(4, 1)$ 14. $P(-1, -2)$; $P'(-3, -1)$

B 15. In a translation of the plane, the image of $P(4, 7)$ is $P'(2, 8)$.
    a. Find a matrix equation of the transformation.
    b. Find the image of $Q(1, 3)$ under the transformation.
    c. Find the preimage of $R'(-2, 1)$ under the transformation.

16. In a translation of the plane, the preimage of $P'(-2, -3)$ is $P(4, 1)$
    a. Find a matrix equation of the transformation.
    b. Find the image of $Q(4, -3)$ under the transformation.
    c. Find the preimage of $R'(0, 2)$ under the transformation.

C 17. Explain why the identity transformation $\begin{bmatrix} x' \\ y' \end{bmatrix} = \begin{bmatrix} x \\ y \end{bmatrix}$ can be considered
    to be a translation of the plane.

18. Explain why the inverse of a translation of the plane is a translation o
    the plane.

19. Explain why the transformation resulting from a succession of two trans
    lations of the plane is a translation of the plane.

20. In Exercise 19, is the resulting transformation the same if the two giver
    translations are interchanged?

13-8   *transformations by matrix multiplication*

The system of linear equations

$$x' = 3x - 2y$$
$$y' = 7x - 5y$$

can be written in the matrix form $X' = AX$ as:

$$\begin{bmatrix} x' \\ y' \end{bmatrix} = \begin{bmatrix} 3 & -2 \\ 7 & -5 \end{bmatrix} \begin{bmatrix} x \\ y \end{bmatrix} \tag{1}$$

For each $x, y \in \mathcal{R}$, this matrix equation yields just one $\begin{bmatrix} x' \\ y' \end{bmatrix}$. For example

$$\text{If } \begin{bmatrix} x \\ y \end{bmatrix} = \begin{bmatrix} 3 \\ 5 \end{bmatrix}, \text{ then } \begin{bmatrix} x' \\ y' \end{bmatrix} = \begin{bmatrix} 3 & -2 \\ 7 & -5 \end{bmatrix} \begin{bmatrix} 3 \\ 5 \end{bmatrix} = \begin{bmatrix} -1 \\ -4 \end{bmatrix}.$$

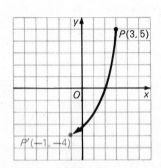

Figure 3

Accordingly, Equation (1) can be considered as defining a mapping function, or transformation of the plane,

$$\begin{bmatrix} x \\ y \end{bmatrix} \rightarrow \begin{bmatrix} x' \\ y' \end{bmatrix},$$

with domain the set of 2×1 matrices $\begin{bmatrix} x \\ y \end{bmatrix}$, where $x, y \in \mathcal{R}$, and range the set of corresponding matrices. (See Figure 3.)

EXAMPLE 1 Under the transformation $\begin{bmatrix} x' \\ y' \end{bmatrix} = \begin{bmatrix} 4 & 1 \\ -2 & -3 \end{bmatrix} \begin{bmatrix} x \\ y \end{bmatrix}$ determine **(a)** the image of $P(3, -5)$; and **(b)** the preimage of $Q'(7, -1)$.

SOLUTION **a.** Substituting $\begin{bmatrix} 3 \\ -5 \end{bmatrix}$ for $\begin{bmatrix} x \\ y \end{bmatrix}$ in the equation for the transformation, you have:

$$\begin{bmatrix} x' \\ y' \end{bmatrix} = \begin{bmatrix} 4 & 1 \\ -2 & -3 \end{bmatrix} \begin{bmatrix} 3 \\ -5 \end{bmatrix}$$

$$\begin{bmatrix} x' \\ y' \end{bmatrix} = \begin{bmatrix} 12 & -5 \\ -6 & +15 \end{bmatrix} = \begin{bmatrix} 7 \\ 9 \end{bmatrix}$$

$\therefore$ the image of $P(3, -5)$ is $P'(7, 9)$. **Answer.**

b. Substituting $\begin{bmatrix} 7 \\ -1 \end{bmatrix}$ for $\begin{bmatrix} x' \\ y' \end{bmatrix}$ in the equation for the transformation, you obtain:

$$\begin{bmatrix} 7 \\ -1 \end{bmatrix} = \begin{bmatrix} 4 & 1 \\ -2 & -3 \end{bmatrix} \begin{bmatrix} x \\ y \end{bmatrix}$$

The multiplicative inverse of $\begin{bmatrix} 4 & 1 \\ -2 & -3 \end{bmatrix}$ is:

$$\frac{1}{-12 + 2} \begin{bmatrix} -3 & -1 \\ 2 & 4 \end{bmatrix}, \quad \text{or} \quad \begin{bmatrix} \frac{3}{10} & \frac{1}{10} \\ -\frac{2}{10} & -\frac{4}{10} \end{bmatrix}$$

Left-multiplying both members of the equation by this multiplicative inverse, you obtain:

$$\begin{bmatrix} \frac{3}{10} & \frac{1}{10} \\ -\frac{2}{10} & -\frac{4}{10} \end{bmatrix} \begin{bmatrix} 7 \\ -1 \end{bmatrix} = \begin{bmatrix} \frac{3}{10} & \frac{1}{10} \\ -\frac{2}{10} & -\frac{4}{10} \end{bmatrix} \begin{bmatrix} 4 & 1 \\ -2 & -3 \end{bmatrix} \begin{bmatrix} x \\ y \end{bmatrix}$$

$$\begin{bmatrix} 2 \\ -1 \end{bmatrix} = \begin{bmatrix} 1 & 0 \\ 0 & 1 \end{bmatrix} \begin{bmatrix} x \\ y \end{bmatrix}$$

$$\begin{bmatrix} x \\ y \end{bmatrix} = \begin{bmatrix} 2 \\ -1 \end{bmatrix}$$

Checking that these values satisfy the original equation is left to you.
$\therefore$ the preimage of $Q'(7, -1)$ is $Q(2, -1)$. **Answer.**

In general, any transformation of the form

$$X' = AX$$

where $X' = \begin{bmatrix} x' \\ y' \end{bmatrix}$, $A = \begin{bmatrix} a_1 & b_1 \\ a_2 & b_2 \end{bmatrix}$, $X = \begin{bmatrix} x \\ y \end{bmatrix}$ and $a_1, b_1, a_2, b_2 \in \mathcal{R}$, is called a linear transformation of the plane.

Each point in the plane has an image under such a transformation, as illustrated in Example 1 (a). In particular, since $AO = O$, the image of the origin is the origin under every linear transformation.

Further, as illustrated in Example 1 (b), if det $A \neq 0$ then each point also has a unique preimage because the matrix A has a unique inverse. In this case, the transformation is a one-to-one mapping of the entire plane onto itself, and is said to be *nonsingular*.

EXAMPLE 2 Describe the mapping of the plane onto itself under the linear transformation of the plane, $X' = AX$, for which **(a)** $A = \begin{bmatrix} 1 & 0 \\ 0 & -1 \end{bmatrix}$; and **(b)** $A = \begin{bmatrix} 0 & 1 \\ 1 & 0 \end{bmatrix}$

SOLUTION a. Substituting $\begin{bmatrix} 1 & 0 \\ 0 & -1 \end{bmatrix}$ for $\begin{bmatrix} a_1 & b_1 \\ a_2 & b_2 \end{bmatrix}$ in

$$\begin{bmatrix} x' \\ y' \end{bmatrix} = \begin{bmatrix} a_1 & b_1 \\ a_2 & b_2 \end{bmatrix} \begin{bmatrix} x \\ y \end{bmatrix},$$

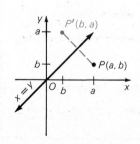

you have

$$\begin{bmatrix} x' \\ y' \end{bmatrix} = \begin{bmatrix} 1 & 0 \\ 0 & -1 \end{bmatrix} \begin{bmatrix} x \\ y \end{bmatrix},$$

$$\begin{bmatrix} x' \\ y' \end{bmatrix} = \begin{bmatrix} x \\ -y \end{bmatrix}, \text{ or } (x', y') = (x, -y).$$

Thus, for each $P(a, b)$ the image is the reflection $P'(a, -b)$ of P in the x-axis, as shown in the figure.

∴ the transformation is a *reflection in the x-axis*. **Answer.**

b. Substituting $\begin{bmatrix} 0 & 1 \\ 1 & 0 \end{bmatrix}$ for $\begin{bmatrix} a_1 & b_1 \\ a_2 & b_2 \end{bmatrix}$, you have

$$\begin{bmatrix} x' \\ y' \end{bmatrix} = \begin{bmatrix} 0 & 1 \\ 1 & 0 \end{bmatrix} \begin{bmatrix} x \\ y \end{bmatrix},$$

$$\begin{bmatrix} x' \\ y' \end{bmatrix} = \begin{bmatrix} y \\ x \end{bmatrix} \text{ or } (x', y') = (y, x).$$

Thus for each $P(a, b)$ the image is the reflection $P'(b, a)$ of P in the line $y = x$, as discussed on page 374 and as shown in the figure.

∴ the transformation is a *reflection in the line* $y = x$. **Answer.**

If det $A = 0$ then the linear transformation $X' = AX$ is said to be *singular*.

EXAMPLE 3 Describe the mapping of the plane under the singular linear transformation for which **(a)** $A = \begin{bmatrix} 0 & 0 \\ 0 & 0 \end{bmatrix}$; and **(b)** $A = \begin{bmatrix} 2 & 1 \\ 4 & 2 \end{bmatrix}$.

SOLUTION **a.** For all $x, y \in \mathcal{R}$, you have:

$$\begin{bmatrix} x' \\ y' \end{bmatrix} = \begin{bmatrix} 0 & 0 \\ 0 & 0 \end{bmatrix} \begin{bmatrix} x \\ y \end{bmatrix}$$

$$\begin{bmatrix} x' \\ y' \end{bmatrix} = \begin{bmatrix} 0 \\ 0 \end{bmatrix}$$

Thus the image of each $P(a, b)$ is $P'(0, 0)$.

$\therefore$ each point of the plane is mapped onto the origin under this transformation. **Answer.**

b. For any x and $y \in \mathcal{R}$, you have

$$\begin{bmatrix} x' \\ y' \end{bmatrix} = \begin{bmatrix} 2 & 1 \\ 4 & 2 \end{bmatrix} \begin{bmatrix} x \\ y \end{bmatrix} = \begin{bmatrix} 2x + y \\ 4x + 2y \end{bmatrix},$$

so that $x' = 2x + y$, $y' = 4x + 2y$. Since $4x + 2y = 2(2x + y)$, you have $y' = 2x'$. Therefore the map of the entire plane lies on the line $y' = 2x'$. Further, each point, say $(c, 2c)$ on this line is the image of many different points; for example, $(c, 2c)$ is the image of $\left(\frac{c}{2}, 0\right)$ and also of $\left(\frac{c}{3}, \frac{c}{3}\right)$.

$\therefore$ under this transformation the plane is mapped onto the line $y' = 2x'$.
Answer.

Examples 2 and 3 illustrate the following result:

Theorem. The linear transformation $AX = X'$, where $A = \begin{bmatrix} a_1 & b_1 \\ a_2 & b_2 \end{bmatrix}$, $X = \begin{bmatrix} x \\ y \end{bmatrix}$, $X' = \begin{bmatrix} x' \\ y' \end{bmatrix}$, and a_1, b_1 $a_2, b_2 \in \mathcal{R}$ is a one-to-one mapping of the plane onto itself if det $A \neq 0$.

If $A = 0$, then the entire plane is mapped onto the origin.

If $A \neq 0$ but det $A = 0$, then the entire plane is mapped onto a line through the origin.

Find the coordinates of the image P' of the given point P under the given linear transformation of the plane.

A
1. $P(0, 2)$; $\begin{bmatrix} x' \\ y' \end{bmatrix} = \begin{bmatrix} 4 & 0 \\ 2 & 3 \end{bmatrix} \begin{bmatrix} x \\ y \end{bmatrix}$ 3. $P(5, -2)$; $\begin{bmatrix} x' \\ y' \end{bmatrix} = \begin{bmatrix} 2 & 4 \\ 0 & 3 \end{bmatrix} \begin{bmatrix} x \\ y \end{bmatrix}$

2. $P(3, 0)$; $\begin{bmatrix} x' \\ y' \end{bmatrix} = \begin{bmatrix} 3 & 1 \\ 0 & 1 \end{bmatrix} \begin{bmatrix} x \\ y \end{bmatrix}$ 4. $P(-1, -3)$; $\begin{bmatrix} x' \\ y' \end{bmatrix} = \begin{bmatrix} 0.6 & 0.5 \\ 1.3 & 2.8 \end{bmatrix} \begin{bmatrix} x \\ y \end{bmatrix}$

Find the coordinates of the preimage P of the given point P' under the given linear transformation of the plane.

5. $P'(-4, 0)$; $\begin{bmatrix} x' \\ y' \end{bmatrix} = \begin{bmatrix} 4 & 7 \\ 0 & 1 \end{bmatrix} \begin{bmatrix} x \\ y \end{bmatrix}$ 7. $P'(1, -3)$; $\begin{bmatrix} x' \\ y' \end{bmatrix} = \begin{bmatrix} 5 & 0 \\ 0 & 5 \end{bmatrix} \begin{bmatrix} x \\ y \end{bmatrix}$

6. $P'(0, -5)$; $\begin{bmatrix} x' \\ y' \end{bmatrix} = \begin{bmatrix} 3 & 0 \\ 5 & 2 \end{bmatrix} \begin{bmatrix} x \\ y \end{bmatrix}$ 8. $P'(-2, -1)$; $\begin{bmatrix} x' \\ y' \end{bmatrix} = \begin{bmatrix} 0 & 4 \\ 4 & 0 \end{bmatrix} \begin{bmatrix} x \\ y \end{bmatrix}$

B
9. Show that for the singular linear transformation $\begin{bmatrix} x' \\ y' \end{bmatrix} = \begin{bmatrix} 3 & -2 \\ 9 & -6 \end{bmatrix} \begin{bmatrix} x \\ y \end{bmatrix}$, the image P' of each point $P(x, y)$ lies on the line $y' = 3x'$.

10. Show that for the singular linear transformation $\begin{bmatrix} x' \\ y' \end{bmatrix} = \begin{bmatrix} 3 & 5 \\ -6 & -10 \end{bmatrix} \begin{bmatrix} x \\ y \end{bmatrix}$ the image P' of each point $P(x, y)$ lies on the line $y' = -2x'$.

Describe the mapping of the plane onto itself under the following linear transformations.

11. $\begin{bmatrix} x' \\ y' \end{bmatrix} = \begin{bmatrix} -1 & 0 \\ 0 & 1 \end{bmatrix} \begin{bmatrix} x \\ y \end{bmatrix}$ 14. $\begin{bmatrix} x' \\ y' \end{bmatrix} = \begin{bmatrix} \frac{1}{2} & 0 \\ 0 & \frac{1}{2} \end{bmatrix} \begin{bmatrix} x \\ y \end{bmatrix}$

12. $\begin{bmatrix} x' \\ y' \end{bmatrix} = \begin{bmatrix} -1 & 0 \\ 0 & -1 \end{bmatrix} \begin{bmatrix} x \\ y \end{bmatrix}$ 15. $\begin{bmatrix} x' \\ y' \end{bmatrix} = \begin{bmatrix} 1 & 0 \\ 0 & 0 \end{bmatrix} \begin{bmatrix} x \\ y \end{bmatrix}$

13. $\begin{bmatrix} x' \\ y' \end{bmatrix} = \begin{bmatrix} 2 & 0 \\ 0 & 2 \end{bmatrix} \begin{bmatrix} x \\ y \end{bmatrix}$ 16. $\begin{bmatrix} x' \\ y' \end{bmatrix} = \begin{bmatrix} 1 & 2 \\ 0 & 0 \end{bmatrix} \begin{bmatrix} x \\ y \end{bmatrix}$

Every linear transformation, $X' = AX$, of the plane for which $A \neq O$ maps each straight line on a straight line. Use this fact in solving Exercises 17 and 18.

17. Determine the image of the square with vertices $(0, 0)$, $(1, 0)$, $(1, 1)$, and $(0, 1)$ under the *shear* transformation
$$\begin{bmatrix} x' \\ y' \end{bmatrix} = \begin{bmatrix} 1 & 2 \\ 0 & 1 \end{bmatrix} \begin{bmatrix} x \\ y \end{bmatrix}.$$

18. Determine the image of the square with vertices $(0, 0)$, $(1, 0)$, $(1, 1)$ and $(0, 1)$ under the shear transformation
$$\begin{bmatrix} x' \\ y' \end{bmatrix} = \begin{bmatrix} 1 & 0 \\ 3 & 1 \end{bmatrix} \begin{bmatrix} x \\ y \end{bmatrix}.$$

C 19. Explain why the identity transformation $\begin{bmatrix} x' \\ y' \end{bmatrix} = \begin{bmatrix} x \\ y \end{bmatrix}$ can be considered to be a linear transformation of the plane.

20. Explain why the inverse of a nonsingular linear transformation of the plane is a nonsingular linear transformation of the plane.

21. Explain why the transformation resulting from a succession of two linear transformations of the plane is a linear transformation of the plane, and why the resulting transformation is nonsingular if each of the given transformations is nonsingular.

22. In Exercise 21, explain why the resulting transformation is not necessarily the same if the two given transformations are interchanged.

SELF-TEST 3 Give the meaning of each of the following.

1. translation
2. linear transformation
3. image
4. preimage
5. singular linear transformation

Objective 1, page 465 6. Determine an equation of the translation of the plane for which the image of $P(2, 7)$ is $P'(5, 3)$.

Objective 2, page 465 7. Find the coordinates of the image P' of the point $P(\tfrac{3}{2}, -\tfrac{1}{2})$ under the translation of the plane given by

$$\begin{bmatrix} x' \\ y' \end{bmatrix} = \begin{bmatrix} x \\ y \end{bmatrix} + \begin{bmatrix} -5 \\ 3 \end{bmatrix}.$$

8. Find the coordinates of the preimage P of the point $P'(-4, -5)$ under the translation of the plane given by

$$\begin{bmatrix} x' \\ y' \end{bmatrix} = \begin{bmatrix} x \\ y \end{bmatrix} + \begin{bmatrix} -2 \\ -6 \end{bmatrix}.$$

Objective 3, page 465 9. Find the coordinates of the image P' of the point $P(0, 2)$ under the linear transformation

$$\begin{bmatrix} x' \\ y' \end{bmatrix} = \begin{bmatrix} 5 & -3 \\ -2 & 4 \end{bmatrix}\begin{bmatrix} x \\ y \end{bmatrix}.$$

Objective 4, page 465 10. Find the coordinates of the preimage P of the point $P'(4, -2)$ under the linear transformation

$$\begin{bmatrix} x' \\ y' \end{bmatrix} = \begin{bmatrix} 3 & 4 \\ 4 & 5 \end{bmatrix}\begin{bmatrix} x \\ y \end{bmatrix}.$$

Check your answers with those printed at the back of the book.

chapter summary

1. A rectangular array of numerals is a **matrix** (plural, **matrices**). The numerals are the **entries** of the matrix, and the number of (horizontal) rows and the number of (vertical) columns are its **dimensions**.

2. Two matrices are **equal** if and only if they have the same dimensions and all their corresponding entries are equal.

3. If two matrices have the same dimensions, then their **sum** is a matrix of the same dimensions, whose entries are the sums of the corresponding entries of the given matrices.

4. In the set $\mathcal{S}_{m \times n}$ of all $m \times n$ matrices with real-number entries, the **identity matrix for addition** is the zero matrix $O_{m \times n}$ all of whose entries are zero. The **additive inverse**, or **negative**, of the matrix $A_{m \times n}$ is the $m \times n$ matrix $-A_{m \times n}$ each of whose entries is the negative of the corresponding entry of $A_{m \times n}$. The **difference** $A_{m \times n} - B_{m \times n}$ is defined to be the sum $A_{m \times n} + (-B_{m \times n})$.

5. The set $\mathcal{S}_{m \times n}$ of all $m \times n$ matrices with real-number entries has the same addition properties as the set of all real numbers: closure, commutative, associative, additive-identity, and additive-inverse.

6. In dealing with matrices, we often refer to real numbers as **scalars**. The **product** of a scalar c and a matrix A, is denoted by cA; it is the matrix of the same dimensions as A whose entries are the products of c and the corresponding entries of A. Basic properties of these products follow from the definition and the properties of real numbers.

7. The **product** AB of matrices A and B can be described as ''row by column'' multiplication. The product is defined only if the number of columns in A is equal to the number of rows in B. The product matrix then has the same number of rows as A and the same number of columns as B. Thus:

$$A_{m \times p} \times B_{p \times n} = C_{m \times n}$$

8. The set $\mathcal{S}_{2 \times 2}$ is closed under matrix multiplication, and the associative and distributive properties hold for matrix multiplication. The **identity element for multiplication** is $\begin{bmatrix} 1 & 0 \\ 0 & 1 \end{bmatrix}$. But multiplication in $\mathcal{S}_{2 \times 2}$ **is not commutative**, though certain products do commute. The product of two matrices can be the zero matrix without either factor being the zero matrix.

9. The determinant having the same entries as a given square matrix A is the **determinant** of the matrix. The matrix A is **singular** if det $A = 0$; otherwise A is **nonsingular**. A has a **multiplicative inverse**, that is, there is a square matrix A^{-1} such that $AA^{-1} = I$ and $A^{-1}A = I$, if and only if A is nonsingular.

$$\text{If } A = \begin{bmatrix} a_1 & a_2 \\ b_1 & b_2 \end{bmatrix}, \text{ then } A^{-1} = \frac{1}{\det A} \begin{bmatrix} b_2 & -a_2 \\ -b_1 & a_1 \end{bmatrix}.$$

10. A system of two linear equations in two variables can be written in matrix form: $AX = B$. If det $A \neq 0$ then the system has the unique solution $X = A^{-1}B$. Higher-order systems can be treated similarly.

11. A transformation, or mapping of the plane defined by an equation of the form $\begin{bmatrix} x' \\ y' \end{bmatrix} = \begin{bmatrix} x \\ y \end{bmatrix} + \begin{bmatrix} h \\ k \end{bmatrix}$, where $h, k \in \mathfrak{R}$, is called a **translation**. Under the transformation, the point $P'(x', y')$ is called the **image** of the point $P(x, y)$, and P is called the **preimage** of P'.

12. A transformation defined by an equation of the form $\begin{bmatrix} x' \\ y' \end{bmatrix} = \begin{bmatrix} a & b \\ c & d \end{bmatrix} \begin{bmatrix} x \\ y \end{bmatrix}$, where $a, b, c, d \in \mathfrak{R}$, is called a **linear transformation**. Such a transformation is one-to-one if and only if $\begin{bmatrix} a & b \\ c & d \end{bmatrix}$ is nonsingular; that is, if and only if det $\begin{bmatrix} a & b \\ c & d \end{bmatrix} \neq 0$.

chapter test and review

13–1 1. Solve: $[x - 3 \quad y] = [2 \quad x + 4]$

Simplify:

2. $\begin{bmatrix} 4 & -5 \\ -6 & 3 \end{bmatrix} + \begin{bmatrix} 2 & 0 \\ -3 & -4 \end{bmatrix}$ 3. $\begin{bmatrix} 4 & -5 \\ -6 & 3 \end{bmatrix} - \begin{bmatrix} 2 & 0 \\ -3 & -4 \end{bmatrix}$

13–2 4. Solve over $\mathcal{S}_{2\times3}$: $X + \begin{bmatrix} -2 & 1 & 0 \\ 3 & 4 & -3 \end{bmatrix} = \begin{bmatrix} 2 & 2 & 3 \\ -4 & -3 & 2 \end{bmatrix}$

13–3 5. Solve over $\mathcal{S}_{3\times3}$: $2X - \begin{bmatrix} 4 & 1 & 7 \\ 2 & 9 & -8 \\ 3 & 0 & -6 \end{bmatrix} = 3X + \begin{bmatrix} 0 & 2 & 1 \\ -1 & 3 & 1 \\ 2 & 4 & 3 \end{bmatrix}$

13–4 6. Simplify: $\begin{bmatrix} -2 & 1 \\ 3 & -4 \end{bmatrix} \times \begin{bmatrix} 5 & -6 \\ 2 & 0 \end{bmatrix}$

13–5 7. For $A = \begin{bmatrix} 1 & 2 \\ -3 & 0 \end{bmatrix}$ and $B = \begin{bmatrix} -2 & 4 \\ 5 & -1 \end{bmatrix}$, compute $(3A)B$ and $A(3B)$ and determine whether or not $(3A)B = A(3B)$.

13–6 **8.** Determine the multiplicative inverse of the matrix $\begin{bmatrix} 4 & 7 \\ 1 & 3 \end{bmatrix}$.

9. Solve the matrix equation: $\begin{bmatrix} 3 & 2 \\ 1 & 4 \end{bmatrix} X = \begin{bmatrix} 5 & 9 \\ 15 & -7 \end{bmatrix}$

10. Use a matrix equation to solve the system:

$$3x - 4y = -1$$
$$2x - 3y = -2$$

13–7 **11.** A translation of the plane maps $P(7, -3)$ on $P'(2, -1)$.

  a. What is an equation of the translation?
  b. What is the image of $Q(-4, -6)$?
  c. What is the preimage of $R'(-3, 5)$?

13–8 **12.** Under the linear transformation $\begin{bmatrix} x' \\ y' \end{bmatrix} = \begin{bmatrix} 3 & -2 \\ 6 & 1 \end{bmatrix} \begin{bmatrix} x \\ y \end{bmatrix}$,

  a. What are the coordinates of the image P' of $P(-4, 1)$?
  b. What are the coordinates of the preimage Q of $Q'(0, 2)$?

cumulative review Simplify.
chapters 1–13

  1. $-3(7 - 12) + 2(8 - 15)$
  2. $(2z^2 - 3z + 5) + (z^2 - 7) - 2(z^2 + 3z + 1)$

Solve over $\mathcal{R}$.

  3. $\dfrac{x - 3}{2} + \dfrac{x + 5}{3} = 17$ **4.** $z(z - 3) - (z^2 + 3) = 6$

  5. If $f(x) = 3x^2 - 5x + 1$, find **(a)** $f(0)$, **(b)** $f(-1)$, and **(c)** $f(t)$.
  6. Find an equation for the line with slope $-\frac{4}{3}$ and y-intercept 3.
  7. Solve by substitution: $2x - 3y = -7$
                 $3x + y = -5$
  8. Factor completely: $4b^2 + 10b - 24$
  9. Find the solution set of $x^2 - 5x \le 24$ over $\mathcal{R}$ and draw its graph.

Simplify.

  10. $\dfrac{x^2 - 6x + 5}{x^2 + 2x - 3} \cdot \dfrac{x^2 - 4x - 21}{x^2 - 10x + 25}$ **11.** $\dfrac{1}{2y + 1} - \dfrac{3}{y - 2}$

  12. Find the value of $\displaystyle\sum_{j=1}^{12} (2j - 5)$.

  13. Find a common fraction for $0.\overline{325}$.

Simplify.

14. $\sqrt[3]{4ty^2} \cdot \sqrt[3]{4t^4y}$

15. $\dfrac{2 - \sqrt{3}}{1 + 2\sqrt{3}}$

16. Solve $2k^2 - 3k + 3 = 0$ using the quadratic formula.

17. If $Q(x) = 2x^3 - 3x^2 + 7$, use synthetic substitution to find $Q(2i)$.

18. Find the distance between $(1, -3)$ and $(7, 5)$.

19. Transform the equation $x^2 + y^2 - 2x + 6y = 6$ into an equation of the form $(x - h)^2 + (y - k)^2 = r^2$, and state the coordinates of the center of its graph and the radius of the graph.

20. Sketch the graph of $\{(x, y): 16x^2 + y^2 = 64\}$.

21. If y varies jointly as x and z^2, and $y = 8$ when $x = 2$ and $z = 1$, find y when $x = 1$ and $z = 3$.

22. Evaluate $(9^{\frac{3}{2}}) \cdot (16^{\frac{3}{4}})$.

23. Give the equation defining the inverse of $\{(x, y): y = 3x - 4\}$.

Solve for x.

24. $\log_x 3 = \frac{1}{2}$

25. $\log_5 x = 3$

26. How many different three-digit numerals for even numbers can be formed from the digits 0, 1, 2, 3, 4, 5?

27. In how many ways can 2 white marbles and 3 blue marbles be selected from an urn containing 5 white and 5 blue marbles?

28. What is the probability that a random linear arrangement of the letters "a," "d," "e," "r" will spell either the word "read" or the word "dare"?

29. A card is drawn from a standard 52-card bridge deck. Without replacing the first card, a second card is drawn. What is the probability that both cards are kings?

Simplify.

30. $\begin{bmatrix} 8 & -1 & 2 \\ 0 & 1 & 4 \end{bmatrix} + 2\begin{bmatrix} 1 & 3 & -1 \\ 0 & 2 & 1 \end{bmatrix}$

31. $\begin{bmatrix} -2 & 3 \\ 0 & 1 \end{bmatrix}\begin{bmatrix} 4 & -2 \\ 1 & 5 \end{bmatrix}$

32. Find the multiplicative inverse of $\begin{bmatrix} 5 & -1 \\ 4 & -1 \end{bmatrix}$

33. Solve for X: $\begin{bmatrix} -5 & -3 \\ 2 & 1 \end{bmatrix} X = \begin{bmatrix} -2 & 1 \\ 0 & 3 \end{bmatrix}$

34. Solve using matrices: $\begin{aligned} 3x - 2y &= -2 \\ x + 3y &= 14 \end{aligned}$

This is one section of a telephone call switching center. The circuits on either side of the corridor are used to process local and long-distance calls. Computers switch calls to "alternate routes" when direct circuits are busy.

14 trigonometric and circular functions

angles and their measurement

Objectives | After completing the next two sections, you should be able to:
1. Find the distance traveled during a given number of revolutions by a point on the rim of a wheel.
2. Convert radian measure to degree measure, and vice versa.

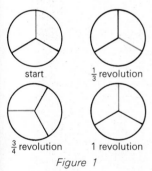

start

$\frac{1}{3}$ revolution

$\frac{3}{4}$ revolution

1 revolution

Figure 1

14–1 *rotations and angles*

How can you measure the distance traveled by a wheeled vehicle in going from one point to another? One way may be described as follows: First, count the number of times a wheel on which the vehicle travels has rotated through a complete revolution in making the trip. Count partial revolutions as fractions of complete revolutions. Then multiply this number of revolutions by the circumference of the wheel. The result will be (in the absence of slippage, of course) the distance the wheel, and hence the vehicle, has moved.

EXAMPLE A tractor wheel has a diameter of 2 meters. How far will the tractor travel as the wheel makes 18.6 revolutions?

SOLUTION To find the circumference C of the wheel, we use $C = \pi d$ where $\pi \doteq 3.14$. Thus,

$$C \doteq 3.14(2) = 6.28.$$

Then the distance the tractor travels in 18.6 revolutions is

$$s \doteq 6.28(18.6) = 116.8.$$

∴ the distance traveled is approximately 117 meters. **Answer.**

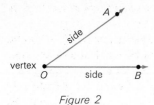

Figure 2

To study rotating objects, we need to reconsider the concept of *angle*. An angle may have been defined in your geometry course as the union of two noncollinear rays that have the same endpoint, as suggested by ∠*AOB* pictured in Figure 2. We shall now define a directed angle as an *ordered pair* of rays with a common endpoint, one ray called the initial side of the angle and the other called the terminal side of the angle, together with a *rotation* from the initial side to the terminal side (see Figure 3). For this definition we drop the restriction that the rays be noncollinear.

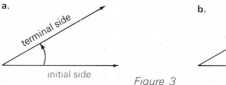

Figure 3

The rotation of the directed angle pictured in Figure 3b is *clockwise;* the rotation pictured in Figure 3a is *counterclockwise*. The angle in Figure 4 has a rotation of $\frac{1}{4}$ of a revolution *counterclockwise*. An angle having a rotation of $\frac{1}{4}$ of a revolution is a right angle.

The sides of any geometric angle form the sides of many different directed angles. (Greek letters such as α (alpha) and β (beta) are often used to name angles.) In Figure 5, the sides of ∠*AOB* are those of angle α_1, which has a counterclockwise rotation of $\frac{1}{8}$ of a revolution; angle α_2, which has a clockwise rotation of $\frac{1}{8}$ of a revolution; angle β_1, which has a clockwise rotation of $\frac{7}{8}$ of a revolution; and angle β_2, which has a counterclockwise rotation of $\frac{7}{8}$ of a revolution.

Angles that have the same initial side and the same terminal side are called coterminal angles. In Figure 5, α_1 and β_1 are coterminal angles, as are α_2 and β_2.

To study an angle, it is convenient to consider it as placed on a rectangular coordinate system with the vertex, *O*, of the angle at the origin and the initial side of the angle as the positive part of the horizontal axis, as shown in Figure 6. The angle is then said to be in standard position.

Figure 4

Figure 5

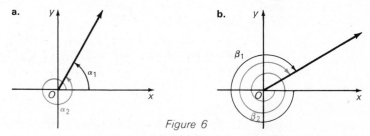

Figure 6

In Figure 6a, angle α_1 and angle α_2 are coterminal. Angle α_1 has a counterclockwise rotation of $\frac{1}{6}$ of a revolution, and angle α_2 has a counterclockwise rotation of $1\frac{1}{6}$ revolutions.

In Figure 6b, angles β_1 and β_2 are coterminal, with angle β_1 having a clockwise rotation of $\frac{11}{12}$ of a revolution and angle β_2 having a clockwise rotation of $1\frac{11}{12}$ of a revolution.

If the terminal side of an angle in standard position lies in a given quadrant, then the angle is said to lie *in* that quadrant. If the terminal side of an angle coincides with a coordinate axis, then the angle is called a quadrantal angle. The angles in Figure 6 all lie in the first quadrant. Angle α_1 in Figure 7a lies in the second quadrant; angle α_2 lies in the third quadrant. Angle β_1 in Figure 7b is a quadrantal angle having $\frac{1}{2}$ of a revolution; its terminal side lies in the negative *x*-axis. It is called a straight angle. Angle β_2 is a quadrantal angle having $1\frac{3}{4}$ revolutions; its terminal side lies in the negative *y*-axis.

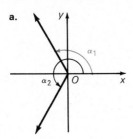
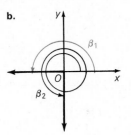

Figure 7

How far will a wheel with the given radius roll as it makes the given number of revolutions? Give your result to the nearest unit in the same unit of measure as that given for the radius. Use $\pi \doteq \frac{22}{7}$.

A

1. 14 cm; $2\frac{1}{2}$ revolutions

2. 35 m; $4\frac{1}{5}$ revolutions

3. 105 mm; 7.2 revolutions

4. 9.1 m; 6.3 revolutions

5. 21.7 cm; 1.3 revolutions

6. 1.26 mm; 3.2 revolutions

7. $\frac{7}{5}$ m; 10 revolutions

8. $\frac{14}{11}$ cm; 23 revolutions

Find the diameter of a wheel that will roll the given distance in the given number of revolutions. Use $\pi \doteq \frac{22}{7}$. Give your result to the nearest unit in the same unit of measure as that given for the distance rolled.

EXAMPLE   33 m; $3\frac{1}{2}$ revolutions

SOLUTION   Using the fact that the distance rolled, s, is given by $s = Ck$, where C is the circumference of the wheel, and k is the number of revolutions turned, and, further, that $C = \pi d$, where d is the diameter of the wheel, you have

$$s = \pi dk.$$

Then, since $s = 33$, $\pi \doteq \frac{22}{7}$, and $k = 3\frac{1}{2} = \frac{7}{2}$, you find that $33 \doteq \frac{22}{7}d(\frac{7}{2})$. Solving for d, you obtain

$$d \doteq \frac{2 \cdot 7 \cdot 33}{7 \cdot 22} = 3.$$

∴ the diameter of the wheel is approximately 3 meters. **Answer.**

9. 286 cm; $3\frac{1}{4}$ revolutions   **11.** 154 cm; $6\frac{2}{3}$ revolutions

10. 66 m; $4\frac{1}{5}$ revolutions   **12.** $28\frac{3}{5}$ m; 14 revolutions

Sketch each angle in standard position, indicating the number of revolutions by a curved arrow.

13. $\frac{1}{4}$ revolution counterclockwise   **16.** $\frac{5}{6}$ revolution clockwise

14. $\frac{3}{5}$ revolution counterclockwise   **17.** $1\frac{3}{4}$ revolutions clockwise

15. $\frac{2}{3}$ revolution clockwise   **18.** $2\frac{3}{10}$ revolutions counterclockwise

B   **19.** The tip of the minute hand on a watch travels 180 centimeters in 36 hours. What is the length of the minute hand to the nearest centimeter?

20. A ferris wheel makes one revolution in 15 seconds. The radius of the wheel is 6 meters. What is the speed in kilometers per hour of a person riding on the ferris wheel?

21. The earth spins on its axis, making one complete revolution every 24 hours. The diameter of the earth at the equator is approximately 13,000 kilometers. What is the speed in kilometers per hour of a point on the equator?

22. A record turns at a rate of $33\frac{1}{3}$ revolutions per minute. The recording plays for 15 minutes. The average distance from the center of the record to the grooves of the record is $10\frac{1}{2}$ centimeters. How long is the path over which the needle travels?

C   **23.** The radius of an automobile wheel and tire is 30 centimeters. A set of tires lasts approximately 55,000 kilometers. How many complete revolutions do the tires make in their lifetime?

24. Each time the pedals of a bicycle make one complete revolution, the rear wheel makes three complete revolutions. The rear wheel is 70 centimeters in diameter. How many complete revolutions must you make with the pedals to ride up a $\frac{1}{2}$-kilometer hill?

14–2   *measurement of angles*

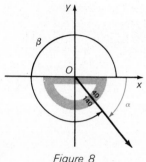

Figure 8

In Section 14–1, angles were described in terms of complete revolutions and fractions of revolutions. However, in order to make effective use of angles, we need some system of measurement that is based on a smaller unit than a complete revolution. Two such systems will be described in this section.

In one system a complete revolution is divided into 360 equal parts, each of which is called a degree of rotation or simply a degree. If the rotation is counterclockwise, the measure is ordinarily taken as positive. If the rotation is clockwise, the measure is negative. In Figure 8, the measure of angle α is negative 40 degrees, written as $-40°$, and the measure of angle β is $320°$.

For more precise measurements, a degree is subdivided into minutes and seconds as follows:

$$1° = 60 \text{ minutes (written } 60')$$
$$1' = 60 \text{ seconds (written } 60'')$$

The equals sign is used to indicate that we have written two names for the same amount of rotation.

EXAMPLE 1   **Find the measure in the degree system of an angle formed by a rotation of:**
a. $2\frac{1}{4}$ **revolutions clockwise.**
b. $\frac{17}{54}$ **revolution counterclockwise.**

SOLUTION   **a.** $2\frac{1}{4} \times (-360°) = -(\frac{9}{4} \times 360°) = -810°$ **Answer.**

b. $\frac{17}{54} \times 360° = \frac{340°}{3} = 113\frac{1}{3}° = 113°20'$ **Answer.**

Several notations exist for recording angle measurements. If angle α has $35°$, you may write

or $m°(\alpha) = 35$, read the measure in degrees of α is 35
      $m(\alpha) = 35°$, read the measure of α is $35°$.

If angle α has $35°23'$, you may write

$$m°(\alpha) = 35\tfrac{23}{60} \qquad \text{or} \qquad m(\alpha) = 35°23'.$$

If α and β are coterminal angles, you may write

$$m°(\beta) = m°(\alpha) + k \cdot 360, k \in \{\text{the integers}\}.$$

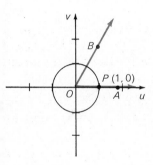

Figure 9

For a second system of measuring angles, consider $\angle AOB$ placed in standard position on the uv-coordinate axes (Figure 9). On the same set of axes, picture the unit circle, that is, the circle with center at (0, 0) and radius 1. Notice that any angle in standard position is determined by the point of intersection of its terminal side with the unit circle. We will measure angles by measuring the length of the arc of the unit circle intercepted by the angle.

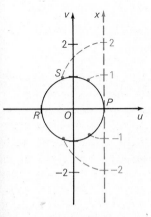

Figure 10

Imagine a flexible x number line tangent to the unit circle at $P(1, 0)$, with origin at P and the same scale, or unit length as on the u and v axes. Think of the number line as being wound around the unit circle as a thread would be wound on a spool. The positive ray would be wound in the counterclockwise direction, and the negative ray in the clockwise direction (Figure 10). This winding procedure pairs each real number (with graph on the flexible number line) with one and only one point on the unit circle. For example, 2 is paired with point S.

As the flexible number line is wound around the unit circle, more than one number will be paired with the same point. Thus, both π and $-\pi$ are paired with point R. Moreover, S is paired with 2, $2 + 2\pi$, $2 - 2\pi$, and so on, and P with 0, 2π, -2π, 4π, and so on.

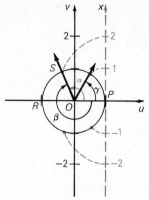

Figure 11

Now we can assign a measure to any angle in standard position as follows: If the *length of an arc* on the unit circle measured from point P is a units, then the *measure of the angle* intercepting that arc is said to be *a* radians. For example, the measure of the angle α in Figure 11 is 2 radians, written 2^R. The angle for a complete revolution is measured by $2\pi^R$.

A notation similar to that for degree measure is used. Thus, you may write

$$m^R(\alpha) = 2 \quad \text{or} \quad m(\alpha) = 2^R.$$

Also, in Figure 11,

$$m^R(\beta) = 2 - 2\pi \quad \text{or} \quad m(\beta) = (2 - 2\pi)^R.$$

In general, if α and β are coterminal angles, you may write:

$$m^R(\beta) = m^R(\alpha) + 2k\pi, \ k \in \{\text{the integers}\}$$

Since an angle for a complete revolution is also measured by $360°$, you have

$$360° = 2\pi^R,$$

or

$$180° = \pi^R.$$

Thus,

$$1° = \frac{\pi^R}{180} \quad \text{and} \quad 1^R = \frac{180°}{\pi}.$$

To change from degrees to radians, or from radians to degrees, we use the above to get conversion equations:

$$m°(\alpha) = \frac{180}{\pi} m^R(\alpha) \qquad m^R(\alpha) = \frac{\pi}{180} m°(\alpha)$$

Since $\pi \doteq 3.14159$, you have $1° \doteq 0.01745^R$ and $1^R \doteq 57°17'45''$. In Figure 11, $m(\gamma) = 60° = \frac{\pi}{180} \cdot 60^R = \frac{\pi^R}{3}$. Thus, γ is slightly greater than an angle that measures 1^R.

EXAMPLE 2   **a.** If $m^R(\alpha) = \dfrac{5\pi}{6}$, find $m°(\alpha)$.

b. If $m°(\beta) = 240$, find $m^R(\beta)$.

SOLUTION   **a.** $m°(\alpha) = \dfrac{180}{\pi} m^R(\alpha) = \dfrac{180}{\pi}\left(\dfrac{5\pi}{6}\right) = 150.$ **Answer.**

b. $m^R(\beta) = \dfrac{\pi}{180} m°(\beta) = \dfrac{\pi}{180}(240) = \dfrac{4\pi}{3}.$ **Answer.**

EXAMPLE 3   Find the length of arc intercepted by a central angle with measure $\frac{7}{3}\pi^R$ in a circle whose radius is 18 cm. Use $\pi \doteq \frac{22}{7}$.

SOLUTION $C = 2\pi r = 2\pi(18) \doteq 2(\frac{22}{7})(18) = \frac{792}{7} \doteq 113.$

The angle contains $\dfrac{\frac{7\pi}{3}}{2\pi}$ or $\frac{7}{6}$ of a revolution, so the length of the arc is $\frac{7}{6}$ of the circumference. $\frac{7}{6}(113) \doteq 132.$

$\therefore$ the length of the arc is approximately 132 cm. **Answer.**

In general, you can show (Exercise 35, page 486) that in a circle of radius r, the length, s, of arc intercepted by a central angle α is given by the formula

$$s = r \cdot m^R(\alpha).$$

WRITTEN EXERCISES   Express each given degree measure as a radian measure using π.

A   1. 135°   3. −270°   5. −150°   7. 90°   9. −330°
     2. 210°   4. −60°   6. −225°   8. 180°   10. −300°

Express each given radian measure as a degree measure.

11. $\dfrac{2\pi^R}{9}$ 15. $-\dfrac{3\pi^R}{2}$ 18. $\dfrac{11\pi^R}{9}$

12. $\dfrac{5\pi^R}{18}$ 16. $-\dfrac{\pi^R}{2}$ 19. $-\dfrac{7\pi^R}{4}$

13. $-\dfrac{7\pi^R}{6}$ 17. $\dfrac{7\pi^R}{12}$ 20. $-\dfrac{11\pi^R}{4}$

14. $-\dfrac{5\pi^R}{3}$

Find the length of the arc on a circle with the given radius which is intercepted by a central angle having the given measurement. Use $\pi \doteq 3.14$.

21. 12 cm; 90°   25. 8 m; $\dfrac{3\pi^R}{4}$

22. 4 km; 120°   26. 15 cm; $\dfrac{5\pi^R}{9}$

23. 20 m; 240°   27. 18.2 km; $\dfrac{7\pi^R}{3}$

24. 24 cm; 420°   28. 16.1 m; $\dfrac{16\pi^R}{3}$

Find the measurement in degrees of a central angle intercepting an arc with the length as given in a circle having the given radius.

EXAMPLE $\overset{\frown}{AB}$: 8π m; r: 6 m

SOLUTION You know that $s = r \cdot m^R(\alpha)$. Since $s = AB = 8\pi$, you have

$$8\pi = 6[m^R(\alpha)] \quad \text{or} \quad m^R(\alpha) = \frac{8\pi}{6} = \frac{4\pi}{3}.$$

Then $\frac{4\pi}{3} \times \frac{180}{\pi} = 240$, so $m°(\alpha) = 240$. **Answer.**

29. $\overset{\frown}{AB}$: $\frac{16\pi}{5}$ m; r: 12 m $\qquad$ 32. $\overset{\frown}{AB}$: $\frac{8\pi}{3}$ km; r: 3 km

30. $\overset{\frown}{AB}$: $\frac{8\pi}{3}$ cm; r: 8 cm $\qquad$ 33. $\overset{\frown}{AB}$: 24 m; r: $\frac{12}{\pi}$ m

31. $\overset{\frown}{AB}$: $\frac{6\pi}{5}$ m; r: 15 m $\qquad$ 34. $\overset{\frown}{AB}$: 18 cm; r: $\frac{7}{6\pi}$ cm

B 35. Derive the formula $s = r \cdot m^R(\alpha)$.

programming in BASIC

1. Write a program to change an angle measurement in degrees and minutes to the corresponding measurement in radians. (Use $\pi = 3.14159$.)

2. Write a program to change an angle measurement in radians to the corresponding measurement in degrees and minutes.

3. You can use a defined function to round a result to a given number of decimal places. For example, to round to tenths, use:

DEF FNR(X) = INT (10* X + 5)/10

Add this function to the program of Exercise 2 and give the measurement correct to tenths of a minute. That is, if D is the integral number of degrees and M the number of minutes, then use:

PRINT D; " DEGREES"; FNR(M); " MINUTES"

SELF-TEST 1 Give the meaning of each of the following.

1. directed angle $\qquad$ 3. quadrantal angle $\qquad$ 5. radian
2. coterminal angles $\qquad$ 4. degree

Objective 1, page 479 6. How far will a wheel with a radius of 14 cm roll in 12 revolutions?

Objective 2, page 479 7. What is the radian measure for an angle whose degree measure is 390?

8. What is the degree measure of an angle whose radian measure is $-\frac{8\pi}{3}$?

Check your answers with those printed at the back of the book.

the sine and cosine trigonometric and circular functions

After completing the next six sections, you should be able to:

Objectives

1. Determine the sine and cosine of an angle in standard position given the coordinates of a point other than the origin on the terminal side of the angle.
2. Determine one of the values $\sin \alpha$ or $\cos \alpha$ given the other value and the quadrant in which α lies.
3. Find values or approximate values for $\cos \alpha$ and $\sin \alpha$ for specified angles α.
4. Sketch the graph of $\{(x, y): y = A \sin Bx\}$ and $\{(x, y): y = A \cos Bx\}$ for given constants A and B.

14-3   the sine and cosine functions

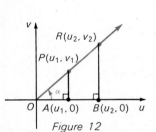

Figure 12

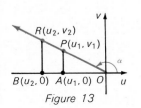

Figure 13

Figure 12 shows an angle α in standard position on a uv-coordinate system. $P(u_1, v_1)$ and $R(u_2, v_2)$ are two distinct points different from the origin on the terminal side of α. $\overline{PA}$ and $\overline{RB}$ are perpendicular to the u-axis. Since right triangles OAP and OBR share a common acute angle, α, they are similar. Therefore their sides are proportional; that is:

$$\frac{v_1}{\sqrt{u_1^2 + v_1^2}} = \frac{v_2}{\sqrt{u_2^2 + v_2^2}} \quad \text{and} \quad \frac{u_1}{\sqrt{u_1^2 + v_1^2}} = \frac{u_2}{\sqrt{u_2^2 + v_2^2}}.$$

Although the terminal side of angle α is pictured in Quadrant I in Figure 12, the preceding proportions hold for an angle in any quadrant (see Figure 13, for example) and for quadrantal angles as well. The ratios above are independent of the points chosen in the terminal side of α, and so for each angle α there are unique values

$$\frac{v_1}{\sqrt{u_1^2 + v_1^2}} \quad \text{and} \quad \frac{u_1}{\sqrt{u_1^2 + v_1^2}}.$$

Thus, we can define two functions as follows:

If α is an angle in standard position, with $P(u, v)$ any point other than the origin on the terminal side of α, and if $\sqrt{u^2 + v^2} = r$, then:

$$\text{sine: } \alpha \to \frac{v}{r} \qquad \text{cosine: } \alpha \to \frac{u}{r}$$

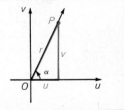

To represent function values of these functions, the following notation is used

$\sin \alpha$ (read "sine of α") $\qquad \cos \alpha$ (read "cosine of α")

The preceding definitions tell you what is meant by the sine and cosine of any angle *in standard position*. But any angle can be put into standard position, and so *the domain of each of these functions is the set of all angles.* Because of their relation to triangles, these functions are called trigonometric functions, where the word "trigonometric" comes from the Greek (*trigonon*, meaning *triangle*, and *metron*, meaning *measure*). There are several other trigonometric functions, which will be defined later in this chapter.

EXAMPLE — If α is an angle in standard position and its terminal side contains the point $(-5, 3)$, find $\sin \alpha$ and $\cos \alpha$.

SOLUTION — Using -5 for u and 3 for v in these definitions of the functions, and noting that

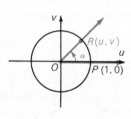

$$\sqrt{u^2 + v^2} = \sqrt{(-5)^2 + 3^2} = \sqrt{34},$$

you have

$$\sin \alpha = \frac{3}{\sqrt{34}} \text{ and } \cos \alpha = -\frac{5}{\sqrt{34}}. \text{ Answer.}$$

By computation, you find that for the angle α in the foregoing example,

$$\sin \alpha \doteq 0.5145 \qquad \text{and} \qquad \cos \alpha \doteq 0.8575.$$

The definitions of $\sin \alpha$ and $\cos \alpha$ make it clear that these values are positive or negative depending on the quadrant in which the terminal side of α lies. Thus, since $u > 0$ and $v < 0$ in the fourth quadrant (and you always have $r > 0$ except at the origin), it follows that in the fourth quadrant,

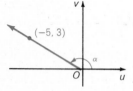

$$\sin \alpha = \frac{v}{r} < 0 \qquad \text{and} \qquad \cos \alpha = \frac{u}{r} > 0.$$

Figure 14

These inequalities and corresponding ones for the other quadrants are shown in Figure 14.

Let us now find the ranges of the sine and cosine functions. Suppose that $R(u, v)$ is the point of intersection of the terminal side of an angle α in standard position with the unit circle (Figure 15). Then you have

$$u^2 + v^2 = 1.$$

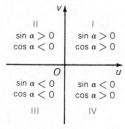

$$\sin \alpha = \frac{v}{\sqrt{u^2 + v^2}} = \frac{v}{1} = v,$$

$$\cos \alpha = \frac{u}{\sqrt{u^2 + v^2}} = \frac{u}{1} = u.$$

Figure 15

This means that the coordinates of R are $(\cos \alpha, \sin \alpha)$. Thus, the ranges of the sine and cosine functions are given, respectively, by

$$-1 \leq \sin \alpha \leq 1 \qquad \text{and} \qquad -1 \leq \cos \alpha \leq 1.$$

Since the coordinates of R must satisfy $u^2 + v^2 = 1$, you have

$$(\sin \alpha)^2 + (\cos \alpha)^2 = 1,$$

which is usually written

$$\sin^2 \alpha + \cos^2 \alpha = 1.$$

This statement is one of the fundamental trigonometric identities. (Recall that an identity is an equation which is true for all real values of the variables.)

Theorem. For every angle α,

$$\sin^2 \alpha + \cos^2 \alpha = 1.$$

There is an alternative way to define sine and cosine functions, a way in which the elements of the domains of the functions are real numbers instead of angles. Recall that when we set up the system of radian measure, each real number was paired with one and only one point on the unit circle. Thus, with each real number $m^R(\alpha)$, you can pair a value $\sin \alpha$ and a value $\cos \alpha$ to define functions

$$\text{sine: } m^R(\alpha) \rightarrow \sin \alpha \qquad \text{cosine: } m^R(\alpha) \rightarrow \cos \alpha$$

which each have $\mathcal{R}$ as domain. Each range is, as before,

$$-1 \leq \sin \alpha \leq 1 \qquad \text{and} \qquad -1 \leq \cos \alpha \leq 1.$$

Although $m^R(\alpha)$ was used in defining these functions, it is customary to represent them by using a single variable, x, y, z, etc., in place of $m^R(\alpha)$ and writing, for example:

$$\text{sine: } x \rightarrow \sin x \qquad \text{cosine: } x \rightarrow \cos x$$

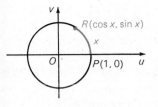

Figure 16

Because, in this context, values in the domains of these functions can be pictured as lengths of arcs on the unit circle (Figure 16), these functions are sometimes called circular functions to distinguish them from the trigonometric functions with the set of angles as domains.

The fact that each angle α has one and only one measure in radians ensures that the circular functions and angle functions have identical properties. Since it is sometimes convenient (and easier) to study properties of one of these kinds of functions in preference to the other, we shall, hereafter, use whichever seems best suited for our purposes, with the understanding that fundamental properties developed using one kind are equally applicable to the other.

WRITTEN EXERCISES   The given points lie on the terminal side of an angle α in standard position. For each problem sketch the angle and find $\sin \alpha$ and $\cos \alpha$.

A
1. $(3, 4)$ 4. $(-5, 12)$ 7. $(-8, 15)$ 10. $(-2, -3)$
2. $(4, 3)$ 5. $(-2, -2)$ 8. $(12, 13)$ 11. $(-6, 8)$
3. $(12, 5)$ 6. $(3, -4)$ 9. $(0, -4)$ 12. $(-2, 2\sqrt{3})$

In Exercises 13–20 find $\sin \alpha$ or $\cos \alpha$, whichever is not given, and state the quadrant in which α lies.

EXAMPLE $\sin \alpha = -\frac{3}{5}$, $\cos \alpha > 0$

SOLUTION   Since $\sin^2 \alpha + \cos^2 \alpha = 1$ for every angle α, replace $\sin \alpha$ with $-\frac{3}{5}$ in the identity to obtain

$$(-\tfrac{3}{5})^2 + \cos^2 \alpha = 1$$
$$\cos^2 \alpha = 1 - \tfrac{9}{25} = \tfrac{16}{25}.$$

Therefore,

$$\cos \alpha = \tfrac{4}{5} \quad \text{or} \quad \cos \alpha = -\tfrac{4}{5}.$$

Since you are given that $\cos \alpha > 0$, choose the positive value.
$\therefore \cos \alpha = \frac{4}{5}$ and α lies in Quadrant IV.   **Answer.**

13. $\cos \alpha = \frac{5}{13}$, $\sin \alpha > 0$ 18. $\cos \alpha = \dfrac{-\sqrt{3}}{2}$, $\sin \alpha > 0$

14. $\cos \alpha = \frac{12}{13}$, $\sin \alpha < 0$

15. $\sin \alpha = -\frac{3}{5}$, $\cos \alpha > 0$ 19. $\cos \alpha = \dfrac{\sqrt{2}}{2}$, $\sin \alpha < 0$

16. $\sin \alpha = -\frac{5}{13}$, $\cos \alpha < 0$

17. $\sin \alpha = \dfrac{1}{\sqrt{13}}$, $\cos \alpha < 0$ 20. $\sin \alpha = -\dfrac{\sqrt{10}}{10}$, $\cos \alpha < 0$

In Exercises 21–26, find $\sin \alpha$ and $\cos \alpha$ if α is an angle in standard position whose terminal side is the graph of the given set.

EXAMPLE $\{(u, v): 2u - v = 0, u \leq 0\}$

SOLUTION   Sketch the graph of the given set and show the unit circle on your sketch. Then use the fact that $R(u, v)$, the point of intersection of the terminal side of α and the unit circle, has as coordinates $(\cos \alpha, \sin \alpha)$.
Solve $2u - v = 0$ for v to get $v = 2u$. Replace v with $2u$ in $u^2 + v^2 = 1$:

$$u^2 + (2u)^2 = 1$$
$$u^2 + 4u^2 = 1$$
$$5u^2 = 1$$
$$u^2 = \tfrac{1}{5}$$

$u^2 + v^2 = 1$

$R(u, v)$

Hence,

$$u = \dfrac{1}{\sqrt{5}} \quad \text{or} \quad u = -\dfrac{1}{\sqrt{5}}.$$

Since R lies in Quadrant III, choose the negative value. Then

$$v = 2u = 2\left(-\frac{1}{\sqrt{5}}\right) = -\frac{2}{\sqrt{5}}.$$

$\therefore \sin \alpha = -\dfrac{2}{\sqrt{5}}$ and $\cos \alpha = -\dfrac{1}{\sqrt{5}}$. **Answer.**

B 21. $\{(u, v): u - 3v = 0, u \geq 0\}$ 24. $\{(u, v): 5u + 2v = 0, u \leq 0\}$
  22. $\{(u, v): 3u - 4v = 0, u \geq 0\}$ 25. $\{(u, v): u - v = 0, u \geq 0\}$
  23. $\{(u, v): u + 4v = 0, u \leq 0\}$ 26. $\{(u, v): u + v = 0, u \leq 0\}$

C 27. Use the fact that corresponding sides of similar triangles are proportional to show that if (u_1, v_1) and (u_2, v_2) are any two points other than the origin on the terminal side of a first-quadrant angle α in standard position, then

$$\frac{u_1}{v_1} = \frac{u_2}{v_2}, \quad \frac{u_1}{\sqrt{u_1^2 + v_1^2}} = \frac{u_2}{\sqrt{u_2^2 + v_2^2}},$$

and

$$\frac{v_1}{\sqrt{u_1^2 + v_1^2}} = \frac{v_2}{\sqrt{u_2^2 + v_2^2}}.$$

  28. Make a sketch showing appropriate triangles, and repeat Problem 27 for a second-quadrant angle in standard position.

14–4 *special values of sine and cosine*

We use shortened notation to refer to the values of trigonometric functions for specific angles. The notation "sin 30°" means "the value of the sine of the angle whose measure is 30°." "Cos $\dfrac{\pi^R}{4}$" means "the value of the cosine of the angle whose measure is $\dfrac{\pi^R}{4}$."

   In geometry, you learned that if one acute angle of a right triangle measures 30° $\left(\text{or } \dfrac{\pi^R}{6}\right)$, then the lengths of the sides of the triangle are in the ratio

$$1 : \sqrt{3} : 2,$$

and that in a right triangle with an acute angle measuring 45° $\left(\text{or } \dfrac{\pi^R}{4}\right)$, the lengths of the sides are in the ratio

$$1 : 1 : \sqrt{2}.$$

You can use these facts to find $\sin \alpha$ and $\cos \alpha$ when the measure of α is a multiple of 30° $\left(\text{or } \dfrac{\pi^R}{6}\right)$ or of 45° $\left(\text{or } \dfrac{\pi^R}{4}\right)$.

EXAMPLE Find **(a)** sin 45° and **(b)** cos $\dfrac{5\pi^R}{6}$.

SOLUTION In each case, sketch an angle α in standard position with the given measure

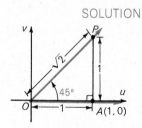

a. Since the measure of the angle is 45°, take point $A(1, 0)$ on the u-axis and complete the right triangle AOP dimensions as shown at the left.

$$\therefore \sin 45° = \frac{v}{r} = \frac{1}{\sqrt{2}}. \quad \text{Answer.}$$

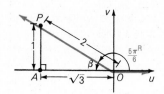

b. Since the measure of the given angle is $\dfrac{5\pi^R}{6}$, the measure of angle β i the diagram is

$$\left(\pi - \frac{5\pi}{6}\right)^R, \text{ or } \frac{\pi}{6}^R.$$

Take point P at a distance of 2 units from the origin on the terminal sid of the given angle, and complete the right triangle AOP with the dimension as shown. Since cos α is negative in the second quadrant

$$\cos \frac{5\pi^R}{6} = -\frac{\sqrt{3}}{2}. \quad \text{Answer.}$$

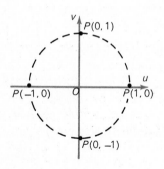

Figure 17

For quadrantal angles, that is, angles with measures which are multiple of 90° $\left(\text{or } \dfrac{\pi}{2}^R\right)$, the definitions of sin α and cos α are sufficient to provid these values by inspection. Thus, you can see from a particular point P o the unit circle (Figure 17) that:

cos 0° = 1	cos 90° = 0	cos 180° = −1	cos 270° = 0
sin 0° = 0	sin 90° = 1	sin 180° = 0	sin 270° = −1

Using these function values for quadrantal angles and procedures such a those supplied in the Example above, you can construct the table shown o the opposite page.

You can use this table for circular functions also, since

$$\sin m^R(\alpha) = \sin \alpha, \qquad \cos m^R(\alpha) = \cos \alpha.$$

For example,

$$\text{if } x = \frac{\pi}{3}, \text{ then } \sin x = \frac{\sqrt{3}}{2} \text{ and } \cos x = \frac{1}{2}.$$

On the other hand, for values of x between 0 and 2π,

$$\text{if } \sin x = \frac{1}{\sqrt{2}}, \text{ then } x = \frac{\pi}{4} \text{ or } x = \frac{3\pi}{4}.$$

Since coterminal angles differ in measure by multiples of 360°, or 2 radians, it follows that for any angle α

$$\sin (\alpha + k \cdot 360°) = \sin \alpha, \qquad \sin (\alpha + 2k\pi^R) = \sin \alpha,$$
$$\cos (\alpha + k \cdot 360°) = \cos \alpha, \qquad \cos (\alpha + 2k\pi^R) = \cos \alpha.$$

Measure of α		sin α	cos α	Measure of α		sin α	cos α
0°	0^R	0	1	180°	π^R	0	-1
30°	$\dfrac{\pi^R}{6}$	$\dfrac{1}{2}$	$\dfrac{\sqrt{3}}{2}$	210°	$\dfrac{7\pi^R}{6}$	$-\dfrac{1}{2}$	$-\dfrac{\sqrt{3}}{2}$
45°	$\dfrac{\pi^R}{4}$	$\dfrac{1}{\sqrt{2}}$	$\dfrac{1}{\sqrt{2}}$	225°	$\dfrac{5\pi^R}{4}$	$-\dfrac{1}{\sqrt{2}}$	$-\dfrac{1}{\sqrt{2}}$
60°	$\dfrac{\pi^R}{3}$	$\dfrac{\sqrt{3}}{2}$	$\dfrac{1}{2}$	240°	$\dfrac{4\pi^R}{3}$	$-\dfrac{\sqrt{3}}{2}$	$-\dfrac{1}{2}$
90°	$\dfrac{\pi^R}{2}$	1	0	270°	$\dfrac{3\pi^R}{2}$	-1	0
120°	$\dfrac{2\pi^R}{3}$	$\dfrac{\sqrt{3}}{2}$	$-\dfrac{1}{2}$	300°	$\dfrac{5\pi^R}{3}$	$-\dfrac{\sqrt{3}}{2}$	$\dfrac{1}{2}$
135°	$\dfrac{3\pi^R}{4}$	$\dfrac{1}{\sqrt{2}}$	$-\dfrac{1}{\sqrt{2}}$	315°	$\dfrac{7\pi^R}{4}$	$-\dfrac{1}{\sqrt{2}}$	$\dfrac{1}{\sqrt{2}}$
150°	$\dfrac{5\pi^R}{6}$	$\dfrac{1}{2}$	$-\dfrac{\sqrt{3}}{2}$	330°	$\dfrac{11\pi^R}{6}$	$-\dfrac{1}{2}$	$\dfrac{\sqrt{3}}{2}$
180°	π^R	0	-1	360°	$2\pi^R$	0	1

Sine and cosine are examples of *periodic* functions. A function *f* is periodic if there is some nonzero constant *p* such that $f(x + p) = f(x)$ for all *x* in the domain of *f*. *p* is called a period of the function. If there is a smallest positive constant *p* for which *f* is periodic, then *p* is called the fundamental period of *f*. Sine and cosine both have fundamental periods of 360° or $2\pi^R$. If their domains are each $\mathcal{R}$, the fundamental period is 2π.

WRITTEN EXERCISES Use the periodic properties of sine and cosine, together with the table above, to find the given function value.

EXAMPLE   **a.** sin 840°   **b.** $\cos\left(-\dfrac{13\pi^R}{3}\right)$

SOLUTION   **a.** First note that positive multiples of 360° are 360°, 720°, and 1080°. Since 720° < 840° < 1080°, and 840° − 720° = 120°, you can write:

$$\sin 840° = \sin(120° + 720°) = \sin[120° + 2(360°)] = \sin 120°$$

From the table, $\sin 840° = \sin 120° = \dfrac{\sqrt{3}}{2}$. Answer.

b. Since negative multiples of 2π are -2π, -4π, and -6π, and $-6\pi < -\dfrac{13\pi}{3} < -4\pi$, you can express $-\dfrac{13\pi}{3}$ as $-6\pi + \dfrac{5\pi}{3}$. Then,

$$\cos\left(-\dfrac{13\pi^R}{3}\right) = \cos\left[\dfrac{5\pi^R}{3} - 3(2\pi)^R\right] = \cos\dfrac{5\pi^R}{3} = \dfrac{1}{2}. \quad \text{Answer.}$$

A

1. $\sin 780°$
2. $\cos 1110°$
3. $\cos 690°$
4. $\sin 870°$
5. $\cos 11\pi$

6. $\sin \dfrac{9\pi}{4}$
7. $\cos \dfrac{11\pi}{3}$
8. $\sin \dfrac{29\pi}{6}$

9. $\sin(-300°)$
10. $\cos(-600°)$
11. $\cos(-1125°)$
12. $\sin(-855°)$
13. $\cos(-5\pi)$

14. $\sin\left(\dfrac{15\pi}{2}\right)$
15. $\sin\left(\dfrac{27\pi}{6}\right)$
16. $\cos\left(\dfrac{21\pi}{4}\right)$

Evaluate.

17. $3\cos 45° + 2\sin 30°$
18. $3(\cos 60° - \sin 120°)$
19. $4(\sin 120° - \cos 240°)$

20. $-2(\cos 135° - \sin 225°)$
21. $\cos 45°(\sin 135° - \cos 225°)$
22. $\sin 60°(\cos 240° - \sin 330°)$

Use a process similar to those shown in the example on page 492 to verify each of the following.

B

23. $\cos\dfrac{3\pi^R}{4} = -\dfrac{1}{\sqrt{2}}$, $\sin\dfrac{3\pi^R}{4} = \dfrac{1}{\sqrt{2}}$

24. $\cos 150° = -\dfrac{\sqrt{3}}{2}$, $\sin 150° = \dfrac{1}{2}$

14–5 *using tables*

In the preceding section, you computed values of sine and cosine for some special angles. Values in general can be computed to any desired accuracy by the methods of advanced mathematics. Some of these values have been collected in the tables given at the back of this book.

Table 6, at the back of the book, gives approximate values of the sine and cosine functions (together with those for other functions that you will study later) for angles whose measures run from 0° to 90° in multiples of 10'. (Methods of finding function values for angles outside this range will be discussed in the next section.) The left-hand column, beginning at the top of page 602 and continuing to the bottom of page 606, lists such angle measures from 0°0' to 45°0'. The right-hand column, beginning at the bottom of page 606 and continuing to the top of page 602, lists angle measures from 45°0' to 90°0'. Most of the values are approximate and are given correct to four significant digits. Of course, the values of sin 0°, cos 0°, sin 30°, cos 60°, sin 90°, and cos 90° are exact.

To find a four-significant-digit approximation for the value of sin α or cos α for an angle α whose measure is listed in Table 6:

1. **a.** If $0° \leq m(\alpha) \leq 45°$, find $m(\alpha)$ in the left-hand column, and read across the top to identify the column containing values of the specified function.
   b. If $45° \leq m(\alpha) \leq 90°$, find $m(\alpha)$ in the right-hand column, and read across the bottom to identify the column containing values of the specified function.

2. The intersection of the row containing the angle measure and the column for the specified function contains the desired function value.

EXAMPLE 1   Find sin 61°10'.

SOLUTION   In the right-hand column of Table 6 you find ''61°10'.'' In the row opposite this, *above* the label sin α at the bottom of the page, you find ''0.8760.''
∴ sin 61°10' $\doteq$ 0.8760.   **Answer.**

If you wish to find the approximate value of a given function for an angle measure that is not a multiple of 10', you may use the process of *linear interpolation* as you did for logarithms on page 385. In so doing, you must be careful to take into account whether the values of the given function increase or decrease when $m(\alpha)$ increases from 0° to 90°.

EXAMPLE 2   Find cos 37°18'.

SOLUTION   cos 37°10' > cos 37°18' > cos 37°20'. Using a convenient vertical arrangement for the linear interpolation, you can write:

$$10'\left[8'\begin{bmatrix}\begin{array}{c|c} m(\alpha) & \cos\alpha \\ \hline 37°10' & 0.7969 \\ 37°18' & \underline{\ ?\ } \\ 37°20' & 0.7951 \end{array}\end{bmatrix}d\right]-0.0018 \left\{\begin{array}{l}\text{A negative number,}\\ \text{because}\\ \cos 37°20' < \cos 37°10'.\end{array}\right.$$

$$\frac{8}{10} \doteq \frac{d}{-0.0018}; \ d \doteq \frac{8}{10}(-0.0018) \doteq -0.0014$$

cos 37°18' $\doteq$ 0.7969 + (−0.0014), or 0.7955.   **Answer.**

You can also use Table 6 to approximate to the nearest minute the measure of an angle α with measure between 0° and 90° when you are given the value for a trigonometric function of α.

EXAMPLE 3   Find $m(\alpha)$, where $0° \leq m(\alpha) \leq 90°$, if $\sin \alpha = 0.3891$.

SOLUTION   You first locate the nearest values given for $\sin \alpha$ that are above and below 0.3891. Then you arrange the values as follows:

$$10' \left[d \begin{bmatrix} \begin{array}{c|c} m(\alpha) & \sin \alpha \\ \hline 22°50' & 0.3881 \\ \underline{\quad ? \quad} & 0.3891 \\ 23°00' & 0.3907 \end{array} \end{bmatrix} 0.0010 \right] 0.0026 \begin{cases} \text{Positive numbers,} \\ \text{because} \\ \sin 23°0' > \sin 22°50' \end{cases}$$

$$\frac{d}{10} \doteq \frac{0.0010}{0.0026} \doteq \frac{10}{26}; \ d \doteq \frac{10}{26}(10) \doteq 4$$

$$m(\alpha) \doteq 22°50' + 4', \text{ or } 22°54'. \quad \textbf{Answer.}$$

Table 7 gives values of circular functions for

$$0 \leq x \leq \frac{\pi}{2}$$

together with values of trigonometric functions for angles such that

$$0 \leq m^R(\alpha) \leq \frac{\pi}{2}$$

at intervals of 0.01.

EXAMPLE 4   Find $\cos 0.42^R$.

SOLUTION   Locate "0.42" in the left-hand column on page 607. In the row opposite this, below the label "$\cos x$ or $\cos \alpha$," you find "0.9131."

$$\therefore \cos 0.42^R \doteq 0.9131. \quad \textbf{Answer.}$$

By using linear interpolation in Table 7, you can find approximate function values for x (or $m^R(\alpha)$) given as multiples of 0.001.

ORAL EXERCISES   Use Tables 6 and 7 at the back of the book to find an approximation for each function value.

1. $\cos 22°10'$ 4. $\cos 27°00'$ 7. $\cos 0.21^R$ 10. $\sin 1^R$

2. $\sin 14°20'$ 5. $\sin 44°30'$ 8. $\sin 1.23^R$ 11. $\sin 1.56^R$

3. $\sin 72°50'$ 6. $\cos 58°40'$ 9. $\cos 0.98^R$ 12. $\cos 0.03^R$

Use Table 6 to find an approximation in degrees and minutes for the value of α in each equation.

13. $\cos \alpha = 0.8884$ 16. $\cos \alpha = 0.9989$

14. $\sin \alpha = 0.3854$ 17. $\sin \alpha = 0.9555$

15. $\sin \alpha = 0.6539$ 18. $\cos \alpha = 0.4436$

Use Table 7 to find an approximation to hundredths of radians for the value of α in each equation.

19. $\cos \alpha = 0.7038$
20. $\sin \alpha = 0.9580$
21. $\sin \alpha = 0.9995$

22. $\cos \alpha = 0.3058$
23. $\cos \alpha = 0.7712$
24. $\sin \alpha = 0.7771$

WRITTEN EXERCISES

For Exercises 1–24, use Table 6 at the back of the book and linear interpolation as necessary.

Find a four-significant-digit approximation to the given function value.

A
1. $\cos 24°38'$
2. $\sin 43°12'$
3. $\sin 71°13'$

4. $\cos 55°15'$
5. $\cos 12°47'$
6. $\sin 1°8'$

7. $\sin 69°57'$
8. $\cos 42°14'$
9. $\sin 57°22'$

10. $\sin 45°23'$
11. $\cos 44°57'$
12. $\cos 89°24'$

Find the measure of α in degrees and minutes (to the nearest minute) for the first-quadrant angle with the given function value.

13. $\cos \alpha \doteq 0.9485$
14. $\sin \alpha \doteq 0.4705$
15. $\sin \alpha \doteq 0.6000$
16. $\cos \alpha \doteq 0.9800$
17. $\cos \alpha \doteq 0.2712$
18. $\sin \alpha \doteq 0.8104$

19. $\sin \alpha \doteq 0.9915$
20. $\cos \alpha \doteq 0.0035$
21. $\sin \alpha \doteq 0.5980$
22. $\sin \alpha \doteq 0.2731$
23. $\cos \alpha \doteq 0.5873$
24. $\cos \alpha \doteq 0.7090$

For Exercises 25–48, use Table 7 at the back of the book and linear interpolation as necessary.

Find a four-significant-digit approximation to the given function value.

25. $\cos 1.231^R$
26. $\sin 0.732^R$
27. $\sin 0.794^R$

28. $\cos 1.005^R$
29. $\cos 0.247^R$
30. $\sin 0.564^R$

31. $\cos 1.118^R$
32. $\sin 1.413^R$
33. $\cos 0.109^R$

34. $\cos 1.481^R$
35. $\sin 0.088^R$
36. $\sin 1.492^R$

Find to the nearest thousandth the approximate value of the real number x, $0 \leq x \leq \dfrac{\pi}{2}$, for which the given sentence is true.

37. $\sin x \doteq 0.9350$
38. $\cos x \doteq 0.1352$
39. $\cos x \doteq 0.7912$
40. $\sin x \doteq 0.1420$
41. $\sin x \doteq 0.5560$
42. $\cos x \doteq 0.1275$

43. $\cos x \doteq 0.6462$
44. $\sin x \doteq 0.9505$
45. $\cos x \doteq 0.9876$
46. $\cos x \doteq 0.0925$
47. $\sin x \doteq 0.9895$
48. $\sin x \doteq 0.2965$

programming in BASIC

The BASIC language contains built-in functions SIN(X) and COS(X), with X given in radians. Here is a program that will find the value of sine for a whole number of degrees.

```
10   PRINT ''INPUT D IN DEGREES'';
20   INPUT D
30   LET X=D*3.14159/180
40   PRINT ''SIN '';D;''(D) = '';SIN(X)
50   END
```

EXERCISES

1. Rewrite the program given above to allow you to input numbers of degrees and minutes, and use your program to check Example 1 on page 495.

2. Write a program to find the cosine of an angle measured in degrees and minutes, and use the program to check Example 2 on page 495.

14–6 *reference angles and arcs*

We shall now discuss how to find values for the sine and cosine functions for angles with measures outside the range

$$0° \leq m(\alpha) \leq 90°.$$

First consider an angle in each of Quadrants II, III, and IV, as in Figure 18. Let $P(a, b)$ be any point other than the origin on the terminal side of α. Let T be the point with coordinates $(|a|, |b|)$; thus, T lies in the first quadrant. Then let θ (Greek *theta*) be the angle whose terminal side contains T.

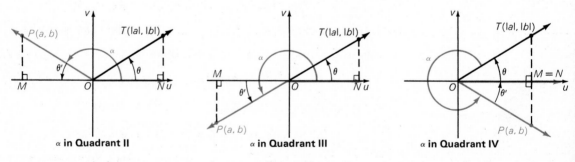

Figure 18

Now, notice that for α in Quadrant II, right triangles OMP and ONT are congruent and $\theta' \cong \theta$. Thus, the v-coordinates of P and T are equal, but their u-coordinates are negatives of each other; that is, $a = -|a|$. This means that, by definition,

$$\sin \alpha = \frac{b}{\sqrt{a^2 + b^2}} = \frac{|b|}{\sqrt{|a|^2 + |b|^2}} = \sin \theta$$

and

$$\cos \alpha = \frac{a}{\sqrt{a^2 + b^2}} = \frac{-|a|}{\sqrt{|a|^2 + |b|^2}} = -\cos \theta.$$

By observing similar relationships between a and $|a|$ and b and $|b|$ in each quadrant, and noting that in any quadrant

$$\sqrt{a^2 + b^2} = \sqrt{|a|^2 + |b|^2},$$

you can see that the sines and cosines of α and θ are related as shown in the table below. Either θ or θ' is called a reference angle for α, because you can use it to determine values for trigonometric functions of α. The *reference angle* will hereafter be denoted by θ.

Function value	Quadrant in which α lies			
	I	II	III	IV
$\sin \alpha$	$\sin \theta$	$\sin \theta$	$-\sin \theta$	$-\sin \theta$
$\cos \alpha$	$\cos \theta$	$-\cos \theta$	$-\cos \theta$	$\cos \theta$

EXAMPLE   Find an approximation for **(a)** cos 153° and **(b)** sin 312°.

SOLUTION   Use a sketch to help you picture the angle.

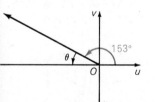

a. From the sketch you see that

$$m°(\theta) = 180 - m°(\alpha) = 180 - 153 = 27.$$

From the table above, $\cos 153° = -\cos 27°$. Then, from Table 6,

$$\cos 27° = 0.8910.$$

∴ cos 153° = −0.8910. **Answer.**

b. From the sketch you can see that

$$m°(\theta) = 360 - m°(\alpha) = 360 - 312 = 48.$$

From the table above, $\sin 312° = -\sin 48°$. Then, from Table 6,

$$\sin 48° = 0.7431.$$

∴ sin 312° = −0.7431. **Answer.**

For angles with measures outside the range $0° \leq m(\alpha) \leq 360°$, you use the periodic properties of the trigonometric functions (page 492) to find first an equivalent function value for an angle with measure in the range $0° \leq m(\alpha) < 360°$, and then use an appropriate reference angle. For example, to find sin 672°, you would first write

$$\sin 672° = \sin (672° - 360°) = \sin 312°,$$

and then proceed as in Example b, above.

When angle measures are given in radians, measures for reference angles can be approximated by using

$$\frac{\pi}{2} \doteq 1.57, \ \pi \doteq 3.14, \ \frac{3\pi}{2} \doteq 4.71, \text{ and } 2\pi \doteq 6.28.$$

When finding values of circular functions, you may think of the real number x as the measure of an arc on the unit circle, and use a **reference arc** with measure x', as shown in Figure 19. For example,

$$\cos 4 = -\cos (4 - \pi)$$
$$\doteq -\cos (4.00 - 3.14)$$
$$\doteq -\cos 0.86.$$

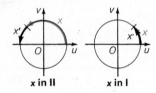

x in II   x in I

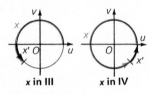

x in III   x in IV

Figure 19

Then from Table 7

$$\cos 0.86 \doteq 0.6524.$$
$$\therefore \cos 4 \doteq -0.6524.$$

WRITTEN EXERCISES

Express the given function value in terms of the same function of an angle with measure between 0° and 90° or between 0^R and 1.57^R. Make a sketch showing the given angle together with its reference angle.

EXAMPLE   sin 208°

SOLUTION   From the table on page 499, $\sin \alpha = -\sin \theta$.

$$\therefore \sin 208° = -\sin 28°. \text{ Answer.}$$

A
1. sin 103°   4. sin 199°   7. sin 310°30′   10. sin 219°6′
2. cos 171°   5. sin 280°   8. cos 142°20′   11. sin 2.57^R
3. cos 257°   6. cos 343°   9. cos 105°50′   12. cos 4.2^R

13–24. Use Tables 6 and 7 to find a four-decimal-digit approximation for each function value found in Exercises 1–12.

Find a four-significant-digit approximation for the given function value.

25. cos 471°   28. sin 743°   31. sin 4.71^R 34. cos 3.2^R
26. sin 533°   29. sin $(-2)^R$ 32. cos 5.55^R 35. cos 1352°
27. cos 817°   30. cos $(-3)^R$ 33. sin 6^R 36. sin 1111°

In Exercises 37–44 use Table 6 to find the measure of α in degrees and minutes (to the nearest 10') such that α is in the given quadrant and $0° \leq m(\alpha) < 360°$.

EXAMPLE   II; cos $\alpha = -0.7790$

SOLUTION   Since α is in Quadrant II, you seek first the measurement of the reference angle θ. From Table 6, if cos $\theta = 0.7790$, then $m(\theta) = 38°50'$. Thus, $m(\alpha) = 180° - m(\theta) = 180° - 38°50' = 141°10'$. Answer.

37. III; sin $\alpha = -0.4094$ 41. IV; sin $\alpha = -0.9886$

38. IV; cos $\alpha = 0.4488$ 42. III; cos $\alpha = -0.0785$

39. II; cos $\alpha = -0.9483$ 43. II; sin $\alpha = 0.3365$

40. II; sin $\alpha = 0.1161$ 44. III; cos $\alpha = -0.5831$

Use Table 7 to find x to the nearest thousandth, $-3.14 \leq x \leq -1.57$, for the given function value.

45. cos $x = -0.8961$ 46. sin $x = -0.7243$

14-7   graphs of sine and cosine I

The sine and cosine circular functions, when specified as sets of ordered pairs of real numbers, are represented respectively by

$$\text{sine} = \{(x, y): y = \sin x\}$$

and

$$\text{cosine} = \{(x, y): y = \cos x\}.$$

Each has as domain $\mathcal{R}$, and as range the set of real numbers $\{y: |y| \leq 1\}$. Therefore, each can be graphed in the coordinate plane. Because both functions are periodic with fundamental period 2π, we need to determine their graphs only over the interval $0 \leq x \leq 2\pi$; the pattern over this interval then repeats endlessly in both directions along the x-axis.

From the table on page 493, you can determine the ordered pairs in

$$\{(x, y): y = \sin x\}$$

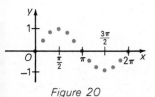

Figure 20

that have multiples of $\dfrac{\pi}{6}$ or $\dfrac{\pi}{4}$ as first components.

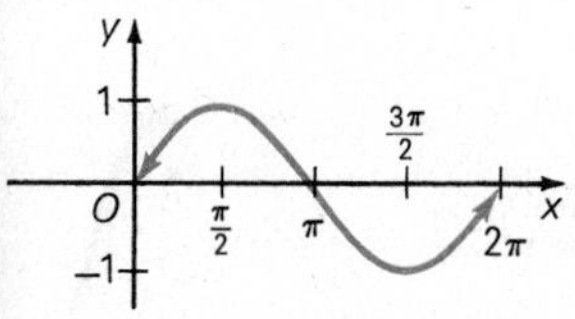

When all such ordered pairs with first components in the interval $0 \leq x \leq 2\pi$ are graphed, you obtain Figure 20. Assuming that the graph of sine is a smooth unbroken curve (as it is), you can connect the points shown in Figure 20 to produce the graph shown in Figure 21, which represents one fundamental period.

Figure 21

Now you need only to duplicate the pattern shown in Figure 21 over successive intervals of length 2π along the x-axis to obtain as much of the graph of the sine function as you wish. Figure 22 pictures the graph of sine over $-4\pi \le x \le 4\pi$. Do you see why this graph is called a sine wave?

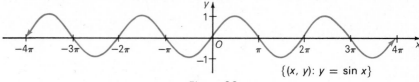

$$\{(x, y): y = \sin x\}$$

Figure 22

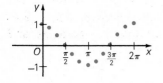

Figure 23

To graph $\{(x, y): y = \cos x\}$,

you can use the same procedure as for the sine function. Graphing points for ordered pairs from the table on page 493, you obtain the pattern shown in Figure 23, and, upon connecting the points, you have the graph of one fundamental period of the cosine function as shown in Figure 24.

Drawing three more periods produces the graph of cosine over $-4\pi \le x \le 4\pi$, as shown in Figure 25. This graph is also an example of a sine wave but displaced along the x-axis $\dfrac{\pi}{2}$ to the left.

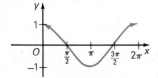

Figure 24

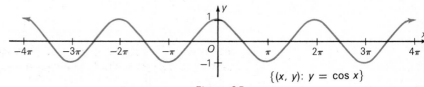

$$\{(x, y): y = \cos x\}$$

Figure 25

Notice that both curves (Figures 22 and 25) lie between the graphs of the *maximum* ordinate, 1, and the *minimum* ordinate, -1. When a periodic function attains a maximum value M and a minimum value m, you say that the function has an amplitude of

$$\frac{M - m}{2}.$$

Thus, the amplitude of sine and cosine is $\dfrac{1 - (-1)}{2}$, or 1.

Notice that the maximum ordinate in the graph of $y = \sin x$ occurs at $\frac{1}{4}$ of the distance across the fundamental periodic interval, $0 \le x \le 2\pi$ (see Figure 21), that is,

$$\sin \frac{\pi}{2} = 1,$$

and the minimum ordinate at $\frac{3}{4}$ of the distance across that interval, that is,

$$\sin \frac{3\pi}{2} = -1.$$

Correspondingly, the maximum ordinates in the graph of $y = \cos x$ occur at the beginning and the end of the interval (see Figure 24), that is,

$$\cos 0 = 1 \quad \text{and} \quad \cos 2\pi = 1,$$

and the minimum at the midpoint of the interval, that is,

$$\cos \pi = -1.$$

Next consider

$$\{(x, y): y = 2 \cos x\} \quad \text{and} \quad \{(x, y): y = -2 \sin x\}.$$

Notice that the y-component of each solution of $y = 2 \cos x$ is 2 times the y-component of the corresponding solution of $y = \cos x$. Similarly, the y-component of $y = -2 \sin x$ is -2 times the y-component of the corresponding solution of $y = \sin x$. Their graphs are shown in Figures 26 and

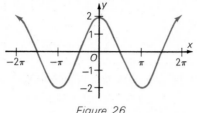

Figure 26

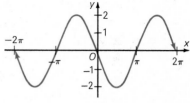

Figure 27

27, respectively. The fundamental period of each of these functions is 2π, and the amplitudes are each 2. Notice also that the graph of

$$\{(x, y): y = -2 \sin x\}$$

is a *reflection* with respect to the x-axis of the graph that would be drawn for

$$\{(x, y): y = 2 \sin x\}.$$

Hence, for $J = \{\text{the integers}\}$, in Figure 27

the *maximum* ordinates occur at $\sin\left(\dfrac{3\pi}{2} + 2k\pi\right) = 2, k \in J,$

and the *minimum* ordinates at $\sin\left(\dfrac{\pi}{2} + 2k\pi\right) = -2, k \in J.$

Similarly, in Figure 26

the *maximum* ordinates occur at $\cos(2k\pi) = 2, k \in J,$
and the *minimum* ordinates at $\cos(\pi + 2k\pi) = -2, k \in J.$

In general, the functions

$$\{(x, y): y = A \sin x\} \quad \text{and} \quad \{(x, y): y = A \cos x\}, A \neq 0,$$

have fundamental period 2π and amplitude $|A|$.

Sketch the graph of the function defined by the given equation over the two-period intervals $-2\pi \le x \le 2\pi$. State the amplitude.

A
1. $y = 4 \sin x$
2. $y = 3 \cos x$
3. $y = \frac{1}{2} \cos x$
4. $y = \frac{2}{3} \sin x$

5. $y = -3 \cos x$
6. $y = -\cos x$
7. $y = -\frac{1}{2} \cos x$
8. $y = -\frac{2}{3} \cos x$

9. $y = \frac{3}{2} \sin x$
10. $y = \frac{5}{2} \cos x$
11. $y = -\frac{4}{3} \cos x$
12. $y = -\frac{5}{3} \sin x$

14-8 graphs of sine and cosine II

In Section 14-7 you saw that the graphs of

$$\{(x, y)\}: y = A \sin x\} \qquad \text{and} \qquad \{(x, y): y = A \cos x\}$$

were sine waves with amplitude $|A|$ and period 2π.
   Next consider

$$\{(x, y): y = \sin 2x\}.$$

Notice that as x varies from 0 to π, $2x$ varies from 0 to 2π. Hence, $\sin 2x$ will assume all the values of sine while in the interval $0 \le x \le \pi$. Thus, the fundamental period of this function is π rather than 2π. The graph is shown in Figure 28.

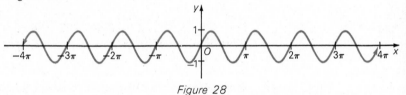

Figure 28

In general, the functions

$$\{(x, y): y = \sin Bx\} \qquad \text{and} \qquad \{(x, y): y = \cos Bx\}, B \ne 0$$

have fundamental period $\dfrac{2\pi}{|B|}$ and amplitude 1.
   Combining these results with those in Section 14-7, you have:

The functions

$$\{(x, y): y = A \sin Bx\} \qquad \qquad (1)$$
$$\{(x, y): y = A \cos Bx\} \qquad \qquad (2)$$

each have amplitude $|A|$ and fundamental period $\dfrac{2\pi}{|B|}$. Their graphs are sine waves.

These facts can be used to make a rapid sketch of such a graph.

EXAMPLE   Sketch the graph of $\{(x, y): y = 3 \cos \frac{1}{2}x\}$ over one fundamental period.

SOLUTION   The amplitude is 3 and the fundamental period is $\frac{2\pi}{\frac{1}{2}} = 4\pi$. Then over the interval $0 \le x \le 4\pi$:

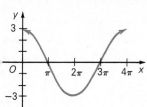

1. The maximum points are $(0, 3)$ and $(4\pi, 3)$.
2. The minimum point occurs when $x = \frac{1}{2} \times 4\pi = 2\pi$; it is $(2\pi, -3)$.
3. The intercepts are midway between the turning points, i.e., at $(\pi, 0)$ and $(3\pi, 0)$. These facts yield the curve shown at the left. **Answer.**

To graph the trigonometric functions sine and cosine, each having as domain the set of all angles, we represent each angle by its measure. If the angles are measured in radians, the graphs are the same as those of the associated circular functions. If the angles are measured in the degree system, the scale on the horizontal axis must be labeled accordingly. At the left is the graph of one fundamental period of

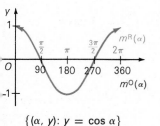

$$\{(\alpha, y): y = \cos \alpha\},$$

where $m^R(\alpha)$ and $m^\circ(\alpha)$ are shown along the horizontal axis in red and black, respectively.

WRITTEN EXERCISES   Find the amplitude $|A|$ and fundamental period P of the function defined by the given equation, and sketch the graph over the two-period interval $-P \le x \le P$.

A   1. $y = \sin 3x$ 5. $y = \frac{1}{2} \cos 2x$

2. $y = \cos 4x$ 6. $y = \frac{3}{4} \sin 3x$

3. $y = \cos \frac{1}{2}x$ 7. $y = -2 \sin 3x$

4. $y = \sin \frac{1}{5}x$ 8. $y = -3 \sin 2x$

B   9. $y = 2 \cos (-3x)$ 12. $y = \cos \pi x$

10. $y = -3 \sin (-2x)$ 13. $y = \cos \frac{\pi}{3} x$

11. $y = \sin \pi x$ 14. $y = \sin \frac{\pi}{2} x$

C   15. $y = 2 + \cos 2x$ 18. $y = \sin \left(x + \frac{\pi}{3}\right)$

16. $y = 2 \sin x - 2$ 19. $y = \cos \left(2x + \frac{\pi}{4}\right)$

17. $y = \cos \left(x - \frac{\pi}{6}\right)$ 20. $y = \cos \left(2x - \frac{\pi}{3}\right)$

SELF-TEST 2   Give the meaning of each of the following.

1. sine
2. cosine
3. trigonometric function
4. circular function

5. periodic function
6. reference angle
7. sine wave
8. amplitude

Objective 1, page 487   **9.** If the terminal side of an angle α contains the point $(2, -5)$, find $\cos \alpha$ and $\sin \alpha$.

Objective 2, page 487   **10.** If α is in quadrant IV and $\cos (\alpha) = \frac{5}{13}$ find $\sin (\alpha)$.

Objective 3, page 487   **11.** Find **(a)** $\cos 390°$, and **(b)** $\sin \dfrac{8\pi^R}{3}$.

Use Tables 6 and 7 at the back of the book to find:

12. $\cos 63°17'$ **13.** $\sin 0.273^R$ **14.** $\sin 411°10'$ **15.** $\cos 4^R$

Objective 4, page 487   **16.** Graph $\{(x, y): y = 2 \cos \frac{1}{3}x\}$.

Check your answers with those printed at the back of the book.

other trigonometric and circular functions and applications

Objectives

After completing the next two sections, you should be able to:
1. Find values for $\sec x$, $\tan x$, $\csc x$, and $\cot x$ for certain specified values of x.
2. Solve and apply solutions of right triangles.

14-9   *the tangent, cotangent, secant, and cosecant functions*

Several other trigonometric functions in common use are defined in terms of sine and cosine as follows:

tangent: $\alpha \to \dfrac{\sin \alpha}{\cos \alpha}$, $\cos \alpha \neq 0$ secant: $\alpha \to \dfrac{1}{\cos \alpha}$, $\cos \alpha \neq 0$

cotangent: $\alpha \to \dfrac{\cos \alpha}{\sin \alpha}$, $\sin \alpha \neq 0$ cosecant: $\alpha \to \dfrac{1}{\sin \alpha}$, $\sin \alpha \neq 0$

Values of these functions are denoted by:

$\tan \alpha$ (read "tangent of α") $\sec \alpha$ (read "secant of α")
$\cot \alpha$ (read "cotangent of α") $\csc \alpha$ (read "cosecant of α")

Notice that tangent and secant are not defined when $m(\alpha)$ is 90°, 270°, etc. $\left(or \dfrac{\pi^R}{2}, \text{ etc.}\right)$, and cotangent and cosecant are not defined when $m(\alpha)$ is 0°, 180°, etc. (or π^R, etc.).

EXAMPLE   If $\sin \alpha = \frac{3}{5}$ and $\cos \alpha = \frac{4}{5}$, find:

a. tan α.   **b.** cot α.   **c.** sec α.   **d.** csc α.

SOLUTION   **a.** $\tan \alpha = \dfrac{\sin \alpha}{\cos \alpha} = \dfrac{\frac{3}{5}}{\frac{4}{5}} = \dfrac{3}{4}.$ **c.** $\sec \alpha = \dfrac{1}{\cos \alpha} = \dfrac{1}{\frac{4}{5}} = \dfrac{5}{4}.$

            b. $\cot \alpha = \dfrac{\cos \alpha}{\sin \alpha} = \dfrac{\frac{4}{5}}{\frac{3}{5}} = \dfrac{4}{3}.$ **d.** $\csc \alpha = \dfrac{1}{\sin \alpha} = \dfrac{1}{\frac{3}{5}} = \dfrac{5}{3}.$

By using the definitions of sine and cosine on page 487,

$$\text{sine: } \alpha \to \frac{v}{r}, \text{ cosine: } \alpha \to \frac{u}{r},$$

you can verify (Exercises 29–30, page 510) the following:

Theorem. If α is an angle in standard position, with $P(u, v)$ any point other than the origin on the terminal side of α, and if $\sqrt{u^2 + v^2} = r$, then:

         tangent: $\alpha \to \dfrac{v}{u}, u \neq 0$ secant: $\alpha \to \dfrac{r}{u}, u \neq 0$

         cotangent: $\alpha \to \dfrac{u}{v}, v \neq 0$ cosecant: $\alpha \to \dfrac{r}{v}, v \neq 0$

Do you see why tangent and cotangent are called reciprocal functions? Sine and cosecant are also reciprocal functions, as are cosine and secant.

Although the theorem above is stated for angles in standard position, the domain of each of the functions is the set of all angles, since any angle can be put into standard position.

We can now extend Figure 14 as shown in Figure 29.

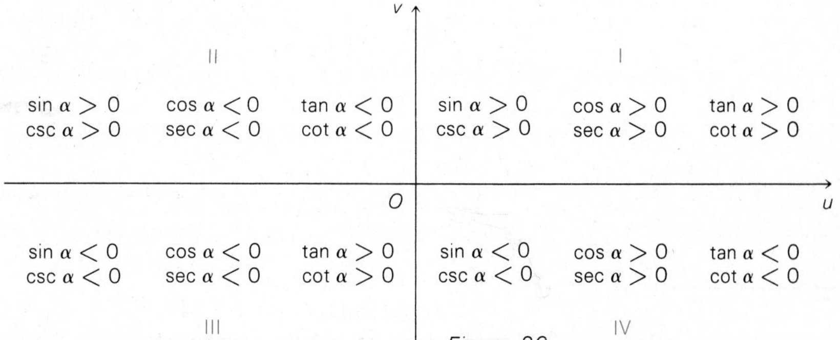

	II				I	
$\sin \alpha > 0$	$\cos \alpha < 0$	$\tan \alpha < 0$		$\sin \alpha > 0$	$\cos \alpha > 0$	$\tan \alpha > 0$
$\csc \alpha > 0$	$\sec \alpha < 0$	$\cot \alpha < 0$		$\csc \alpha > 0$	$\sec \alpha > 0$	$\cot \alpha > 0$
			O			u
$\sin \alpha < 0$	$\cos \alpha < 0$	$\tan \alpha > 0$		$\sin \alpha < 0$	$\cos \alpha > 0$	$\tan \alpha < 0$
$\csc \alpha < 0$	$\sec \alpha < 0$	$\cot \alpha > 0$		$\csc \alpha < 0$	$\sec \alpha > 0$	$\cot \alpha < 0$
	III				IV	

Figure 29

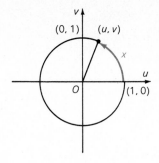

Figure 30

Circular functions tangent, cotangent, secant, and cosecant are defined in terms of arc length on the unit circle (Figure 30); since $\sin x = v$ and $\cos x = u$:

$$\tan x = \frac{v}{u}, u \neq 0 \qquad \sec x = \frac{1}{u}, u \neq 0$$

$$\cot x = \frac{u}{v}, v \neq 0 \qquad \csc x = \frac{1}{v}, v \neq 0$$

Special values for $\tan \alpha$, $\cot \alpha$, $\sec \alpha$, and $\csc \alpha$ can be computed from the values for $\sin \alpha$ and $\cos \alpha$ given in the table on page 493 (for example, see Exercises 9–16, page 510). You can use these values in sketching graphs of these functions:

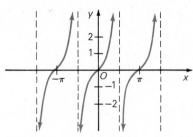

Figure 31 $\{(x, y): y = \tan x\}$

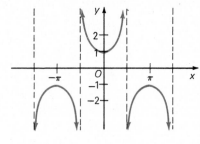

Figure 32 $\{(x, y): y = \sec x\}$

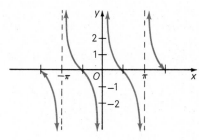

Figure 33 $\{(x, y): y = \cot x\}$

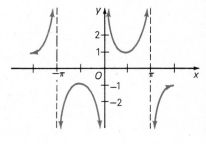

Figure 34 $\{(x, y): y = \csc x\}$

Compare the graph in Figure 31 with the graph of the reciprocal function in Figure 32. Also, compare the graph in Figure 33 with the graph in Figure 25 and the graph in Figure 34 with the graph in Figure 22.

The dashed lines in Figures 31, 32, 33, and 34 are asymptotes (see page 348).

We can now summarize the properties of the six circular functions that we have discussed ($J = \{$the integers$\}$).

sine: Domain: $\mathcal{R}$
Range: $\{y: y \in \mathcal{R}, |y| \leq 1\}$
Fundamental period: 2π

cosine: Domain: $\mathcal{R}$
Range: $\{y: y \in \mathcal{R}, |y| \leq 1\}$
Fundamental period: 2π

tangent: Domain: $\left\{x: x \in \mathcal{R}, x \neq \dfrac{(2k+1)\pi}{2}, k \in J\right\}$

Range: $\mathcal{R}$
Fundamental period: π

cotangent: Domain: $\{x: x \in \mathcal{R}, x \neq k\pi, k \in J\}$
Range: $\mathcal{R}$
Fundamental period: π

secant: Domain: $\left\{x: x \in \mathcal{R}, x \neq \dfrac{(2k+1)\pi}{2}, k \in J\right\}$

Range: $\{y: y \in \mathcal{R}, |y| \geq 1\}$
Fundamental period: 2π

cosecant: Domain: $\{x: x \in \mathcal{R}, x \neq k\pi, k \in J\}$
Range: $\{y: y \in \mathcal{R}, |y| \geq 1\}$
Fundamental period: 2π

Notice that the fundamental period of tangent and cotangent is π rather than 2π, and that each of the latter four functions has certain real numbers excluded from its domain.

Furthermore, as x increases from 0 to $\dfrac{\pi}{2}$, the function values vary as follows:

sin x increases,   tan x increases, sec x increases,
cos x decreases, cot x decreases, csc x decreases.

Values of tangent, cotangent, secant, and cosecant can be found from Tables 6 and 7 at the back of the book.

EXAMPLE   Find x where $0 \leq x \leq \dfrac{\pi}{2}$, if tan $x \doteq 1.305$.

SOLUTION   Use Table 7.

x	tan x

$$0.010 \left[n \begin{bmatrix} 0.910 & 1.286 \\ \underline{\quad ? \quad} & 1.305 \\ 0.920 & 1.313 \end{bmatrix} 0.019 \right] 0.027 \left\{ \begin{array}{l} \text{A positive number} \\ \text{because} \\ \tan 0.920 > \tan 0.910. \end{array} \right.$$

$$\frac{n}{0.010} \doteq \frac{0.019}{0.027}, \; n \doteq 0.007$$

$\therefore x \doteq 0.910 + 0.007 = 0.917.$ **Answer.**

Find values for the six trigonometric functions of the angle α in standard position whose terminal side contains the point with given coordinates.

A
1. (9, 12)   3. (−3, 1)   5. (1, 6)   7. (0, 3)
2. (−3, 3)   4. (−2, −5)   6. (3, −5)   8. (5, 0)

Using the values of $\sin \alpha$ and $\cos \alpha$ in the table on page 493, compute the values of $\tan \alpha$, $\cot \alpha$, $\sec \alpha$, and $\csc \alpha$ for the angle having the given measurement.

9. 45°   11. 150°   13. $\dfrac{\pi^R}{6}$ 15. $\dfrac{7\pi^R}{6}$

10. 120°   12. 240°   14. $\dfrac{\pi^R}{3}$ 16. $\dfrac{7\pi^R}{4}$

Use Table 6 or Table 7, the periodic properties of the trigonometric functions, reference angles, and linear interpolation as needed to find four-significant-digit approximations to the given function values. In each exercise, sketch the appropriate angle in standard position.

17. sec 98°   21. sec 172° 15′   25. csc 3.12^R
18. csc 223°   22. csc 314° 37′   26. sec 2.78^R
19. tan 341° 50′   23. cot (−0.12)^R 27. tan (−3.413)^R
20. cot 104° 10′   24. tan (−1.32)^R 28. cot (−1.082)^R
29. Verify that with the conditions of the theorem on page 507:

$$\text{tangent: } \alpha \rightarrow \frac{v}{u}, u \neq 0 \qquad \text{cotangent: } \alpha \rightarrow \frac{u}{v}, v \neq 0$$

30. Verify that with the conditions of the theorem on page 507:

$$\text{secant: } \alpha \rightarrow \frac{r}{u}, u \neq 0 \qquad \text{cosecant: } \alpha \rightarrow \frac{r}{v}, v \neq 0$$

Use Table 6 and linear interpolation as necessary to find the measurement of α in degrees and minutes, $0° \leq m(\alpha) \leq 90°$, for which the given sentence is true.

31. sec α = 1.800   33. cot α = 0.5000   35. tan α = 1.152
32. csc α = 2.545   34. tan α = 1.382   36. cot α = 0.8697

Use Table 7 and linear interpolation as necessary to find to the nearest 0.001 the real number x, $0 \leq x \leq \dfrac{\pi}{2}$, for which the given sentence is true.

37. cot x = 1.600   39. csc x = 1.042   41. sec x = 12.00
38. tan x = 1.255   40. sin x = 0.120   42. tan x = 0.5500

Find $m(\alpha)$ or the real number x for which the given compound sentence is true.

B **43.** $\cot \alpha = 3.412$ and $180° < m(\alpha) < 270°$.

44. $\sec \alpha = 1.210$ and $180° < m(\alpha) < 360°$.

45. $\csc x = -1.162$ and $\dfrac{3\pi}{2} < x < 2\pi$.

46. $\tan x = -0.3660$ and $\dfrac{\pi}{2} < x < \pi$.

Determine the period of each function, and sketch the graph over an interval of two successive periods (one with $x \leq 0$ and one with $x \geq 0$).

47. $y = \frac{1}{2} \tan x$

48. $y = -2 \sec x$

49. $y = -\tan 2x$

50. $y = \sec \frac{1}{3} x$

51. $y = 2 \cot \frac{1}{3} x$

52. $y = -3 \csc 3x$

programming in BASIC

BASIC provides the function TAN(X) as well as SIN(X) and COS(X). It also provides the function ATN(X), which will give the measurement in radians between $-\dfrac{\pi}{2}$ and $\dfrac{\pi}{2}$ of the angle whose tangent is X. For example, you can use this program to check the Example on page 509.

```
10   PRINT "IF TAN X = ";
20   INPUT T
30   PRINT "THEN X(R) = ";ATN(T)
40   END
```

EXERCISES

1. To see how ATN(X) works, try the program given above for values of $\tan x$:

0.6249   0.8693   1.150   2.145

Round your results to 4 decimal places, and compare them with the corresponding values in Table 6.

2. Repeat Exercise 1 using the negatives of the values given.

14–10 *solving right triangles*

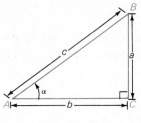

Figure 35

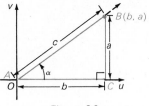

Figure 36

To solve a right triangle means to find the measures (or approximations to these) of various parts (angles and sides) when measures of other parts are given. In working with right triangles, it is customary to use either capital letters or Greek letters to identify the angles, and the corresponding lowercase Roman letters to represent the lengths of the sides opposite these angles (see Figure 35). It is also common practice to label the vertex of the right angle as C. The trigonometric functions discussed earlier in this chapter can be used to solve right triangles.

Any right triangle is congruent to a right triangle placed with an acute angle in standard position (Figure 36). If α of right triangle ABC is placed in standard position with side $\overline{AC}$ along the positive u-axis, then the definitions of the six trigonometric functions can be interpreted as follows:

If α is an acute angle of a right triangle, then:

$$\sin \alpha = \frac{\text{length of side opposite } \alpha}{\text{length of hypotenuse}}$$

$$\cos \alpha = \frac{\text{length of side adjacent to } \alpha}{\text{length of hypotenuse}}$$

$$\tan \alpha = \frac{\text{length of side opposite } \alpha}{\text{length of side adjacent to } \alpha}$$

$$\cot \alpha = \frac{\text{length of side adjacent to } \alpha}{\text{length of side opposite } \alpha}$$

$$\sec \alpha = \frac{\text{length of hypotenuse}}{\text{length of side adjacent to } \alpha}$$

$$\csc \alpha = \frac{\text{length of hypotenuse}}{\text{length of side opposite } \alpha}$$

From these statements, you can see that for right triangle ABC in Figure 35:

$$\sin \beta = \frac{b}{c} = \cos \alpha \qquad \cot \beta = \frac{a}{b} = \tan \alpha$$

$$\cos \beta = \frac{a}{c} = \sin \alpha \qquad \sec \beta = \frac{c}{a} = \csc \alpha$$

$$\tan \beta = \frac{b}{a} = \cot \alpha \qquad \csc \beta = \frac{c}{b} = \sec \alpha$$

Angles α and β are complementary angles, and the pairs of functions sine and cosine, tangent and cotangent, secant and cosecant are called cofunctions.

EXAMPLE 1   Solve the right triangle pictured, stating lengths of sides correct to the nearest hundredth of a unit of length and angle measures to the nearest minute.

SOLUTION   Since $m(A) + m(B) = 90°$,

$$m(B) = 90° - m(A) = 90° - 42° = 48°.$$

To find c you can use

$$\csc A = \frac{c}{9} \quad \text{or} \quad c = 9 \csc 42°.$$

From Table 6, $\csc 42° \doteq 1.494$, so that

$$c \doteq 9(1.494) = 13.446 \doteq 13.45.$$

To find b, you can use

$$\tan B = \frac{b}{9} \quad \text{or} \quad b = 9 \tan 48°.$$

From Table 6, $\tan 48° \doteq 1.111$, so that

$$b \doteq 9(1.111) = 9.999 \doteq 10.00.$$

$\therefore$ the measures of the remaining parts of the right triangle are $m(B) = 48°$, $c \doteq 13.45$, and $b \doteq 10.00$. **Answer.**

In theoretical examples like Example 1, the given measures (in this case, the measures of side $\overline{BC}$, angle α, and the right angle at C) are taken to be exact. Notice also that the cotangent and cosecant were used instead of tangent and cosine to avoid long divisions.

In using Table 6 in the solution of triangles or in solving real-life problems, lengths need be stated to no more than four significant digits, since this is the limit of the accuracy of the entries in this table. The following relationships between angle measure and length can be used as a guide in the exercises in this and later sections.

Angle measure to nearest	corresponds to	length to
1°	. . . .	2 significant digits
10′	. . . .	3 significant digits
1′	. . . .	4 significant digits

EXAMPLE 2   Solve the right triangle pictured.

SOLUTION   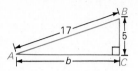 Assume that the given measures are exact. Thus, with the tables in this book, you may compute b to 4 significant digits and the measures of angles A and B to the nearest $1'$, according to the chart given above. To find $m(A)$, you can use $\sin A = \frac{5}{17} \doteq 0.2941$. From Table 6, you find that $m(A) \doteq 17°6'$. Since $m(A) + m(B) = 90°$, you have

$$m(B) = 90° - m°(A) \doteq 90° - 17°6' = 72°54'.$$

To find b, you can use

$$\cos A = \frac{b}{17} \quad \text{or} \quad b = 17 \cos 17°6'.$$

From Table 6, $\cos 17°6' \doteq 0.9558$, so that

$$b \doteq 17(0.9558) \doteq 16.25.$$

$\therefore m(A) \doteq 17°6'$, $m(B) \doteq 72°54'$, and $b \doteq 16.25$.   **Answer.**

In many practical problems applying trigonometric function values an angle is described as an *angle of elevation*, or an *angle of depression* (see Figure 37). Since the point B is elevated with respect to the observer at A, $\angle CAB$, the angle between the horizontal ray AC through A and the line of sight is an angle of elevation. The point T is depressed with respect to the observer at R; therefore, $\angle TRS$, the angle between the line of sight and the horizontal ray RS, is an angle of depression.

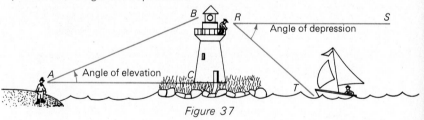

Figure 37

WRITTEN EXERCISES   Solve the right triangle with given parts. In each case, $m(C) = 90°$. Make and label a sketch of a right triangle showing the data.

A   1. $m(A) = 54°$; $b = 120$

2. $m(A) = 32°$; $a = 18$

3. $m(B) = 80°$; $b = 10$

4. $m(B) = 61°$; $a = 18$

5. $m(A) = 23°$; $c = 32$

6. $m(B) = 75°$; $c = 44$

7. $m(A) = 37°20'$; $a = 24$

8. $m(A) = 54°40'$; $b = 18$

9. $m(B) = 9°20'$; $c = 20$

10. $m(A) = 83°30'$; $c = 30$

11. $a = 6$; $c = 10$

12. $a = 8$; $c = 10$

13. $b = 10$; $c = 26$

14. $b = 24$; $c = 26$

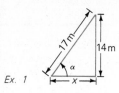

Ex. 1

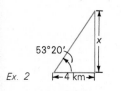

Ex. 2

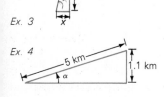

Ex. 3

Ex. 4

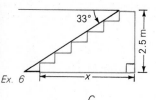

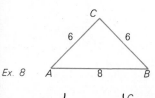

Ex. 6

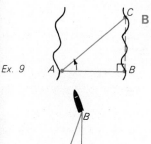

Ex. 8

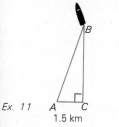

Ex. 9

Ex. 11

15. $a = 15$; $b = 20$

16. $a = 24$; $b = 13$

17. $a = 9.1$; $b = 7.2$

18. $a = 15.3$; $c = 18.7$

19. $b = 7.28$; $c = 9.04$

20. $a = 4.58$; $b = 6.76$

PROBLEMS

A   **1.** A support wire to a TV transmission antenna is 17 meters long and is attached to the antenna 14 meters from the ground. How far from the base of the antenna is the support wire attached to the ground? What is the measure of the angle that the support wire forms with the ground?

2. The angle of elevation from an observer at ground level to a vertically ascending rocket measures 53°20′. If the observer is located 4 kilometers from the lift-off point of the rocket, what is the altitude of the rocket?

3. The angle of depression from the top of a building 98 meters high to the base of a building across the street measures 78°10′. How wide is the street?

4. Hikers climb a 5-kilometer path to the top of a mountain. The top of the mountain is 1.1 kilometers higher than the base. What is the angle α (to the nearest degree) that the path makes with the horizontal?

5. What is the measure of the angle of elevation from the top of a building 12 meters high to the top of a building across a street 10 meters wide if the second building is 28 meters high?

6. The top of a stairway is 2.5 meters higher than the bottom. The angle of depression from the top of the stairway to the bottom is 33°. How far in meters do you move horizontally in walking from the bottom to the top of the stairway?

7. What is the measure of the angle of depression from an airplane flying at an altitude of 2500 meters to a lake located 4200 meters from a point on the ground directly beneath the airplane?

8. Find the measure of angle A in the isosceles triangle pictured at the left.

B   **9.** From a point A directly opposite a point B on the banks of a straight river, the angle CAB to a point, C, 50 meters upstream from B measures 38°52′. How wide (in meters) is the river?

10. The angles of elevation from a point on the ground 55 meters from the base of a building to the top and bottom of a television antenna located on top of the building are 68°18′ and 71°4′, respectively. How tall in meters is the antenna?

11. At a time 15 seconds after launching, a ground-control observer located 1.5 kilometers from a launch-pad finds that the angle of elevation of a rocket moving vertically from the pad is 78°42′. How high (in kilometers) is the rocket at that time? How far (in kilometers) is the observer from the rocket at the given time?

programming in BASIC

In BASIC you have these trigonometric functions to work with:

SIN(X), COS(X), TAN(X), ATN(X)

Write a program to solve a right triangle *ABC* with angles measured in degrees when given:

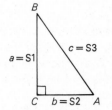

1. $m(A)$, a 2. $m(A)$, b 3. $m(A)$, c 4. a, b 5. a, c

(Suggestions: Represent a, b, c by S1, S2, S3, and use conversion factors C1 = 3.14159/180 and C2 = 180/3.14159.)

6. Write a program that combines the preceding programs into one that solves a triangle when given angle, adjacent leg; angle, opposite leg; and so on. (Suggestions: To guide choices through the program, use questions that can be answered 1 for *yes*, 0 for *no*.)

SELF-TEST 3

Give the meaning of each of the following.

1. tangent   3. secant   5. reciprocal functions
2. cotangent   4. cosecant   6. cofunctions

Objective 1, page 506 7. Find values for the six trigonometric functions of the angle α in standard position if the terminal side of α contains $(3, -5)$.

Objective 2, page 506 8. Solve the right triangle *ABC* in which $m(A) = 35°10'$ and $b = 12$.

Check your answers with those printed at the back of the book.

---

chapter summary

1. A **directed angle** is an ordered pair of rays with a common endpoint, one ray called the **initial side** and the other the **terminal side** of the angle, together with a rotation from the initial side to the terminal side. Angle measures are ordinarily expressed in either **degrees** or **radians**. These measures are related by the **conversion equations**:

$$m°(\alpha) = \frac{180}{\pi} m^R(\alpha) \qquad m^R(\alpha) = \frac{\pi}{180} m°(\alpha)$$

2. If α is an angle in standard position, with $P(u, v)$ any point other than the origin on the terminal side of α, and if $\sqrt{u^2 + v^2} = r$, then the six trigonometric functions are:

$$\sin: \alpha \rightarrow \sin \alpha = \frac{v}{r} \qquad \text{cotangent: } \alpha \rightarrow \cot \alpha = \frac{u}{v}, v \neq 0$$

$$\cos: \alpha \rightarrow \cos \alpha = \frac{u}{r} \qquad \text{secant: } \alpha \rightarrow \sec \alpha = \frac{r}{u}, u \neq 0$$

$$\text{tangent: } \alpha \rightarrow \tan \alpha = \frac{v}{u}, u \neq 0 \qquad \text{cosecant: } \alpha \rightarrow \csc \alpha = \frac{r}{v}, v \neq 0$$

3. Associated with each trigonometric function T is a correspondingly named **circular function** C, and for each angle α in standard position for which a given function is defined, $T(\alpha) = C[m^R(\alpha)]$.

4. Trigonometric and circular functions are **periodic**, and values for these functions can be found from tables in terms of **reference angles** or **reference arcs**.

5. Graphs of periodic functions consist of basic patterns repeated over each interval having a length of one fundamental period. The graphs of sine and cosine are **sine waves**. For a sine wave, the absolute value of one-half the difference of the minimum and maximum ordinates on the curve is called the **amplitude** of the wave.

6. Many practical problems can be solved by applying trigonometric function values.

chapter test and review

14–1   **1.** To the nearest centimeter how far will a wheel with a radius of 72 cm roll in $3\frac{1}{2}$ revolutions? Use $\pi \doteq \frac{22}{7}$.

14–2   **2.** Express $225°$ in radian measure as a multiple of π.

         3. Express $\dfrac{6\pi^R}{5}$ in degree measure.

14–3   **4.** Find $\sin \alpha$ and $\cos \alpha$ if the terminal side of α contains the point $(-5, 1)$.

         5. If $\cos \alpha = -\dfrac{3}{\sqrt{10}}$ and $\sin \alpha > 0$, find $\sin \alpha$ and state the quadrant in which α lies.

14–4   **6.** Evaluate $5 \sin 45° - \cos 315°$.

14–5   **7.** Given $\cos 40°10' \doteq 0.7642$ and $\cos 40°20' = 0.7623$, find an approximation for $\cos 40°17'$.

14–6   **8.** Express $\sin 300°$ in terms of the sine of an angle with a measurement between $0°$ and $90°$.

14–7   **9.** Graph $\{(x, y): y = 2 \cos x\}$.

14–8   **10.** Graph $\{(x, y): y = \sin(-\frac{1}{2}x)\}$.

14–9   **11.** If the terminal side of an angle α contains $(5, -7)$, find $\sec \alpha$, $\csc \alpha$, $\tan \alpha$, and $\cot \alpha$.

14–10   **12.** Use Table 6 to solve the right triangle for which $m(A) = 17°$ and $b = 10$.

Woodwind instruments have been crafted and played in many of the world's cultures. The vibrations which produce musical tones can be described by equations involving the sine and cosine functions.

15 *trigonometric identities and formulas*

identities

After completing the next two sections, you should be able to:
1. Prove simple trigonometric identities.

15-1 *fundamental identities*

Following are listed the eight fundamental trigonometric identities, some of which you have already met. You saw in Section 14-3 that the values of the sine and cosine functions are related by the identity

$$\sin^2 \alpha + \cos^2 \alpha = 1. \tag{1}$$

In Section 14-9, the following statements were made as definitions:

$$\tan \alpha = \frac{\sin \alpha}{\cos \alpha}, \ \cos \alpha \neq 0 \quad (2) \qquad \sec \alpha = \frac{1}{\cos \alpha}, \ \cos \alpha \neq 0 \quad (4)$$

$$\cot \alpha = \frac{\cos \alpha}{\sin \alpha}, \ \sin \alpha \neq 0 \quad (3) \qquad \csc \alpha = \frac{1}{\sin \alpha}, \ \sin \alpha \neq 0 \quad (5)$$

Since values of trigonometric functions are real numbers, the properties of real numbers can be used to find other relationships between the function values. From (2) and (3) you have

$$\frac{\sin \alpha}{\cos \alpha} = \frac{1}{\dfrac{\cos \alpha}{\sin \alpha}}, \ \sin \alpha \neq 0, \ \cos \alpha \neq 0,$$

that is,

$$\tan \alpha = \frac{1}{\cot \alpha}, \ \tan \alpha \neq 0, \ \cot \alpha \neq 0. \tag{6}$$

The last two of the eight fundamental trigonometric identities can be obtained from (1) as follows. For angles α for which $\cos \alpha \neq 0$, you have

$$\frac{\sin^2 \alpha}{\cos^2 \alpha} + \frac{\cos^2 \alpha}{\cos^2 \alpha} = \frac{1}{\cos^2 \alpha},$$

or

$$\tan^2 \alpha + 1 = \sec^2 \alpha, \cos \alpha \neq 0. \tag{7}$$

Similarly, for angles α for which $\sin \alpha \neq 0$, you have

$$\frac{\sin^2 \alpha}{\sin^2 \alpha} + \frac{\cos^2 \alpha}{\sin^2 \alpha} = \frac{1}{\sin^2 \alpha},$$

or

$$1 + \cot^2 \alpha = \csc^2 \alpha, \sin \alpha \neq 0. \tag{8}$$

Of course, Identities (1)–(8) are equally valid for the circular functions. You know that for every real number x,

$$\sin^2 x + \cos^2 x = 1,$$

because $\sin x$ and $\cos x$ are coordinates of points on the unit circle. The fact that the remaining circular functions are defined in precisely the same way as the corresponding trigonometric functions of angles guarantees that every trigonometric identity is as valid for values of circular functions as it is for values of those functions with the same names whose domains are the set of angles.

EXAMPLE 1 **Express $\tan \alpha \csc \alpha$ in terms of $\cos \alpha$, noting any restrictions.**

SOLUTION The given expression is defined provided $\cos \alpha \neq 0$ and $\sin \alpha \neq 0$. Thus, from Identities (2) and (5), you have

$$\tan \alpha \csc \alpha = \frac{\sin \alpha}{\cos \alpha} \cdot \frac{1}{\sin \alpha} = \frac{1}{\cos \alpha}, \cos \alpha \neq 0, \sin \alpha \neq 0. \text{ \textbf{Answer.}}$$

EXAMPLE 2 **Express $\cos \alpha$ in terms of $\sin \alpha$.**

SOLUTION From Identity (1), $\qquad \sin^2 \alpha + \cos^2 \alpha = 1$

$$\cos^2 \alpha = 1 - \sin^2 \alpha$$

$$\therefore \cos \alpha = \sqrt{1 - \sin^2 \alpha} \quad \text{or} \quad \cos \alpha = -\sqrt{1 - \sin^2 \alpha}. \text{ \textbf{Answer.}}$$

Notice that, in Example 2, the result is a disjunction of sentences. Since $\sqrt{1 - \sin^2 \alpha}$ always represents a nonnegative number, and $-\sqrt{1 - \sin^2 \alpha}$ always represents a nonpositive number, it is customary to use the information in Figure 29 on page 507 and express this disjunction as follows:

$$\cos \alpha = \sqrt{1 - \sin^2 \alpha} \text{ if } \alpha \text{ lies in Quadrants I or IV.}$$

$$\cos \alpha = -\sqrt{1 - \sin^2 \alpha} \text{ if } \alpha \text{ lies in Quadrants II or III.}$$

State the first expression equivalently in terms of the given function value, noting any restrictions.

1. $\sec \alpha$; $\cos \alpha$

2. $\csc \alpha$; $\sin \alpha$

3. $\cot \alpha$; $\tan \alpha$

4. $\sin \alpha$; $\cos \alpha$

5. $\sin \alpha \cot \alpha$; $\cos \alpha$

6. $\sec x \tan x$; $\sin x$

7. $\tan^2 x$; $\cos x$

8. $\cot^2 x$; $\sin x$

9. $\dfrac{\sin^2 x}{\tan^2 x}$; $\cos x$

10. $\dfrac{\cos^2 x}{\cot^2 x}$; $\sin x$

WRITTEN EXERCISES Write the first expression equivalently in terms of the given function value, noting any restrictions.

A

1. $\tan \alpha \csc \alpha$; $\sec \alpha$

2. $\cot \alpha \sec \alpha$; $\csc \alpha$

3. $\sin x \sec x$; $\tan x$

4. $\cos x \tan x$; $\sin x$

5. $\cot^2 x$; $\cos x$

6. $\tan^2 x$; $\sin x$

7. $\tan^2 x \sin^2 x$; $\cos x$

8. $\cot^2 x \cos^2 x$; $\sin x$

9. $1 - \sin^2 x$; $\sec x$

10. $1 - \cos^2 x$; $\csc x$

11. $\dfrac{1 + \tan^2 x}{\tan^2 x}$; $\sin x$

12. $\dfrac{\sin^2 x}{1 - \cos x}$; $\sec x$

In each of Exercises 13–18, find a single function value or a constant equivalent to the given expression, noting any restrictions.

EXAMPLE $\dfrac{\sin \alpha}{\cos \alpha \tan \alpha} - 1$

SOLUTION In the given expression, replace $\tan \alpha$ with $\dfrac{\sin \alpha}{\cos \alpha}$ ($\cos \alpha \neq 0$) to obtain

$$\frac{\sin \alpha}{\cos \alpha \left(\dfrac{\sin \alpha}{\cos \alpha}\right)} - 1 = \frac{\sin \alpha}{\sin \alpha} - 1 = 1 - 1 = 0.$$

Thus, for all angles α for which $\cos \alpha \neq 0$ and $\tan \alpha \neq 0$,

$$\frac{\sin \alpha}{\cos \alpha \tan \alpha} - 1 = 0. \quad \text{Answer.}$$

13. $\cos \alpha \tan \alpha \sec \alpha$

14. $\sec \alpha \csc \alpha - \cot \alpha$

15. $\dfrac{\sin x - \cos x}{\cos x} + 1$

16. $\dfrac{\sec x - \cos x}{\sin x}$

17. $(\csc \alpha - \cot \alpha)(\csc \alpha + \cot \alpha)$

18. $(\sec \alpha - \tan \alpha)(\sec \alpha + \tan \alpha)$

Express in terms of sin α and cos α only, and simplify.

B **19.** $\cos \alpha \cot \alpha + \sin \alpha$

20. $(\cot \alpha)(\cos \alpha + \tan \alpha \sin \alpha)$

21. $\dfrac{\csc \alpha - \sin \alpha}{\cot \alpha}$

22. $(\cot \alpha + \cos \alpha)(1 - \sin \alpha) + \dfrac{\sin \alpha}{\sec \alpha}$

23. $\dfrac{\tan^2 \alpha \csc^2 \alpha - 1}{\sec \alpha \tan^2 \alpha \cos \alpha}$

24. $(\cos \alpha \csc \alpha)\left(\sin \alpha + \dfrac{\sec \alpha}{\csc^2 \alpha}\right)$

25. If α lies in Quadrant II, express in terms of sin α:

a. $\tan \alpha$ b. $\cot \alpha$ c. $\sec \alpha$ d. $\csc \alpha$

26. If α lies in Quadrant III, express in terms of cos α:

a. $\tan \alpha$ b. $\cot \alpha$ c. $\sec \alpha$ d. $\csc \alpha$

15–2 *proving identities*

Is the equation

$$\frac{1}{1 + \sin x} + \frac{1}{1 - \sin x} = 2 \sec^2 x$$

true for every real number x for which both members are defined? That is, is it an identity? One method of proving that an equation is an identity is to transform the more complicated member to the form of the simpler member.

EXAMPLE 1   Prove that $\dfrac{1}{1 + \sin x} + \dfrac{1}{1 - \sin x} = 2 \sec^2 x$ is an identity, noting any restrictions on values for x.

SOLUTION   First notice that the left-hand member is not defined for numbers x for which $\sin x = 1$ or $\sin x = -1$, and the right-hand member is not defined for those x for which $\cos x = 0$. For all other values of x we can rewrite the left-hand member to obtain

$$\frac{1 (1 - \sin x)}{(1 + \sin x)(1 - \sin x)} + \frac{1 (1 + \sin x)}{(1 - \sin x)(1 + \sin x)}$$

$$= \frac{(1 - \sin x) + (1 + \sin x)}{1 - \sin^2 x} = \frac{2}{1 - \sin^2 x}$$

$$= \frac{2}{\cos^2 x} = 2 \sec^2 x,$$

which is the right-hand member. Since no new restrictions on x were introduced in the process, the original sentence is an identity when $\sin x \neq -1$, $\sin x \neq 1$, and $\cos x \neq 0$.

You can also prove that a given equation is an identity by showing that it is equivalent to a known identity.

EXAMPLE 2 Prove that $(\sec \alpha)(\sec \alpha - \cos \alpha) = \tan^2 \alpha$, noting any restrictions on values for α.

SOLUTION Begin by noting that neither member is defined for $\cos \alpha = 0$; then write both expressions entirely in terms of $\sin \alpha$ and $\cos \alpha$.

$$\frac{1}{\cos \alpha}\left(\frac{1}{\cos \alpha} - \cos \alpha\right) = \frac{\sin^2 \alpha}{\cos^2 \alpha}$$

Apply the distributive property to the left-hand member to get

$$\frac{1}{\cos^2 \alpha} - 1 = \frac{\sin^2 \alpha}{\cos^2 \alpha}.$$

Multiplying each member by $\cos^2 \alpha$ then produces

$$1 - \cos^2 \alpha = \sin^2 \alpha$$

or $\sin^2 \alpha + \cos^2 \alpha = 1$, which is an identity for all values of α.

$\therefore$ for all values of α for which $\cos \alpha \neq 0$, the given sentence is an identity.

In proving trigonometric identities, it is helpful to observe the following items.

1. Use the eight fundamental trigonometric identities to simplify the more complicated member.

2. Use the transformations that produce equivalent equations.

3. Observe restrictions on variables and make sure that no new ones are introduced in your work.

4. If no other approach suggests itself, express all function values in terms of values of sine and cosine.

5. Introduce radicals only when absolutely necessary.

WRITTEN EXERCISES Prove each identity. State all necessary restrictions on the variable(s) involved. (If the variable x is used, the functions involved are understood to be circular functions.)

A 1. $\sin^2 \alpha \cot^2 \alpha = \cos^2 \alpha$

2. $\dfrac{\sin x \sec x}{\tan x} = 1$

3. $\tan^2 x - \sin^2 x = \sin^2 x \tan^2 x$

4. $\cot^2 x + \sec^2 x = \tan^2 x + \csc^2 x$

5. $(\cos x)(\sec x - \cos x) = \sin^2 x$

6. $(\csc x)(\csc x - \sin x) = \cot^2 x$

7. $1 + \sin x \tan x \sec x = \sec^2 x$

8. $1 - \cos \alpha \sin \alpha \cot \alpha = \sin^2 \alpha$

9. $\cos \alpha + \sin \alpha \tan \alpha = \sec \alpha$

13. $\sin x \cos x = \dfrac{\tan x}{1 + \tan^2 x}$

10. $\dfrac{\sec x + \csc x}{1 + \tan x} = \csc x$

14. $\dfrac{1}{\sin x \cos x} = \tan x + \cot x$

11. $\dfrac{1 - \tan^2 x}{1 + \tan^2 x} = \cos^2 x - \sin^2 x$

15. $\dfrac{1 + \tan^2 x}{\csc^2 x} = \tan^2 x$

12. $\csc x - \cot x = \dfrac{1}{\csc x + \cot x}$

16. $\dfrac{1 + \tan^2 x}{\tan^2 x} = \csc^2 x$

B 17. $\cos^4 \alpha - \sin^4 \alpha = \cos^2 \alpha - \sin^2 \alpha$

18. $\dfrac{2 \sin \alpha \cos \alpha}{1 - \cos^2 \alpha + \sin^2 \alpha} = \cot \alpha$

19. $\dfrac{\sin x \cot x + \cos x}{\sin x} = 2 \cot x$

20. $\dfrac{1 + 2 \sin x \cos x}{\sin x + \cos x} = \sin x + \cos x$

21. $\dfrac{\sin x \cos x}{1 + \cos x} - \dfrac{\sin x}{1 - \cos x} = -(\cot x \cos x + \csc x)$

22. $\dfrac{\sin x + \cos x}{\sec x + \tan x} + \dfrac{\cos x - \sin x}{\sec x - \tan x} = 2 - 2 \sin^2 x \sec x$

23. $\dfrac{1 + \sec \beta}{\sec \beta - 1} + \dfrac{1 + \cos \beta}{\cos \beta - 1} = 0$

24. $\dfrac{(\sec^2 \beta)(1 + \csc \beta) - (\tan \beta)(\sec \beta + \tan \beta)}{\csc \beta (1 + \sin \beta)} - 1 = 0$

C 25. $\dfrac{\tan A - \sin A}{\tan A \sin A} = \dfrac{\tan A \sin A}{\tan A + \sin A}$

26. $\dfrac{\csc A}{1 + \sec A} = \dfrac{\cot A}{1 + \cos A}$

27. $\dfrac{\csc C + \cot C}{\csc C - \cot C} = (\csc^2 C)(1 + 2 \cos C + \cos^2 C)$

28. $\dfrac{\sin C + \cos C - 1}{\sin C - \cos C + 1} = \dfrac{\cos C}{\sin C + 1}$

SELF-TEST 1 Prove each identity.

Objective 1, page 519

1. $\sin x \sec x = \tan x$

2. $\cos x(\sec x - \cos x) = \sin^2 x$

3. $\sec x - \cos x = \sin x \tan x$

4. $\sec x + \tan x = \dfrac{\cos x}{1 - \sin x}$

Check your answers with those printed at the back of the book.

functions: sums and differences

After completing the next four sections, you should be able to:

Objectives

1. Use reduction formulas to find function values in quadrants other than Quadrant I.
2. Use formulas of sums and differences of trigonometric function values to evaluate expressions involving such sums or differences.
3. Prove simple trigonometric identities involving double- and half-angle formulas.

15–3   *the cosine of a sum or a difference*

If $m^R(\alpha_1) = x_1$ and $m^R(\alpha_2) = x_2$, then the sum of α_1 and α_2, denoted by $\alpha_1 + \alpha_2$, is an angle whose measure in radians is $x_1 + x_2$:

$$m^R(\alpha_1 + \alpha_2) = x_1 + x_2.$$

Similarly, the difference of α_1 and α_2, denoted by $\alpha_1 - \alpha_2$, has measure $x_1 - x_2$:

$$m^R(\alpha_1 - \alpha_2) = x_1 - x_2.$$

Angles α_1, α_2, $\alpha_1 + \alpha_2$, $\alpha_1 - \alpha_2$, where all are in the first quadrant, are pictured in Figure 1.

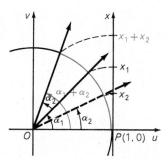 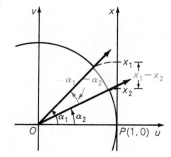

Figure 1

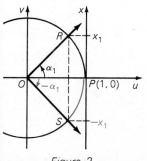

Figure 2

The negative of α_1, denoted by $-\alpha_1$, has measure $-x_1$:

$$m^R(-\alpha_1) = -x_1.$$

Angles α_1 (in the first quadrant) and angle $-\alpha_1$ (in the fourth quadrant) are pictured in Figure 2.

Figure 2 can be used to deduce two very important properties of sin $(-x)$ and cos $(-x)$ and of sin $(-\alpha)$ and cos $(-\alpha)$. Because of the symmetry of the unit circle with respect to the axes, the points R and S have *equal abscissas*, but *ordinates* which are the *negatives* of each other. Since a similar

situation exists if α is in any of the other quadrants, you can assert that fo
each real number x,

$$\sin(-x) = -\sin x \qquad \text{and} \qquad \cos(-x) = \cos x.$$

In terms of angles, for each angle α you have

$$\sin(-\alpha) = -\sin\alpha \qquad \text{and} \qquad \cos(-\alpha) = \cos\alpha.$$

A function for which

$$f(-x) = -f(x)$$

for every x in the domain of f is called an odd function, while a function for
which

$$f(-x) = f(x)$$

for every x in the domain of f is called an even function (see Section 8–1).
Thus, sine is an *odd* function, and cosine is an *even* function.

Figure 3 shows $x_1 - x_2$ when x_1 corresponds to a second-quadrant angle
and x_2 to a first-quadrant angle:

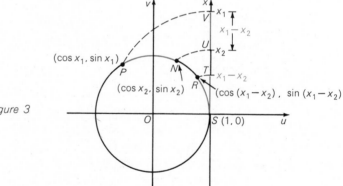

Figure 3

Observe that the segment $\overline{UV}$, whose endpoints are the graphs of x_2 and x_1
on the x number line, is congruent to the segment $\overline{ST}$ with endpoints corresponding to 0 and $x_1 - x_2$. Therefore, the arc of the unit circle from S to
R is congruent to the arc from N to P, and consequently chord $\overline{SR}$ is congruent
to chord $\overline{NP}$. Expressing this latter fact by means of the distance formula
(page 334), you have

$$\sqrt{[\cos(x_1 - x_2) - 1]^2 + [\sin(x_1 - x_2) - 0]^2}$$
$$= \sqrt{(\cos x_1 - \cos x_2)^2 + (\sin x_1 - \sin x_2)^2}.$$

Squaring both members of this equation, you find that

$$\cos^2(x_1 - x_2) - 2\cos(x_1 - x_2) + 1 + \sin^2(x_1 - x_2)$$
$$= \cos^2 x_1 - 2\cos x_1 \cos x_2 + \cos^2 x_2$$
$$+ \sin^2 x_1 - 2\sin x_1 \sin x_2 + \sin^2 x_2.$$

On rearranging terms, you have

$$\cos^2(x_1 - x_2) + \sin^2(x_1 - x_2) - 2\cos(x_1 - x_2) + 1$$
$$= \cos^2 x_1 + \sin^2 x_1 - 2\cos x_1 \cos x_2$$
$$+ \cos^2 x_2 + \sin^2 x_2 - 2\sin x_1 \sin x_2.$$

Because $\cos^2 x + \sin^2 x = 1$ for every real number x, you can replace each of the three pairs of terms shown in red in the preceding equation with "1" and simplify the result to obtain the following:

$$\cos(x_1 - x_2) = \cos x_1 \cos x_2 + \sin x_1 \sin x_2$$

Since the development given is not limited by the particular values of x_1 and x_2 shown in Figure 3, the preceding equation is an identity. It is sometimes called the formula for the cosine of a difference. In terms of angles, this formula could be written:

$$\cos(\alpha_1 - \alpha_2) = \cos \alpha_1 \cos \alpha_2 + \sin \alpha_1 \sin \alpha_2$$

EXAMPLE 1   Find $\cos \dfrac{\pi}{12}$.

SOLUTION   Express $\dfrac{\pi}{12}$ as the difference of two numbers for which you know the sine and cosine. (Refer to the table on page 493.) Thus,

$$\frac{\pi}{12} = \frac{4\pi}{12} - \frac{3\pi}{12} = \frac{\pi}{3} - \frac{\pi}{4}.$$

Then, replacing x_1 and x_2 in the formula for the cosine of a difference with $\dfrac{\pi}{3}$ and $\dfrac{\pi}{4}$, respectively, you get

$$\cos\left(\frac{\pi}{3} - \frac{\pi}{4}\right) = \cos \frac{\pi}{3} \cos \frac{\pi}{4} + \sin \frac{\pi}{3} \sin \frac{\pi}{4}.$$

From the table, you have

$$\cos \frac{\pi}{3} = \frac{1}{2}, \ \cos \frac{\pi}{4} = \frac{\sqrt{2}}{2},$$

$$\sin \frac{\pi}{3} = \frac{\sqrt{3}}{2}, \ \sin \frac{\pi}{4} = \frac{\sqrt{2}}{2}.$$

Therefore,

$$\cos \frac{\pi}{12} = \cos\left(\frac{\pi}{3} - \frac{\pi}{4}\right) = \left(\frac{1}{2}\right)\left(\frac{\sqrt{2}}{2}\right) + \left(\frac{\sqrt{3}}{2}\right)\left(\frac{\sqrt{2}}{2}\right)$$

$$= \frac{\sqrt{2}}{4} + \frac{\sqrt{6}}{4} = \frac{1}{4}(\sqrt{2} + \sqrt{6}). \ \text{Answer.}$$

By replacing x_2 with $-x_2$ in the difference formula, you obtain

$$\cos [x_1 - (-x_2)] = \cos x_1 \cos (-x_2) + \sin x_1 \sin (-x_2).$$

Then, since $\cos (-x) = \cos x$ and $\sin (-x) = -\sin x$ (page 526), you have the formula for the cosine of a sum:

$$\cos (x_1 + x_2) = \cos x_1 \cos x_2 - \sin x_1 \sin x_2$$

In terms of angles, this formula could be written

$$\cos (\alpha_1 + \alpha_2) = \cos \alpha_1 \cos \alpha_2 - \sin \alpha_1 \sin \alpha_2.$$

You can develop a number of other valuable identities by using the formulas for the cosine of a difference and the cosine of a sum.

For example, if you let $x_1 = \pi$ and $x_2 = x$ in the difference formula, you have

$$\cos (\pi - x) = \cos \pi \cos x + \sin \pi \sin x$$
$$= (-1) \cos x + (0) \sin x = -\cos x.$$

Similarly, if $m(\alpha_1) = 180°$ and $\alpha_2 = \alpha$, you find from the difference formula that

$$\cos (180° - \alpha) = \cos 180° \cos \alpha + \sin 180° \sin \alpha$$
$$= (-1) \cos \alpha + (0) \sin \alpha = -\cos \alpha.$$

You can also show (Exercise 33, page 530) that

$$\cos (\pi + x) = -\cos x \qquad \text{and} \qquad \cos (180° + \alpha) = -\cos \alpha.$$

These identities are valid for all real numbers x and all angles α. However, if $0 < x < \dfrac{\pi}{2}$, then $\pi - x$ is the measure of a unit-circle arc in Quadrant II and $\pi + x$ is the measure of a unit-circle arc in Quadrant III, and x becomes the measure of the *reference arc* for the arcs with measures $\pi - x$ and $\pi + x$. Compare Figures 4 and 5 with parts **a** and **c** of Figure 19, page 500, where the reference arc has measure x'.

Now if you let $x_1 = \dfrac{\pi}{2}$ and $x_2 = x$ in the difference formula, you have

$$\cos \left(\frac{\pi}{2} - x\right) = \cos \frac{\pi}{2} \cos x + \sin \frac{\pi}{2} \sin x$$
$$= (0) \cos x + (1) \sin x = \sin x.$$

Notice that since the measures of the acute angles of a right triangle can be expressed as x and $\dfrac{\pi}{2} - x$ radians, the preceding formula is a generalization of the corresponding one given on page 512.

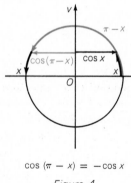

$$\cos (\pi - x) = -\cos x$$

Figure 4

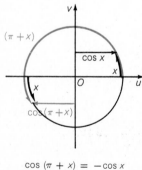

$$\cos (\pi + x) = -\cos x$$

Figure 5

You can also show (Exercise 34, page 530) that

$$\cos\left(\frac{\pi}{2} + x\right) = -\sin x.$$

For $0 < x < \frac{\pi}{2}$, these results are pictured in Figures 6 and 7.

By letting $x_1 = \frac{3\pi}{2}$ in the sum and difference formulas, you can find two more identities (Exercises 35 and 36, page 530). Because all these formulas can be used to "reduce" a given circular or trigonometric function value in any quadrant to a function value in Quadrant I, they are called reduction formulas. Here is a list of the most useful reduction formulas for cosine. From now on we shall work primarily with formulas stated in terms of x, where x is a real number, with the understanding that corresponding formulas hold in terms of angles.

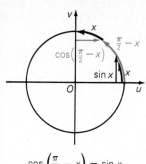

$$\cos\left(\frac{\pi}{2} - x\right) = \sin x$$

Figure 6

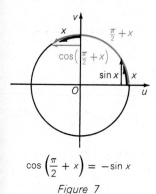

$$\cos\left(\frac{\pi}{2} + x\right) = -\sin x$$

Figure 7

$$\cos\left(\frac{\pi}{2} + x\right) = -\sin x \qquad\qquad \cos\left(\pi - x\right) = -\cos x$$

$$\cos\left(\frac{\pi}{2} - x\right) = \sin x \qquad\qquad \cos\left(\frac{3\pi}{2} + x\right) = \sin x$$

$$\cos\left(\pi + x\right) = -\cos x \qquad\qquad \cos\left(\frac{3\pi}{2} - x\right) = -\sin x$$

EXAMPLE   Reduce $\cos\dfrac{13\pi}{9}$ to an equal function value for a number x such that $0 \le x \le \dfrac{\pi}{2}$.

SOLUTION   Because $\pi < \dfrac{13\pi}{9} < \dfrac{3\pi}{2}$, you can use either

$$\frac{13\pi}{9} = \pi + \frac{4\pi}{9} \qquad \text{or} \qquad \frac{13\pi}{9} = \frac{3\pi}{2} - \frac{\pi}{18}.$$

METHOD I   Using $\dfrac{4\pi}{9}$, from $\cos\left(\pi + x\right) = -\cos x$ you have

$$\cos\frac{13\pi}{9} = \cos\left(\pi + \frac{4\pi}{9}\right) = -\cos\frac{4\pi}{9}. \text{ Answer.}$$

METHOD II   Using $\dfrac{\pi}{18}$, from $\cos\left(\dfrac{3\pi}{2} - x\right) = -\sin x$ you have

$$\cos\frac{13\pi}{9} = \cos\left(\frac{3\pi}{2} - \frac{\pi}{18}\right) = -\sin\frac{\pi}{18}. \text{ Answer.}$$

Note: $-\sin\dfrac{\pi}{18} = -\cos\dfrac{4\pi}{9}$ because $\dfrac{\pi}{18} + \dfrac{4\pi}{9} = \dfrac{\pi}{2}.$

Use an identity to reduce the given value to a function value for a number

x such that $0 \leq x \leq \dfrac{\pi}{2}$, and then state the value.

A   1. $\cos \dfrac{7\pi}{6}$ 3. $\cos \dfrac{3\pi}{2}$ 5. $\cos\left(-\dfrac{2\pi}{3}\right)$ 7. $\cos 2\pi$

        2. $\cos \dfrac{5\pi}{4}$ 4. $\cos \dfrac{11\pi}{6}$ 6. $\cos\left(-\dfrac{3\pi}{4}\right)$ 8. $\cos \pi$

Use an identity to reduce the given value to a function value for an angle α such that $0° \leq m(\alpha) \leq 90°$, and then state the value.

      9. $\cos 225°$ 11. $\cos 300°$ 13. $\cos(-135°)$ 15. $\cos 330°$

     10. $\cos 120°$ 12. $\cos 315°$ 14. $\cos(-150°)$ 16. $\cos 240°$

Express the given function value as a function value for a number x such that $0 \leq x \leq \dfrac{\pi}{4}$.

     17. $\cos \dfrac{5\pi}{7}$ 19. $\cos \dfrac{7\pi}{15}$ 21. $\cos\left(-\dfrac{3\pi}{5}\right)$ 23. $\cos 1.3\pi$

     18. $\cos \dfrac{7\pi}{5}$ 20. $\cos \dfrac{11\pi}{8}$ 22. $\cos\left(-\dfrac{6\pi}{13}\right)$ 24. $\cos 1.9\pi$

Express the given function value as a function value for an angle α such that $0° < m(\alpha) < 90°$.

     25. $\cos 93°$ 27. $\cos 231°$ 29. $\cos 241°10'$ 31. $\cos(-105°)$

     26. $\cos 152°$ 28. $\cos 196°$ 30. $\cos 315°20'$ 32. $\cos(-207°)$

Prove each of the following identities. In each exercise, sketch a geometric representation of the identity similar to that in Figure 7 showing the significance of the identities.

B   33. $\cos(\pi + x) = -\cos x$ 36. $\cos\left(\dfrac{3\pi}{2} - x\right) = -\sin x$

        34. $\cos\left(\dfrac{\pi}{2} + x\right) = -\sin x$ 37. $\cos\left(x - \dfrac{\pi}{2}\right) = \sin x$

        35. $\cos\left(\dfrac{3\pi}{2} + x\right) = \sin x$ 38. $\cos(x - \pi) = -\cos x$

In each of Exercises 39–42, represent the given expression as a numerical value. Refer to the table on page 493 as necessary.

EXAMPLE $\cos \dfrac{2\pi}{3} \cos \dfrac{\pi}{6} - \sin \dfrac{2\pi}{3} \sin \dfrac{\pi}{6}$

SOLUTION   The form of the given expression suggests the identity

$$\cos (x_1 + x_2) = \cos x_1 \cos x_2 - \sin x_1 \sin x_2.$$

Setting $x_1 = \dfrac{2\pi}{3}$ and $x_2 = \dfrac{\pi}{6}$, you have

$$\cos \frac{2\pi}{3} \cos \frac{\pi}{6} - \sin \frac{2\pi}{3} \sin \frac{\pi}{6} = \cos \left(\frac{2\pi}{3} + \frac{\pi}{6} \right) = \cos \frac{5\pi}{6}.$$

$\therefore$ the value is $\cos \dfrac{5\pi}{6}$ or $-\dfrac{\sqrt{3}}{2}$.   **Answer.**

39. $\cos \dfrac{5\pi}{6} \cos \dfrac{\pi}{2} - \sin \dfrac{5\pi}{6} \sin \dfrac{\pi}{2}$

40. $\cos \dfrac{\pi}{3} \cos \left(-\dfrac{\pi}{6} \right) + \sin \dfrac{\pi}{3} \sin \left(-\dfrac{\pi}{6} \right)$

41. $\cos \dfrac{\pi}{4} \cos \dfrac{\pi}{4} + \sin \dfrac{\pi}{4} \sin \dfrac{\pi}{4}$

42. $\cos 150° \cos (-30°) + \sin 150° \sin (-30°)$

In each of Exercises 43–46, let $\cos x_1 = \frac{4}{5}$ and $\cos x_2 = \frac{12}{13}$, and use any available identities to find a value for the given expression.

EXAMPLE $\cos (x_1 + x_2), \ 0 < x_1 < \dfrac{\pi}{2}, \dfrac{3\pi}{2} < x_2 < 2\pi.$

SOLUTION   Using $\cos (x_1 + x_2) = \cos x_1 \cos x_2 - \sin x_1 \sin x_2$, you have at once

$$\cos (x_1 + x_2) = (\tfrac{4}{5})(\tfrac{12}{13}) - \sin x_1 \sin x_2.$$

To find $\sin x_1$ and $\sin x_2$, you can use $\cos^2 x + \sin^2 x = 1$.

$$(\tfrac{4}{5})^2 + \sin^2 x_1 = 1 \qquad \text{and} \qquad (\tfrac{12}{13})^2 + \sin^2 x_2 = 1$$
$$\sin^2 x_1 = 1 - \tfrac{16}{25} \qquad\qquad\qquad \sin^2 x_2 = 1 - \tfrac{144}{169}$$
$$\sin^2 x_1 = \tfrac{9}{25} \qquad\qquad\qquad\qquad \sin^2 x_2 = \tfrac{25}{169}$$

Since x_1 is in Quadrant I and x_2 is in Quadrant IV, you have

$$\sin x_1 = \tfrac{3}{5} \quad \text{and} \quad \sin x_2 = -\tfrac{5}{13}.$$

$\therefore \cos (x_1 + x_2) = (\tfrac{4}{5})(\tfrac{12}{13}) - (\tfrac{3}{5})(-\tfrac{5}{13}) = \tfrac{48}{65} + \tfrac{15}{65} = \tfrac{63}{65}.$ **Answer.**

43. $\cos (x_1 - x_2), \ 0 < x_1 < \dfrac{\pi}{2}, \ 0 < x_2 < \dfrac{\pi}{2}$

44. $\cos (x_1 - x_2), \ 0 < x_1 < \dfrac{\pi}{2}, \dfrac{3\pi}{2} < x_2 < 2\pi$

45. $\cos (x_2 + x_1), \ \dfrac{3\pi}{2} < x_1 < 2\pi, \dfrac{3\pi}{2} < x_2 < 2\pi$

46. $\cos (x_2 - x_1), \ \dfrac{3\pi}{2} < x_1 < 2\pi, \ 0 < x_2 < \dfrac{\pi}{2}$

15-4   *the sine and tangent of a sum or a difference*

To find formulas for the sine of a sum and of a difference, first recall (page 528) that

$$\cos \left(\frac{\pi}{2} - x\right) = \sin x.$$

If you replace x with $\frac{\pi}{2} - x$, you obtain

$$\cos \left(\frac{\pi}{2} - \left(\frac{\pi}{2} - x\right)\right) = \sin \left(\frac{\pi}{2} - x\right), \quad \text{or} \quad \sin \left(\frac{\pi}{2} - x\right) = \cos x.$$

To find a formula for $\sin (x_1 + x_2)$, use the above and the formula for the cosine of a difference to get:

$$\sin (x_1 + x_2) = \cos \left(\frac{\pi}{2} - (x_1 + x_2)\right) = \cos \left(\left(\frac{\pi}{2} - x_1\right) - x_2\right)$$

$$= \cos \left(\frac{\pi}{2} - x_1\right) \cos x_2 + \sin \left(\frac{\pi}{2} - x_1\right) \sin x_2$$

But $\cos \left(\frac{\pi}{2} - x_1\right) = \sin x_1$ and $\sin \left(\frac{\pi}{2} - x_1\right) = \cos x_1$, so you have the formula for the sine of a sum:

$$\sin (x_1 + x_2) = \sin x_1 \cos x_2 + \cos x_1 \sin x_2$$

In terms of angles, you have

$$\sin (\alpha_1 + \alpha_2) = \sin \alpha_1 \cos \alpha_2 + \cos \alpha_1 \sin \alpha_2.$$

If, in the formula for the sine of a sum, you replace x_2 with $-x_2$, you obtain

$$\sin (x_1 + (-x_2)) = \sin x_1 \cos (-x_2) + \cos x_1 \sin (-x_2).$$

Then, because $\sin (-x) = -\sin x$ and $\cos (-x) = \cos x$ (page 526), you have the formula for the sine of a difference:

$$\sin (x_1 - x_2) = \sin x_1 \cos x_2 - \cos x_1 \sin x_2$$

In terms of angles, you have:

$$\sin (\alpha_1 - \alpha_2) = \sin \alpha_1 \cos \alpha_2 - \cos \alpha_1 \sin \alpha_2$$

EXAMPLE 1   Find $\sin \dfrac{11\pi}{12}$.

SOLUTION $\dfrac{11\pi}{12}$ can be expressed as the sum of two numbers for which you know the sine and cosine, namely,

$$\frac{11\pi}{12} = \frac{\pi}{6} + \frac{3\pi}{4}.$$

Then, you can replace x_1 and x_2 in the sum formula with $\dfrac{\pi}{6}$ and $\dfrac{3\pi}{4}$ respectively, to obtain

$$\sin \frac{11\pi}{12} = \sin\left(\frac{\pi}{6} + \frac{3\pi}{4}\right) = \sin\frac{\pi}{6}\cos\frac{3\pi}{4} + \cos\frac{\pi}{6}\sin\frac{3\pi}{4}.$$

Since

$$\sin\frac{\pi}{6} = \frac{1}{2}, \quad \cos\frac{3\pi}{4} = -\frac{\sqrt{2}}{2}, \quad \cos\frac{\pi}{6} = \frac{\sqrt{3}}{2}, \quad \text{and } \sin\frac{3\pi}{4} = \frac{\sqrt{2}}{2}$$

you have

$$\sin\frac{11\pi}{12} = \sin\left(\frac{\pi}{6} + \frac{3\pi}{4}\right) = \left(\frac{1}{2}\right)\left(-\frac{\sqrt{2}}{2}\right) + \left(\frac{\sqrt{3}}{2}\right)\left(\frac{\sqrt{2}}{2}\right)$$

$$= \frac{\sqrt{2}}{4}(\sqrt{3} - 1). \quad \textbf{Answer.}$$

Following are the reduction formulas for sine corresponding to those for cosine given on page 529. The second of these was derived above. You can prove the others (Exercises 57–61, pages 536–537).

$$\sin\left(\frac{\pi}{2} + x\right) = \cos x \qquad\qquad \sin(\pi - x) = \sin x$$

$$\sin\left(\frac{\pi}{2} - x\right) = \cos x \qquad\qquad \sin\left(\frac{3\pi}{2} + x\right) = -\cos x$$

$$\sin(\pi + x) = -\sin x \qquad\qquad \sin\left(\frac{3\pi}{2} - x\right) = -\cos x$$

Two of these are pictured in Figures 8 and 9.

Sum, difference, and reduction formulas for the functions tangent, cotangent, secant, and cosecant can be obtained by using appropriate formulas established for sine and cosine, in conjunction with the definitions of the other functions. While the formulas for sine and cosine hold for all values of the variable, there are certain restrictions placed on the domains of the variables in formulas for the other functions.

In practice, the only ones of these additional formulas that are of much concern to us are those for tangent, because to find values for cotangent, secant, or cosecant, you need only take the reciprocal of the corresponding values of tangent, cosine, or sine.

To start, notice that tangent, like sine, is an odd function (page 526), since

$$\tan(-x) = \frac{\sin(-x)}{\cos(-x)} = \frac{-\sin x}{\cos x} = -\frac{\sin x}{\cos x}.$$

Thus,

$$\tan(-x) = -\tan x, \quad \cos x \neq 0.$$

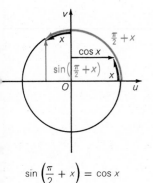

$$\sin\left(\frac{\pi}{2} + x\right) = \cos x$$

Figure 8

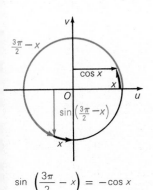

$$\sin\left(\frac{3\pi}{2} - x\right) = -\cos x$$

Figure 9

To obtain a difference formula for the tangent function, you can replac x with $(x_1 - x_2)$ in the definition of $\tan x$ to obtain

$$\tan (x_1 - x_2) = \frac{\sin (x_1 - x_2)}{\cos (x_1 - x_2)}, \quad \cos (x_1 - x_2) \neq 0.$$

From this, you find

$$\tan (x_1 - x_2) = \frac{\sin x_1 \cos x_2 - \cos x_1 \sin x_2}{\cos x_1 \cos x_2 + \sin x_1 \sin x_2}.$$

Then, if $\cos x_1 \cos x_2 \neq 0$, you can divide the numerator and denominato of the right-hand member of this identity by this product to obtain

$$\tan (x_2 - x_1) = \frac{\dfrac{\sin x_1 \cos x_2}{\cos x_1 \cos x_2} - \dfrac{\cos x_1 \sin x_2}{\cos x_1 \cos x_2}}{\dfrac{\cos x_1 \cos x_2}{\cos x_1 \cos x_2} + \dfrac{\sin x_1 \sin x_2}{\cos x_1 \cos x_2}}, \quad \cos x_1 \cos x_2 \neq 0.$$

From this and the definition of $\tan x$, you have the formula for the tangen of a difference:

$$\tan (x_1 - x_2) = \frac{\tan x_1 - \tan x_2}{1 + \tan x_1 \tan x_2}, \quad \begin{cases} \cos (x_1 - x_2) \neq 0 \\ \cos x_1 \neq 0, \cos x_2 \neq 0 \end{cases}$$

Using the fact that tangent is an odd function, you can replace x_2 with $-x_2$ in the formula for the tangent of a difference to deduce that

$$\tan [x_1 - (-x_2)] = \frac{\tan x_1 - \tan (-x_2)}{1 + \tan x_1 \tan (-x_2)},$$

from which you have the formula for the tangent of a sum:

$$\tan (x_1 + x_2) = \frac{\tan x_1 + \tan x_2}{1 - \tan x_1 \tan x_2}, \quad \begin{cases} \cos (x_1 + x_2) \neq 0 \\ \cos x_1 \neq 0, \cos x_2 \neq 0 \end{cases}$$

You saw from the graph of tangent on page 508 that the period of tangen is π (or $180°$) rather than 2π (or $360°$). You can readily verify that π is a period by replacing x_1 with π and x_2 with x in the formula for $\tan (x_1 + x_2$ to obtain

$$\tan (\pi + x) = \frac{\tan \pi + \tan x}{1 - \tan \pi \tan x} = \frac{0 + \tan x}{1 - (0)(\tan x)} = \tan x, \quad \cos x \neq 0.$$

This latter relationship can then be used to obtain a reduction formula fo $\tan (\pi - x)$. If you replace x with $-x$, you have

$$\tan (\pi - x) = \tan (-x),$$

or

$$\tan (\pi - x) = -\tan x, \quad \cos x \neq 0.$$

Notice that the formula for tan $(x_1 + x_2)$ cannot be used to produce reduction formulas for tangent for values $\frac{\pi}{2} \pm x$ or $\frac{3\pi}{2} \pm x$, because $\tan \frac{\pi}{2}$ and $\tan \frac{3\pi}{2}$ are not defined. Such formulas, however, for tangent can be found directly from the definition of $\tan x$.

EXAMPLE 2 **Prove that** $\tan\left(\frac{\pi}{2} - x\right) = \cot x$, $\sin x \neq 0$.

SOLUTION By definition,

$$\tan\left(\frac{\pi}{2} - x\right) = \frac{\sin\left(\frac{\pi}{2} - x\right)}{\cos\left(\frac{\pi}{2} - x\right)} = \frac{\cos x}{\sin x}, \quad \sin x \neq 0.$$

$$\therefore \tan\left(\frac{\pi}{2} - x\right) = \cot x, \quad \sin x \neq 0.$$

Following are reduction formulas for tangent. Three were derived above. You can prove the others (Exercises 65–67, page 537).

$$\tan\left(\frac{\pi}{2} + x\right) = -\cot x, \quad \sin x \neq 0 \qquad \tan(\pi - x) = -\tan x, \quad \cos x \neq 0$$

$$\tan\left(\frac{\pi}{2} - x\right) = \cot x, \quad \sin x \neq 0 \qquad \tan\left(\frac{3\pi}{2} + x\right) = -\cot x, \quad \sin x \neq 0$$

$$\tan(\pi + x) = \tan x, \quad \cos x \neq 0 \qquad \tan\left(\frac{3\pi}{2} - x\right) = \cot x, \quad \sin x \neq 0$$

WRITTEN EXERCISES Express the given function value as a function value of a number x such that $0 < x < \frac{\pi}{4}$.

A
1. $\sin \frac{3\pi}{7}$ 4. $\sin \frac{7\pi}{13}$ 7. $\sin\left(-\frac{6\pi}{13}\right)$ 10. $\sin\left(-\frac{6\pi}{11}\right)$

2. $\sin \frac{7\pi}{5}$ 5. $\sin \frac{11\pi}{18}$ 8. $\sin\left(-\frac{11\pi}{5}\right)$ 11. $\sin 1.4\pi$

3. $\sin \frac{7\pi}{10}$ 6. $\sin \frac{8\pi}{9}$ 9. $\sin\left(-\frac{\pi}{8}\right)$ 12. $\sin 0.9\pi$

Express the given function value as a function value of an angle for which $0° \leq m(\alpha) \leq 45°$.

13. $\cos 68°$ 16. $\sin 109°$ 19. $\sin 217°$ 22. $\sin 244°40'$
14. $\sin 75°$ 17. $\sin 143°$ 20. $\cos 341°$ 23. $\cos (-71°)$
15. $\cos 93°$ 18. $\cos 171°$ 21. $\cos 143°15'$ 24. $\sin (-102°)$

Use an identity to reduce the given function value to a function value of a number x for which $0 \leq x \leq \dfrac{\pi}{2}$ and then determine the value.

25. $\sin \dfrac{7\pi}{6}$ 27. $\sin \dfrac{5\pi}{4}$ 29. $\sin \dfrac{7\pi}{2}$ 31. $\sin \left(-\dfrac{4\pi}{3}\right)$

26. $\sin \dfrac{5\pi}{3}$ 28. $\sin \dfrac{13\pi}{3}$ 30. $\sin \dfrac{8\pi}{3}$ 32. $\sin \left(-\dfrac{7\pi}{6}\right)$

Use an identity to reduce the given function value to a function value of an angle α for which $0° \leq m(\alpha) \leq 90°$, and then determine the value.

33. $\sin 150°$ 35. $\sin 225°$ 37. $\sin 390°$ 39. $\sin (-480°)$

34. $\sin 210°$ 36. $\sin 300°$ 38. $\sin 405°$ 40. $\sin (-750°)$

Use the formulas for tangent of a sum and tangent of a difference to find the given function value.

41. $\tan \dfrac{\pi}{12}$ 43. $\tan \dfrac{7\pi}{12}$ 45. $\tan 15°$ 47. $\tan 75°$

42. $\tan \dfrac{5\pi}{12}$ 44. $\tan \dfrac{11\pi}{12}$ 46. $\tan 105°$ 48. $\tan 165°$

Use the definition of the function involved and appropriate reduction formulas to find the given function value.

EXAMPLE $\sec \dfrac{\pi}{12}$

SOLUTION $\sec \dfrac{\pi}{12} = \dfrac{1}{\cos \dfrac{\pi}{12}} = \dfrac{1}{\cos \left(\dfrac{\pi}{3} - \dfrac{\pi}{4}\right)} = \dfrac{1}{\cos \dfrac{\pi}{3} \cos \dfrac{\pi}{4} + \sin \dfrac{\pi}{3} \sin \dfrac{\pi}{4}}$

$$= \dfrac{1}{\dfrac{1}{2} \cdot \dfrac{1}{\sqrt{2}} + \dfrac{\sqrt{3}}{2} \cdot \dfrac{1}{\sqrt{2}}} = \dfrac{2\sqrt{2}\,(1 - \sqrt{3})}{(1 + \sqrt{3})(1 - \sqrt{3})}$$

$$= \dfrac{2\sqrt{2} - 2\sqrt{6}}{-2} = \sqrt{6} - \sqrt{2}.\ \text{Answer.}$$

49. $\csc \dfrac{\pi}{12}$ 51. $\sec \dfrac{5\pi}{12}$ 53. $\sec 15°$ 55. $\cot 15°$

50. $\cot \dfrac{\pi}{12}$ 52. $\csc \dfrac{11\pi}{12}$ 54. $\csc 75°$ 56. $\sec 105°$

Prove the identity and write it also in terms of angles. Make a sketch illustrating it.

B   57. $\sin \left(\dfrac{\pi}{2} + x\right) = \cos x$ 59. $\sin \left(\dfrac{3\pi}{2} + x\right) = -\cos x$

       58. $\sin (\pi + x) = -\sin x$ 60. $\sin (\pi - x) = \sin x$

61. $\sin\left(\dfrac{3\pi}{2} - x\right) = -\cos x$ 65. $\tan\left(\dfrac{\pi}{2} + x\right) = -\cot x, \sin x \neq 0$

62. $\sin\left(x - \dfrac{\pi}{2}\right) = -\cos x$ 66. $\tan\left(\dfrac{3\pi}{2} + x\right) = -\cot x, \sin x \neq 0$

63. $\sin(x - \pi) = -\sin x$ 67. $\tan\left(\dfrac{3\pi}{2} - x\right) = \cot x, \sin x \neq 0$

64. $\sin\left(x - \dfrac{3\pi}{2}\right) = \cos x$ 68. $\tan\left(x - \dfrac{\pi}{2}\right) = -\cot x, \sin x \neq 0$

Find the value of the given expression.

69. $\cos\dfrac{3\pi}{12}\cos\dfrac{\pi}{12} - \sin\dfrac{3\pi}{12}\sin\dfrac{\pi}{12}$

73. $\dfrac{\tan\dfrac{5\pi}{3} - \tan\dfrac{\pi}{3}}{1 + \tan\dfrac{5\pi}{3}\tan\dfrac{\pi}{3}}$

70. $\sin\dfrac{\pi}{3}\cos\dfrac{\pi}{12} - \cos\dfrac{\pi}{3}\sin\dfrac{\pi}{12}$

71. $\sin 132° \cos 12° - \cos 132° \sin 12°$

74. $\dfrac{\tan 10° + \tan 20°}{1 - \tan 10° \tan 20°}$

72. $\sin 70° \cos 80° + \cos 70° \sin 80°$

Show that for appropriately restricted values of x_1, x_2, and $x_1 + x_2$, each of the following is an identity.

C   75. $\cot(x_1 + x_2) = \dfrac{\cot x_1 \cot x_2 - 1}{\cot x_1 + \cot x_2}$

76. $\sec(x_1 + x_2) = \dfrac{\sec x_1 \sec x_2}{1 - \tan x_1 \tan x_2}$

15-5   *double-angle and half-angle formulas*

All the identities derived in the preceding sections of this chapter result from the basic sum and difference identities:

$$\sin(x_1 \pm x_2) = \sin x_1 \cos x_2 \pm \cos x_1 \sin x_2$$
$$\cos(x_1 \pm x_2) = \cos x_1 \cos x_2 \mp \sin x_1 \sin x_2$$

We shall now derive still more identities.
   If $x_1 = x_2 = x$, then

$$\sin(x + x) = \sin x \cos x + \sin x \cos x,$$

or

$$\sin 2x = 2 \sin x \cos x.$$

Similarly,

$$\cos(x + x) = \cos x \cos x - \sin x \sin x,$$

or

$$\cos 2x = \cos^2 x - \sin^2 x.$$

You can easily obtain two additional expressions for cos 2x. Since $\sin^2 x + \cos^2 x = 1$, you have

$$\sin^2 x = 1 - \cos^2 x \qquad \text{and} \qquad \cos^2 x = 1 - \sin^2 x.$$

Therefore, on replacing $\sin^2 x$ with $(1 - \cos^2 x)$, in the identity for cos 2x you have

$$\cos 2x = \cos^2 x - (1 - \cos^2 x),$$

or

$$\cos 2x = 2 \cos^2 x - 1.$$

On the other hand, if you replace $\cos^2 x$ with $(1 - \sin^2 x)$, you have

$$\cos 2x = (1 - \sin^2 x) - \sin^2 x,$$

or

$$\cos 2x = 1 - 2 \sin^2 x.$$

Also, for all x for which tan x is defined and $|\tan x| \neq 1$,

$$\tan (x + x) = \frac{\tan x + \tan x}{1 - \tan x \tan x},$$

or

$$\tan 2x = \frac{2 \tan x}{1 - \tan^2 x}.$$

Corresponding identities can, of course, be written in terms of angles, and so these identities are often referred to as the double-angle formulas (or identities) for sine, cosine, and tangent.

Now, on replacing x with $\frac{x}{2}$ in $\cos 2x = 2 \cos^2 x - 1$, you have

$$\cos x = 2 \cos^2 \frac{x}{2} - 1,$$

or

$$\cos^2 \frac{x}{2} = \frac{1 + \cos x}{2}.$$

Therefore,

$$\cos \frac{x}{2} = \pm \sqrt{\frac{1 + \cos x}{2}}.$$

If you replace x with $\frac{x}{2}$ in $\cos 2x = 1 - 2 \sin^2 x$, you can use a similar process to find that

$$\sin \frac{x}{2} = \pm \sqrt{\frac{1 - \cos x}{2}}.$$

In applying the formulas for $\sin \frac{x}{2} \left(\text{or } \sin \frac{\alpha}{2} \right)$ and $\cos \frac{x}{2} \left(\text{or } \cos \frac{\alpha}{2} \right)$, the choice of the positive or negative root depends on the quadrant in which $\frac{x}{2}$ $\left(\text{or } \frac{\alpha}{2} \right)$ lies. For example, if $0 < \frac{x}{2} < \frac{\pi}{2} \left(\text{or } 0° < m \left(\frac{\alpha}{2} \right) < 90° \right)$, you would select the positive root for each, but if $\frac{\pi}{2} < \frac{x}{2} < \pi$ (or $90° < m\left(\frac{\alpha}{2}\right) < 180°$), you would select the positive root for sine and the negative root for cosine, and so on.

For tangent, if x is a value for which $\tan \frac{x}{2}$ is defined, you have

$$\tan^2 \frac{x}{2} = \frac{\sin^2 \frac{x}{2}}{\cos^2 \frac{x}{2}} = \frac{\frac{1 - \cos x}{2}}{\frac{1 + \cos x}{2}} = \frac{1 - \cos x}{1 + \cos x},$$

from which

$$\tan \frac{x}{2} = \pm \sqrt{\frac{1 - \cos x}{1 + \cos x}}.$$

Again, the choice of root is determined by the location of $\frac{x}{2}$ (or $\frac{\alpha}{2}$).

A simpler formula for $\tan \frac{x}{2}$ (or $\tan \frac{\alpha}{2}$) can be found by using the double-angle formulas as follows:

$$2 \sin \frac{x}{2} \cos \frac{x}{2} = \sin x \qquad 2 \cos^2 \frac{x}{2} = 1 + \cos x$$

Then

$$\tan \frac{x}{2} = \frac{\sin \frac{x}{2}}{\cos \frac{x}{2}} = \frac{2 \sin \frac{x}{2} \cos \frac{x}{2}}{2 \cos^2 \frac{x}{2}},$$

and so

$$\tan \frac{x}{2} = \frac{\sin x}{1 + \cos x}.$$

Corresponding identities can be written in terms of angles, and so these identities are often called the half-angle formulas (or identities).

WRITTEN EXERCISES In Exercises 1–12 find each function value.

EXAMPLE $\tan \frac{\pi}{8}$

SOLUTION   Using $\tan \frac{x}{2} = \frac{\sin x}{1 + \cos x}$ with $x = \frac{\pi}{4}$, you have

$$\tan \frac{\frac{\pi}{4}}{2} = \frac{\sin \frac{\pi}{4}}{1 + \cos \frac{\pi}{4}} = \frac{\frac{\sqrt{2}}{2}}{1 + \frac{\sqrt{2}}{2}} = \frac{\sqrt{2}}{2 + \sqrt{2}}.$$

(Solution continued on page 540.)

Rationalizing the denominator yields

$$\tan \frac{\pi}{8} = \frac{\sqrt{2}(2 - \sqrt{2})}{(2 + \sqrt{2})(2 - \sqrt{2})} = \frac{2\sqrt{2} - 2}{2} = \sqrt{2} - 1. \quad \text{Answer.}$$

A   1. $\sin \dfrac{\pi}{8}$ 4. $\tan \dfrac{3\pi}{8}$ 7. $\tan 15°$ 10. $\tan 112\frac{1}{2}°$

    2. $\cos \dfrac{\pi}{8}$ 5. $\cos \dfrac{7\pi}{12}$ 8. $\sin 67\frac{1}{2}°$ 11. $\cos 75°$

    3. $\sin \dfrac{3\pi}{8}$ 6. $\sin \dfrac{5\pi}{12}$ 9. $\cos 22\frac{1}{2}°$ 12. $\sin 165°$

Evaluate.

13. $2 \sin \dfrac{\pi}{8} \cos \dfrac{\pi}{8}$

14. $\cos^2 \dfrac{\pi}{12} - \sin^2 \dfrac{\pi}{12}$

15. $2 \cos^2 15° - 1$

16. $1 - 2 \sin^2 75°$

17. $\dfrac{2 \tan 22\frac{1}{2}°}{1 - \tan^2 22\frac{1}{2}°}$

18. $\dfrac{\tan 75°}{\frac{1}{2} - \frac{1}{2}\tan^2 75°}$

19. $\sqrt{\dfrac{1 - \cos 180°}{2}}$

20. $\sqrt{\dfrac{1 + \cos 300°}{2}}$

21. $-\sqrt{\dfrac{1 - \cos 300°}{1 + \cos 300°}}$

22. $\dfrac{\sin 420°}{1 + \cos 420°}$

If $0 \le x \le \dfrac{\pi}{2}$, and $\sin x = \dfrac{4}{5}$, find each function value.

23. $\sin 2x$ 25. $\tan 2x$ 27. $\cos 4x$

24. $\cos 2x$ 26. $\sin 4x$ 28. $\tan 4x$

If $90° \le x \le 180°$, and $\sin x = \frac{4}{5}$, find each function value.

29. $\sin \dfrac{x}{2}$ 31. $\tan \dfrac{x}{2}$ 33. $\cos \dfrac{x}{4}$

30. $\cos \dfrac{x}{2}$ 32. $\sin \dfrac{x}{4}$ 34. $\tan \dfrac{x}{4}$

Prove each identity. In each case, state necessary restrictions.

B   35. $\sec 2x = \dfrac{\sec^2 x}{2 - \sec^2 x}$

    36. $\csc 2x = \dfrac{\csc x}{2 \cos x}$

    37. $\cot 2\alpha = \dfrac{\cot^2 \alpha - 1}{2 \cot \alpha}$

38. $\cot \dfrac{x}{2} = \pm\sqrt{\dfrac{1 + \cos x}{1 - \cos x}}$

39. $\sec \dfrac{x}{2} = \pm\dfrac{\sqrt{2 + 2\cos x}}{1 + \cos x}$

40. $\tan \dfrac{\alpha}{2} = \dfrac{1 - \cos \alpha}{\sin \alpha}$

15–6 *more on identities*

The following is a list of useful identities to which you can refer as needed. These identities hold for all values of the variables for which the function values are defined. Corresponding identities hold in terms of angles under similar restrictions.

SUMMARY OF USEFUL IDENTITIES

Quotient Identities

$$\tan x = \frac{\sin x}{\cos x}$$

$$\cot x = \frac{\cos x}{\sin x}$$

Reciprocal Identities

$$\sin x \csc x = 1$$

$$\cos x \sec x = 1$$

$$\tan x \cot x = 1$$

Pythagorean Identities

$$\sin^2 x + \cos^2 x = 1$$
$$\tan^2 x + 1 = \sec^2 x$$
$$1 + \cot^2 x = \csc^2 x$$

Negatives

$$\sin(-x) = -\sin x$$
$$\cos(-x) = \cos x$$
$$\tan(-x) = -\tan x$$

Sum and Difference Identities

$$\sin(x_1 \pm x_2) = \sin x_1 \cos x_2 \pm \cos x_1 \sin x_2$$
$$\cos(x_1 \pm x_2) = \cos x_1 \cos x_2 \mp \sin x_1 \sin x_2$$
$$\tan(x_1 \pm x_2) = \frac{\tan x_1 \pm \tan x_2}{1 \mp \tan x_1 \tan x_2}$$

Double-Angle Identities

$$\sin 2x = 2 \sin x \cos x$$
$$\cos 2x = \cos^2 x - \sin^2 x$$
$$= 1 - 2 \sin^2 x$$
$$= 2 \cos^2 x - 1$$
$$\tan 2x = \frac{2 \tan x}{1 - \tan^2 x}$$

Half-Angle Identities

$$\sin \frac{x}{2} = \pm \sqrt{\frac{1 - \cos x}{2}}$$

$$\cos \frac{x}{2} = \pm \sqrt{\frac{1 + \cos x}{2}}$$

$$\tan \frac{x}{2} = \pm \sqrt{\frac{1 - \cos x}{1 + \cos x}}$$

$$= \frac{\sin x}{1 + \cos x}$$

WRITTEN EXERCISES Prove each identity. In each case, state the necessary restrictions.

EXAMPLE $\dfrac{\sin 2\alpha}{2 \sin^2 \alpha} = \cot \alpha$

SOLUTION You have $\sin 2\alpha = 2 \sin \alpha \cos \alpha$, so

$$\frac{2 \sin \alpha \cos \alpha}{2 \sin^2 \alpha} = \frac{\cos \alpha \, (2 \sin \alpha)}{\sin \alpha \, (2 \sin \alpha)} = \frac{\cos \alpha}{\sin \alpha} = \cot \alpha$$

for all values of α for which $\sin \alpha \neq 0$, by the definition of cotangent.

A 1. $\csc \alpha \, (\sin \alpha + \sin 2\alpha) = 1 + 2 \cos \alpha$

2. $\dfrac{2}{\sin 2\alpha} = \sec \alpha \csc \alpha$

3. $2 - 2 \sin^2 \alpha = \sin 2\alpha \csc \alpha \cos \alpha$

4. $\sin^2 \alpha = \frac{1}{2} \tan \alpha \sin 2\alpha$

5. $\dfrac{2}{\tan 2\alpha} = \cot \alpha - \tan \alpha$

6. $\dfrac{1 - \sin 2\alpha}{\cos 2\alpha} = \dfrac{1 - \tan \alpha}{1 + \tan \alpha}$

7. $\cos \alpha + \sin^2 \frac{1}{2}\alpha = \dfrac{1 + \cos \alpha}{2}$

8. $2 \, (\cos^2 \frac{1}{2}\alpha - \cos \alpha) = 1 - \cos \alpha$

9. $\sin 2\alpha = \dfrac{2 \tan \alpha}{1 + \tan^2 \alpha}$

10. $\cos 2\alpha = \dfrac{1 - \tan^2 \alpha}{1 + \tan^2 \alpha}$

11. $\dfrac{2}{1 + \cos 2\alpha} = \sec^2 \alpha$

12. $\dfrac{1 + \cos 2\alpha}{\sin 2\alpha} = \cot \alpha$

13. $\cos 4\alpha = 1 - 2 \sin^2 2\alpha$

14. $\tan 2\alpha = \dfrac{\sin 4\alpha}{1 + \cos 4\alpha}$

B 15. $\sin 3\alpha = 3 \sin \alpha - 4 \sin^3 \alpha$

16. $\cos 3\alpha = 4 \cos^3 \alpha - 3 \cos \alpha$

17. $\tan 3\alpha = \csc 6\alpha - \cot 6\alpha$

18. $\tan 2\alpha = \dfrac{1}{1 - \tan \alpha} - \dfrac{1}{1 + \tan \alpha}$

19. $\cot \alpha = \csc \alpha - \tan \dfrac{\alpha}{2}$

20. $\sin 2\alpha - 2 \sin^3 \alpha \cos \alpha = 2 \sin \alpha \cos^3 \alpha$

C 21. $\sin (x_1 + x_2) \sin (x_1 - x_2) = \sin^2 x_1 - \sin^2 x_2$

22. $\cos (x_1 + x_2) \cos (x_1 - x_2) = \cos^2 x_1 - \sin^2 x_2$

The following are sometimes called the **sum and product identities.**

23. $\sin (x_1 + x_2) + \sin (x_1 - x_2) = 2 \sin x_1 \cos x_2$

24. $\sin (x_1 + x_2) - \sin (x_1 - x_2) = 2 \cos x_1 \sin x_2$

25. $\cos (x_1 + x_2) + \cos (x_1 - x_2) = 2 \cos x_1 \cos x_2$

26. $\cos (x_1 + x_2) - \cos (x_1 - x_2) = -2 \sin x_1 \sin x_2$

27. $\sin A + \sin B = 2 \sin \dfrac{A + B}{2} \cos \dfrac{A - B}{2}$.

(*Hint:* Let $A = x_1 + x_2$ and $B = x_1 - x_2$ and use Exercise 23.)

28. $\sin A - \sin B = 2 \cos \dfrac{A + B}{2} \sin \dfrac{A - B}{2}$

29. $\cos A + \cos B = 2 \cos \dfrac{A + B}{2} \cos \dfrac{A - B}{2}$

30. $\cos A - \cos B = -2 \sin \dfrac{A + B}{2} \sin \dfrac{A - B}{2}$

SELF-TEST 2 Give the meaning of each of the following.

1. odd function
2. even function
3. reduction formula

4. double-angle formula
5. half-angle formula

Objective 1, page 525

6. Reduce $\cos 150°$ to a function value of an angle in Quadrant I.

7. Reduce $\sin \dfrac{14\pi}{3}$ to a function value of an angle in Quadrant I.

Objective 2, page 525

8. Evaluate $1 - 2 \sin^2 15°$.

9. If α is a first-quadrant angle, and $\cos \alpha = \frac{3}{5}$, find $\sin 2\alpha$.

Objective 3, page 525

10. Prove that $\csc 2\alpha = \dfrac{\csc \alpha}{2 \cos \alpha}$ is an identity with suitable restrictions on $\cos \alpha$.

Check your answers with those printed at the back of the book.

Hilda Geiringer von Mises
1894–1973

Hilda von Mises was born and educated in Vienna. She taught at Berlin University, and after moving to the United States in 1939 she taught at Bryn Mawr College and at Wheaton College in Massachusetts. She published many articles (under the name Hilda Geiringer) dealing with probability and statistics, and also studied fluids and the plasticity of solids. She later worked as a research assistant at Harvard University, where she compiled and edited the works of her husband, Richard von Mises, after his death.

solving general triangles

Objectives

After completing the next two sections, you should be able to:
1. Apply the law of cosines and the law of sines to solve general triangles
2. Apply the law of cosines and the law of sines to solve simple practical problems.

15–7 the law of cosines

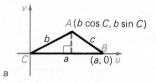

a

b

c

Figure 10

The Pythagorean Theorem enables you to find the length of one side of a *right* triangle when you know the lengths of the other two sides. To find a more general relationship between the lengths of the three sides of any triangle, look at Figure 10. In Figure 10a, $\angle BCA$ is in standard position and so the coordinates of point A are $(b \cos C, b \sin C)$. By the distance formula then,

$$c = \sqrt{(b \cos C - a)^2 + (b \sin C - 0)^2}$$

Squaring and simplifying the right-hand member, you have

$$c^2 = b^2 \cos^2 C - 2ab \cos C + a^2 + b^2 \sin^2 C$$
$$= a^2 + b^2 (\cos^2 C + \sin^2 C) - 2ab \cos C,$$

or, since $\cos^2 C + \sin^2 C = 1$,

$$c^2 = a^2 + b^2 - 2ab \cos C. \qquad (1)$$

By reorienting the axes so that angles A and B are, in turn, in standard position (Figures 10b and 10c), you can obtain the analogous relationships:

$$b^2 = a^2 + c^2 - 2ac \cos B \qquad (2)$$
$$a^2 = b^2 + c^2 - 2bc \cos A \qquad (3)$$

These three relationships together are the law of cosines.
Notice that if one of the angles of the triangle, say C, is a right angle, then $\cos C = 0$ and you have $c^2 = a^2 + b^2$, which is the Pythagorean Theorem. Thus, the Pythagorean Theorem is a "special case" of the law of cosines.

EXAMPLE   **Solve the triangle pictured, assuming the data to be exact.**

SOLUTION $\cos C = \cos 102° = -\cos (180 - 102)° = -\cos 78°$. From Table 6 at the back of the book, $-\cos 78° \doteq -0.2079$. Then, using the law of cosines, you have

$$c^2 \doteq (16)^2 + (13)^2 - 2(16)(13)(-0.2079)$$
$$\doteq 256 + 169 + 86.5 = 511.5.$$
$$\therefore c \doteq \sqrt{511.5}.$$

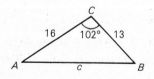

From Table 3 you find that to the nearest unit, $c \doteq 23$. To find $m(A)$, you can use

$$a^2 = b^2 + c^2 - 2bc \cos A,$$

from which

$$\cos A = \frac{b^2 + c^2 - a^2}{2\ bc} \doteq \frac{256 + 511.5 - 169}{736} = \frac{598.5}{736} \doteq 0.8132$$

$\therefore m(A) \doteq 36°$.

Since in any triangle, $m(A) + m(B) + m(C) = 180°$, you have

$$36° + m(B) + 102° = 180° \text{ or } m(B) \doteq 42°$$

$\therefore c \doteq 23$, $m(A) \doteq 36°$, and $m(B) \doteq 42°$.   Answer.

Notice that solving (3) for $\cos A$ gives

$$\cos A = \frac{b^2 + c^2 - a^2}{2bc}, \tag{4}$$

which, as illustrated in the Example above, can be used to find $m(A)$, when a, b, and c are given. Similarly, solving (1) and (2) for $\cos C$ and $\cos B$ gives formulas for finding $m(C)$ and $m(B)$, respectively.

WRITTEN EXERCISES   Find the required part of $\triangle ABC$ either to the nearest tenth or to the nearest 10'. Assume that the data are exact.

A   1. $a = 10$, $b = 4$, $m(C) = 30°$; $c =$ __?__

2. $a = 1$, $b = 4$, $m(C) = 60°$; $c =$ __?__

3. $a = 3$, $b = 2$, $m(C) = \dfrac{\pi^R}{3}$; $c =$ __?__

4. $a = 6$, $b = 9$, $m(C) = \dfrac{\pi^R}{4}$; $c =$ __?__

5. $b = 7$, $c = 12$, $m(A) = 52°$; $a =$ __?__

6. $a = 12$, $c = 16$, $m(B) = 78°$; $b =$ __?__

7. $a = 15$, $b = 7$, $c = 9$; $m(B) =$ __?__

8. $a = 9$, $b = 5$, $c = 6$; $m(A) =$ __?__

Solve each triangle completely. Give measurements to the nearest unit of length and the nearest degree.

B   9. $a = 14$, $c = 8$, $m(B) = 64°$ 12. $a = 4$, $b = 5$, $c = 2$

10. $b = 24$, $c = 10$, $m(A) = 148°$ 13. $a = 6$, $b = 9$, $m(C) = 53°$

11. $a = 5$, $b = 8$, $c = 7$ 14. $a = 12$, $c = 5$, $m(B) = 80°$

In each problem, give answers to the nearest tenth of a unit of length or to the nearest 10′.

A

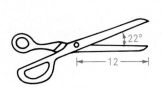

1. In sailing from Harbor City to Eagle Island, a distance of 200 kilometers, Mr. Thomas sails 20° off course for 50 kilometers. How far is he then from Eagle Island? By how much must he change his course to correct his error?

2. The blades on a pair of shears are 12 centimeters long. How far apart are the tips of the shears when the angle formed by the blades measures 22°?

3. Two sides of a triangular plot of land measure 40 meters and 30 meters, respectively, and the angle between these sides measures 42°. What is the perimeter of the plot of land?

4. From a point near one end of a pond, a surveyor observes that the angle determined by her transit and points A and B on opposite sides of the pond measures 28°. The transit is located 200 meters from point A and 180 meters from point B. How wide is the pond?

5. A clock pendulum is 50 centimeters long. From one end of its swing to the other, the straight-line separation measures 20 centimeters. What is the angle through which the pendulum swings?

6. Two ships sail from a harbor at the same time, one at a speed of 8 knots (nautical miles per hour), and the other at a speed of 10 knots. After two hours, they are 12 nautical miles apart. What is the measure of the angle by which their courses diverge?

B

7. The perimeter of a triangular lot is 1500 meters. If the length of the longest side of the lot is 100 meters less than the sum of the lengths of the other two sides, while the length of the shortest side is 50 meters less than $\frac{1}{2}$ that of the longest side, what is the degree measure of the angle formed by the shortest and longest sides?

8. A 150-meter television antenna is being raised into a vertical position by a cable. If the cable is anchored to the level ground at a distance of 170 meters from the base of the antenna, what is the measure of the acute angle the tower forms with the ground in the plane of the cable and tower when the supporting cable is 300 meters in length?

15-8   *the law of sines*

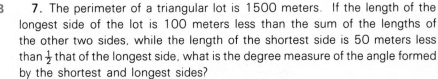

As noted in Section 15-7, by choosing the coordinate system appropriately, you can position any triangle ABC so that any one of the angles A, B, or C is in standard position. Because the area of a triangle is equal to one-half the product of the length of a base and the corresponding altitude, you can express the area of triangle ABC in Figure 11 by

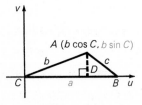

Figure 11

$$\text{Area} = \tfrac{1}{2}ab \sin C.$$

Similarly, with angles A or B in standard position, we get

$$\text{Area} = \tfrac{1}{2}bc \sin A \qquad \text{and} \qquad \text{Area} = \tfrac{1}{2}ca \sin B.$$

Thus, in general, we have the following.

> **Theorem.** The area of a triangle is equal to one-half the product of the lengths of two sides and the sine of their included angle.

EXAMPLE 1   Find the area of a triangle in which $a = 8$, $b = 14$, and $m(C) = 23°10'$.

SOLUTION   From Table 6, $\sin 23°10' \doteq 0.3934$, so that

$$\text{Area} = \tfrac{1}{2}ab \sin C \doteq \tfrac{1}{2}(8)(14)(0.3934) \doteq 22.03. \quad \textbf{Answer.}$$

Since each of the three expressions for the area of triangle ABC represents the same number, you know that

$$\tfrac{1}{2}bc \sin A = \tfrac{1}{2}ac \sin B = \tfrac{1}{2}ab \sin C.$$

Dividing each member of this compound sentence by $\tfrac{1}{2}abc$ produces

$$\frac{\sin A}{a} = \frac{\sin B}{b} = \frac{\sin C}{c}.$$

This relationship is formalized in the following theorem.

> **Law of Sines**
>
> The sines of the angles of a triangle are proportional to the lengths of the opposite sides.

Notice that if one of the angles of the triangle, say C, is a right angle, then $\sin C = 1$, and the law of sines yields the familiar right-triangle relationships

$$\sin A = \frac{a}{c} \qquad \text{and} \qquad \sin B = \frac{b}{c}.$$

EXAMPLE 2   Solve the triangle pictured.

SOLUTION   Since $m(A) + m(B) + m(C) = 180°$, you have

$$27°20' + 48°10' + m(C) = 180° \qquad \text{or} \qquad m(C) = 104°30'.$$

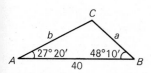

From the law of sines:

$$\frac{\sin 27°20'}{a} = \frac{\sin 48°10'}{b} = \frac{\sin 104°30'}{40}$$

(Solution continued on page 548.)

Solving separately for a and b, you find:

$$\frac{\sin 27°20'}{a} = \frac{\sin 104°30'}{40} \qquad \frac{\sin 48°10'}{b} = \frac{\sin 104°30'}{40}$$

$$a = \frac{40 \sin 27°20'}{\sin 104°30'} \qquad b = \frac{40 \sin 48°10'}{\sin 104°30'}$$

$$\doteq \frac{40(0.4592)}{0.9681} \doteq 18.97 \qquad \doteq \frac{40(0.7451)}{0.9681} \doteq 30.79$$

$\therefore m(C) = 104°30'$, $a \doteq 18.97$, and $b \doteq 30.79$. **Answer.**

The law of sines gives you a way to solve any triangle if you know
(a) the measurements of two angles and the length of any one side, as illustrated in Example 2 on the previous page, or
(b) the lengths of two sides and the measurement of an angle opposite one of them—insofar as there is a solution.

In the latter case, the data may be ambiguous. Figure 12 illustrates the possibilities for a triangle when you are given a, b, and $m(A)$.

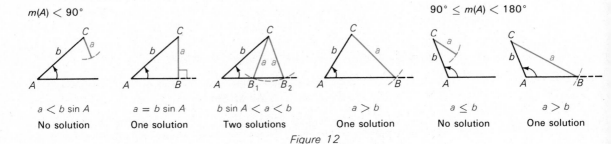

$m(A) < 90°$				$90° \leq m(A) < 180°$	
$a < b \sin A$	$a = b \sin A$	$b \sin A < a < b$	$a > b$	$a \leq b$	$a > b$
No solution	One solution	Two solutions	One solution	No solution	One solution

Figure 12

EXAMPLE 3   **Solve the triangle for which $a = 40$, $b = 42$, and $m(A) = 27°$.**

SOLUTION   A sketch of the triangle, roughly to scale, suggests that there are two solutions. This can be verified by noting that $b \sin A \doteq 42(0.4540) \doteq 19.07$ and $19.07 < 40 < 42$ (see Figure 12, part 3).

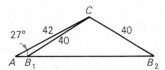

To find $m(B)$, we use

$$\frac{\sin A}{a} = \frac{\sin B}{b} \qquad \text{or} \qquad \sin B = \frac{b \sin A}{a} \doteq \frac{19.07}{40} \doteq 0.4768.$$

$\therefore$ either $m(B) \doteq 28°28'$ or $m(B) \doteq 180° - 28°28' = 151°32'$.

If $m(B) = 28°28'$, then $m(C) = 180° - 27° - 28°28' = 124°32'$.
If $m(B) = 151°32'$, then $m(C) = 180° - 27° - 151°32' = 1°28'$.

From

$$\frac{\sin A}{a} = \frac{\sin C}{c}, \qquad \text{or} \qquad c = \frac{a \sin C}{\sin A},$$

taking $m(C) = 124°32'$, you find that $c \doteq \dfrac{40(0.8238)}{0.4540} \doteq 72.58$, and

taking $m(C) = 1°28'$, you find that $c \doteq \dfrac{40(0.0256)}{0.4540} \doteq 2.26$.

∴ the two possible triangles have the following parts:

$$m(B) \doteq 28°28', \ m(C) \doteq 124°32', \ c \doteq 72.58;$$

and $\qquad m(B) \doteq 151°32', \ m(C) \doteq 1°28', \ c \doteq 2.26.$ **Answer.**

WRITTEN EXERCISES Solve the triangle with parts as given. Give lengths to the nearest tenth of a unit and angle measurements to the nearest 10'. Assume the data are exact. Use the law of cosines and/or the law of sines as necessary. If no solution exists, so state; and if two solutions exist, give both.

A 1. $m(A) = 70°$, $m(B) = 30°$, $a = 20$

2. $m(A) = 24°$, $m(C) = 63°$, $c = 10$

3. $a = 15$, $c = 30$, $m(C) = 120°$

4. $a = 15$, $b = 20$, $m(A) = 30°$

5. $m(A) = 58°50'$, $m(C) = 63°10'$, $c = 78$

6. $m(A) = 41°10'$, $m(B) = 96°50'$, $c = 0.9$

7. $a = 4$, $b = 5$, $m(B) = 30°$

8. $b = 26$, $c = 29$, $m(B) = 59°$

9. $a = 20$, $b = 22$, $m(A) = 57°40'$

10. $a = 14$, $b = 18$, $m(A) = 35°$

11–16. In each of the Exercises 1–6, find the area of the triangle.

Show that each relationship is true for any triangle ABC.

B 17. $\dfrac{a + b}{b} = \dfrac{\sin A + \sin B}{\sin B}$ $\left(\textit{Hint: } \text{Add 1 to each member of } \dfrac{a}{b} = \dfrac{\sin A}{\sin B}.\right)$

18. $\dfrac{a - b}{b} = \dfrac{\sin A - \sin B}{\sin B}$

19. $\dfrac{a - b}{a + b} = \dfrac{\sin A - \sin B}{\sin A + \sin B}$

20. $\dfrac{a - b}{a + b} = \dfrac{\cos \frac{1}{2}(A + B) \sin \frac{1}{2}(A - B)}{\sin \frac{1}{2}(A + B) \cos \frac{1}{2}(A - B)} = \dfrac{\tan \frac{1}{2}(A - B)}{\tan \frac{1}{2}(A + B)}$

(This relationship is called the Law of Tangents.)

21. Show that the area of a triangle is given by $\text{Area} = \dfrac{b^2 \sin A \sin C}{2 \sin B}$, by starting with the fact that $\text{Area} = \frac{1}{2}bc \sin A$.

PROBLEMS   Give answers to the nearest tenth of a unit of length or nearest 10′. Assume that the data are exact.

A   1. From two observation points 8 kilometers apart, the angles between an observed column of smoke and the other observation point measure 34°30′ and 50°20′, respectively. How far is the column of smoke from the nearer observation point?

2. When the liner Mohawk is 100 kilometers from the radio station on Carson's Island, it takes a bearing on the station and finds that the measure of the angle between the station and the Mohawk's course is 52°50′. After sailing at 12 kilometers per hour for two hours on the same course, it finds the bearing on the station to be 65°30′. How far is the Mohawk from the station at that time?

3. The diagonal of a parallelogram is 40 centimeters long, and makes angles of 33° and 40° with the sides. Find the perimeter of the parallelogram.

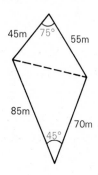

4. Find the perimeter of an isosceles triangle in which the base is 12 centimeters long, and for which each of the base angles measures 62°10′.

5. A surveyor measures an irregular plot of land. The four sides measure 45 meters, 55 meters, 70 meters, and 85 meters. The angle included between the two longest sides is 45°. The angle included between the two shortest sides is 75°. What is the area of the plot?

6. Mr. Matilsky wants to buy a piece of land for a service station. Building codes require that the plot be at least 2500 square meters. He finds a well-located triangular plot whose sides measure 60 meters, 85 meters, and 95 meters. Is it sufficiently large?

B   7. Radio station A is 120 kilometers due north of station B. Station A receives a distress message from a ship located 40° south of due east of the station, while station B receives the same message from a direction 47° east of north. How long would it take a helicopter flying at 110 kilometers per hour to reach the ship from station A?

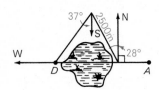

8. A surveyor laying a road due west from A changes direction to 28° west of north to avoid a swamp. After proceeding 2500 meters in this new direction, he turns and moves in a direction 37° west of south. How far must he continue in this direction to reach point D on the east-west line through A?

SELF-TEST 3   Give a statement of each of the following.

1. law of cosines   2. law of sines

Objective 1, page 544   3. In a triangle, if $a = 7$, $b = 10$, and $m(C) = 72°$, find c.

4. In a triangle, if $m(A) = 84°$, $m(B) = 65°$, and $c = 12$, find a.

5. Find the area of the triangle described in Problem 4.

Objective 2, page 544

6. Two ships sail from the same harbor at the same time on courses diverging by 83°. If the ships sail at constant speeds of 10 knots and 12 knots, how many nautical miles apart are they after 1 hour?

7. Find the perimeter of an isosceles triangle with base of length 30 centimeters and vertex angle 30°.

Check your answers with those printed at the back of the book.

chapter summary

1. You use the **fundamental trigonometric identities** together with properties of real numbers to establish additional identities.

2. The formula $\cos(x_1 - x_2) = \cos x_1 \cos x_2 + \sin x_1 \sin x_2$ is the **formula for the cosine of a difference.** You can use this formula to derive **reduction formulas** and formulas for values of functions of **sums** and then for **double-** and **half-angle formulas.**

3. If you know the measures of three parts of a triangle, including the length of at least one side, you can find the measures of the remaining parts by using the **Law of Cosines,** $c^2 = a^2 + b^2 - 2ab \cos C$, or the **Law of Sines,** $\dfrac{\sin A}{a} = \dfrac{\sin B}{b} = \dfrac{\sin C}{c}$.

When given data for a triangle consist of the lengths of two sides and the measure of an angle opposite one of them, there may exist no, one, or two triangles with the given measurements.

4. The **area of a triangle** is equal to one-half the product of the lengths of two sides and the sine of their included angle.

chapter test and review

15–1 **1.** Express $\cos^2 \alpha$ in terms of $\csc \alpha$.

15–2 **2.** Prove that $\dfrac{\csc^2 \alpha - 1}{\csc \alpha} = \cos \alpha \cot \alpha$ is an identity and state any necessary restrictions on $m°(\alpha)$.

15–3 **3.** Express $\cos 305°$ as a function of a first-quadrant angle.

15–4 **4.** Express $\sin 141°$ as a function of an angle α for which $0° \le m(\alpha) \le 45°$.

15–5 **5.** Given $\sin x = \dfrac{3}{5}$, and $0^R \le m(x) \le \dfrac{\pi^R}{4}$, find $\cos 2x$.

15–6 **6.** Prove that $\cos 2\alpha = \dfrac{\csc^2 \alpha - 2}{\csc^2 \alpha}$ is an identity and state all necessary restrictions on α.

15–7 **7.** In triangle ABC, if $a = 10$, $b = 20$, and $m(C) = 30°$, find c.

15–8 **8.** In triangle ABC, if $m(A) = 45°$, $m(B) = 60°$, and $a = 40$, find b.

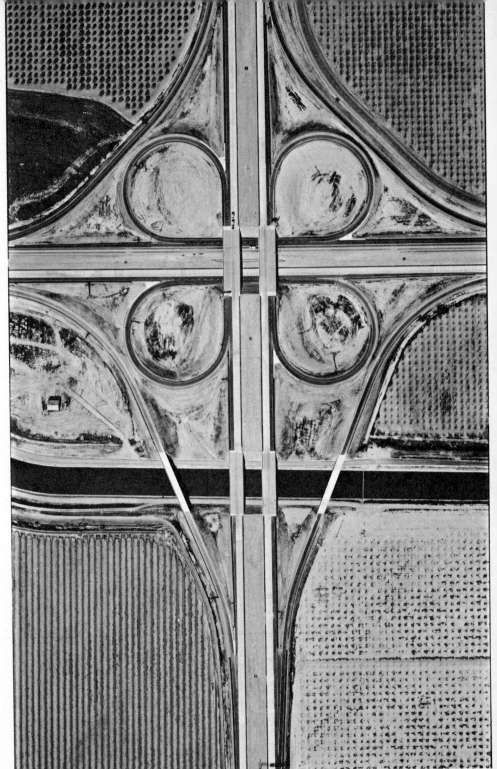

Highway systems have increased our mobility and facilitated transportation of goods. They have also created new problems—traffic congestion, air pollution, fuel shortages. We are now working to balance the benefits and the adverse effects of automobile transportation.

552

16 *inverses of periodic functions; polar coordinates and vectors*

inverses of periodic functions

Objectives

After completing the next two sections, you should be able to:
1. Find values of inverses of periodic functions.
2. Solve simple trigonometric sentences.

16–1 *inverses of periodic functions; principal values*

You find the inverse of the periodic function specified by

$$\{(x, y): y = \sin x\}$$

by interchanging the x and the y in the defining equation, thus obtaining the relation specified by

$$\{(x, y): x = \sin y\}.$$

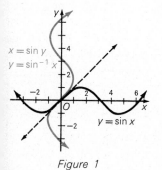

Figure 1

Both relations are graphed in Figure 1. The inverse relation is denoted either by $\{(x, y): y = \sin^{-1} x\}$ (read "$y =$ the inverse sine of x") or by $\{(x, y): y = \arcsin x\}$ (read "$y =$ the arcsine of x"). Notice that the inverse relation $\{(x, y): y = \sin^{-1} x\}$ is *not* a function.

Inverses of the other circular functions that you have studied are defined similarly:

$$\{(x, y): y = \cos^{-1} x\} \qquad \{(x, y): y = \sec^{-1} x\}$$
$$\{(x, y): y = \tan^{-1} x\} \qquad \{(x, y): y = \csc^{-1} x\}$$
$$\{(x, y): y = \cot^{-1} x\}$$

You can see from the graphs in Figures 2 through 6 that none of these inverse relations is a function.

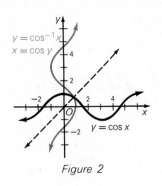

Figure 2

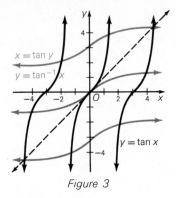

Figure 3

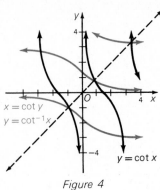

Figure 4

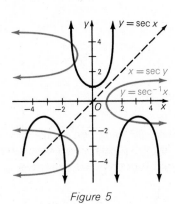

Figure 5

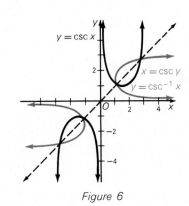

Figure 6

However, by suitably restricting the ranges of the inverses of the circular and trigonometric functions, you can define for each such function any number of inverse functions. For example, as suggested by Figure 7, if the range is restricted to a suitable interval of length π, the resulting relation will then be a function.

According to custom, the principal-value inverse function for sine is defined for real numbers to be

$$\left\{(x,\ y)\colon x = \sin y \text{ and } -\frac{\pi}{2} \le y \le \frac{\pi}{2}\right\}$$

and is denoted by ''Arcsin'' or ''Sin^{-1},'' with capital letters, and read ''principal arcsine of x'' and ''principal inverse sine of x,'' respectively. In terms of angles, you have:

$$\text{Arcsin} = \text{Sin}^{-1} = \{(x,\ \alpha)\colon x = \sin \alpha \text{ and } -90° \le m(\alpha) \le 90°\}.$$

The domain of Sin^{-1} is $\{x\colon |x| \le 1\}$.

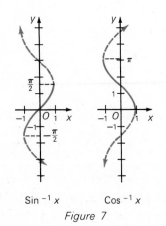

Sin$^{-1}\,x$ Cos$^{-1}\,x$

Figure 7

On the other hand, it is customary to define the principal-value inverse function for cosine to be

$$\text{Arccos} = \text{Cos}^{-1} = \{(x, y): x = \cos y \text{ and } 0 \leq y \leq \pi\}.$$

In terms of angles, you have

$$\text{Arccos} = \text{Cos}^{-1} = \{(x, \alpha): x = \cos \alpha \text{ and } 0° \leq m(\alpha) \leq 180°\}$$

The domain of Cos^{-1} is also $\{x: |x| \leq 1\}$.

The graphs and definitions of the remaining principal-value inverses for the circular functions are shown in Figures 8 through 11.

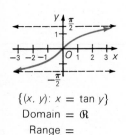

$\{(x, y): x = \tan y\}$

Domain = $\mathcal{R}$

Range =

$\left\{y: -\dfrac{\pi}{2} < y < \dfrac{\pi}{2}\right\}$

Figure 8

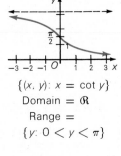

$\{(x, y): x = \cot y\}$

Domain = $\mathcal{R}$

Range =

$\{y: 0 < y < \pi\}$

Figure 9

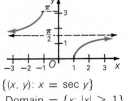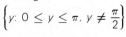

$\{(x, y): x = \sec y\}$

Domain = $\{x: |x| \geq 1\}$

Range =

$\left\{y: 0 \leq y \leq \pi, y \neq \dfrac{\pi}{2}\right\}$

Figure 10

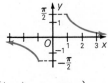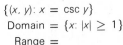

$\{(x, y): x = \csc y\}$

Domain = $\{x: |x| \geq 1\}$

Range =

$\left\{y: -\dfrac{\pi}{2} \leq y \leq \dfrac{\pi}{2}, y \neq 0\right\}$

Figure 11

When 0, $\dfrac{\pi}{2}$, π, etc., are replaced with $0°$, $90°$, $180°$, etc., and y with $m(\alpha)$, in the foregoing definitions, the results will define the principal-value inverse functions for the corresponding trigonometric functions.

EXAMPLE 1   a. Specify the members of $\{y: \cos y = -\frac{1}{2}, y \in \mathcal{R}\}$.

b. Find $\text{Cos}^{-1}\left(-\frac{1}{2}\right)$ for both the inverse circular and the inverse trigonometric function.

SOLUTION   a. First, find all values of y such that $\cos y = -\frac{1}{2}$ and $0 \leq y \leq 2\pi$. These are the values $\dfrac{2\pi}{3}$ and $\dfrac{4\pi}{3}$ because

$$\cos \frac{2\pi}{3} = -\tfrac{1}{2} \text{ and } \cos \frac{4\pi}{3} = -\tfrac{1}{2}.$$

$\therefore \{y: \cos y = -\frac{1}{2}, y \in \mathcal{R}\} =$

$$\left\{y: y = \frac{2\pi}{3} + 2k\pi\right\} \cup \left\{y: y = \frac{4\pi}{3} + 2k\pi\right\}, \text{ where } k \in \{\text{the integers}\}.$$

Answer.

b. For Cos^{-1} the range is $0 \leq y \leq \pi$, or $0° \leq m(\alpha) \leq 180°$, and thus

$$\text{Cos}^{-1}\left(-\tfrac{1}{2}\right) = \frac{2\pi}{3} \text{ or } \text{Cos}^{-1}\left(-\tfrac{1}{2}\right) = 120°. \text{ Answer.}$$

Throughout the remainder of this chapter, the variable k will always have $\{\text{the integers}\}$ as its replacement set.

Sometimes you must use a table of function values to approximate element
in the range of an inverse relation.

EXAMPLE 2   a. Specify to the nearest hundredth the members of $\{y: \sin y = \frac{7}{8}, y \in \mathcal{R}\}$

    b. Find $\text{Sin}^{-1} \frac{7}{8}$ for both the inverse circular and inverse trigonometri
function.

SOLUTION   a. Using $\frac{7}{8} = 0.8750$, you find from Table 7 that, for $0 \leq y \leq \frac{\pi}{2}$

$y \doteq 1.07$. Moreover, since in Quadrant II sin y is positive, you also have

$$y \doteq \pi - 1.07 \doteq 3.14 - 1.07 = 2.07.$$

$\therefore \{y: \sin y = \frac{7}{8}, y \in \mathcal{R}\} =$

$$\{y: y \doteq 1.07 + 2k\pi\} \cup \{y: y \doteq 2.07 + 2k\pi\}. \quad \textbf{Answer}$$

b. For Sin^{-1}, the range is $-\frac{\pi}{2} \leq y \leq \frac{\pi}{2}$, or $-90° \leq m(\alpha) \leq 90°$, and

thus

$$\text{Sin}^{-1} \frac{7}{8} \doteq 1.07 \text{ or } \text{Sin}^{-1} \frac{7}{8} \doteq 61°2'. \quad \textbf{Answer.}$$

Thinking of principal-value inverses in terms of angles instead of number
gives the easiest way to obtain values for such compositions of functions a

$$\sin (\text{Cos}^{-1}), \quad \text{and} \quad \text{Tan}^{-1} (\sin).$$

For example, Figure 12 pictures the angle function value $\alpha = \text{Cos}^{-1} \left(\frac{2}{3}\right)$
After using the Pythagorean theorem to compute the length of side $\overline{AB}$ c
$\triangle AOB$ to be $\sqrt{5}$, you can read from the diagram such values as

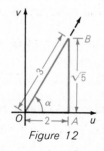

Figure 12

$$\sin \left(\text{Cos}^{-1} \frac{2}{3}\right) = \frac{\sqrt{5}}{3}, \quad \tan \left(\text{Cos}^{-1} \frac{2}{3}\right) = \frac{\sqrt{5}}{2}, \quad \text{and}$$

$$\csc \left(\text{Cos}^{-1} \frac{2}{3}\right) = \frac{3}{\sqrt{5}}.$$

EXAMPLE 3   Simplify $\sin (\text{Cos}^{-1} a + \text{Sin}^{-1} b)$.

SOLUTION   By the sum formula for $\sin (\alpha_1 + \alpha_2)$, you have

$\sin (\text{Cos}^{-1} a + \text{Sin}^{-1} b)$
$$= [\sin (\text{Cos}^{-1} a)][\cos (\text{Sin}^{-1} b)] + [\cos (\text{Cos}^{-1} a)][\sin (\text{Sin}^{-1} b)]$$

Now $\text{Cos}^{-1} a$ represents an angle in either Quadrant I or Quadrant II, so tha
$\sin (\text{Cos}^{-1} a)$ is positive. Thus, you need only depict $\text{Cos}^{-1} a$ as an angle in
a right triangle as shown. By inspection,

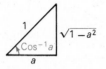

$$\sin (\text{Cos}^{-1} a) = \sqrt{1 - a^2}.$$

Similarly, $\text{Sin}^{-1} b$ lies in Quadrant I or Quadrant IV; in either case, $\cos (\text{Sin}^{-1} b$
is positive, so that, from the sketch at the left, you see that

$$\cos (\text{Sin}^{-1} b) = \sqrt{1 - b^2}.$$

Then, because for every $a \in \mathcal{R}$ and $b \in \mathcal{R}$, $\sin(\text{Sin}^{-1} a) = a$ and $\cos(\text{Cos}^{-1} b) = b$, you find

$$\sin(\text{Cos}^{-1} a + \text{Sin}^{-1} b) = (\sqrt{1 - a^2})(\sqrt{1 - b^2}) + ab$$
$$= \sqrt{(1 - a^2)(1 - b^2)} + ab. \text{ Answer.}$$

WRITTEN EXERCISES Identify the members of each set of real numbers. Use Table 7 for approximations when necessary.

A
1. $\{y: \cos y = 1, y \in \mathcal{R}\}$
2. $\{y: \sin y = -1, y \in \mathcal{R}\}$
3. $\{x: \tan x = 1, x \in \mathcal{R}\}$
4. $\{x: \cot x = 0, x \in \mathcal{R}\}$
5. $\{z: \sec z = \frac{3}{2}, z \in \mathcal{R}\}$
6. $\{z: \csc z = 2.138, z \in \mathcal{R}\}$

Identify by means of degree-measures the set of angles in standard position in each set. Use Table 6 for approximations when necessary.

7. $\{\alpha: \sin \alpha = \frac{1}{2}\}$
8. $\left\{\alpha: \cos \alpha = \dfrac{1}{\sqrt{2}}\right\}$
9. $\{\alpha: \tan \alpha = 1\}$
10. $\{\alpha: \cot \alpha = 1\}$
11. $\{\alpha: \sin \alpha = 0.3852\}$
12. $\{\alpha: \cos \alpha = -0.1783\}$

State the value of each of the following for both the inverse circular and inverse angle function. Use Tables 6 and 7 for approximations as needed.

13. $\text{Cos}^{-1} \dfrac{\sqrt{3}}{2}$
14. $\text{Sin}^{-1} \dfrac{\sqrt{3}}{2}$
15. $\text{Tan}^{-1} 2$
16. $\text{Cot}^{-1}(-1)$

17. $\text{Arccos} \frac{1}{2}$
18. $\text{Arcsin} \dfrac{\sqrt{2}}{2}$
19. $\text{Cos}^{-1} 0.6675$
20. $\text{Tan}^{-1} 3.467$

21. $\text{Arcsec } 1.053$
22. $\text{Arccsc } 2.187$
23. $\text{Arcsin}(-0.8882)$
24. $\text{Arccot}(-1.342)$

Find each of the following values. Where applicable, give both inverse circular and inverse trigonometric function values.

25. $\text{Sin}^{-1}\left(\cos \dfrac{\pi}{4}\right)$
26. $\text{Cos}^{-1}\left(\sin \dfrac{\pi}{2}\right)$
27. $\text{Tan}^{-1}\left(\tan \dfrac{\pi}{3}\right)$
28. $\text{Cot}^{-1}\left(\tan \dfrac{\pi}{6}\right)$

29. $\text{Sec}^{-1}\left(\tan \dfrac{\pi}{4}\right)$
30. $\text{Csc}^{-1}\left(\cot \dfrac{3\pi}{4}\right)$
31. $\tan\left(\text{Arcsin} \dfrac{\sqrt{3}}{2}\right)$
32. $\sec(\text{Arccos} \frac{1}{2})$

33. $\sin(\text{Tan}^{-1}(-1))$
34. $\cos(\text{Cot}^{-1}(-\sqrt{3}))$
35. $\cot(\text{Arccot } 2)$
36. $\csc(\text{Arccsc } 3)$

Simplify.

B
37. $\sin(\text{Sin}^{-1} \frac{1}{2} + \text{Cos}^{-1} \frac{3}{5})$
38. $\sin(\text{Sin}^{-1} \frac{5}{13} + \text{Tan}^{-1} \frac{1}{2})$

39. $\cos \left(\mathrm{Sin}^{-1} \dfrac{1}{\sqrt{2}} + \mathrm{Cos}^{-1} \dfrac{4}{5} \right)$

41. $\sin (2 \, \mathrm{Cos}^{-1} \frac{3}{5})$

40. $\tan \left(\mathrm{Tan}^{-1} \dfrac{2}{5} + \dfrac{\pi}{3} \right)$

42. $\cos (2 \, \mathrm{Sin}^{-1} \frac{12}{13})$

Verify each of the following.

43. $\mathrm{Cos}^{-1} x = \mathrm{Sec}^{-1} \left(\dfrac{1}{x} \right)$

45. $\mathrm{Arcsin} \, x = \dfrac{\pi}{2} - \mathrm{Arccos} \, x$

44. $\cos \mathrm{Sin}^{-1} x = \sin \mathrm{Cos}^{-1} x$

46. $\mathrm{Arcsin} \, x = \mathrm{Arctan} \dfrac{x}{\sqrt{1 - x^2}}$

C **47.** Is it true that for all x, $\mathrm{Sin}^{-1} (\sin x) = x$? (*Hint:* Look at some specifi values for x, for example, $x = \dfrac{3\pi}{4}$.)

48. Is it true that for all x, $\mathrm{Cos}^{-1} (\cos x) = x$? (*Hint:* Look at $x = -\dfrac{\pi}{3}$.)

16–2 *equations involving circular and trigonometric functions*

The equation $\cos x = c$, where $c \in \mathfrak{R}$ is a constant, either has an empt solution set (if $|c| > 1$), or else has a solution set containing infinitely man members. For example, the solution set over $\mathfrak{R}$ of

$$\cos x = -\tfrac{1}{2}$$

was found in part **a** of Example 1 in Section 16–1 to be

$$\left\{ x : x = \dfrac{2\pi}{3} + 2k\pi \right\} \cup \left\{ x : x = \dfrac{4\pi}{3} + 2k\pi \right\}, \quad \text{where } k \in \{\text{the integers}\}$$

Over the set of angles, the solution set of $\cos \alpha = -\tfrac{1}{2}$ is

$$\{\alpha : m(\alpha) = 120° + k \cdot 360°\} \cup \{\alpha : m(\alpha) = 240° + k \cdot 360°\},$$
$$\text{where } k \in \{\text{the integers}\}$$

In either case, such a solution set is referred to as the general solution c the equation. The subset consisting of the solutions in a specified interva is called a particular solution. The particular solution of the equatio $\cos x = -\tfrac{1}{2}$ in the interval $0 \leq x < 2\pi$ is

$$\left\{ \dfrac{2\pi}{3}, \dfrac{4\pi}{3} \right\}.$$

In the interval $0° \leq m(\alpha) < 360°$, the particular solution of $\cos \alpha = -\tfrac{1}{2}$ i

$$\{\alpha : m(\alpha) = 120°\} \cup \{\alpha : m(\alpha) = 240°\}.$$

In the latter case, we shall use the abbreviated notation $\{120°, 240°\}$ (Compare this with the abbreviated notation introduced in Section 14–4.

EXAMPLE 1   a. Find the general solution over $\Re$ of $3 \sin x + \cos x = 0$.
                b. Find the particular solution in the interval $0 \leq x < 2\pi$.

SOLUTION   a. To obtain an equation involving a single function value, you can add $-\cos x$ to each member to obtain:

$$3 \sin x = -\cos x$$

Then, observing that $\cos x \neq 0$ (because if $\cos x = 0$, $\sin x \neq 0$), you can divide each member by $3 \cos x$ to obtain

$$\frac{\sin x}{\cos x} = -\frac{1}{3}.$$

Since $\dfrac{\sin x}{\cos x} = \tan x$, you have $\tan x = -\frac{1}{3} \doteq -0.3333$. From Table 7 you see that $\tan (0.322) \doteq \frac{1}{3}$. From Section 15–4 you know that $\tan (-x) = -\tan x$, so $\tan (-0.322) \doteq -\frac{1}{3}$. Since -0.322 is in the range of Tan^{-1},

$$\text{Tan}^{-1} \left(-\tfrac{1}{3}\right) \doteq -0.322.$$

Tangent has period π, so you have, as a general solution,

$$\{x: x \doteq -0.322 + k\pi\}. \quad \textbf{Answer.}$$

b. Particular solutions in the interval $0 \leq x < 2\pi$ are obtained by letting $k = 1$ and $k = 2$. The particular solutions are $\{2.82, 5.96\}$. **Answer.**

EXAMPLE 2   a. Find the general solution over the set of angles of

$$\cos 2x + \sin x - 1 = 0.$$

b. Find the particular solution over the interval

$$0° \leq m(\alpha) < 360°.$$

SOLUTION   a. You can begin by replacing $\cos 2x$ with $1 - 2 \sin^2 x$ to obtain $1 - 2 \sin^2 x + \sin x - 1 = 0$, from which $2 \sin^2 x - \sin x = 0$. Factoring the left-hand member yields

$$\sin x (2 \sin x - 1) = 0,$$

which is equivalent to

$$\sin x = 0 \quad \text{or} \quad 2 \sin x - 1 = 0.$$

Since $\sin x = 0$ for $x = k \cdot 180°$, and $\sin x = \frac{1}{2}$ for $x = 30° + k \cdot 360°$ and $x = 150° + k \cdot 360°$, the general solution set is

$$\{x: x = k \cdot 180°\} \cup \{x: x = 30° + k \cdot 360°\}$$
$$\cup \{x: x = 150° + k \cdot 360°\} \text{ for } k \in \{\text{the integers}\}. \quad \textbf{Answer.}$$

b. Over the interval $0° \leq m(\alpha) < 360°$, the set of particular solutions is $\{0°, 30°, 150°, 180°\}$. **Answer.**

Find the general solution of each equation for **(a)** $x \in \mathcal{R}$, and **(b)** $m(\alpha)$ in degrees.

A

1. $\sin x - 1 = 0$
2. $\cos x + 1 = 0$
3. $\sqrt{2} \sin x - 1 = 0$
4. $2 + \sec x = 0$

5. $2 \sec x - 2\sqrt{2} = 0$
6. $\sqrt{3} \sec x + 2 = 0$
7. $4 \sin^2 x - 1 = 0$
8. $2 \cos^2 x = 1 + \cos^2 x$

Find the particular solution over $0 \leq x < 2\pi$.

9. $2 \cos^2 x + 3 \cos x + 1 = 0$
10. $\sin 2x - 2 \cos x = 0$
11. $\sin 2x = \sin x$

12. $\sin 2x = \cos x$
13. $\sin^2 x - \cos^2 x = 1$
14. $\sin x + \cos x \tan x = 1$

Find the particular solution in $0 \leq x < 2\pi$ or in $0° \leq m(\alpha) < 360°$. Use Table 6 or 7 as necessary for approximations.

15. $2 \cos^2 x - \cos x = 1$
16. $\sin^2 x - 2 \sin x + 1 = 0$
17. $\tan 3\alpha = 0$
18. $\sin 4\alpha = 1$

19. $\sin x \cos x = \frac{1}{2} \cos 2x$
20. $\cos 2x + \sin 2x = 0$
21. $2 \cot x = 3 \csc 2x$
22. $\sec^2 2x = 1 - \tan 2x$

B

23. $\sin x = 1 + \sqrt{3} \cos x$
   (*Hint:* Square both members.)
24. $\sin x + \cos x = 1$
25. $3 \tan \frac{x}{2} = \cot \frac{x}{2}$
26. $\sin \frac{x}{2} - \cos \frac{x}{2} = \sqrt{2}$
27. $\tan^2 2\alpha + 2 \tan 2\alpha + 1 = 0$

28. $2 \cos^2 2\alpha = 1 - \cos 2\alpha$
29. $\sin x < \tan x$
30. $\sin x \leq \cos x$
31. $\text{Tan}^{-1} (x - 2) = \frac{\pi}{3}$
32. $\text{Cos}^{-1} 2x = \frac{\pi}{3} - \text{Cos}^{-1} x$

C

33. $0 \leq \sin x \leq 1$
34. $\tan^2 x - 1 \leq 0$
35. $\sin 3x + \sin x = \sin 2x$

36. $\cos 2x = \cos 3x - \cos 4x$
37. $2 \tan x + \sec x = 1$
38. $3 \cot x + 5 \csc x = 4$

(*Hint for Ex.* 35: $\sin x_1 + \sin x_2 = 2 \sin \dfrac{x_1 + x_2}{2} \cos \dfrac{x_1 - x_2}{2}$.)

SELF-TEST 1 Give the meaning of each of the following:

1. $\text{Sin}^{-1} x$
2. Arctan x
3. $\text{Cos}^{-1} x$

Objective 1, page 553 4. Specify the members of $\left\{ y\colon \tan y = \dfrac{1}{\sqrt{3}}, y \in \mathcal{R} \right\}$.

5. State the value of Arcsin $\frac{1}{2}$ for the inverse *angle* function.

Objective 2, page 553   **6.** Solve $\tan^2 x = 1$ over $\mathcal{R}$.

7. Solve $\sin 2\alpha - \cos \alpha = 0$ over $0° \leq m(\alpha) < 360°$.

Check your answers with those printed at the back of the book.

polar coordinates

Objectives

After completing the next three sections, you should be able to:
1. Express the coordinates of a point in Cartesian or polar form when it is given in the other form.
2. Use De Moivre's Theorem to find powers and roots of complex numbers.
3. Resolve a given vector into horizontal and vertical components, and find the sum of two given vectors.

16–3 *polar coordinates; polar graphs*

In Section 3–2 you learned that each point in a plane can be paired uniquely with an ordered pair of real numbers (x, y) in a given Cartesian coordinate system for the plane. Another coordinate system can be developed as follows.

Each point in the plane lies on a ray with initial point at the origin. If r represents the distance from the origin to a point P, and if an angle having the nonnegative x-axis as its initial side and the ray $\overrightarrow{OP}$ as its terminal side is denoted by θ, then the ordered pair

$$(r, m(\theta))$$

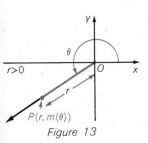
Figure 13

clearly specifies the location of P in the plane (Figure 13). The components of the ordered pair $(r, m(\theta))$, usually written as simply (r, θ), are called a pair of **polar coordinates** of P. The nonnegative x-axis is then called the **polar axis**, and the origin is called the **pole**.

If r is negative, then we measure the distance $|r|$ along the extension of the terminal side of θ through the origin (Figure 14). For example, $(-3, 30°)$ is a pair of polar coordinates for the point P which also has coordinates $(3, 210°)$.

In this system, since θ is coterminal with infinitely many angles having the polar axis as initial side, the location of P can also be given, for example, by any of the ordered pairs

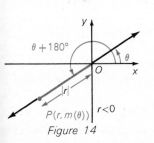
Figure 14

$$(r, \theta + 2k\pi) \qquad \text{or} \qquad (r, \theta + k \cdot 360°).$$

If $r = 0$, then *any* value might be assigned to $m(\theta)$. Thus the pole migh for example, be assigned polar coordinates $(0, 0°)$, $(0, 45°)$, or $(0, \frac{1}{2}\pi)$. I general:

> In a system of polar coordinates, each ordered pair (r, θ) can be associated with one and only one point of the plane, but each point of the plane may be associated with any number of ordered pairs (r, θ).

EXAMPLE 1   List all other polar coordinates of $P(2, 120°)$ for which $-360° \leq m(\theta) \leq 360°$.

SOLUTION   Sketch the graph of $P(2, 120°)$. By inspection, P has the additional coordinates

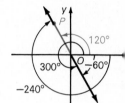

$(-2, 300°)$, $(-2, -60°)$, $(2, -240°)$.   **Answer.**

   When the polar axis of a polar coordinate system coincides with the nor negative *x*-axis of a Cartesian coordinate system, the polar and Cartesia coordinates are related as shown in Figure 15.

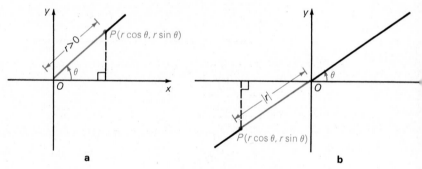

Figure 15

If $r > 0$ (Figure 15a), then $(x, y) = (r \cos \theta, r \sin \theta)$.
If $r = 0$, $(x, y) = (r \cos \theta, r \sin \theta) = (0, 0)$.
If $r < 0$ (Figure 15b), then

$$(x, y) = (|r| \cos (\theta + 180°), |r| \sin (\theta + 180°))$$
$$= (-|r| \cos \theta, -|r| \sin \theta)$$
$$= (r \cos \theta, r \sin \theta).$$

In general:

> The polar and Cartesian coordinates of any point P are related by:
>
> $$\left. \begin{aligned} x &= r \cos \theta \\ y &= r \sin \theta \end{aligned} \right\} \qquad (1)$$

These equations can be used to find Cartesian coordinates for a point whose polar coordinates are given.

EXAMPLE 2   Find the Cartesian coordinates of the point P with polar coordinates $(4, -120°)$.

SOLUTION   Using Equations (1), you have:

$$x = r \cos \theta = 4 \cos (-120°) = 4(-\tfrac{1}{2}) = -2$$

$$y = r \sin \theta = 4 \sin (-120°) = 4\left(-\frac{\sqrt{3}}{2}\right) = -2\sqrt{3}$$

∴ the required Cartesian coordinates are $(-2, -2\sqrt{3})$. **Answer.**

Given the Cartesian coordinates (x, y) of a point other than the origin, a pair of polar coordinates of the point can be found from the equations:

$$r = \pm\sqrt{x^2 + y^2}, \qquad \cos \theta = \frac{x}{\pm\sqrt{x^2 + y^2}}, \qquad (2)$$

$$\sin \theta = \frac{y}{\pm\sqrt{x^2 + y^2}}$$

EXAMPLE 3   Find a pair of polar coordinates of the point P whose Cartesian coordinates are $\left(-\dfrac{3\sqrt{3}}{2}, \dfrac{3}{2}\right)$.

SOLUTION   From Equations (2), using $r = \sqrt{x^2 + y^2}$, you have

$$r = \sqrt{\left(-\frac{3\sqrt{3}}{2}\right)^2 + \left(\frac{3}{2}\right)^2} = \sqrt{\frac{27}{4} + \frac{9}{4}} = \sqrt{\frac{36}{4}} = \sqrt{9} = 3.$$

$$\text{Since } \cos \theta = \frac{-\dfrac{3\sqrt{3}}{2}}{3} = -\frac{\sqrt{3}}{2}, \text{ and } \sin \theta = \frac{\dfrac{3}{2}}{3} = \frac{1}{2},$$

you see by inspection that θ can be an angle measuring $150°$. Thus, a pair of polar coordinates of P is $(3, 150°)$. [By using $r = -\sqrt{x^2 + y^2} = -3$, you would find $\cos \theta = \dfrac{\sqrt{3}}{2}$ and $\sin \theta = -\tfrac{1}{2}$, and so a second pair of coordinates is $(-3, 330°)$.] **Answer.**

Polar equations such as

$$r = 4 \cos \theta, \qquad r = 2, \qquad r \sin \theta = 2, \qquad \text{and} \qquad \theta = 30°$$

have ordered pairs of the form (r, θ) as solutions. The graph of the set of all solutions of such an equation is called the graph of the equation.

EXAMPLE 4   Sketch the graph of $r = 4 \cos \theta$.

SOLUTION   The table below shows selected solutions of the equation for

$$0° \leq m(\theta) \leq 360°.$$

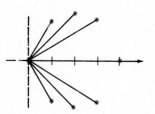

θ	0°	30°	45°	60°	90°	120°	135°	150°	180°
r	4	$2\sqrt{3}$	$2\sqrt{2}$	2	0	-2	$-2\sqrt{2}$	$-2\sqrt{3}$	-4

210°	225°	240°	270°	300°	315°	330°	360°
$-2\sqrt{3}$	$-2\sqrt{2}$	-2	0	2	$2\sqrt{2}$	$2\sqrt{3}$	4

If you plot all these solutions in succession, you will twice plot the points
in the figure at the left (above). That is, the points associated with

$$0° \leq m(\theta) \leq 180°$$

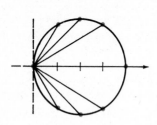

are the same as those associated with

$$180° \leq m(\theta) \leq 360°.$$

Connecting the points with a smooth curve yields the graph shown at the
left (below). You can verify (Exercise 27, page 565) that the graph is a circle.

WRITTEN EXERCISES   Find two sets of polar coordinates with $-180° < m(\theta) \leq 180°$ for the
point whose Cartesian coordinates are given. Show the graph of the point
in the plane.

A   1. (3, 3)

4. $\left(\dfrac{5\sqrt{3}}{2}, \dfrac{5}{2}\right)$

7. (5, -12)

2. (-4, -4)

5. $\left(-\dfrac{3}{2}, -\dfrac{3\sqrt{3}}{2}\right)$

8. ($-4\sqrt{2}$, $-4\sqrt{2}$)

3. $\left(-\dfrac{\sqrt{3}}{2}, \dfrac{1}{2}\right)$

6. (-3, 4)

Find the Cartesian coordinates of the point with the given polar coordinates.

9. (5, 60°)

14. $\left(-3, \dfrac{\pi^{R}}{6}\right)$

10. (3, $-120°$)

11. (-4, $-90°$)

15. $\left(4, \dfrac{11\pi^{R}}{3}\right)$

12. (-1, 330°)

13. (2, π^{R})

16. $\left(-2, -\dfrac{9\pi^{R}}{4}\right)$

In each of Exercises 17–24, use equations (1) on page 562 to transform the given equation into an equation in polar coordinates.

EXAMPLE Transform $x + y - 1 = 0$ into an equation in polar coordinates.

SOLUTION Substitute $x = r \cos \theta$ and $y = r \sin \theta$ into the equation and simplify.

$$r \cos \theta + r \sin \theta - 1 = 0$$
$$r(\cos \theta + \sin \theta) = 1$$
$$r = \frac{1}{\cos \theta + \sin \theta}. \quad \text{Answer.}$$

17. $x^2 + y^2 = 16$
18. $3x^2 + 3y^2 = 27$
19. $y^2 = 8x$
20. $x^2 = 4y$

21. $2x + y - 5 = 0$
22. $x - 2y + 3 = 0$
23. $x^2 + y^2 = 4x$
24. $x^2 + y^2 = -9y$

In each of Exercises 25–32, use equations (2) on page 563 to transform the given equation into an equation in Cartesian coordinates. Identify the graph.

EXAMPLE Transform $r = 2 \sin \theta$ into an equation in Cartesian coordinates and identify the graph.

SOLUTION Substituting $r = \pm \sqrt{x^2 + y^2}$ and $\sin \theta = \dfrac{y}{\pm \sqrt{x^2 + y^2}}$, we get:

$$\pm \sqrt{x^2 + y^2} = \frac{2y}{\pm \sqrt{x^2 + y^2}}$$
$$x^2 + y^2 = 2y$$
$$x^2 + y^2 - 2y + 1 = 1$$
$$x^2 + (y - 1)^2 = 1$$

The graph is a circle with center $(0, 1)$ and radius $= 1$. **Answer.**

25. $r = 5$
26. $r = -2$
27. $r = 4 \cos \theta$

28. $r = 3 \sin \theta$
29. $r = \dfrac{1}{1 - \cos \theta}$
30. $r = 4 \sec \theta$

31. $r = \dfrac{1}{1 - \sin \theta}$
32. $r = -2 \csc \theta$

Sketch the graph of the given polar equation.

33. $\theta = 60°$
34. $\theta = -45°$
35. $r = 3$

36. $r = -7$
37. $r = 2 \sec \theta$
38. $r = -3 \csc \theta$

39. $r = 2(1 - \cos \theta)$
40. $r = 1 - 2 \sin \theta$

41. $r^2 = 4 \sin \theta$

43. $r^2 = \theta$ (θ in radians)

42. $r^2 = \cos 2\theta$

44. $r^2\theta = 1$ (θ in radians)

45. Use the Pythagorean theorem to show that if (x, y) and (r, θ) represent the same point in Cartesian and polar coordinates respectively, then $r = \pm\sqrt{x^2 + y^2}$.

46. Show that if (x, y) and (r, θ) represent the same point in Cartesian and polar coordinates respectively, then

$$\cos \theta = \frac{x}{\pm\sqrt{x^2 + y^2}} \quad \text{and} \quad \sin \theta = \frac{y}{\pm\sqrt{x^2 + y^2}}.$$

16-4 polar form for complex numbers; De Moivre's theorem

In the preceding section you saw that the rectangular coordinates (x, y) of a point can be expressed as $(r \cos \theta, r \sin \theta)$, where (r, θ) are polar coordinates of the point.

A complex number can be expressed in the form $x + yi$ where $x, y \in \mathcal{R}$ (see Section 9–2). If we specify $r \geq 0$, then $x + yi$ can be expressed as $r \cos \theta + (r \sin \theta)i$, or $r(\cos \theta + i \sin \theta)$, where

$$r = \sqrt{x^2 + y^2}, \quad \cos \theta = \frac{x}{\sqrt{x^2 + y^2}}, \quad \text{and} \quad \sin \theta = \frac{y}{\sqrt{x^2 + y^2}}$$

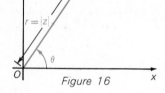

The expression

$$r(\cos \theta + i \sin \theta)$$

is called the polar form or the trigonometric form for denoting the complex number $x + yi$. If

$$z = x + yi,$$

then $r = |z|$ is the modulus or the absolute value of z. An angle θ determined by the equations above is called an amplitude or an argument of z. Thus $x + yi$ may be graphed as the point with rectangular coordinates (x, y) or polar coordinates (r, θ), $r \geq 0$, as shown in Figure 16.

EXAMPLE 1   **Express** $-2\sqrt{3} - 2i$ **in trigonometric form with** $0° \leq m(\theta) < 360°$.

SOLUTION   You have $r = |z| = \sqrt{(-2\sqrt{3})^2 + (-2)^2} = \sqrt{16} = 4$.   Then $\cos \theta = -\frac{2\sqrt{3}}{4} = -\frac{\sqrt{3}}{2}$ and $\sin \theta = -\frac{2}{4} = -\frac{1}{2}$, so that $m(\theta) = 210°$.

$\therefore -2\sqrt{3} - 2i = 4 (\cos 210° + i \sin 210°)$. **Answer.**

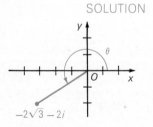

By expressing complex numbers in polar form, you can compute their products and quotients very readily by means of the following:

Theorem. If

$$z_1 = r_1(\cos \theta_1 + i \sin \theta_1) \text{ and } z_2 = r_2(\cos \theta_2 + i \sin \theta_2),$$

then: (1) $z_1 z_2 = r_1 r_2 [\cos (\theta_1 + \theta_2) + i \sin (\theta_1 + \theta_2)]$,

(2) $\dfrac{z_1}{z_2} = \dfrac{r_1}{r_2} [\cos (\theta_1 - \theta_2) + i \sin (\theta_1 - \theta_2)] \quad (z_2 \neq 0)$.

Proof of (1)

$$z_1 \cdot z_2 = r_1(\cos \theta_1 + i \sin \theta_1) \cdot r_2(\cos \theta_2 + i \sin \theta_2)$$

$$= r_1 r_2 [\cos \theta_1 \cos \theta_2 + i \sin \theta_1 \cos \theta_2 + i \cos \theta_1 \sin \theta_2 + i^2 \sin \theta_1 \sin \theta_2]$$

$$= r_1 r_2 [(\cos \theta_1 \cos \theta_2 - \sin \theta_1 \sin \theta_2) + i(\sin \theta_1 \cos \theta_2 + \cos \theta_1 \sin \theta_2)]$$

$$= r_1 r_2 [\cos (\theta_1 + \theta_2) + i \sin (\theta_1 + \theta_2)].$$

Proof of (2)

$$\frac{z_1}{z_2} = \frac{r_1(\cos \theta_1 + i \sin \theta_1)}{r_2(\cos \theta_2 + i \sin \theta_2)} = \frac{r_1(\cos \theta_1 + i \sin \theta_1)(\cos \theta_2 - i \sin \theta_2)}{r_2(\cos \theta_2 + i \sin \theta_2)(\cos \theta_2 - i \sin \theta_2)}$$

$$= \frac{r_1[\cos \theta_1 \cos \theta_2 + i \sin \theta_1 \cos \theta_2 - i \cos \theta_1 \sin \theta_2 - i^2 \sin \theta_1 \sin \theta_2]}{r_2[\cos^2 \theta - i^2 \sin^2 \theta_2]}$$

$$= \frac{r_1[(\cos \theta_1 \cos \theta_2 + \sin \theta_1 \sin \theta_2) + i(\sin \theta_1 \cos \theta_2 - \cos \theta_1 \sin \theta_2)]}{r_2[\cos^2 \theta + \sin^2 \theta]}$$

$$= \frac{r_1}{r_2} [\cos (\theta_1 - \theta_2) + i \sin (\theta_1 - \theta_2)]$$

EXAMPLE 2　If $z_1 = 10(\cos 45° + i \sin 45°)$ and $z_2 = 2(\cos 15° + i \sin 15°)$, express in the form $a + bi$, (a) $z_1 z_2$ and (b) $\dfrac{z_1}{z_2}$.

SOLUTION　a. By Part (1) of the theorem,

$$z_1 \cdot z_2 = 10 \cdot 2[\cos (45° + 15°) + i \sin (45° + 15°)]$$

$$= 20(\cos 60° + i \sin 60°) = 20 \left(\frac{1}{2} + \frac{\sqrt{3}}{2} i \right)$$

$$= 10 + 10\sqrt{3}i. \text{ Answer.}$$

b. By Part (2) of the theorem,

$$\frac{z_1}{z_2} = \frac{10}{2} [\cos (45° - 15°) + i \sin (45° - 15°)]$$

$$= 5(\cos 30° + i \sin 30°)$$

$$= 5 \left(\frac{\sqrt{3}}{2} + \frac{1}{2} i \right) = \frac{5\sqrt{3}}{2} + \frac{5}{2} i. \text{ Answer.}$$

If $z = r(\cos \theta + i \sin \theta)$, you can see that successive applications of Part (1) of the theorem on page 567 yield

$$z^2 = z \cdot z = r(\cos \theta + i \sin \theta) \cdot r(\cos \theta + i \sin \theta)$$
$$= r^2(\cos 2\theta + i \sin 2\theta),$$
$$z^3 = z^2 \cdot z = r^2(\cos 2\theta + i \sin 2\theta) \cdot r(\cos \theta + i \sin \theta)$$
$$= r^3(\cos 3\theta + i \sin 3\theta),$$

and

$$z^4 = z^3 \cdot z = r^3(\cos 3\theta + i \sin 3\theta) \cdot r(\cos \theta + i \sin \theta)$$
$$= r^4(\cos 4\theta + i \sin 4\theta).$$

Continuing this process suggests the general statement

$$z^n = z^{n-1}z = r^{n-1}[\cos (n - 1)\theta + i \sin (n - 1)\theta]r(\cos \theta + i \sin \theta)$$
$$= r^n \cos n\theta + i \sin n\theta.$$

This result was first published by the French mathematician De Moivre.

De Moivre's Theorem

If $z = r(\cos \theta + i \sin \theta)$ and $n \in$ {the natural numbers}, then

$$z^n = r^n(\cos n\theta + i \sin n\theta).$$

A formal proof of this theorem requires mathematical induction, which is discussed in more advanced courses.

EXAMPLE 3   Express $(-1 + i)^4$ in the form $a + bi$.

SOLUTION   Expressing $-1 + i$ in polar form, you have

$$r = \sqrt{(-1)^2 + (1)^2} = \sqrt{2}, \cos \theta = -\frac{1}{\sqrt{2}}, \text{ and } \sin \theta = \frac{1}{\sqrt{2}}.$$

so that $-1 + i = \sqrt{2} (\cos 135° + i \sin 135°).$

Then, applying De Moivre's Theorem, you see that

$$(-1 + i)^4 = [\sqrt{2}(\cos 135° + i \sin 135°)]^4$$
$$= (\sqrt{2})^4[\cos (4 \cdot 135°) + i \sin (4 \cdot 135°)]$$
$$= 4(\cos 540° + i \sin 540°)$$
$$= 4(\cos 180° + i \sin 180°) = 4(-1 + 0i) = -4. \textbf{ Answer}$$

By defining $z^0 = 1$ and $z^{-n} = \dfrac{1}{z^n}$, it is possible to extend De Moivre's Theorem to include all integral powers of nonzero complex numbers.

> **Theorem.** If $z = r(\cos \theta + i \sin \theta) \neq 0 + 0i$ and $n \in \{\text{the integers}\}$, then
> $$z^n = r^n(\cos n\theta + i \sin n\theta).$$

The proof, which depends on the fact that

$$\frac{1}{z} = \frac{1}{r} [\cos(-\theta) + i \sin(-\theta)]$$

(Exercise 36, page 571), is left for you (Exercise 43, page 572).

EXAMPLE 4   **Express** $\left(\dfrac{3\sqrt{3}}{2} + \dfrac{3}{2} i\right)^{-4}$ **in the form** $a + bi$.

SOLUTION   First, you express $\dfrac{3\sqrt{3}}{2} + \dfrac{3}{2} i$ in polar form:

$$r = |z| = \sqrt{\left(\frac{3\sqrt{3}}{2}\right)^2 + \left(\frac{3}{2}\right)^2} = \sqrt{\frac{27}{4} + \frac{9}{4}} = \sqrt{9} = 3,$$

$$\cos \theta = \frac{\frac{3\sqrt{3}}{2}}{3} = \frac{\sqrt{3}}{2}, \qquad \text{and} \qquad \sin \theta = \frac{\frac{3}{2}}{3} = \frac{1}{2}.$$

$$\therefore \frac{3\sqrt{3}}{2} + \frac{3}{2} i = 3(\cos 30° + i \sin 30°).$$

Then by the extended form of De Moivre's theorem,

$$[3(\cos 30° + i \sin 30°)]^{-4} = 3^{-4}[\cos(-4 \cdot 30°) + i \sin(-4 \cdot 30°)]$$
$$= \tfrac{1}{81}[\cos(-120°) + i \sin(-120°)]$$
$$= \frac{1}{81}\left(-\frac{1}{2} - \frac{\sqrt{3}}{2} i\right) = -\frac{1}{162} - \frac{\sqrt{3}}{162} i. \quad \text{Answer.}$$

To find roots of complex numbers using De Moivre's theorem, you can reason as in the following example.

EXAMPLE 5   **Find all cube roots of 1 and express them in the form** $a + bi$.

SOLUTION   Expressing $1 = 1 + 0i$ in polar form, you have $r = 1$, $\cos \theta = \frac{1}{1} = 1$, and $\sin \theta = \frac{0}{1} = 0$. $\therefore 1 = \cos 0° + i \sin 0°$.

Now let $w = r(\cos \theta + i \sin \theta)$ represent a cube root of 1. Then

$$w^3 = r^3(\cos 3\theta + i \sin 3\theta)$$
$$= 1^3(\cos 0° + i \sin 0°).$$

(Solution continued on page 570.)

Since two complex numbers are equal if and only if their moduli are equal and their arguments differ in degree measure by a multiple of 360°, you have

$$r^3 = 1 \quad \text{and} \quad 3\theta = 3 \cdot 0 + k \cdot 360°.$$

$$\therefore r = \sqrt[3]{1} = 1 \text{ and } \theta = \frac{3 \cdot 0 + k \cdot 360°}{3} = 0 + k \cdot 120°, \text{ and}$$

$$w = 1[\cos (0° + k \cdot 120°) + i \sin (0° + k \cdot 120°)].$$

Replacing k in turn with "0", "1", "2", "3", and so on, you find that:

If $k = 0$, then $w = 1(\cos 0° + i \sin 0°) = 1(1 + 0i) = 1$.
If $k = 1$, then $w = 1[\cos (0° + 120°) + i \sin (0° + 120)]$
$$= 1(\cos 120° + i \sin 120°)$$

$$= 1\left(-\frac{1}{2} + \frac{\sqrt{3}}{2} i\right) = -\frac{1}{2} + \frac{\sqrt{3}}{2} i.$$

If $k = 2$, then $w = 1[\cos (0° + 240°) + i \sin (0° + 240°)]$
$$= 1(\cos 240° + i \sin 240°)$$

$$= 1\left(-\frac{1}{2} - \frac{\sqrt{3}}{2} i\right) = -\frac{1}{2} - \frac{\sqrt{3}}{2} i.$$

If $k = 3$, then $w = 1[\cos (0° + 360°) + i \sin (0° + 360°)]$
$$= 1(\cos 360° + i \sin 360°)$$
$$= 1(1 + 0i) = 1,$$

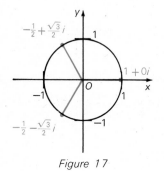

$-\frac{1}{2} + \frac{\sqrt{3}}{2} i$

$1 + 0i$

$-\frac{1}{2} - \frac{\sqrt{3}}{2} i$

Figure 17

which is the same as the value when $k = 0$. Additional replacements for k will simply duplicate the three values of w already obtained. Therefore, the three cube roots of 1 are $1, -\frac{1}{2} + \frac{\sqrt{3}}{2} i$, and $-\frac{1}{2} - \frac{\sqrt{3}}{2} i$. **Answer.**

The three cube roots of 1 obtained in Example 5 above can be graphed as shown in Figure 17. The points are equally spaced around a circle with center at the origin and with radius 1.

The process used in Example 5 can be generalized as follows:

Theorem. The equation $z^n = r(\cos \theta + i \sin \theta)$, where $n \in \{\text{the natural numbers}\}$, $r \in \mathcal{R}$, $r > 0$, has n roots:

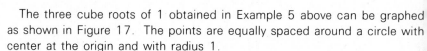

$$z = \sqrt[n]{r} \left(\cos \frac{\theta + k(360°)}{n} + i \sin \frac{\theta + k(360°)}{n}\right)$$

for $k = 0, 1, 2, \ldots, n - 1$.

WRITTEN EXERCISES Express the given complex number in polar form. Use Table 6 if necessary.

A 1. -1 3. $1 - i$ 5. $5i$ 7. $3 + 4i$

     2. $1 + i$ 4. $-2 + 2i$ 6. $-1 - \sqrt{3}i$ 8. $5 - 12i$

Express the given complex number in the form $a + bi$. Use Tables 6 and 7 as necessary.

9. $2(\cos 60° + i \sin 60°)$

10. $4(\cos 30° + i \sin 30°)$

11. $9(\cos 120° + i \sin 120°)$

12. $3(\cos 225° + i \sin 225°)$

13. $\cos \left(\dfrac{5\pi}{6}\right)^R + i \sin \left(\dfrac{5\pi}{6}\right)^R$

14. $2\left[\cos \left(\dfrac{5\pi}{3}\right)^R + i \sin \left(\dfrac{5\pi}{3}\right)^R\right]$

15. $3(\cos 42°40' + i \sin 42°40')$

16. $5(\cos 176°10' + i \sin 176°10')$

For z_1 and z_2 as given, compute (a) $z_1 z_2$ and (b) $\dfrac{z_1}{z_2}$. Leave your result in polar form.

17. $z_1 = 2(\cos 60° + i \sin 60°)$, $z_2 = 5(\cos 30° + i \sin 30°)$
18. $z_1 = 3(\cos 110° + i \sin 110°)$, $z_2 = 3(\cos 20° + i \sin 20°)$
19. $z_1 = 15(\cos 275° + i \sin 275°)$, $z_2 = 5(\cos 5° + i \sin 5°)$
20. $z_1 = 30(\cos 310° + i \sin 310°)$, $z_2 = 6(\cos 20° + i \sin 20°)$

Use De Moivre's Theorem or its extension to express each of the following in the form $a + bi$.

21. $[3(\cos 10° + i \sin 10°)]^6$

22. $[2(\cos 15° + i \sin 15°)]^6$

23. $[\tfrac{1}{3}(\cos 20° + i \sin 20°)]^{-3}$

24. $[\tfrac{1}{2}(\cos 30° + i \sin 30°)]^{-4}$

25. $(1 + \sqrt{3}i)^3$

26. $(1 + i)^4$

27. $(\sqrt{3} + i)^4$

28. $(-\tfrac{1}{5} - \tfrac{1}{5}i)^{-4}$

29. $(\sqrt{3} - i)^{-5}$

30. $(1 + \sqrt{3}i)^{-4}$

Find the required roots in the form $r(\cos \theta + i \sin \theta)$ and show the graphs of the roots on a circle.

31. The four fourth roots of i.

32. The three cube roots of $1 + \sqrt{3}i$.

33. The four fourth roots of $16(\cos 120° + i \sin 120°)$.

34. The three cube roots of $27(\cos 240° + i \sin 240°)$.

B 35. Show that if $z = a + bi = r(\cos \theta + i \sin \theta)$, then

$$\bar{z} = a - bi = r(\cos \theta - i \sin \theta).$$

36. Show that if $z = r(\cos \theta + i \sin \theta)$, then

$$\dfrac{1}{z} = \dfrac{1}{r}[\cos (-\theta) + i \sin (-\theta)] = \dfrac{1}{r}(\cos \theta - i \sin \theta).$$

Find the solution set of the given equation over the set of complex numbers.

37. $z^4 + 16 = 0$

38. $z^4 + 81 = 0$

39. $z^2 - 16 - 16\sqrt{3}i = 0$

40. $z^3 + 4 + 4\sqrt{3}i = 0$

41. Show that the three cube roots of 1 can be represented in the form 1, w, and w^2.

42. Use the results of Exercise 41 to find the value of $1 + w + w^2$ and of $w + w^2 + w \cdot w^2$.

43. Prove that if, for $z \neq 0$, z^0 is defined to equal 1 and z^{-n} is defined to equal $\dfrac{1}{z^n}$, then De Moivre's Theorem is valid for all integral exponents.

16–5 *vectors*

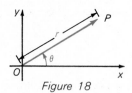

Figure 18

In order to describe a physical quantity such as velocity or force, you must give both its direction and its magnitude. In Figure 18 the arrow from O to P is a directed line segment which might represent, say, a velocity of meters per second in a direction of θ with the x-axis. Any directed line segment in the plane (or space) is called a vector and is considered to point from one endpoint, called the initial point, to the other endpoint, called the terminal point.

A vector may be identified by means of a notation naming its endpoints, initial point first, such as $\overrightarrow{AB}$ (read "the vector AB"), or else by means of a lowercase letter in boldface type, such as

$$\mathbf{v} \text{ (read "the vector } \mathbf{v}\text{")}$$

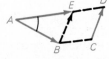

Figure 19

(see Figure 19). The length of a vector is called its norm and is denoted by $\|\overrightarrow{AB}\|$ or $\|\mathbf{v}\|$. In the plane, you ordinarily specify the direction of the vector by identifying the angle θ, where

$$-180° < m(\theta) \leq 180°,$$

that it determines with a ray directed parallel to, and in the direction of, the positive x-axis, as suggested by Figure 19. In particular, in Figure 19, $\mathbf{v}$ and $\overrightarrow{AB}$ have the same norm and the same direction. Such vectors are called equivalent.

For every vector $\mathbf{v}$ in the plane, each point in the plane is the initial point of a vector equivalent to $\mathbf{v}$. In particular, every vector $\mathbf{v}$ in the plane is equivalent to a vector in standard position, that is, a vector with initial point at the origin.

The sum, or resultant, $\overrightarrow{AB} + \overrightarrow{CD}$ of two vectors is defined as pictured in Figure 20. That is, if $\overrightarrow{AB}$ and $\overrightarrow{CD}$ are vectors, and $\overrightarrow{BE}$ is the vector equivalent to $\overrightarrow{CD}$ that has initial endpoint B, then

$$\overrightarrow{AB} + \overrightarrow{CD} = \overrightarrow{AE}.$$

Figure 20

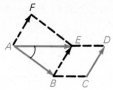

Figure 21.

The vectors $\overrightarrow{AB}$ and $\overrightarrow{CD}$ are called components of $\overrightarrow{AE}$. Notice that the sum $\overrightarrow{AE}$ of vectors $\overrightarrow{AB}$ and $\overrightarrow{CD}$ can be pictured as the diagonal of a parallelogram with adjacent sides having the same lengths as $\overrightarrow{AB}$ and $\overrightarrow{CD}$ and parallel to them, as illustrated in Figure 21. You can use this fact to help you find the norm and direction of a vector sum.

EXAMPLE 1 Given that $\|\mathbf{u}\| = 5$ and the direction angle of $\mathbf{u}$ measures $70°$, $\|\mathbf{v}\| = 8$ and the direction angle of $\mathbf{v}$ measures $-10°$, find an approximation to the nearest tenth of a unit for $\|\mathbf{u} + \mathbf{v}\|$, and to the nearest degree for the measure of the direction angle of $\mathbf{u} + \mathbf{v}$.

SOLUTION Make a sketch of the given vectors. By inspection, $m\angle DOB = 80°$ so that in the parallelogram $OBCD$,

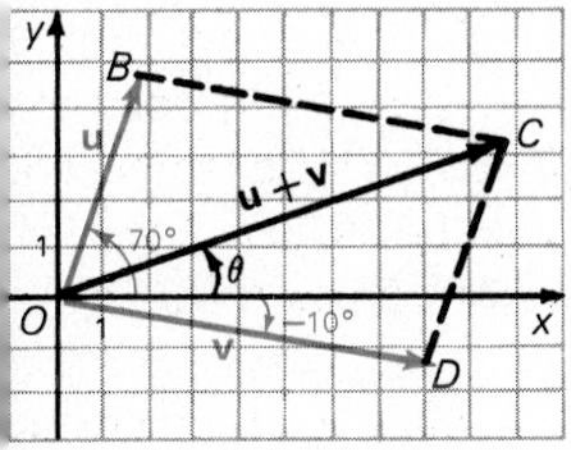

$$m\angle ODC = 180° - 80° = 100°.$$

Then, to find $\|\mathbf{u} + \mathbf{v}\|$, you use the law of cosines:

$$
\begin{aligned}
\|\mathbf{u} + \mathbf{v}\|^2 &= \|\mathbf{u}\|^2 + \|\mathbf{v}\|^2 - 2\|\mathbf{u}\| \cdot \|\mathbf{v}\| \cos 100° \\
&\doteq 5^2 + 8^2 - 2(5)(8)(-0.1736) \\
&\doteq 25 + 64 + 13.888 \doteq 102.89 \\
\therefore \|\mathbf{u} + \mathbf{v}\| &\doteq \sqrt{102.89} \doteq 10.1
\end{aligned}
$$

To find the measure of the direction angle θ of $\mathbf{u} + \mathbf{v}$, use the law of sines first to find $m\angle COD$:

$$\frac{\sin \angle COD}{5} \doteq \frac{\sin 100°}{10.1}; \ \sin \angle COD \doteq \frac{5\sin 100°}{10.1} \doteq \frac{5(0.9848)}{10.1}$$
$$\doteq 0.4875$$

Then $m\angle COD \doteq 29°$.
$\therefore m(\theta) \doteq 29° - 10° \doteq 19°$, and $\|\mathbf{u} + \mathbf{v}\| \doteq 10.1$. **Answer.**

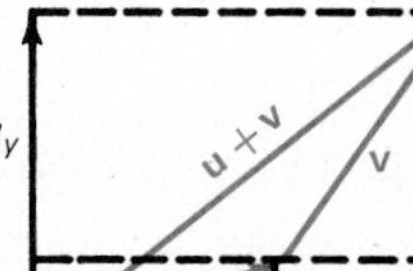

An alternative means of determining the norm and direction angle for the sum $\mathbf{u} + \mathbf{v}$ of two vectors is first to resolve $\mathbf{u}$ and $\mathbf{v}$ into sums of horizontal (parallel to x-axis) and vertical (parallel to y-axis) components. Figure 22 pictures a vector $\mathbf{u}$ together with its horizontal and vertical components $\mathbf{u}_x$ and $\mathbf{u}_y$. Do you see that

$$\|\mathbf{u}_x\| = \|\mathbf{u}\| \, |\cos \theta|, \qquad \|\mathbf{u}_y\| = \|\mathbf{u}\| \, |\sin \theta|?$$

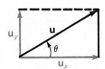

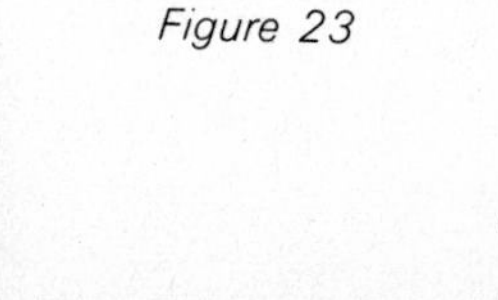

Figure 22

Now, examining Figure 23, you can see that the horizontal and vertical components of the sum $\mathbf{u} + \mathbf{v}$ of two vectors are the sums of the corresponding components of $\mathbf{u}$ and $\mathbf{v}$:

$$(\mathbf{u} + \mathbf{v})_x = \mathbf{u}_x + \mathbf{v}_x \qquad \text{and} \qquad (\mathbf{u} + \mathbf{v})_y = \mathbf{u}_y + \mathbf{v}_y$$

so that

$$\|\mathbf{u} + \mathbf{v}\| = \sqrt{\|\mathbf{u}_x + \mathbf{v}_x\|^2 + \|\mathbf{u}_y + \mathbf{v}_y\|^2}.$$

Figure 23

Notice also that, for the direction angle θ of $\mathbf{u} + \mathbf{v}$, you have

$$|\cos \theta| = \frac{\|\mathbf{u}_x + \mathbf{v}_x\|}{\|\mathbf{u} + \mathbf{v}\|} \quad \text{and} \quad |\sin \theta| = \frac{\|\mathbf{u}_y + \mathbf{v}_y\|}{\|\mathbf{u} + \mathbf{v}\|},$$

or

$$|\tan \theta| = \frac{\|\mathbf{u}_y + \mathbf{v}_y\|}{\|\mathbf{u}_x + \mathbf{v}_x\|}.$$

EXAMPLE 2   Given that $\|\mathbf{v}\| = 10$ and the direction angle of $\mathbf{v}$ measures $10°$, $\|\mathbf{w}\| = 8$, and the direction angle of $\mathbf{w}$ measures $55°$, find an approximation to the nearest tenth for $\|\mathbf{v} + \mathbf{w}\|$, and to the nearest degree for the measure of the direction angle of $\mathbf{v} + \mathbf{w}$.

SOLUTION   Make a sketch showing the given vectors. Find the norms of the horizontal and vertical components of $\mathbf{v}$ and $\mathbf{w}$.

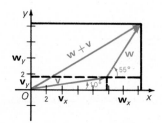

$$\begin{aligned} \|\mathbf{v}_x\| &= 10 \cos 10° \\ &\doteq 10(0.9848) \\ &\doteq 9.8 \end{aligned}$$

$$\begin{aligned} \|\mathbf{w}_x\| &= 8 \cos 55° \\ &\doteq 8(0.5736) \\ &\doteq 4.6 \end{aligned}$$

$$\begin{aligned} \|\mathbf{v}_y\| &= 10 \sin 10° \\ &\doteq 10(0.1736) \\ &\doteq 1.7 \end{aligned}$$

$$\begin{aligned} \|\mathbf{w}_y\| &= 8 \sin 55° \\ &\doteq 8(0.8192) \\ &\doteq 6.6 \end{aligned}$$

Then for the norm and direction of horizontal and vertical components of $\mathbf{v} + \mathbf{w}$, you find:

$$\|\mathbf{v}_x + \mathbf{w}_x\| \doteq 9.8 + 4.6 = 14.4; \text{ direction } 0°$$
$$\|\mathbf{v}_y + \mathbf{w}_y\| \doteq 1.7 + 6.6 = 8.3; \text{ direction } 90°$$

For θ, the direction angle of $\mathbf{v} + \mathbf{w}$, you find that

$$|\tan \theta| \doteq \frac{8.3}{14.4} \doteq 0.5764$$

from which you obtain $m(\theta) \doteq 30°$.

Knowing $m(\theta)$, you can find the norm of $\mathbf{v} + \mathbf{w}$ by using

$$\cos \theta \doteq \frac{14.4}{\|\mathbf{v} + \mathbf{w}\|},$$

so that

$$\|\mathbf{v} + \mathbf{w}\| \doteq \frac{14.4}{\cos 30°} \doteq \frac{14.4}{0.866} \doteq 16.6.$$

Alternatively, you can compute $\|\mathbf{v} + \mathbf{w}\|$ as follows:

$$\|\mathbf{v} + \mathbf{w}\| = \sqrt{(14.4)^2 + (8.3)^2} = \sqrt{276} \doteq 16.6$$

$\therefore \|\mathbf{v} + \mathbf{w}\| \doteq 16.6$, $m(\theta) = 30°$. **Answer.**

Find, to the nearest tenth, the norms of the horizontal and vertical components of the given vector **u**.

A 1. $\|u\| = 3$; direction of u, $60°$
   2. $\|u\| = 5$; direction of u, $45°$
   3. $\|u\| = 7$; direction of u, $120°$
   4. $\|u\| = 10$; direction of u, $140°$
   5. $\|u\| = \frac{1}{2}$; direction of u, $110°$
   6. $\|u\| = \frac{3}{4}$; direction of u, $150°$
   7. $\|u\| = 12$; direction of u, $82°$
   8. $\|u\| = 12$; direction of u, $142°$

Find the sum of the given vectors **u** and **v**. State $\|u + v\|$ to the nearest tenth and $m(\theta)$ to the nearest degree.

9. $\|u\| = 8$; direction of u, $30°$; $\|v\| = 10$, direction of v, $45°$
10. $\|u\| = 12$; direction of u, $60°$; $\|v\| = 8$, direction of v, $30°$
11. $\|u\| = 20$; direction of u, $150°$; $\|v\| = 10$, direction of v, $45°$
12. $\|u\| = 10$, direction of u, $150°$; $\|v\| = 12$, direction of v, $-30°$
13. $\|u\| = 24$, direction of u, $90°$; $\|v\| = 12$, direction of v, $120°$
14. $\|u\| = 32$, direction of u, $0°$; $\|v\| = 24$, direction of v, $135°$
15. $\|u\| = 10$, direction of u, $40°$; $\|v\| = 5$, direction of v, $-70°$
16. $\|u\| = 8$, direction of u, $-110°$; $\|v\| = 10$, direction of v, $-40°$

programming in BASIC

EXERCISES

1. Complete the program that will find, to the nearest tenth, the norms and direction angles of the horizontal and vertical components of a vector when its norm and direction angle are given. Refer to the discussion of Figure 22. (Recall that in using COS(A) and SIN(A) in BASIC, A is in radians.)

```
30  LET X = U*COS(A)
40  LET Y = U*SIN(A)
```

2. Complete the program that will find, to the nearest tenth, the norm of the sum of two vectors whose norms and direction angles are given. Refer to Example 1.

```
60  LET S = SQR(U↑2 + V↑2 − 2*U*V*COS(B))
```

Give the meaning of:

1. polar coordinates
2. modulus, or absolute value
3. amplitude, or argument
4. vector

5. equivalent vectors
6. resultant
7. components of a vector

Objective 1, page 561

8. Find two sets of polar coordinates for $P(-3, 2)$.

9. Transform to polar form, $x^2 = 8y$.

Objective 2, page 561

10. Express in polar form and find $z_1 z_2$, $\dfrac{z_1}{z_2}$, and $z_1{}^3$, where

$$z_1 = -1 + i \text{ and } z_2 = -3 - 3i.$$

11. Find the three cube roots of $-4\sqrt{2} + 4\sqrt{2}\,i$.

Objective 3, page 561

12. Give $\|u + v\|$ correct to the nearest tenth, and $m(\theta)$ for $u + v$ to the nearest degree:

$$\|u\| = 20, \text{ direction of } u, 45°$$
$$\|v\| = 10, \text{ direction of } v, -30°$$

Check your answers with those printed at the back of the book.

chapter summary

1. The inverse of each of the circular or trigonometric functions discussed in this chapter is a relation that is not a function unless the range is restricted. For the **principal-value inverse functions** the ranges are:

$\text{Sin}^{-1}: -\dfrac{\pi}{2} \le y \le \dfrac{\pi}{2}$ $\qquad$ $\text{Cos}^{-1}: 0 \le y \le \pi$

$\text{Tan}^{-1}: -\dfrac{\pi}{2} < y < \dfrac{\pi}{2}$ $\qquad$ $\text{Cot}^{-1}: 0 < y < \pi$

$\text{Csc}^{-1}: -\dfrac{\pi}{2} \le y \le \dfrac{\pi}{2}, y \ne 0$ $\qquad$ $\text{Sec}^{-1}: 0 \le y \le \pi, y \ne \dfrac{\pi}{2}$

2. Using trigonometric identities and the usual algebraic transformations, you can solve equations involving the circular or trigonometric functions.

3. Coordinates of points may be given in the Cartesian system as (x, y) or in the polar system as (r, θ), related as follows:

$$x = r \cos \theta$$
$$y = r \sin \theta$$

$$r = \pm\sqrt{x^2 + y^2}$$

$$\cos \theta = \frac{x}{\pm\sqrt{x^2 + y^2}} \qquad \sin \theta = \frac{y}{\pm\sqrt{x^2 + y^2}}$$

4. If $z_1 = r_1(\cos \theta_1 + i \sin \theta_1)$ and $z_2 = r_2(\cos \theta_2 + i \sin \theta_2)$, then:

$$z_1 z_2 = r_1 r_2 [\cos (\theta_1 + \theta_2) + i \sin (\theta_1 + \theta_2)]$$

$$\frac{z_1}{z_2} = \frac{r_1}{r_2} [\cos (\theta_1 - \theta_2) + i \sin (\theta_1 - \theta_2)]$$

5. De Moivre's theorem states that if $z = r(\cos \theta + i \sin \theta)$ and $n \in \{$the natural numbers$\}$, then $z^n = r^n(\cos n\theta + i \sin n\theta)$.

6. The equation $z^n = r(\cos \theta + i \sin \theta)$, where $n \in \{$the natural numbers$\}$, $r \in \mathcal{R}$, $r > 0$, has n solutions:

$$z = \sqrt[n]{r} \left(\cos \frac{\theta + k(360°)}{n} + i \sin \frac{\theta + k(360°)}{n} \right)$$

for $k = 0, 1, 2, \ldots, n - 1$.

7. A **vector** may be written in the form $\overrightarrow{AB}$ or $\mathbf{u}$; its **norm**, or length, is denoted by $\|\overrightarrow{AB}\|$ or by $\|\mathbf{u}\|$.

8. If $\overrightarrow{AB}$ and $\overrightarrow{CD}$ are any two vectors in the plane, and if $\overrightarrow{BE}$ is equivalent to $\overrightarrow{CD}$, then $\overrightarrow{AB} + \overrightarrow{CD} = \overrightarrow{AE}$. Vectors $\overrightarrow{AB}$ and $\overrightarrow{CD}$ are called **components** of $\overrightarrow{AE}$.

chapter test 16–1 **1.** Specify the members of the set $\left\{ y: \sin y = -\dfrac{\sqrt{3}}{2}, y \in \mathcal{R} \right\}$.
and review

                  2. Find $\text{Sin}^{-1} \left(-\dfrac{\sqrt{3}}{2} \right)$.

                  3. Find $\text{Cos}^{-1} \left(\tan \dfrac{\pi}{4} \right)$.

16–2 **4.** Solve $\tan x \sec x - \tan x = 0$ over $\mathcal{R}$.

       5. Solve $2 \sin^2 \alpha + 3 \sin \alpha + 1 = 0$ over $0° \le m(\alpha) < 360°$.

16–3 **6.** Find the Cartesian coordinates of the point with polar coordinates $(-3, 120°)$.

       7. Transform $y(2 - x) = 1$ into an equation in polar coordinates.

16–4 **8.** If $z_1 = \sqrt{3} + i$ and $z_2 = 2i$, find **(a)** $z_1 z_2$, **(b)** $\dfrac{z_1}{z_2}$, and **(c)** $z_1{}^3$. Leave your results in polar form.

16–5 **9.** Given $\|\mathbf{u}\| = 10$, direction of $\mathbf{u}$, $45°$; $\|\mathbf{v}\| = 8$, direction of $\mathbf{v}$, $-60°$, find $\|\mathbf{u} + \mathbf{v}\|$ and the direction of $\mathbf{u} + \mathbf{v}$.

comprehensive test
chapters 1–16

1. Which of the following is *not* equivalent to the statement "*x* is less than or equal to zero?"

   a. *x* is negative.
   b. $x \leq 0$
   c. *x* is nonpositive.
   d. $x \not> 0$

2. If $z = -3$, then $|2z + 3|$ is equal to:

   a. 9 b. 3 c. -3 d. -9

3. In simple form, $(x^2 + xy) + (2xy - 3y^2)$ is equal to:

   a. $-2x^2 + 3xy$
   b. $-2x^4 + 2x^2y^2$
   c. $-4x^2 + 3xy$
   d. $x^2 + 3xy - 3y^2$

4. Over $\mathcal{R}$, the solution set of $3[x - (2 - x)] = 5(x - 4)$ is:

   a. $\{\frac{14}{5}\}$ b. $\{-\frac{2}{5}\}$ c. $\{-\frac{14}{5}\}$ d. $\{-14\}$

5. Over $\mathcal{R}$, the solution set of $\frac{x}{2} + x < \frac{x}{3} - 1$ is:

   a. $\{x\colon x < -2\}$
   b. $\{x\colon x < -\frac{6}{7}\}$
   c. $\{x\colon x > -\frac{6}{7}\}$
   d. $\{x\colon x < \frac{6}{7}\}$

6. If one of two supplementary angles measures $20°$ more than 4 times the other, then the angle of lesser measure measures __?__ .

   a. $38°$ b. $41°$ c. $32°$ d. $25°$

7. If $g(x) = x^2 - x + 1$, then $g(-1)$ is equal to:

   a. 3 b. 1 c. -1 d. $-x^2 + x - 1$

8. The sketch shows the graph of:

   a. $3y - 2x = 6$
   b. $2x + 3y = 6$
   c. $2x + 3y = -6$
   d. $2x - 3y = 6$

9. The graph of the line $\ell\colon 2x - 3y \geq 6$ consists of the half-plane:

   a. Above and including the graph of ℓ
   b. Below and including the graph of ℓ
   c. Above and excluding the graph of ℓ
   d. Below and excluding the graph of ℓ

10. An equation for the line containing $(-2, 4)$ and with slope 4 is:

    a. $x - 4y + 12 = 0$
    b. $4x - y + 4 = 0$
    c. $4x - y + 12 = 0$
    d. $x - 4y + 4 = 0$

11. The solution set of the system $\begin{aligned} 2x - 3y &= 6 \\ 2x + y &= 14 \end{aligned}$ is:

    a. $\{(3, 0)\}$
    b. $\{(6, 2)\}$
    c. $\emptyset$
    d. $\{(x, y)\colon 2x - 3y = 6$

12. The value of $\begin{vmatrix} 2 & -3 \\ 4 & 2 \end{vmatrix}$ is:

    a. -8 b. 16 c. 8 d. -16

13. To solve for y in the system $\begin{aligned} x - 2y &= 3 \\ 2x + y &= 5 \end{aligned}$ you would use:

    a. $y = \dfrac{\begin{vmatrix} 1 & -2 \\ 2 & 1 \end{vmatrix}}{\begin{vmatrix} 1 & 3 \\ 2 & 5 \end{vmatrix}}$
    b. $y = \dfrac{\begin{vmatrix} 1 & -2 \\ 2 & 1 \end{vmatrix}}{\begin{vmatrix} -2 & 3 \\ 1 & 5 \end{vmatrix}}$
    c. $y = \dfrac{\begin{vmatrix} 1 & 3 \\ 2 & 5 \end{vmatrix}}{\begin{vmatrix} 1 & -2 \\ 2 & 1 \end{vmatrix}}$
    d. $y = \dfrac{\begin{vmatrix} 3 & -2 \\ 5 & 1 \end{vmatrix}}{\begin{vmatrix} 1 & -2 \\ 2 & 1 \end{vmatrix}}$

14. The value of x in the solution of the system
$$\begin{aligned} 2x - y + z &= 4 \\ 3x + 2y + z &= 5 \\ x + 2y - 3z &= -5 \end{aligned}$$ is:

    a. -1 b. 2 c. -2 d. 1

15. The value of $\begin{vmatrix} 3 & -2 & 1 \\ 1 & 0 & 2 \\ -1 & 0 & 4 \end{vmatrix}$ is:

    a. -4 b. 12 c. 4 d. -12

16. The expression $\dfrac{r^3 s^{-2} t}{r^{-1} s t^{-3}}$ is equivalent to:

    a. $\dfrac{s^3}{r^4 t^4}$ b. $\dfrac{r^4 t^4}{s^3}$ c. $\dfrac{-s^3}{r^4 t^4}$ d. $\dfrac{-r^4 t^4}{s^3}$

17. As a polynomial in simple form, $(z - 2)(3z + 5)$ is equal to:

    a. $3z^2 - 10$ c. $3z^2 - 7z - 10$

    b. $3z^2 - z - 10$ d. $3z^2 + 11z - 10$

18. A complete factorization of $x^4 + x^2y^2 - 2y^4$ is:

    a. $(x^2 + 2y^2)(x^2 - y^2)$

    b. $(x^2 - 2y^2)(x^2 + y^2)$

    c. $(x + y)(x - y)(x^2 + 2y^2)$

    d. $(x + y)(x - y)(x + 2y)(x + y)$

19. As a single fraction in lowest terms, $\dfrac{2a + b}{4a} - \dfrac{a - b}{8a}$ is equal to:

    a. $\dfrac{a + b}{8a}$ c. $\dfrac{3b}{8a}$

    b. $\dfrac{3(a + b)}{8a}$ d. $\dfrac{3a + 2b}{8a}$

20. The solution set over $\Re$ of $\dfrac{y}{y + 1} - \dfrac{y}{y - 1} = \dfrac{3}{4}$ is:

    a. $\{-3, -\frac{1}{3}\}$ c. $\{3, \frac{1}{3}\}$

    b: $\{3, -\frac{1}{3}\}$ d. $\{-3, \frac{1}{3}\}$

21. A general term for the sequence 7, 9, 11, 13, . . . is:

    a. $6n + 1$ c. $2n + 5$

    b. $3n + 4$ d. $4n + 3$

22. The twentieth term in the arithmetic sequence 1, 6, 11, . . . is:

    a. 96   b. 105   c. 115   d. 95

23. The value of $\displaystyle\sum_{j=2}^{7} \left(\frac{1}{2}\right)^j$ is:

    a. $\frac{63}{64}$ b. $\frac{31}{64}$ c. $\frac{63}{256}$ d. $\frac{63}{128}$

24. The "sum" of the infinite geometric series $18 + 6 + 2 + \ldots$ is:

    a. 26   b. 27   c. 28   d. infinite

25. In simple form, $\sqrt[5]{-243z^{10}}$ is equal to:

    a. $-\frac{243}{5}z^5$ c. $-\frac{243}{5}z^2$

    b. $-3z^5$ d. $-3z^2$

26. The expression $\sqrt{18a^3} - \sqrt{8a^3} - 4\sqrt{50a^3}$ is equivalent to:

    a. $19\sqrt{2a^3}$ c. $a\sqrt{-190a}$

    b. $-19a\sqrt{2a}$ d. $\sqrt{-190a^3}$

27. The solution set of $\sqrt{x - 3} + 5 = x$ is:

    a. $\{7, 4\}$ b. $\{4\}$ c. $\{7\}$ d. $\emptyset$

28. In the form $a + bi$, the complex expression $(2 - \sqrt{-9}) - (5 - \sqrt{-16})$ is equal to:

    a. -4 c. $-3 - 7i$

    b. $-3 + i$ d. 4

29. The solutions of $x^2 - x - 4 = 0$ are:

    a. rational and equal   c. complex

    b. real and unequal   d. integers

30. The equation for the axis of symmetry of the graph of $\{(x, y): y = 2x^2 - 3x + 5\}$ is:

    a. $x = 0$ c. $x = \frac{3}{2}$

    b. $x = \frac{2}{3}$ d. $x = \frac{3}{4}$

31. If $P(x) = 2x^3 + x^2 - 6x - 3$, then $P(-\frac{1}{2})$ is equal to:

    a. -3 b. $-\frac{11}{2}$ c. 0   d. 2

32. The distance between the points $P_1(1, -3)$ and $P_2(2, -1)$ is:

    a. $\sqrt{2}$ b. 5   c. $\sqrt{5}$ d. $\sqrt{3}$

33. The line through $(2, -1)$ that is perpendicular to the graph of $2x - y = 4$ has an equation:

    a. $2x + y = 3$ c. $x + 2y = 4$

    b. $x + 2y = 0$ d. $x - 2y = 0$

34. The graph of $x^2 = 25 + y^2$ is a(an):

    a. circle   c. ellipse

    b. parabola   d. hyperbola

35. The solution set of the system $\begin{aligned} x^2 + y^2 &= 25 \\ x^2 - y^2 &= -7 \end{aligned}$ is:

    a. $\{(3, 4)\}$

    b. $\{(3, 4), (3, -4)\}$

    c. $\{(3, 4), (3, -4), (-3, 4), (-3, -4)\}$

    d. $\{(4, 3), (4, -3), (-4, 3), (-4, -3)\}$

36. The expression $\log_b \dfrac{y\sqrt{x}}{z}$ is equivalent to:

  a. $\log_b y + \frac{1}{2}\log_b x - \frac{1}{2}\log_b z$

  b. $(\log_b y \cdot \frac{1}{2}\log_b x) \div \log_b z$

  c. $\log_b y + \frac{1}{2}\log_b x - \log_b z$

  d. $\frac{1}{2}\log_b y + \frac{1}{2}\log_b x - \frac{1}{2}\log_b z$

37. If $\log 4.25 \doteq 0.6284$ and $\log 4.26 \doteq 0.6294$, then $\log 4.257$ is approximately equal to:

  a. 0.6287   c. 0.6292

  b. 0.6291   d. 0.6293

38. The solution set of $3^{z+1} = 5$ over $\Re$ is:

  a. $\log 5 - \log 3 - 1$ c. $\dfrac{\log 5}{\log 3} + 1$

  b. $\dfrac{\log 3}{\log 5} - 1$ d. $\dfrac{\log 5}{\log 3} - 1$

39. The number of ways that 5 horses can be placed in 5 stalls is:

  a. 120   b. 24   c. 6   d. 1

40. The number of distinguishable permutations of the letters in the word "pronoun" is:

  a. 1260   b. 720   c. 360   d. 180

41. The probability that both of two cards drawn at random from a standard 52-card bridge deck will be diamonds is:

  a. $\frac{1}{17}$ b. $\frac{3}{17}$ c. $\frac{13}{52}$ d. $\frac{13}{51}$

42. The inverse of $\begin{bmatrix} 3 & -1 \\ 2 & -1 \end{bmatrix}$ is:

  a. $\begin{bmatrix} 3 & 2 \\ -1 & -1 \end{bmatrix}$ c. $-\begin{bmatrix} -1 & 1 \\ -2 & 3 \end{bmatrix}$

  b. $-\begin{bmatrix} 3 & 2 \\ -1 & -1 \end{bmatrix}$ d. $\begin{bmatrix} -1 & 1 \\ -2 & 3 \end{bmatrix}$

43. If $\begin{bmatrix} 4 & -5 \\ -2 & 3 \end{bmatrix} X = \begin{bmatrix} 2 & 0 \\ 1 & 1 \end{bmatrix}$ then X is equal to:

  a. $\begin{bmatrix} 11 & 5 \\ 8 & 4 \end{bmatrix}$ c. $\frac{1}{22}\begin{bmatrix} 11 & 5 \\ 8 & 4 \end{bmatrix}$

  b. $\begin{bmatrix} \frac{11}{2} & \frac{5}{2} \\ 4 & 2 \end{bmatrix}$ d. $\begin{bmatrix} \frac{1}{2} & 0 \\ 0 & \frac{1}{2} \end{bmatrix}$

44. Under the transformation $\begin{bmatrix} x' \\ y' \end{bmatrix} = \begin{bmatrix} 4 & 1 \\ 7 & 2 \end{bmatrix}\begin{bmatrix} x \\ y \end{bmatrix}$ the preimage of $Q'\ (5, -2)$ is:

  a. $(-2, 5)$ c. $(8, 27)$

  b. $(12, -43)$ d. $(-8, -27)$

45. If the terminal side of α contains the point $(-5, 2)$, then:

  a. $\sin \alpha = -\dfrac{5}{\sqrt{29}}$ c. $\cos \alpha = \dfrac{5}{\sqrt{29}}$

  b. $\sin \alpha = \dfrac{2}{\sqrt{29}}$ d. $\cos \alpha = \dfrac{-2}{\sqrt{29}}$

46. $\sin 305°$ is the same as:

  a. $\sin 55°$ c. $\sin 35°$

  b. $-\sin 55°$ d. $-\sin 35°$

47. If $\cos \alpha = \frac{3}{5}$, and $0° \le m(\alpha) \le 45°$, then $\sin 2\alpha$ is equal to:

  a. $\frac{24}{25}$ b. $\frac{7}{25}$ c. $\frac{21}{25}$ d. $\frac{12}{25}$

48. In a triangle ABC, if $a = 5$, $b = 10$, and $\cos C = 0.2$, then c is equal to:

  a. $\sqrt{14}$ b. $\sqrt{105}$ c. 15   d. $\sqrt{145}$

49. The solution set over $\Re$ of $\sin^2 x - \sin x = 0$ is (for $k \in \{\text{the integers}\}$):

  a. $\{x: x = k\pi\}$

  b. $\left\{x: x = k\dfrac{\pi}{2}\right\}$

  c. $\{x: x = k\pi\} \cup \left\{x: x = \dfrac{\pi}{2} + 2k\pi\right\}$

  d. $\left\{x: x = k\dfrac{\pi}{2}\right\} \cup \{x: x = 2k\pi\}$

50. In polar coordinates, $x^2 - y^2 = 4$ is given by:

  a. $r^2 = \dfrac{4}{\cos 2\theta.}$

  b. $r^2 = 4 \sec \theta$

  c. $r^2 = 4(\cos^2\theta - \sin^2\theta)$

  d. $r^2 = 4 \sin 2\theta$

extra practice

For use after Section 1–6

Simplify the given expression.

1. $23 + (-17)$
2. $-42 + (-81)$
3. $-38 + 45$
4. $27 + (-82)$
5. $36 + (-18) + (-27)$
6. $-54 + 81 + (-17)$
7. $108 + (-101) + (-53)$
8. $-86 + (-123) + (-18)$
9. $28 + (-17) + 19 + (-41)$
10. $-23 + (-28) + 37 + (-4)$

11. $(-15)(7)$
12. $(-24)(-11)$
13. $3(-9)(-41)$
14. $-2(-6)(21)$
15. $(24)(-\frac{1}{8})(-2)$
16. $-36(-\frac{1}{12})(-7)$
17. $14(-11)(\frac{1}{7})(\frac{1}{22})$
18. $-8(-24)(\frac{1}{4})(-1)$
19. $23(-\frac{1}{5})(35)(0)$
20. $72(-1)(0)(\frac{1}{36})$

Find the sum.

21.	22.	23.	24.	25.	26.	27.	28.
51	-8	61	-12	-18	-23	91	-211
-16	25	-38	-71	7	33	-122	182
3	37	-42	-38	-24	41	138	-68
27	-23	11	92	-11	-37	-87	-109
				5	-43	-12	88
				12			

For use after Section 1–8

Simplify.

1. $18 - 31$
2. $-16 - 8$
3. $-5 - (-3)$
4. $-7 - (-21)$
5. $-22 - (-8)$
6. $21 - (-3)$
7. $-18 - 21 + 3$
8. $41 + 17 - 51$
9. $-2(7 - 3)$
10. $-18(8 - 9)$
11. $6[-3 + (7 - 1)] + 1$
12. $2[5 - (8 - 11)] - 6$
13. $-3[2 + (6 - 9)] - 3$
14. $4[-8 - (5 - 2)] + 7$

15. $2[-7(8 + 3) - 5] + 1$
16. $-5[3 - 2(7 - 11)] - 6$
17. $3 \cdot (-7) + 6 \cdot 5$
18. $-3(8 - 2) + 6 \cdot 8$
19. $27 \div 9 \cdot 3$
20. $27 \div (9 \cdot 3)$
21. $27 \cdot 9 \div 3$
22. $27 \cdot (9 \div 3)$
23. $-6 + 3 \cdot 8 \div 2$
24. $5 \cdot (-8 \div 2) + 6$
25. $-36 \div (-6 \cdot 3) - 2$
26. $-40 \div (-3)[6 - 2(1 - 4)]$
27. $\frac{3}{5} \cdot \frac{1}{3} \div (-\frac{1}{5})$
28. $48 \div (\frac{6}{5}) \cdot \frac{2}{5}$

For use after Section 2–1

Simplify.

1. $(2x - 3) + (-x + 5)$
2. $(t - 2) + (2t - 3) - (3t + 1)$
3. $(2x - 3y + 2) - (5x + 3y + 2)$
4. $(t^2 - 3t + 5) - (3t^2 + 1) + (t^2 - t)$
5. $(3n^2 + 5) - (2n^2 - 3n) + (n - 2)$

6. $(3z^2 + 5z - 7) - (2 + 7z + z^2)$
7. $(4n^3 + 3n^2 - 2n) - (2n^2 + 3n - 5)$
8. $2z - 3(z + 1) + 2[3z - 4(z + 2) - 1]$
9. $-2[3a - 2(a + 1)] + 3[-a + 3(2 - a)]$

10. $(2r^2 - 3r + 7) - (6r + 3 - 2r^2) + (3 + r - r^2)$
11. $(2a^2 - 3ab + b^2) + (4a^2 - ab - 2b^2) - (a^2 + ab + b^2)$
12. $(2x^4 - 3x^3 + 2x^2 - 3x + 2) - (x^4 - 2x^3 + x - 3) - (x^3 - x^2)$

For use after Section 2–2

Solve over $\mathcal{R}$.

1. $7t + 3 = 17$
2. $3r - (2 + r) = 8$
3. $6z + 5 - 7z = 10 - 2z + 3$
4. $\dfrac{5y}{2} - 1 = y + \dfrac{1}{2}$
5. $\dfrac{2y}{3} - \dfrac{1}{4} = \dfrac{25}{12} + \dfrac{y}{3}$

6. $5b + 5 = 61 - 3b$
7. $2(5r + 1) + 16 = 4 + 3(r - 7)$
8. $5x - 6(3 - 4x) = x - 7(4 + x)$
9. $\frac{1}{2}(y + 5) - \frac{1}{4}(y + 1) = 3$
10. $\frac{1}{6}(11 + t) - \frac{1}{3}(10 - t) = 1$
11. $\frac{1}{3}(x + 2) - \frac{1}{5}(x - 2) = 2$

For use after Section 2–5

Solve over $\mathcal{R}$ and graph the solution set.

1. $6 - t > 8$
2. $2n - 1 < -13$
3. $-3t - 6t \geq -10t + 10$
4. $3(2b - 2) \leq 2b + 9$
5. $7(3b - 1) \geq 14$

6. $11k - (k + 1) \leq 3(k - 5)$
7. $1 < 2z - 7 < 11$
8. $0 \leq 6(b - 2) \leq 6$
9. $t - 3 < 2t + 5 < t + 7$
10. $2k - 4 < 3k - 2 < 2k + 1$

For use after Section 2–7

Simplify.

1. $|7 - 3|$
2. $|6 - 18|$
3. $-|-3 + 5|$
4. $-|17 - 8|$

5. $|6| - |-7|$
6. $-|3| + |7 - 2|$
7. $|7 - 12| - 3|6 - 1| + |-6|$
8. $2|13 - 3| - 3|5 - 8| - |-3|$

9. $\dfrac{|8 + 3| - 2|2 - 5|}{|7 - 2|}$

10. $\dfrac{2|6 + 1| - |5 - 1|}{|6 - 8|}$

Solve over $\mathcal{R}$ and graph the solution set.

11. $|x| = 3$
12. $-|z| = -7$

13. $|y - 5| = 3$
14. $|n + 2| = 8$

15. $|3 + t| = 11$
16. $|7 - x| = 3$

17. $|2t + 7| = 1$
18. $|5 - 2t| = 7$

If $f: x \rightarrow 3 - 4x + 2x^2$, find:

1. $f(0)$ 2. $f(-1)$ 3. $f(-2)$ 4. $f(2)$ 5. $f(a)$ 6. $f(-a)$

Graph each sentence.

7. $x + y = 8$ 11. $3x - y = 9$ 15. $y = 4x$ 19. $y < -x$
8. $x - y = 3$ 12. $2x + 3y = 12$ 16. $x = -2$ 20. $2x - y \leq 8$
9. $y - x = 5$ 13. $3x - 4y = 24$ 17. $x - 2y \leq 4$ 21. $3x + 4y \geq 12$
10. $2x + y = 6$ 14. $2x - 3y = 1$ 18. $2x + y > 6$ 22. $x - 4y < 8$

Determine the slope of:

23. The line containing $(-5, 4)$ and $(3, 1)$.
24. The line containing $(3, 7)$ and $(0, -1)$.
25. The line with equation $7x - 2y = 4$.
26. The line with equation $3x + 2y = 8$.

Write an equation for the line:

27. Containing $(2, -1)$ and $(3, 2)$.
28. Containing $(0, 6)$ and $(2, 1)$.
29. Containing $(-5, -2)$ and $(-3, 1)$.
30. Containing $(1, -3)$ and $(2, 4)$.
31. Containing $(-2, 3)$ and having slope $\frac{1}{2}$.
32. Containing $(5, -2)$ and having slope $\frac{2}{3}$.
33. Containing $(-1, -2)$ and having slope -2.
34. Containing $(2, -3)$ and having slope $-\frac{1}{3}$.
35. Having slope $\frac{1}{5}$ and y-intercept 2.
36. Having slope -3 and y-intercept -1.
37. Having slope $\frac{2}{3}$ and y-intercept 4.
38. Having slope $-\frac{2}{5}$ and y-intercept -2.

Determine a rule for pairing in a linear function f, if:

39. $f(2) = 6$ and $f(3) = 9$ 43. $f(4) = -2$ and $f(-10) = 5$
40. $f(3) = 2$ and $f(6) = 4$ 44. $f(5) = 3$ and $f(0) = -2$
41. $f(-4) = -5$ and $f(8) = 10$ 45. $f(6) = 13$ and $f(-3) = -5$
42. $f(4) = 14$ and $f(-2) = -7$ 46. $f(-4) = 5$ and $f(4) = 1$

If y varies directly as x, and:

47. $y = 4$ when $x = 3$, find y when $x = 5$.
48. $y = 12$ when $x = \frac{1}{2}$, find y when $x = 2$.
49. $y = 6$ when $x = \frac{1}{3}$, find x when $y = 18$.
50. $y = 3$ when $x = \frac{3}{20}$, find x when $y = 7$.

Solve by graphing.

1. $2x - y = -7$
   $x + 3y = 7$

2. $5x + 3y = 2$
   $x - 6y = 7$

3. $2x - y = 9$
   $2x + 3y = 13$

Solve by the linear-combination method.

4. $7x - 2y = 11$
   $x + y = -1$

5. $3x + y = 14$
   $x - y = 6$

6. $2x + y = 3$
   $x + 2y = 0$

7. $3x - 7y = 16$
   $5x - 7y = 36$

8. $7x + 5y = 2$
   $8x - 9y = 17$

9. $3x - 2y = 13$
   $7x + 3y = 15$

Solve by substitution.

10. $2x + y = 7$
    $2x - y = 13$

11. $3x + 2y = -6$
    $x + 2y = -6$

12. $2x - y = -1$
    $x + y = -2$

13. $x + 2y = 7$
    $x - y = 5$

14. $x - y = 2$
    $2x - 2y = 4$

15. $3x + y = 2$
    $6x + 2y = 5$

Evaluate.

16. $\begin{vmatrix} 3 & -1 \\ 5 & 2 \end{vmatrix}$

17. $\begin{vmatrix} 6 & 7 \\ -1 & 5 \end{vmatrix}$

18. $\begin{vmatrix} 8 & 3 \\ 2 & 1 \end{vmatrix}$

19. $\begin{vmatrix} 2 & 8 \\ 1 & 16 \end{vmatrix}$

20. $\begin{vmatrix} 2 & 4 \\ 8 & 16 \end{vmatrix}$

21. $\begin{vmatrix} 3 & -2 \\ 1 & 5 \end{vmatrix}$

Solve by Cramer's Rule.

22. $3x + y = 11$
    $5x - y = 13$

23. $4x + 3y = -1$
    $5x + y = 7$

24. $x - 6y = -10$
    $2x - 7y = -15$

25. $5x + 4y = 22$
    $3x + y = 9$

26. $7x - 2y = 31$
    $4x - 3y = 27$

27. $5x + 3y = -9$
    $10x + 6y = 8$

Graph the solution set of each system.

28. $x - 2y \le 4$
    $x + y > 2$

29. $x - 3y \le 6$
    $x + y \ge 3$

30. $2 \le x \le 4$
    $3 \le y \le 5$

For use after Chapter 5

Sketch the segment whose endpoints have the given coordinates.

1. $(0, 1, 0)$; $(2, 0, 0)$

2. $(0, 2, 2)$; $(2, 0, 1)$

3. $(2, -2, 0)$; $(1, 1, 1)$

Solve each system.

4. $x + y + z = 2$
   $2x - y + z = -1$
   $x - y - z = 0$

5. $a + b + c = 1$
   $2a - b + 3c = 2$
   $2a - b - c = 2$

6. $2x - y + z = 5$
   $3x + 2y + 3z = 7$
   $4x - 3y - 5z = -3$

7.
$$a - 2b + c = 0$$
$$a - b + 2c = -11$$
$$2a - b + c = -9$$

9.
$$5b - 8c = -19$$
$$5a - 8c = 6$$
$$3a - 2b = 12$$

11.
$$\frac{1}{x} + \frac{1}{y} + \frac{1}{z} = \frac{1}{3}$$
$$\frac{1}{x} - \frac{1}{y} - \frac{1}{z} = -\frac{5}{3}$$
$$-\frac{1}{x} + \frac{1}{y} - \frac{1}{z} = \frac{25}{3}$$

8.
$$x + y + 2z = 0$$
$$2x - 2y + z = 8$$
$$3x + 2y + z = 2$$

10.
$$2x + z = 7$$
$$y - z = -2$$
$$x + y = 2$$

Evaluate.

12. $\begin{vmatrix} 2 & 2 & 3 \\ -2 & -4 & -11 \\ 5 & -6 & 2 \end{vmatrix}$

14. $\begin{vmatrix} 1 & 1 & -1 \\ 4 & 3 & -1 \\ 6 & -5 & -1 \end{vmatrix}$

16. $\begin{vmatrix} 2 & 1 & 3 \\ 0 & 2 & -1 \\ 0 & 0 & 2 \end{vmatrix}$

13. $\begin{vmatrix} 3 & 1 & -1 \\ 1 & 3 & -1 \\ 1 & 1 & -3 \end{vmatrix}$

15. $\begin{vmatrix} 4 & -3 & 0 \\ 0 & 4 & -3 \\ -3 & 0 & 4 \end{vmatrix}$

17. $\begin{vmatrix} 2 & -1 & 0 \\ 0 & 2 & -1 \\ 0 & 0 & 2 \end{vmatrix}$

Solve using Cramer's Rule.

18.
$$x + y = 2$$
$$2x - z = 1$$
$$2y - 3z = -1$$

20.
$$3x - 2y + 5z = 6$$
$$4x - 4y + 3z = 0$$
$$5x - 4y + z = -5$$

22.
$$2x + y - z = 3$$
$$3x + 4y + z = 6$$
$$2x - 3y + z = 1$$

19.
$$2a + 5c = 9$$
$$4a + 3b = -1$$
$$3b - 4c = -13$$

21.
$$3x + y - z = 14$$
$$x + 3y - z = 16$$
$$x + y - 3z = -10$$

23.
$$3x + 2y + 2z = 10$$
$$2x - 3y + 3z = -6$$
$$5x + 4y + 4z = 14$$

For use after Chapter 6

Give an equivalent expression containing only positive exponents. Assume that no variable in a denominator has 0 as a value.

1. $\dfrac{x^{-4}z}{y^3}$

3. $3x^4(-5x^3)$

5. $\dfrac{(3xy^2)^4}{(-12x^2y)^2}$

2. $\dfrac{6m^4n^{-3}}{7p^{-2}}$

4. $(10rs^{-1}t^2)(-3r^2st^{-2})$

6. $\left(\dfrac{12a^2b^3}{20a^4b^2}\right)^3$

Write each product as a polynomial in simple form.

7. $(x + 3)(x + 1)$
8. $(r - 2)(r - 5)$
9. $(\frac{1}{3}r - 6)(\frac{1}{3}r + 3)$
10. $(0.3a + 1)(0.3a - 1)$

11. $(2x + 3)^2(x^2 - 1)$
12. $(n^2 - 2)^2$
13. $(t^3 + 3)^2$
14. $(n^{2a} + 3)^2$

15. $(n + 2)(n - 3)^2$
16. $(r - 2)^2(r^2 - s^2)$
17. $2r(r - 4)^3$
18. $(2n - 1)^2(n + 3)^2$

Factor completely.

19. $n^2 - 2n - 15$
20. $4 - x^2$
21. $x^4y^2 - 9$

22. $x^4 - 16$
23. $3x^2 + 4x + 1$
24. $3x^2 - 7bx + 2b^2$

25. $2a^2 + 3a - 2ab - 3b$
26. $27a^3 + 64b^3$
27. $(x + y)^3 - z^3$

Solve by factoring.

28. $x^2 - 5x = 0$

29. $3x^2 - 27 = 0$

30. $12y^2 = 8y + 15$

31. $z(2z - 3) = -1$

32. $r(3r + 2) = (r + 2)^2$

33. $3n(n + 1) = 2n + 2$

Solve over $\mathcal{R}$ and graph the solution set.

34. $x^2 - 2x - 3 < 0$

35. $x^2 + x - 2 > 0$

36. $t^2 \leq 25$

37. $x^2 \geq 4x$

38. $x^2 - 4x < 5$

39. $r^2 + 3r > 10$

Express using a decimal numeral.

40. 2.3×10^3

41. 7.19×10^{-2}

42. 1.503×10^5

43. 8.01×10^{-7}

Simplify.

44. $27(3)^{-2}$

45. $\dfrac{-3b^2}{24a^3b}$

46. $2^{-1}(4x - 10)$

47. $\dfrac{2 - b^2}{b^2 - 2}$

48. $(18 - 12a)(9 - 6a)^{-1}$

49. $\dfrac{9x^3 - x}{3x^2 + 8x - 3}$

Transform the given rational expression into a sum by dividing.

50. $\dfrac{bx^2 - bx}{bx}$

51. $\dfrac{3x^3 - 6x^2 + 3x}{-3x}$

52. $\dfrac{x^2 + 5x + 6}{x + 3}$

53. $\dfrac{x^2 + 17x + 52}{x + 4}$

54. $\dfrac{n^2 + 15n + 36}{n + 3}$

55. $\dfrac{t^2 + t - 8}{t - 3}$

56. $\dfrac{6r^2 + 11r - 35}{3r - 5}$

57. $\dfrac{12t^2 - 4t - 1}{2t - 1}$

58. $\dfrac{6a^3 + 5a^2 + 9}{2a + 3}$

Simplify.

59. $\dfrac{10x}{12y} \cdot \dfrac{3x^2z}{5x^3z} \cdot \dfrac{6y^2x}{3yz}$

60. $\dfrac{-12a^2b}{5c} \cdot \dfrac{10b^2c}{24a^3b}$

61. $\dfrac{3b}{4ab - 6b^2} \cdot \dfrac{2a - 3b}{12a}$

62. $28a^2b^3 \div \dfrac{21a^2b^2}{5}$

63. $\dfrac{4x^2 + 8x + 3}{2x^2 - 5x + 3} \cdot \dfrac{6x^2 - 9x}{1 - 4x^2}$

64. $\dfrac{2}{ax} + \dfrac{5}{ax}$

65. $\dfrac{x - 1}{2y} + \dfrac{x}{2y}$

66. $\dfrac{a - 2}{6} - \dfrac{a + 1}{3}$

67. $\dfrac{a - 4}{6a} - \dfrac{3 + 5a}{5a} + \dfrac{1}{10a}$

68. $\dfrac{2}{b - 1} + \dfrac{2}{b + 1}$

69. $\dfrac{a + 1}{a + 2} - \dfrac{a + 2}{a + 3}$

70. $\dfrac{1 + 2a^{-1}}{1 - 4a^{-2}}$

71. $\dfrac{x + xy^{-1}}{y^{-1} + 1}$

72. $a + \dfrac{1}{a - 1} - \dfrac{1}{(a - 1)^2}$

73. $z - \dfrac{2z}{z^2 - 1} + \dfrac{3}{z + 1}$

Solve over $\mathcal{R}$.

74. $\dfrac{x}{5} - \dfrac{x}{2} = 9$

75. $\dfrac{2x}{3} - \dfrac{2x + 5}{6} = \dfrac{1}{2}$

76. $\dfrac{1}{z} + \dfrac{1}{2z} = \dfrac{1}{6}$

77. $\dfrac{7}{3a} + \dfrac{3}{a} = 1$

78. $\dfrac{2}{x - 9} = \dfrac{9}{x + 12}$

79. $\dfrac{2}{3} = 6 - \dfrac{x + 10}{x - 3}$

Find the first four terms of an arithmetic sequence for which:

1. $a_1 = 6$; $d = 3$

2. $a_1 = -8$; $d = 5$

3. $a_1 = 6.3$; $d = -3.8$

Find the specified term a_n of the indicated arithmetic sequence.

4. $7, 11, 15, \ldots$; a_{10}

5. $5, 1, -3, \ldots$; a_{12}

6. $-12, -9, -6, \ldots$; a_{25}

Express each sum using summation notation.

7. $7 + 10 + 13 + 16 + 19$

8. $-3 - 5 - 7 - 9 - 11 - 13$

9. $2 + 4 + 6 + \cdots + 98 + 100$

Find the first four terms in the indicated geometric sequence.

10. $a_1 = 3$; $r = 2$

11. $a_1 = \frac{1}{3}$; $r = \frac{1}{3}$

12. $a_1 = -8$; $r = -\frac{1}{4}$

Find the specified term a_n for the indicated geometric sequence.

13. $a_1 = 81$; $r = \frac{1}{3}$; a_5

14. $a_1 = 6$; $r = 2$; a_6

15. $a_1 = -3$; $r = 3$; a_5

Find the common ratio of a geometric sequence of real numbers having the indicated terms.

16. $a_1 = -3$, $a_4 = -192$

17. $a_1 = 5$; $a_4 = \frac{1}{25}$

18. $a_1 = 27$; $a_4 = 0$

Insert the stated number of geometric means between the given numbers.

19. One, between 4 and 64

20. Two, between 3 and 24

21. Two, between 4 and $\frac{1}{16}$

22. Three, between $-\frac{1}{5}$ and $-\frac{1}{80}$

Evaluate.

23. $\displaystyle\sum_{i=1}^{8} (2i + 3)$

24. $\displaystyle\sum_{j=1}^{12} \left(-\tfrac{1}{2}j + 2\right)$

25. $\displaystyle\sum_{j=1}^{50} (3j - 5)$

26. $\displaystyle\sum_{k=1}^{100} k$

27. $\displaystyle\sum_{i=1}^{4} 5(2)^{i+1}$

28. $\displaystyle\sum_{j=1}^{5} 16(\tfrac{1}{2})^{j-1}$

29. $\displaystyle\sum_{k=1}^{5} -8(\tfrac{1}{3})^{k}$

30. $\displaystyle\sum_{i=1}^{6} 3(0.1)^{i}$

Find the sum of the given infinite series.

31. $\displaystyle\sum_{i=1}^{\infty} 5(-\tfrac{1}{2})^{i-1}$

32. $\displaystyle\sum_{j=1}^{\infty} -3(\tfrac{1}{4})^{j-1}$

33. $\displaystyle\sum_{k=1}^{\infty} 10(\tfrac{3}{4})^{k-1}$

34. $\displaystyle\sum_{j=1}^{\infty} 8(\tfrac{5}{7})^{j-1}$

35. $\displaystyle\sum_{k=1}^{\infty} -6(0.4)^{k-1}$

36. $\displaystyle\sum_{i=1}^{\infty} 12(0.7)^{i-1}$

Express the given repeating decimal as a common fraction.

37. $0.\overline{71}$

38. $0.\overline{38}$

39. $0.\overline{007}$

40. $0.\overline{189}$

For use after Chapter 8

1. If y varies directly as x^2, and $y = -16$ when $x = 2$, find y when $x = -3$.
2. If t varies directly as s^2, and $t = 6$ when $s = 3$, find t when $s = 6$.
3. If p varies directly as r^3, and $p = -1$ when $r = -2$, find p when $r = 4$.
4. If y varies directly as x^4, and $y = a$ when $x = \dfrac{1}{a}$, find y when $x = a$.

Express as a decimal. (Use Tables 3 and 4 where necessary.)

5. $\sqrt{4.3}$ 7. $\sqrt[3]{41}$ 9. $\sqrt{\frac{15}{7}}$ 11. $\frac{5}{6}$ 13. $\frac{3}{14}$

6. $-\sqrt{0.81}$ 8. $\sqrt[3]{-81}$ 10. $\sqrt[3]{(2)^5}$ 12. $\frac{8}{11}$ 14. $-\frac{5}{7}$

Find (a) a rational number and (b) an irrational number between the given numbers.

15. $\frac{1}{4}$ and $\frac{3}{8}$ 16. $\frac{6}{5}$ and $\frac{13}{10}$ 17. $\frac{9}{10}$ and 0.98 18. $0.\overline{45}$ and $\frac{1}{2}$

Simplify.

19. $\sqrt{108}$

20. $6\sqrt{75}$

21. $\sqrt[3]{81}$

22. $\sqrt[4]{\dfrac{32}{81}}$

23. $\sqrt{\dfrac{3}{5}}$

24. $\sqrt[3]{\dfrac{4}{3}}$

25. $\sqrt[5]{\dfrac{64x^6y^7}{z^4}}$

26. $\dfrac{8\sqrt{54x^5}}{15\sqrt{5y^3}}$

27. $\dfrac{1}{\sqrt{3x^2 + 1}}$

28. $\dfrac{2}{\sqrt{5x^2 + 2}}$

29. $\sqrt{4x^2 - 12xy + 9y^2}$

30. $\sqrt{1 - 6n + 9n^2}$

31. $\sqrt{98} - \sqrt{32}$

32. $2\sqrt{80} + \sqrt{180}$

33. $\sqrt[3]{54} + \sqrt[3]{16}$

34. $\sqrt[3]{27x^2} + \sqrt[3]{24x^2}$

35. $\sqrt[4]{32} - \sqrt[4]{162}$

36. $\sqrt[5]{64} - \sqrt[5]{2}$

37. $(5 - \sqrt{3})(5 + \sqrt{3})$

38. $(\sqrt{3} + 7)(\sqrt{3} - 8)$

39. $(4 + \sqrt{5})^2$

40. $(2 - 3\sqrt{7})^2$

41. $(\sqrt{x} - \sqrt{x + 5})^2$

42. $(\sqrt{x + 1} - \sqrt{x - 1})^2$

43. $\dfrac{3}{3 + \sqrt{5}}$

44. $\dfrac{6}{3 + 2\sqrt{5}}$

45. $\dfrac{3 - \sqrt{2}}{4 + \sqrt{2}}$

46. $\dfrac{\sqrt{a + b}}{\sqrt{a - b}}$

Solve over $\Re$.

47. $\sqrt{x} - 3 = 0$

48. $\sqrt[3]{y + 4} = 2$

49. $\sqrt[3]{x - 2} + 3 = 1$

50. $\sqrt[4]{y^2 + y + 4} = 2$

51. $\sqrt[3]{t^2 + 2} - 3 = 0$

52. $\sqrt{n} - 1 = \sqrt{2n + 1}$

53. $\sqrt{t - 5} = \sqrt{t} - 1$

54. $\sqrt{r + 12} + \sqrt{r} = 2$

Solve by completing the square.

55. $x^2 + 3x + 1 = 0$ 56. $x^2 - 2x - 1 = 0$ 57. $3x^2 + x - 4 = 0$

Solve using the quadratic formula.

58. $3t^2 + t - 1 = 0$

59. $5n^2 - n - 1 = 0$

60. $\dfrac{x^2}{3} - \dfrac{x}{12} = \dfrac{1}{24}$

61. $\dfrac{n^2}{5} - \dfrac{n}{6} = \dfrac{1}{30}$

62. $4x^2 - 12x + 9 = 0$

63. $3x^2 + 8x + 2 = 0$

Simplify.

1. $3\sqrt{-8}$ 9. $\sqrt{-2}\sqrt{-8}$ 17. $4\sqrt{-27} - 2\sqrt{-3}$ 25. $-2i(5 - 4i)$

2. $\sqrt{-32}$ 10. $\sqrt{-3}\sqrt{-27}$ 18. $5\sqrt{-32} + 2\sqrt{-8}$ 26. $(5 - 2i)(5 + 2i)$

3. $2\sqrt{-50}$ 11. $\dfrac{i\sqrt{5}}{i\sqrt{2}}$ 19. $(3 + i) + (2 + 3i)$ 27. $(3 - 2i)(5 + i)$

4. $4\sqrt{-18}$ 12. $\dfrac{i\sqrt{6}}{i\sqrt{3}}$ 20. $(3 - 2i) - (5 - 3i)$ 28. $(4 - 3i)(2 - 3i)$

5. i^9 13. $\dfrac{2}{3i}$ 21. $(5 + 3i) - (3 - 2i)$ 29. $\dfrac{3}{2 + i}$

6. i^{23} 14. $\dfrac{5}{2\sqrt{-3}}$ 22. $(4 + \sqrt{-8}) + (2 - \sqrt{-2})$ 30. $\dfrac{2}{3 + 2i}$

7. $(i\sqrt{3})^2$ 15. $3\sqrt{-2} + 2\sqrt{-8}$ 23. $(2 - \sqrt{-3}) - (5 + \sqrt{-12})$ 31. $\dfrac{i}{2 + 3i}$

8. $(2i\sqrt{5})^2$ 16. $2\sqrt{-16} - 3\sqrt{-25}$ 24. $-3i(1 + 2i)$ 32. $\dfrac{2 - i}{3 + i}$

Solve over $\mathbb{C}$.

33. $x^2 - x + 1 = 0$ 35. $r^2 - 3r + 5 = 0$ 37. $2r^2 - 3r + 5 = 0$

34. $2z^2 - z + 3 = 0$ 36. $z^2 - z + 4 = 0$ 38. $k^2 - k + 2 = 0$

Write a quadratic equation having the given solution set.

39. $\{3, -4\}$ 41. $\{2 + \sqrt{2}, 2 - \sqrt{2}\}$ 43. $\{1 + 2i, 1 - 2i\}$

40. $\{-7, 0\}$ 42. $\{\sqrt{3}, -\sqrt{3}\}$ 44. $\{-3i, 3i\}$

Sketch the graph of each function.

45. $\{(x, y): y = x^2 - 2x - 3\}$ 47. $\{(x, y): y = 4 - 4x - x^2\}$ 49. $\{(x, y): y = x^2 + x + 1\}$

46. $\{(x, y): y = 2(x - 1)^2 + 3\}$ 48. $\{(x, y): y = 2 - (x + 1)^2\}$ 50. $\{(x, y): y = 1 - x - x^2\}$

Solve each inequality over $\mathbb{R}$ and graph its solution set on the number line.

51. $x^2 - 9 \leq 0$ 53. $3x^2 - 6x > 0$ 55. $x^2 - x \geq 12$

52. $4x^2 - 25 \leq 0$ 54. $2x - 8x^2 > 0$ 56. $x^2 - 2x \leq 15$

Factor each polynomial over (a) $\mathbb{R}$; (b) $\mathbb{C}$.

57. $x^3 + 2x^2 - 5x - 6$ 59. $x^3 - 4x^2 + x + 6$

58. $x^3 - 6x^2 + 13x - 10$ 60. $x^3 - 4x^2 - 5x + 14$

Find the indicated zero to the nearest tenth.

61. $\{(x, y): y = x^3 - 3x + 1\}$, between 1 and 2

62. $\{(x, y): y = 2x^3 - x^2 + 3x + 1\}$, between 0 and -1

63. $\{(x, y): y = x^3 - 2x - 5\}$, between 2 and 3

64. $\{(x, y): y = x^3 + 2x - 1\}$, between 0 and 1

For use after Chapter 10

Find an equation for the line containing P_3 and perpendicular to the line containing points P_1 and P_2.

1. $P_1(1, 3)$; $P_2(-1, 2)$; $P_3(3, 1)$
2. $P_1(2, -4)$; $P_2(-3, -7)$; $P_3(2, 3)$
3. $P_1(0, -5)$; $P_2(2, 0)$; $P_3(0, 0)$
4. $P_1(-3, 0)$; $P_2(0, 2)$; $P_3(3, 3)$
5. $P_1(-4, -3)$; $P_2(-3, 5)$; $P_3(-2, -2)$
6. $P_1(0, 0)$; $P_2(4, 1)$; $P_3(2, 7)$
7. $P_1(2, 3)$; $P_2(2, -1)$; $P_3(2, 1)$
8. $P_1(3, -1)$; $P_2(-1, -1)$; $P_3(1, -1)$

Write an equation of the form $x^2 + y^2 + ax + ay + c = 0$ for the circle with given center and given radius, and sketch the circle.

9. $(3, -2)$; 2
10. $(-5, 1)$; 3
11. $(-2, -2)$; 2
12. (a, b); b

Sketch the graph of the given relation.

13. $\{(x, y): x^2 + y^2 > 36\}$
14. $\{(x, y): y = 2 + 5x - x^2\}$
15. $\{(x, y): y \leq (x - 2)^2 + 3\}$
16. $\left\{(x, y): \dfrac{x^2}{9} + \dfrac{y^2}{25} = 1\right\}$
17. $\{(x, y): x^2 + 4y^2 = 100\}$
18. $\{(x, y): x = y^2 + 4y\}$
19. $\left\{(x, y): \dfrac{x^2}{16} + \dfrac{y^2}{9} = 1\right\}$
20. $\{(x, y): 9x^2 + y^2 > 9\}$
21. $\left\{(x, y): \dfrac{x^2}{4} - \dfrac{y^2}{9} = 1\right\}$
22. $\{(x, y): x^2 + y^2 - 4x + y = 0\}$
23. $\{(x, y): x^2 + y^2 - 4y \leq 0\}$
24. $\left\{(x, y): \dfrac{y^2}{4} - x^2 = 1\right\}$
25. $\{(x, y): x^2 + 9y^2 \leq 36\}$
26. $\{(x, y): 5x^2 - 5y^2 = 45\}$

Find an equation of the form $y = ax^2 + bx + c$ or $x = ay^2 + by + c$ for the parabola with focus F and directrix the line with the given equation.

27. $F(4, 0)$; $x = -2$
28. $F(0, 3)$; $y = 1$
29. $F(0, 4)$; $y = -2$
30. $F(-5, 0)$; $y = 3$

Find an equation for the ellipse with center at the origin and with the given characteristics.

31. Major axis of length 10; x-intercepts 4 and -4.
32. Foci at $(3, 0)$ and $(-3, 0)$; sum of focal radii 8.

Find an equation for the hyperbola with center at the origin and with the given characteristics.

33. Foci at $(4, 0)$ and $(-4, 0)$; length of conjugate axis 6.
34. Intercepts at $(3, 0)$ and $(-3, 0)$; foci at $(4, 0)$ and $(-4, 0)$.

Solve each system over $\mathcal{R}$ by graphing.

35. $y = \frac{1}{2}x$
    $y = x$
36. $x^2 + y^2 = 13$
    $x + y = 5$
37. $x^2 + 4y^2 = 16$
    $x + 2y = 4$
38. $x^2 + 4y^2 = 17$
    $3x^2 - y^2 = -1$

Solve each system over $\mathcal{C}$.

39. $x^2 + y^2 = 6$
    $x + y = 6$
40. $xy = 12$
    $3x + 4y = 24$
41. $y = x^2 + 2x - 3$
    $y = 2x^2 - x - 1$
42. $x^2 + 2y^2 = 17$
    $x^2 - 2y^2 = 1$

For use after Chapter 11

Write each exponential expression in radical form.

1. $7^{\frac{1}{4}}$,   2. $3^{\frac{1}{2}}x^{\frac{1}{2}}$ 3. $7y^{\frac{1}{5}}$ 4. $(7y)^{\frac{3}{5}}$ 5. $(m^2n^3)^{\frac{1}{4}}$ 6. $(t^2 + 8)^{\frac{3}{4}}$

Simplify.

7. $(2^{\sqrt{3}})^2\sqrt{3}$ 8. $(5^{\sqrt{2}})^{\frac{\sqrt{2}}{2}}$ 9. $(3^{\sqrt{2}+1})(3^{2-\sqrt{2}})$ 10. $(6^{2\sqrt{2}-1}) \div (36^{\sqrt{2}})$

Solve over $\Re$.

11. $9^{r+2} = 3^{r+1}$ 12. $2^{6x^2} = 4^{5x+2}$ 13. $8^{n-1} = 16^{3n}$ 14. $4^{n-1} = 8^n$

Write the equation defining F^{-1} and state whether F and F^{-1} are functions.

15. $F = \{(x, y): y = 3x - 2\}$ 17. $F = \{(x, y): y = x^2 + 2x + 1\}$
16. $F = \{(x, y): y = 1 - \sqrt{x}\}$ 18. $F = \{(x, y): y = 2^x\}$

Compute each of the following. Round results to three significant digits.

19. $\dfrac{(0.9)(18.6)}{21.3}$ 22. $\dfrac{(738)(1425)}{16.27}$ 25. $\sqrt[4]{38,200}$ 28. $(2.138)^{-3}$

20. $\dfrac{(0.618)(9.83)}{0.214}$ 23. $(8.14)^4$ 26. $\sqrt[3]{0.183}$ 29. $\dfrac{\sqrt[5]{23,200}}{\sqrt{0.8324}}$

21. $(41.6)(3.19)(0.072)$ 24. $(0.0814)^2(410)^2$ 27. $\dfrac{21.4\sqrt[3]{73.2}}{\sqrt[4]{9000}}$ 30. $\dfrac{(10.73)^3}{\sqrt[3]{819.3}}$

Solve over $\Re$.

31. $\log (x + 1) + \log 2 = \log 8$ 35. $\log x + \log (x - 3) = 1$
32. $\log t^3 - \log t^2 = \log 5$ 36. $\log_5 x + \log_5 (x - 4) = 1$
33. $\log_4 n^2 + \log_4 2 = 2$ 37. $2 \log x = 4 \log 2$
34. $\log_6 (x - 1) - \log_6 3 = 1$ 38. $3 \log x = 2 \log 3 + \log 6 - \log 2$

Find the real number x for which each sentence is true.

39. $\log_x 8 = 3$ 41. $\log_2 \frac{1}{8} = x$ 43. $\log_6 x = -2$ 45. $\log_{16} 8 = x$
40. $\log_3 9 = x$ 42. $\log_x 10 = 1$ 44. $\log_4 x = -4$ 46. $\log_2 0.5 = x$

Give a one-significant-digit estimate of each of the following.

47. $\dfrac{483 \times 18.1}{510}$ 48. $\dfrac{4205 \times 0.89}{3.94 \times 1.98}$ 49. $\dfrac{(18.3)^2 \times 71.4}{(0.9)^3}$ 50. $\dfrac{(41.3)^3}{(0.093)^2 \times 3100}$

Solve over $\Re$. Use Table 5 as needed and express each solution to three significant figures.

51. $5^x = 30$ 52. $4^{\frac{x}{3}} = 9$ 53. $10^{x+2} = 16.1$ 54. $3^{4-x} = 0.85$

1. In how many ways can you arrange 5 books on a horizontal shelf if you select 3 at a time?

2. In how many different ways can four students be seated in a row?

3. How many three-digit numerals for odd integers can be formed using the numerals 3, 4, 5, and 8?

4. In how many ways can 6 persons be seated about a circular table?

5. How many distinguishable permutations are there of all the letters in the word "AVALANCHE"?

6. How many permutations of the letters in the word "FINEST" end in a vowel?

7. In how many ways can 2 hearts be chosen from a standard deck of 52 cards?

8. In how many ways can 3 face cards be chosen from a standard deck of 52 cards?

9. In how many ways can you select 3 red and 5 blue marbles from an urn containing 6 red and 7 blue marbles?

10. In how many ways can you select 2 hearts and 3 spades from a standard deck of 52 cards?

11. A set of 5 points lies in a circle. In how many ways can you use these points as vertices to inscribe a triangle in the circle?

Expand each binomial and express the result in simplest form.

12. $(x - 4y)^3$

13. $(3x + 5y)^4$

14. $(t^2 - \frac{3}{4})^3$

15. $(n^2 - 1)^5$

Find the given term in the given expansion.

16. Fifth: $(y - 3)^7$

17. Sixth: $(t - \frac{1}{2})^8$

18. Third: $\left(\frac{y}{2} - 2\right)^{12}$

Two cards are drawn at random from a standard deck of 52 cards. What is the probability that:

19. both are red?

20. one is a heart and one is a spade?

21. both are face cards?

22. neither is a heart?

Two dice are thrown. What is the probability that:

23. the sum of the numbers is 7?

24. the sum of the numbers is greater than 9?

25. either the sum of the numbers is 8 or at least one of the dice shows a 1?

Two marbles are drawn successively at random from an urn containing 4 red, 5 white, and 2 blue marbles. The first marble is not replaced before the second is drawn. What is the probability that:

26. both are white?

27. one is white and one is red?

28. one is red and the other is not blue?

29. not both are blue?

1. $\begin{bmatrix} 3 & 4 \\ 1 & -2 \end{bmatrix} + \begin{bmatrix} 5 & -1 \\ 3 & -2 \end{bmatrix}$

2. $\begin{bmatrix} 3 & 1 \\ 2 & -1 \\ 3 & 6 \end{bmatrix} - \begin{bmatrix} -1 & 5 \\ -2 & 3 \\ -6 & 1 \end{bmatrix}$

3. $\begin{bmatrix} -1 & 5 & 7 \\ 2 & -3 & 1 \\ 0 & 5 & 1 \end{bmatrix} - \begin{bmatrix} -3 & 2 & 1 \\ 1 & 1 & 2 \\ 0 & 5 & 7 \end{bmatrix}$

Solve for the matrix X.

4. $X + \begin{bmatrix} 5 & -1 \\ 3 & 2 \end{bmatrix} = \begin{bmatrix} 1 & 6 \\ -1 & 5 \end{bmatrix}$

6. $X - \begin{bmatrix} -1 & 7 & 6 \\ 3 & -2 & 1 \end{bmatrix} = \begin{bmatrix} -1 & 5 & 7 \\ 2 & 0 & -1 \end{bmatrix}$

5. $X - \begin{bmatrix} 4 & -3 \\ 2 & 2 \end{bmatrix} = \begin{bmatrix} 5 & -1 \\ 6 & 7 \end{bmatrix}$

7. $3X - \begin{bmatrix} 5 & 1 \\ 7 & 2 \end{bmatrix} = 2 \begin{bmatrix} 1 & 6 \\ -1 & 5 \end{bmatrix}$

Simplify.

8. $\begin{bmatrix} 3 & 1 \\ -1 & 2 \end{bmatrix} \begin{bmatrix} 1 & 0 \\ 2 & 1 \end{bmatrix}$

10. $\begin{bmatrix} 3 & -1 \\ 6 & 5 \end{bmatrix} \begin{bmatrix} -1 & 1 \\ -2 & 1 \end{bmatrix}$

12. $\begin{bmatrix} 2 & 1 & -3 \\ 0 & 2 & 1 \end{bmatrix} \begin{bmatrix} 1 & 2 \\ -1 & 3 \\ 0 & 1 \end{bmatrix}$

9. $\begin{bmatrix} -4 & 1 \\ 0 & 2 \end{bmatrix} \begin{bmatrix} 1 & -2 \\ 0 & 1 \end{bmatrix}$

11. $\begin{bmatrix} -1 & 4 \\ 6 & 2 \end{bmatrix} \begin{bmatrix} 1 & 0 \\ 0 & -1 \end{bmatrix}$

13. $\begin{bmatrix} 3 & -1 & 2 \\ 1 & 0 & 1 \\ 2 & 1 & 0 \end{bmatrix} \begin{bmatrix} 1 & -1 & 0 \\ 0 & 1 & 1 \\ 1 & 0 & 1 \end{bmatrix}$

Solve for the matrix X.

14. $\begin{bmatrix} 2 & -1 \\ -1 & 1 \end{bmatrix} X = \begin{bmatrix} 1 & 0 \\ -1 & 1 \end{bmatrix}$

15. $\begin{bmatrix} 3 & 1 \\ 4 & 1 \end{bmatrix} X = \begin{bmatrix} 1 & 0 \\ 2 & 1 \end{bmatrix}$

16. $\begin{bmatrix} 5 & 2 \\ 4 & 2 \end{bmatrix} X = \begin{bmatrix} 3 & 1 \\ 1 & 4 \end{bmatrix}$

Solve over $\mathcal{R}$ using matrices.

17. $3x - y = 7$
$x + 3y = -1$

18. $5x + 3y = 19$
$2x - 5y = -11$

19. $5x - y = 2$
$2x + 4y = 14$

20. $x - 5y = -7$
$3x - 2y = -8$

Find the coordinates of the image P' of the given point P under the given translation of the plane.

21. $P(2, -3)$: $\begin{bmatrix} x' \\ y' \end{bmatrix} = \begin{bmatrix} x \\ y \end{bmatrix} + \begin{bmatrix} -1 \\ 4 \end{bmatrix}$

23. $P(8, 6)$: $\begin{bmatrix} x' \\ y' \end{bmatrix} = \begin{bmatrix} x \\ y \end{bmatrix} + \begin{bmatrix} -3 \\ 2 \end{bmatrix}$

22. $P(-4, 1)$: $\begin{bmatrix} x' \\ y' \end{bmatrix} = \begin{bmatrix} x \\ y \end{bmatrix} + \begin{bmatrix} -1 \\ 4 \end{bmatrix}$

Find the equation of translation of the plane for which the image of the given point P is the given point P'.

24. $P(4, 5)$; $P'(1, 7)$ 25. $P(-2, 7)$; $P'(3, -2)$ 26. $P(5, -2)$; $P'(7, -2)$ 27. $P(7, 3)$; $P'(-7, -3)$

Find the coordinates of P (or P') under the given linear transformation of the plane.

28. $P(-1, 3)$: $\begin{bmatrix} x' \\ y' \end{bmatrix} = \begin{bmatrix} 2 & 0 \\ 1 & -3 \end{bmatrix} \begin{bmatrix} x \\ y \end{bmatrix}$

30. $P'(-4, -1)$: $\begin{bmatrix} x' \\ y' \end{bmatrix} = \begin{bmatrix} 1 & 2 \\ -2 & 1 \end{bmatrix} \begin{bmatrix} x \\ y \end{bmatrix}$

29. $P(2, 6)$: $\begin{bmatrix} x' \\ y' \end{bmatrix} = \begin{bmatrix} -1 & 0 \\ 1 & 1 \end{bmatrix} \begin{bmatrix} x \\ y \end{bmatrix}$

For use after Chapter 14

Express the given degree or radian measure in terms of radians or degrees, respectively.

1. $240°$ 2. $310°$ 3. $\dfrac{8\pi^R}{3}$ 4. $-110°$ 5. $-\dfrac{21\pi^R}{4}$ 6. $-\dfrac{17\pi^R}{6}$ 7. $-540°$ 8. $610°$

Find the length of an arc on a circle with the given radius which is intercepted by a central angle having the given measurements.

9. 10 m; $270°$ 10. 18 cm; $\dfrac{7\pi^R}{4}$ 11. 14 m; $\dfrac{2\pi^R}{3}$ 12. 8.3 cm; $800°$

Find the measurement in degrees of a central angle intercepting an arc with length as given in a circle having the given radius.

13. $\overset{\frown}{AB}$: $\dfrac{5\pi}{2}$ cm; r: 6 cm   15. $\overset{\frown}{AB}$: $\dfrac{7\pi}{4}$ mm; r: 12 mm   17. $\overset{\frown}{AB}$: 24 cm; r: $\dfrac{11}{\pi}$ cm

14. $\overset{\frown}{AB}$: $\dfrac{8\pi}{3}$ m; r: 10 m   16. $\overset{\frown}{AB}$: $\dfrac{19\pi}{6}$ m; r: 18 m   18. $\overset{\frown}{AB}$: 12 cm; r: $\dfrac{18}{\pi}$ cm

Under the given conditions, find $\sin \alpha$ or $\cos \alpha$, whichever is not given, and state the quadrant in which α lies.

19. $\cos \alpha = \dfrac{3}{5}$; $\sin \alpha < 0$ 20. $\sin \alpha = -\dfrac{3}{\sqrt{34}}$; $\cos \alpha < 0$ 21. $\cos \alpha = \dfrac{1}{\sqrt{12}}$; $\sin \alpha > 0$

Find the given function value.

22. $\sin 810°$ 24. $\cos 660°$ 26. $\sin \dfrac{15\pi}{4}$ 28. $\cos 9\pi$

23. $\cos 1080°$ 25. $\sin 840°$ 27. $\cos \dfrac{13\pi}{3}$ 29. $\sin \dfrac{25\pi}{6}$

Find a four-significant-digit approximation for each function value.

30. $\cos 132°$ 31. $\sin 225°40'$ 32. $\cos 3.51^R$ 33. $\sin 3.00^R$

Sketch the graph of the function defined by the given equation over the two-period interval $-2\pi \le x \le 2\pi$.

34. $y = 3 \cos x$ 35. $y = 2 \sin x$ 36. $y = -\frac{1}{4} \cos x$ 37. $y = \frac{4}{3} \sin x$

Find the amplitude $|A|$ and fundamental period P of the function defined by the given equations, and sketch the graph over the two-period interval $-P \le x \le P$.

38. $y = \sin 4x$ 39. $y = \cos 3x$ 40. $y = 2 \sin \frac{3}{2}x$ 41. $y = -2 \cos \frac{2}{3}x$

Find values for the six trigonometric functions of the angle α in standard position whose terminal side contains the given points.

42. $(2, 3)$ 43. $(-1, 5)$ 44. $(4, 7)$ 45. $(8, -1)$ 46. $(-1, -6)$ 47. $(0, 3)$ 48. $(5, 0)$ 49. $(-4, 0)$

Solve the right triangle with given parts. In each case, $m(C) = 90°$.

50. $m(B) = 51°$; $a = 80$ 52. $m(A) = 22°$; $b = 30$ 54. $a = 4$; $b = 7$ 56. $a = 2$; $c = \sqrt{5}$
51. $m(A) = 28°$; $b = 40$ 53. $m(B) = 77°$; $a = 25$ 55. $a = 3$; $b = 6$ 57. $b = 4$; $c = 5$

rove each identity.

1. $(1 - \cos^2 \alpha) \cot^2 \alpha + \sin^2 \alpha = 1$

6. $\sec^2 \alpha(1 - \sin^2 \alpha) = 1$

2. $\dfrac{\csc \alpha \cos \alpha}{\cot \alpha} = 1$

7. $\cos^2 \alpha + \sin \alpha \cos \alpha \tan \alpha = 1$

3. $\sec \alpha - \cos \alpha = \sin \alpha \tan \alpha$

8. $\csc \alpha(\csc \alpha + \cot \alpha) = \dfrac{1}{1 - \cos \alpha}$

4. $\sin x \cot x + \cos x = 2 \cot x \sin x$

9. $\sec \alpha + \tan \alpha = \dfrac{\cos \alpha}{1 - \sin \alpha}$

5. $\tan x(\sin x + \cot x \cos x) = \sec x$

10. $\sin^4 \alpha - \cos^4 \alpha = 2 \sin^2 \alpha - 1$

Use an identity to reduce the given value to a function value for an angle α such that either $0° \leq m(\alpha) \leq 90°$ or $0^R \leq m(\alpha) \leq \dfrac{\pi^R}{2}$, and then tate the value.

1. $\cos 135°$ 12. $\cos 210°$ 13. $\cos 240°$ 14. $\cos \dfrac{5\pi}{6}$ 15. $\cos \dfrac{5\pi}{2}$ 16. $\cos \dfrac{9\pi}{4}$

xpress the given function value as a function value of an angle α such hat either $0^R \leq m(\alpha) \leq \dfrac{\pi^R}{4}$ or $0° \leq m(\alpha) \leq 45°$.

7. $\sin 75°$ 18. $\cos 241°$ 19. $\sin 303°$ 20. $\sin \dfrac{5\pi^R}{7}$ 21. $\cos \dfrac{6\pi^R}{13}$ 22. $\sin \dfrac{9\pi^R}{5}$

f $0 \leq x \leq \dfrac{\pi}{2}$, and $\sin x = \dfrac{5}{13}$, find each function value.

23. $\cos 2x$ 24. $\sin 2x$ 25. $\tan 2x$ 26. $\sin 4x$ 27. $\tan \dfrac{x}{2}$ 28. $\cos \dfrac{x}{4}$

Prove each identity.

29. $\sin 2\alpha \sec \alpha = 2 \sin \alpha$ 30. $\dfrac{\sin 2\alpha}{2 \sin^2 \alpha} = \cot \alpha$ 31. $\sec 2\alpha = \dfrac{\sec^2 \alpha}{2 - \sec^2 \alpha}$

Find the required part of $\triangle ABC$ either to the nearest tenth or to the nearest 10'. Assume that the data are exact.

32. $a = 4, b = 5, m(C) = 60°$. $c = $ __?__

34. $a = 12, c = 18, m(B) = 46°$. $b = $ __?__

33. $a = 20, b = 40, m(C) = \dfrac{3\pi^R}{4}$. $c = $ __?__

35. $a = 10, c = 16, m(B) = 63°$. $b = $ __?__

Solve the triangle with parts as given, the lengths to the nearest tenth of a unit and angle measurements to the nearest 10'. Assume that the data are exact. Use the law of cosines and/or the law of sines as necessary.

36. $a = 30, b = 50, c = 60$

38. $a = 20, c = 40, m(B) = 60°$

37. $a = 10, b = 20, m(C) = 40°$

39. $a = 30, b = 15, m(A) = 120°$

For use after Chapter 16.

Find each value.

1. $\sin (\text{Tan}^{-1} 1)$
2. $\cos (\text{Cot}^{-1} (-1))$

3. $\text{Tan}^{-1} (\cot \frac{1}{3}\pi)$
4. $\text{Sin}^{-1} (\cos \frac{1}{2}\pi)$

5. Arccos $(\sin 30°)$
6. Arcsec $(\cos 0°)$

Find the general solution for each equation for $m(\alpha)$ in degrees, or for $x \in \mathfrak{R}$, and then find the particular solution over $0° \le m(\alpha) < 360°$, or $0 \le x < 2\pi$.

7. $\sec \alpha - 1 = 0$
8. $2 \cos \alpha - 1 = 0$
9. $4 \cos^2 \alpha - 1 = 0$
10. $2 \sec x - 2\sqrt{3} = 0$

11. $2 \cos x - \sqrt{3} = 0$
12. $\cot^2 x + \cot x = 0$
13. $2 \sin^2 \alpha = 1 + \sin \alpha$
14. $\cos 3\alpha = \frac{1}{2}$

15. $\sec^2 2\alpha = 1 - \tan 2\alpha$
16. $\sin 2x = \frac{1}{2}\sqrt{3}$
17. $\cot 3x = 1$
18. $\sin^2 x + \sin 2x = 0$

Find two sets of polar coordinates with $-180° < m(\theta) \le 180°$ for the point whose Cartesian coordinates are given.

19. $(3\sqrt{3}, 3)$
20. $(5, 0)$
21. $(\frac{3}{2}\sqrt{3}, -\frac{3}{2})$
22. $(-\frac{5}{2}, \frac{5}{2}\sqrt{3})$
23. $(3, -4)$
24. $(-3, -\frac{3}{2})$

Transform the given equation into an equation in Cartesian coordinates, and identify the graph.

25. $r = 8$
26. $r = 2 \sin \theta$
27. $r(1 - 2 \cos \theta) = 8$
28. $r = 2 \sec \theta$

Express the given complex number in polar form.

29. $-i$
30. $3 + 3i$
31. $\sqrt{3} - i$
32. $1 - i$

Express the given complex number in the form $a + bi$.

33. $3(\cos 45° + i \sin 45°)$
34. $2(\cos 120° + i \sin 120°)$

35. $3[\cos (\frac{2}{3}\pi)^R + i \sin (\frac{2}{3}\pi)^R]$
36. $4[\cos (\frac{7}{6}\pi)^R + i \sin (\frac{7}{6}\pi)^R]$

Use De Moivre's Theorem or its extension to express each of the following in the form $a + bi$.

37. $[2(\cos 270° + i \sin 270°)]^5$
38. $[3(\cos 50° + i \sin 50°)]^{-3}$

39. $(-1 - i)^3$
40. $(1 + \sqrt{3}i)^4$

41. $(\frac{1}{5} - \frac{1}{5}i)^3$
42. $(\frac{1}{2}\sqrt{3} - \frac{1}{2}i)^{-4}$

Resolve **u** into a sum of horizontal and vertical components. Give norms to the nearest tenth.

43. $\|\mathbf{u}\| = 10$; direction of u, $30°$
44. $\|\mathbf{u}\| = 30$; direction of u, $-30°$

45. $\|\mathbf{u}\| = 20$; direction of u, $150°$
46. $\|\mathbf{u}\| = 30$; direction of u, $72°$

Find the sum of **u** and **v**, stating $\|\mathbf{u} + \mathbf{v}\|$ to the nearest tenth and $m(\theta)$ to the nearest degree.

47. $\|\mathbf{u}\| = 5$; direction of u, $30°$
    $\|\mathbf{v}\| = 8$; direction of v, $-30°$

48. $\|\mathbf{u}\| = 10$; direction of u, $-135°$
    $\|\mathbf{v}\| = 20$; direction of v, $90°$

APPENDIX

Circle	$A = \pi r^2$, $C = 2\pi r$	Cube	$V = s^3$
Parallelogram	$A = bh$	Rectangular Box	$V = lwh$
Right Triangle	$A = \frac{1}{2}bh$, $c^2 = a^2 + b^2$	Cylinder	$V = \pi r^2 h$
Square	$A = s^2$	Pyramid	$V = \frac{1}{3}Bh$
Trapezoid	$A = \frac{1}{2}h(b + b')$	Cone	$V = \frac{1}{3}\pi r^2 h$
Triangle	$A = \frac{1}{2}bh$	Sphere	$V = \frac{4}{3}\pi r^3$
Sphere	$A = 4\pi r^2$		

Table 2   Units of Measure

Metric System and Approximate US Conversion Factors

Length	10 millimeters (mm) = 1 centimeter (cm) $\doteq$ 0.3937 inch 100 centimeters = 1 meter (m) $\doteq$ 39.37 inches 1000 meters = 1 kilometer (km) $\doteq$ 0.6 mile astronomical unit 1 AU = 1.496 × 10^{11} m wavelength-ångström 1 Å = 10^{-10} m
Area	100 square millimeters (mm²) = 1 square centimeter (cm²) 100 square centimeters = 1 square decimeter (dm²) 100 square decimeters = 1 square meter (m²) 10,000 square meters = 1 hectare (ha) $\doteq$ 2.47 acres
Volume	1000 cubic centimeters (cm³) = 1 liter (1) = 1 cubic decimeter (dm³) 1000 cubic decimeters = 1000 liters = 1 cubic meter (m³)
Capacity	1000 milliliters (ml) = 1 liter (1) $\doteq$ 1.1 quart 1000 liters $\doteq$ 264.2 gallons
Mass	1000 milligrams (mg) = 1 gram (g) $\doteq$ 0.035 ounce 1000 grams = 1 kilogram (kg) $\doteq$ 2.2 pounds 1000 kilograms = 1 tonne (t) $\doteq$ 2200 pounds

Temperature

	Celsius (°C)	Kelvin (°K)	Fahrenheit (°F)
absolute zero	−273.15	0	−459.67
freezing point of water	0	273.15	32
body temperature	37	310.15	98.6
boiling point of water	100	373.15	212

Table 3   Squares and Square Roots

N	N^2	$\sqrt{N}$	$\sqrt{10N}$	N	N^2	$\sqrt{N}$	$\sqrt{10N}$
1.0	1.00	1.000	3.162	**5.5**	30.25	2.345	7.416
1.1	1.21	1.049	3.317	**5.6**	31.36	2.366	7.483
1.2	1.44	1.095	3.464	**5.7**	32.49	2.387	7.550
1.3	1.69	1.140	3.606	**5.8**	33.64	2.408	7.616
1.4	1.96	1.183	3.742	**5.9**	34.81	2.429	7.681
1.5	2.25	1.225	3.873	**6.0**	36.00	2.449	7.746
1.6	2.56	1.265	4.000	**6.1**	37.21	2.470	7.810
1.7	2.89	1.304	4.123	**6.2**	38.44	2.490	7.874
1.8	3.24	1.342	4.243	**6.3**	39.69	2.510	7.937
1.9	3.61	1.378	4.359	**6.4**	40.96	2.530	8.000
2.0	4.00	1.414	4.472	**6.5**	42.25	2.550	8.062
2.1	4.41	1.449	4.583	**6.6**	43.56	2.569	8.124
2.2	4.84	1.483	4.690	**6.7**	44.89	2.588	8.185
2.3	5.29	1.517	4.796	**6.8**	46.24	2.608	8.246
2.4	5.76	1.549	4.899	**6.9**	47.61	2.627	8.307
2.5	6.25	1.581	5.000	**7.0**	49.00	2.646	8.367
2.6	6.76	1.612	5.099	**7.1**	50.41	2.665	8.426
2.7	7.29	1.643	5.196	**7.2**	51.84	2.683	8.485
2.8	7.84	1.673	5.292	**7.3**	53.29	2.702	8.544
2.9	8.41	1.703	5.385	**7.4**	54.76	2.720	8.602
3.0	9.00	1.732	5.477	**7.5**	56.25	2.739	8.660
3.1	9.61	1.761	5.568	**7.6**	57.76	2.757	8.718
3.2	10.24	1.789	5.657	**7.7**	59.29	2.775	8.775
3.3	10.89	1.817	5.745	**7.8**	60.84	2.793	8.832
3.4	11.56	1.844	5.831	**7.9**	62.41	2.811	8.888
3.5	12.25	1.871	5.916	**8.0**	64.00	2.828	8.944
3.6	12.96	1.897	6.000	**8.1**	65.61	2.846	9.000
3.7	13.69	1.924	6.083	**8.2**	67.24	2.864	9.055
3.8	14.44	1.949	6.164	**8.3**	68.89	2.881	9.110
3.9	15.21	1.975	6.245	**8.4**	70.56	2.898	9.165
4.0	16.00	2.000	6.325	**8.5**	72.25	2.915	9.220
4.1	16.81	2.025	6.403	**8.6**	73.96	2.933	9.274
4.2	17.64	2.049	6.481	**8.7**	75.69	2.950	9.327
4.3	18.49	2.074	6.557	**8.8**	77.44	2.966	9.381
4.4	19.36	2.098	6.633	**8.9**	79.21	2.983	9.434
4.5	20.25	2.121	6.708	**9.0**	81.00	3.000	9.487
4.6	21.16	2.145	6.782	**9.1**	82.81	3.017	9.539
4.7	22.09	2.168	6.856	**9.2**	84.64	3.033	9.592
4.8	23.04	2.191	6.928	**9.3**	86.49	3.050	9.644
4.9	24.01	2.214	7.000	**9.4**	88.36	3.066	9.695
5.0	25.00	2.236	7.071	**9.5**	90.25	3.082	9.747
5.1	26.01	2.258	7.141	**9.6**	92.16	3.098	9.798
5.2	27.04	2.280	7.211	**9.7**	94.09	3.114	9.849
5.3	28.09	2.302	7.280	**9.8**	96.04	3.130	9.899
5.4	29.16	2.324	7.348	**9.9**	98.01	3.146	9.950
5.5	30.25	2.345	7.416	**10**	100.00	3.162	10.000

Table 4 Cubes and Cube Roots

N	N^3	$\sqrt[3]{N}$	$\sqrt[3]{10N}$	$\sqrt[3]{100N}$	N	N^3	$\sqrt[3]{N}$	$\sqrt[3]{10N}$	$\sqrt[3]{100N}$
1.0	1.000	1.000	2.154	4.642	5.5	166.375	1.765	3.803	8.193
1.1	1.331	1.032	2.224	4.791	5.6	175.616	1.776	3.826	8.243
1.2	1.728	1.063	2.289	4.932	5.7	185.193	1.786	3.849	8.291
1.3	2.197	1.091	2.351	5.066	5.8	195.112	1.797	3.871	8.340
1.4	2.744	1.119	2.410	5.192	5.9	205.379	1.807	3.893	8.387
1.5	3.375	1.145	2.466	5.313	6.0	216.000	1.817	3.915	8.434
1.6	4.096	1.170	2.520	5.429	6.1	226.981	1.827	3.936	8.481
1.7	4.913	1.193	2.571	5.540	6.2	238.328	1.837	3.958	8.527
1.8	5.832	1.216	2.621	5.646	6.3	250.047	1.847	3.979	8.573
1.9	6.859	1.239	2.668	5.749	6.4	262.144	1.857	4.000	8.618
2.0	8.000	1.260	2.714	5.848	6.5	274.625	1.866	4.021	8.662
2.1	9.261	1.281	2.759	5.944	6.6	287.496	1.876	4.041	8.707
2.2	10.648	1.301	2.802	6.037	6.7	300.763	1.885	4.062	8.750
2.3	12.167	1.320	2.844	6.127	6.8	314.432	1.895	4.082	8.794
2.4	13.824	1.339	2.884	6.214	6.9	328.509	1.904	4.102	8.837
2.5	15.625	1.357	2.924	6.300	7.0	343.000	1.913	4.121	8.879
2.6	17.576	1.375	2.962	6.383	7.1	357.911	1.922	4.141	8.921
2.7	19.683	1.392	3.000	6.463	7.2	373.248	1.931	4.160	8.963
2.8	21.952	1.409	3.037	6.542	7.3	389.017	1.940	4.179	9.004
2.9	24.389	1.426	3.072	6.619	7.4	405.224	1.949	4.198	9.045
3.0	27.000	1.442	3.107	6.694	7.5	421.875	1.957	4.217	9.086
3.1	29.791	1.458	3.141	6.768	7.6	438.976	1.966	4.236	9.126
3.2	32.768	1.474	3.175	6.840	7.7	456.533	1.975	4.254	9.166
3.3	35.937	1.489	3.208	6.910	7.8	474.552	1.983	4.273	9.205
3.4	39.304	1.504	3.240	6.980	7.9	493.039	1.992	4.291	9.244
3.5	42.875	1.518	3.271	7.047	8.0	512.000	2.000	4.309	9.283
3.6	46.656	1.533	3.302	7.114	8.1	531.441	2.008	4.327	9.322
3.7	50.653	1.547	3.332	7.179	8.2	551.368	2.017	4.344	9.360
3.8	54.872	1.560	3.362	7.243	8.3	571.787	2.025	4.362	9.398
3.9	59.319	1.574	3.391	7.306	8.4	592.704	2.033	4.380	9.435
4.0	64.000	1.587	3.420	7.368	8.5	614.125	2.041	4.397	9.473
4.1	68.921	1.601	3.448	7.429	8.6	636.056	2.049	4.414	9.510
4.2	74.088	1.613	3.476	7.489	8.7	658.503	2.057	4.431	9.546
4.3	79.507	1.626	3.503	7.548	8.8	681.472	2.065	4.448	9.583
4.4	85.184	1.639	3.530	7.606	8.9	704.969	2.072	4.465	9.619
4.5	91.125	1.651	3.557	7.663	9.0	729.000	2.080	4.481	9.655
4.6	97.336	1.663	3.583	7.719	9.1	753.571	2.088	4.498	9.691
4.7	103.823	1.675	3.609	7.775	9.2	778.688	2.095	4.514	9.726
4.8	110.592	1.687	3.634	7.830	9.3	804.357	2.103	4.531	9.761
4.9	117.649	1.698	3.659	7.884	9.4	830.584	2.110	4.547	9.796
5.0	125.000	1.710	3.684	7.937	9.5	857.375	2.118	4.563	9.830
5.1	132.651	1.721	3.708	7.990	9.6	884.736	2.125	4.579	9.865
5.2	140.608	1.732	3.733	8.041	9.7	912.673	2.133	4.595	9.899
5.3	148.877	1.744	3.756	8.093	9.8	941.192	2.140	4.610	9.933
5.4	157.464	1.754	3.780	8.143	9.9	970.299	2.147	4.626	9.967
5.5	166.375	1.765	3.803	8.193	10	1000.000	2.154	4.642	10.000

Table 5 Common Logarithms of Numbers*

x	0	1	2	3	4	5	6	7	8	9
10	0000	0043	0086	0128	0170	0212	0253	0294	0334	0374
11	0414	0453	0492	0531	0569	0607	0645	0682	0719	0755
12	0792	0828	0864	0899	0934	0969	1004	1038	1072	1106
13	1139	1173	1206	1239	1271	1303	1335	1367	1399	1430
14	1461	1492	1523	1553	1584	1614	1644	1673	1703	1732
15	1761	1790	1818	1847	1875	1903	1931	1959	1987	2014
16	2041	2068	2095	2122	2148	2175	2201	2227	2253	2279
17	2304	2330	2355	2380	2405	2430	2455	2480	2504	2529
18	2553	2577	2601	2625	2648	2672	2695	2718	2742	2765
19	2788	2810	2833	2856	2878	2900	2923	2945	2967	2989
20	3010	3032	3054	3075	3096	3118	3139	3160	3181	3201
21	3222	3243	3263	3284	3304	3324	3345	3365	3385	3404
22	3424	3444	3464	3483	3502	3522	3541	3560	3579	3598
23	3617	3636	3655	3674	3692	3711	3729	3747	3766	3784
24	3802	3820	3838	3856	3874	3892	3909	3927	3945	3962
25	3979	3997	4014	4031	4048	4065	4082	4099	4116	4133
26	4150	4166	4183	4200	4216	4232	4249	4265	4281	4298
27	4314	4330	4346	4362	4378	4393	4409	4425	4440	4456
28	4472	4487	4502	4518	4533	4548	4564	4579	4594	4609
29	4624	4639	4654	4669	4683	4698	4713	4728	4742	4757
30	4771	4786	4800	4814	4829	4843	4857	4871	4886	4900
31	4914	4928	4942	4955	4969	4983	4997	5011	5024	5038
32	5051	5065	5079	5092	5105	5119	5132	5145	5159	5172
33	5185	5198	5211	5224	5237	5250	5263	5276	5289	5302
34	5315	5328	5340	5353	5366	5378	5391	5403	5416	5428
35	5441	5453	5465	5478	5490	5502	5514	5527	5539	5551
36	5563	5575	5587	5599	5611	5623	5635	5647	5658	5670
37	5682	5694	5705	5717	5729	5740	5752	5763	5775	5786
38	5798	5809	5821	5832	5843	5855	5866	5877	5888	5899
39	5911	5922	5933	5944	5955	5966	5977	5988	5999	6010
40	6021	6031	6042	6053	6064	6075	6085	6096	6107	6117
41	6128	6138	6149	6160	6170	6180	6191	6201	6212	6222
42	6232	6243	6253	6263	6274	6284	6294	6304	6314	6325
43	6335	6345	6355	6365	6375	6385	6395	6405	6415	6425
44	6435	6444	6454	6464	6474	6484	6493	6503	6513	6522
45	6532	6542	6551	6561	6571	6580	6590	6599	6609	6618
46	6628	6637	6646	6656	6665	6675	6684	6693	6702	6712
47	6721	6730	6739	6749	6758	6767	6776	6785	6794	6803
48	6812	6821	6830	6839	6848	6857	6866	6875	6884	6893
49	6902	6911	6920	6928	6937	6946	6955	6964	6972	6981
50	6990	6998	7007	7016	7024	7033	7042	7050	7059	7067
51	7076	7084	7093	7101	7110	7118	7126	7135	7143	7152
52	7160	7168	7177	7185	7193	7202	7210	7218	7226	7235
53	7243	7251	7259	7267	7275	7284	7292	7300	7308	7316
54	7324	7332	7340	7348	7356	7364	7372	7380	7388	7396

*Mantissas, decimal points omitted. Characteristics are found by inspection.

Table 5 Common Logarithms of Numbers

x	0	1	2	3	4	5	6	7	8	9
55	7404	7412	7419	7427	7435	7443	7451	7459	7466	7474
56	7482	7490	7497	7505	7513	7520	7528	7536	7543	7551
57	7559	7566	7574	7582	7589	7597	7604	7612	7619	7627
58	7634	7642	7649	7657	7664	7672	7679	7686	7694	7701
59	7709	7716	7723	7731	7738	7745	7752	7760	7767	7774
60	7782	7789	7796	7803	7810	7818	7825	7832	7839	7846
61	7853	7860	7868	7875	7882	7889	7896	7903	7910	7917
62	7924	7931	7938	7945	7952	7959	7966	7973	7980	7987
63	7993	8000	8007	8014	8021	8028	8035	8041	8048	8055
64	8062	8069	8075	8082	8089	8096	8102	8109	8116	8122
65	8129	8136	8142	8149	8156	8162	8169	8176	8182	8189
66	8195	8202	8209	8215	8222	8228	8235	8241	8248	8254
67	8261	8267	8274	8280	8287	8293	8299	8306	8312	8319
68	8325	8331	8338	8344	8351	8357	8363	8370	8376	8382
69	8388	8395	8401	8407	8414	8420	8426	8432	8439	8445
70	8451	8457	8463	8470	8476	8482	8488	8494	8500	8506
71	8513	8519	8525	8531	8537	8543	8549	8555	8561	8567
72	8573	8579	8585	8591	8597	8603	8609	8615	8621	8627
73	8633	8639	8645	8651	8657	8663	8669	8675	8681	8686
74	8692	8698	8704	8710	8716	8722	8727	8733	8739	8745
75	8751	8756	8762	8768	8774	8779	8785	8791	8797	8802
76	8808	8814	8820	8825	8831	8837	8842	8848	8854	8859
77	8865	8871	8876	8882	8887	8893	8899	8904	8910	8915
78	8921	8927	8932	8938	8943	8949	8954	8960	8965	8971
79	8976	8982	8987	8993	8998	9004	9009	9015	9020	9025
80	9031	9036	9042	9047	9053	9058	9063	9069	9074	9079
81	9085	9090	9096	9101	9106	9112	9117	9122	9128	9133
82	9138	9143	9149	9154	9159	9165	9170	9175	9180	9186
83	9191	9196	9201	9206	9212	9217	9222	9227	9232	9238
84	9243	9248	9253	9258	9263	9269	9274	9279	9284	9289
85	9294	9299	9304	9309	9315	9320	9325	9330	9335	9340
86	9345	9350	9355	9360	9365	9370	9375	9380	9385	9390
87	9395	9400	9405	9410	9415	9420	9425	9430	9435	9440
88	9445	9450	9455	9460	9465	9469	9474	9479	9484	9489
89	9494	9499	9504	9509	9513	9518	9523	9528	9533	9538
90	9542	9547	9552	9557	9562	9566	9571	9576	9581	9586
91	9590	9595	9600	9605	9609	9614	9619	9624	9628	9633
92	9638	9643	9647	9652	9657	9661	9666	9671	9675	9680
93	9685	9689	9694	9699	9703	9708	9713	9717	9722	9727
94	9731	9736	9741	9745	9750	9754	9759	9763	9768	9773
95	9777	9782	9786	9791	9795	9800	9805	9809	9814	9818
96	9823	9827	9832	9836	9841	9845	9850	9854	9859	9863
97	9868	9872	9877	9881	9886	9890	9894	9899	9903	9908
98	9912	9917	9921	9926	9930	9934	9939	9943	9948	9952
99	9956	9961	9965	9969	9974	9978	9983	9987	9991	9996

Table 6   Values of Trigonometric Functions for Angles in Degrees

m(α) Degrees	m(α) Radians	sin α	csc α	tan α	cot α	sec α	cos α		
0° 00′	.0000	.0000	Undefined	.0000	Undefined	1.000	1.0000	1.5708	90° 00′
10′	.0029	.0029	343.8	.0029	343.8	1.000	1.0000	1.5679	50′
20′	.0058	.0058	171.9	.0058	171.9	1.000	1.0000	1.5650	40′
30′	.0087	.0087	114.6	.0087	114.6	1.000	1.0000	1.5621	30′
40′	.0116	.0116	85.95	.0116	85.94	1.000	.9999	1.5592	20′
50′	.0145	.0145	68.76	.0145	68.75	1.000	.9999	1.5563	10′
1° 00′	.0175	.0175	57.30	.0175	57.29	1.000	.9998	1.5533	89° 00′
10′	.0204	.0204	49.11	.0204	49.10	1.000	.9998	1.5504	50′
20′	.0233	.0233	42.98	.0233	42.96	1.000	.9997	1.5475	40′
30′	.0262	.0262	38.20	.0262	38.19	1.000	.9997	1.5446	30′
40′	.0291	.0291	34.38	.0291	34.37	1.000	.9996	1.5417	20′
50′	.0320	.0320	31.26	.0320	31.24	1.001	.9995	1.5388	10′
2° 00′	.0349	.0349	28.65	.0349	28.64	1.001	.9994	1.5359	88° 00′
10′	.0378	.0378	26.45	.0378	26.43	1.001	.9993	1.5330	50′
20′	.0407	.0407	24.56	.0407	24.54	1.001	.9992	1.5301	40′
30′	.0436	.0436	22.93	.0437	22.90	1.001	.9990	1.5272	30′
40′	.0465	.0465	21.49	.0466	21.47	1.001	.9989	1.5243	20′
50′	.0495	.0494	20.23	.0495	20.21	1.001	.9988	1.5213	10′
3° 00′	.0524	.0523	19.11	.0524	19.08	1.001	.9986	1.5184	87° 00′
10′	.0553	.0552	18.10	.0553	18.07	1.002	.9985	1.5155	50′
20′	.0582	.0581	17.20	.0582	17.17	1.002	.9983	1.5126	40′
30′	.0611	.0610	16.38	.0612	16.35	1.002	.9981	1.5097	30′
40′	.0640	.0640	15.64	.0641	15.60	1.002	.9980	1.5068	20′
50′	.0669	.0669	14.96	.0670	14.92	1.002	.9978	1.5039	10′
4° 00′	.0698	.0698	14.34	.0699	14.30	1.002	.9976	1.5010	86° 00′
10′	.0727	.0727	13.76	.0729	13.73	1.003	.9974	1.4981	50′
20′	.0756	.0756	13.23	.0758	13.20	1.003	.9971	1.4952	40′
30′	.0785	.0785	12.75	.0787	12.71	1.003	.9969	1.4923	30′
40′	.0814	.0814	12.29	.0816	12.25	1.003	.9967	1.4893	20′
50′	.0844	.0843	11.87	.0846	11.83	1.004	.9964	1.4864	10′
5° 00′	.0873	.0872	11.47	.0875	11.43	1.004	.9962	1.4835	85° 00′
10′	.0902	.0901	11.10	.0904	11.06	1.004	.9959	1.4806	50′
20′	.0931	.0929	10.76	.0934	10.71	1.004	.9957	1.4777	40′
30′	.0960	.0958	10.43	.0963	10.39	1.005	.9954	1.4748	30′
40′	.0989	.0987	10.13	.0992	10.08	1.005	.9951	1.4719	20′
50′	.1018	.1016	9.839	.1022	9.788	1.005	.9948	1.4690	10′
6° 00′	.1047	.1045	9.567	.1051	9.514	1.006	.9945	1.4661	84° 00′
10′	.1076	.1074	9.309	.1080	9.255	1.006	.9942	1.4632	50′
20′	.1105	.1103	9.065	.1110	9.010	1.006	.9939	1.4603	40′
30′	.1134	.1132	8.834	.1139	8.777	1.006	.9936	1.4573	30′
40′	.1164	.1161	8.614	.1169	8.556	1.007	.9932	1.4544	20′
50′	.1193	.1190	8.405	.1198	8.345	1.007	.9929	1.4515	10′
7° 00′	.1222	.1219	8.206	.1228	8.144	1.008	.9925	1.4486	83° 00′
10′	.1251	.1248	8.016	.1257	7.953	1.008	.9922	1.4457	50′
20′	.1280	.1276	7.834	.1287	7.770	1.008	.9918	1.4428	40′
30′	.1309	.1305	7.661	.1317	7.596	1.009	.9914	1.4399	30′
40′	.1338	.1334	7.496	.1346	7.429	1.009	.9911	1.4370	20′
50′	.1367	.1363	7.337	.1376	7.269	1.009	.9907	1.4341	10′
8° 00′	.1396	.1392	7.185	.1405	7.115	1.010	.9903	1.4312	82° 00′
10′	.1425	.1421	7.040	.1435	6.968	1.010	.9899	1.4283	50′
20′	.1454	.1449	6.900	.1465	6.827	1.011	.9894	1.4254	40′
30′	.1484	.1478	6.765	.1495	6.691	1.011	.9890	1.4224	30′
40′	.1513	.1507	6.636	.1524	6.561	1.012	.9886	1.4195	20′
50′	.1542	.1536	6.512	.1554	6.435	1.012	.9881	1.4166	10′
9° 00′	.1571	.1564	6.392	.1584	6.314	1.012	.9877	1.4137	81° 00′
		cos α	sec α	cot α	tan α	csc α	sin α	Radians	Degrees

m(α)

Table 6 Values of Trigonometric Functions for Angles in Degrees

m(α) Degrees	m(α) Radians	sin α	csc α	tan α	cot α	sec α	cos α		
9° 00′	.1571	.1564	6.392	.1584	6.314	1.012	.9877	1.4137	81° 00′
10′	.1600	.1593	6.277	.1614	6.197	1.013	.9872	1.4108	50′
20′	.1629	.1622	6.166	.1644	6.084	1.013	.9868	1.4079	40′
30′	.1658	.1650	6.059	.1673	5.976	1.014	.9863	1.4050	30′
40′	.1687	.1679	5.955	.1703	5.871	1.014	.9858	1.4021	20′
50′	.1716	.1708	5.855	.1733	5.769	1.015	.9853	1.3992	10′
10° 00′	.1745	.1736	5.759	.1763	5.671	1.015	.9848	1.3963	80° 00′
10′	.1774	.1765	5.665	.1793	5.576	1.016	.9843	1.3934	50′
20′	.1804	.1794	5.575	.1823	5.485	1.016	.9838	1.3904	40′
30′	.1833	.1822	5.487	.1853	5.396	1.017	.9833	1.3875	30′
40′	.1862	.1851	5.403	.1883	5.309	1.018	.9827	1.3846	20′
50′	.1891	.1880	5.320	.1914	5.226	1.018	.9822	1.3817	10′
11° 00′	.1920	.1908	5.241	.1944	5.145	1.019	.9816	1.3788	79° 00′
10′	.1949	.1937	5.164	.1974	5.066	1.019	.9811	1.3759	50′
20′	.1978	.1965	5.089	.2004	4.989	1.020	.9805	1.3730	40′
30′	.2007	.1994	5.016	.2035	4.915	1.020	.9799	1.3701	30′
40′	.2036	.2022	4.945	.2065	4.843	1.021	.9793	1.3672	20′
50′	.2065	.2051	4.876	.2095	4.773	1.022	.9787	1.3643	10′
12° 00′	.2094	.2079	4.810	.2126	4.705	1.022	.9781	1.3614	78° 00′
10′	.2123	.2108	4.745	.2156	4.638	1.023	.9775	1.3584	50′
20′	.2153	.2136	4.682	.2186	4.574	1.024	.9769	1.3555	40′
30′	.2182	.2164	4.620	.2217	4.511	1.024	.9763	1.3526	30′
40′	.2211	.2193	4.560	.2247	4.449	1.025	.9757	1.3497	20′
50′	.2240	.2221	4.502	.2278	4.390	1.026	.9750	1.3468	10′
13° 00′	.2269	.2250	4.445	.2309	4.331	1.026	.9744	1.3439	77° 00′
10′	.2298	.2278	4.390	.2339	4.275	1.027	.9737	1.3410	50′
20′	.2327	.2306	4.336	.2370	4.219	1.028	.9730	1.3381	40′
30′	.2356	.2334	4.284	.2401	4.165	1.028	.9724	1.3352	30′
40′	.2385	.2363	4.232	.2432	4.113	1.029	.9717	1.3323	20′
50′	.2414	.2391	4.182	.2462	4.061	1.030	.9710	1.3294	10′
14° 00′	.2443	.2419	4.134	.2493	4.011	1.031	.9703	1.3265	76° 00′
10′	.2473	.2447	4.086	.2524	3.962	1.031	.9696	1.3235	50′
20′	.2502	.2476	4.039	.2555	3.914	1.032	.9689	1.3206	40′
30′	.2531	.2504	3.994	.2586	3.867	1.033	.9681	1.3177	30′
40′	.2560	.2532	3.950	.2617	3.821	1.034	.9674	1.3148	20′
50′	.2589	.2560	3.906	.2648	3.776	1.034	.9667	1.3119	10′
15° 00′	.2618	.2588	3.864	.2679	3.732	1.035	.9659	1.3090	75° 00′
10′	.2647	.2616	3.822	.2711	3.689	1.036	.9652	1.3061	50′
20′	.2676	.2644	3.782	.2742	3.647	1.037	.9644	1.3032	40′
30′	.2705	.2672	3.742	.2773	3.606	1.038	.9636	1.3003	30′
40′	.2734	.2700	3.703	.2805	3.566	1.039	.9628	1.2974	20′
50′	.2763	.2728	3.665	.2836	3.526	1.039	.9621	1.2945	10′
16° 00′	.2793	.2756	3.628	.2867	3.487	1.040	.9613	1.2915	74° 00′
10′	.2822	.2784	3.592	.2899	3.450	1.041	.9605	1.2886	50′
20′	.2851	.2812	3.556	.2931	3.412	1.042	.9596	1.2857	40′
30′	.2880	.2840	3.521	.2962	3.376	1.043	.9588	1.2828	30′
40′	.2909	.2868	3.487	.2994	3.340	1.044	.9580	1.2799	20′
50′	.2938	.2896	3.453	.3026	3.305	1.045	.9572	1.2770	10′
17° 00′	.2967	.2924	3.420	.3057	3.271	1.046	.9563	1.2741	73° 00′
10′	.2996	.2952	3.388	.3089	3.237	1.047	.9555	1.2712	50′
20′	.3025	.2979	3.357	.3121	3.204	1.048	.9546	1.2683	40′
30′	.3054	.3007	3.326	.3153	3.172	1.049	.9537	1.2654	30′
40′	.3083	.3035	3.295	.3185	3.140	1.049	.9528	1.2625	20′
50′	.3113	.3062	3.265	.3217	3.108	1.050	.9520	1.2595	10′
18° 00′	.3142	.3090	3.236	.3249	3.078	1.051	.9511	1.2566	72° 00′
		cos α	sec α	cot α	tan α	csc α	sin α	Radians	Degrees
									m(α)

Table 6 Values of Trigonometric Functions for Angles in Degrees

m(α) Degrees	Radians	sin α	csc α	tan α	cot α	sec α	cos α		
18° 00′	.3142	.3090	3.236	.3249	3.078	1.051	.9511	1.2566	72° 00′
10′	.3171	.3118	3.207	.3281	3.047	1.052	.9502	1.2537	50′
20′	.3200	.3145	3.179	.3314	3.018	1.053	.9492	1.2508	40′
30′	.3229	.3173	3.152	.3346	2.989	1.054	.9483	1.2479	30′
40′	.3258	.3201	3.124	.3378	2.960	1.056	.9474	1.2450	20′
50′	.3287	.3228	3.098	.3411	2.932	1.057	.9465	1.2421	10′
19° 00′	.3316	.3256	3.072	.3443	2.904	1.058	.9455	1.2392	71° 00′
10′	.3345	.3283	3.046	.3476	2.877	1.059	.9446	1.2363	50′
20′	.3374	.3311	3.021	.3508	2.850	1.060	.9436	1.2334	40′
30′	.3403	.3338	2.996	.3541	2.824	1.061	.9426	1.2305	30′
40′	.3432	.3365	2.971	.3574	2.798	1.062	.9417	1.2275	20′
50′	.3462	.3393	2.947	.3607	2.773	1.063	.9407	1.2246	10′
20° 00′	.3491	.3420	2.924	.3640	2.747	1.064	.9397	1.2217	70° 00′
10′	.3520	.3448	2.901	.3673	2.723	1.065	.9387	1.2188	50′
20′	.3549	.3475	2.878	.3706	2.699	1.066	.9377	1.2159	40′
30′	.3578	.3502	2.855	.3739	2.675	1.068	.9367	1.2130	30′
40′	.3607	.3529	2.833	.3772	2.651	1.069	.9356	1.2101	20′
50′	.3636	.3557	2.812	.3805	2.628	1.070	.9346	1.2072	10′
21° 00′	.3665	.3584	2.790	.3839	2.605	1.071	.9336	1.2043	69° 00′
10′	.3694	.3611	2.769	.3872	2.583	1.072	.9325	1.2014	50′
20′	.3723	.3638	2.749	.3906	2.560	1.074	.9315	1.1985	40′
30′	.3752	.3665	2.729	.3939	2.539	1.075	.9304	1.1956	30′
40′	.3782	.3692	2.709	.3973	2.517	1.076	.9293	1.1926	20′
50′	.3811	.3719	2.689	.4006	2.496	1.077	.9283	1.1897	10′
22° 00′	.3840	.3746	2.669	.4040	2.475	1.079	.9272	1.1868	68° 00′
10′	.3869	.3773	2.650	.4074	2.455	1.080	.9261	1.1839	50′
20′	.3898	.3800	2.632	.4108	2.434	1.081	.9250	1.1810	40′
30′	.3927	.3827	2.613	.4142	2.414	1.082	.9239	1.1781	30′
40′	.3956	.3854	2.595	.4176	2.394	1.084	.9228	1.1752	20′
50′	.3985	.3881	2.577	.4210	2.375	1.085	.9216	1.1723	10′
23° 00′	.4014	.3907	2.559	.4245	2.356	1.086	.9205	1.1694	67° 00′
10′	.4043	.3934	2.542	.4279	2.337	1.088	.9194	1.1665	50′
20′	.4072	.3961	2.525	.4314	2.318	1.089	.9182	1.1636	40′
30′	.4102	.3987	2.508	.4348	2.300	1.090	.9171	1.1606	30′
40′	.4131	.4014	2.491	.4383	2.282	1.092	.9159	1.1577	20′
50′	.4160	.4041	2.475	.4417	2.264	1.093	.9147	1.1548	10′
24° 00′	.4189	.4067	2.459	.4452	2.246	1.095	.9135	1.1519	66° 00′
10′	.4218	.4094	2.443	.4487	2.229	1.096	.9124	1.1490	50′
20′	.4247	.4120	2.427	.4522	2.211	1.097	.9112	1.1461	40′
30′	.4276	.4147	2.411	.4557	2.194	1.099	.9100	1.1432	30′
40′	.4305	.4173	2.396	.4592	2.177	1.100	.9088	1.1403	20′
50′	.4334	.4200	2.381	.4628	2.161	1.102	.9075	1.1374	10′
25° 00′	.4363	.4226	2.366	.4663	2.145	1.103	.9063	1.1345	65° 00′
10′	.4392	.4253	2.352	.4699	2.128	1.105	.9051	1.1316	50′
20′	.4422	.4279	2.337	.4734	2.112	1.106	.9038	1.1286	40′
30′	.4451	.4305	2.323	.4770	2.097	1.108	.9026	1.1257	30′
40′	.4480	.4331	2.309	.4806	2.081	1.109	.9013	1.1228	20′
50′	.4509	.4358	2.295	.4841	2.066	1.111	.9001	1.1199	10′
26° 00′	.4538	.4384	2.281	.4877	2.050	1.113	.8988	1.1170	64° 00′
10′	.4567	.4410	2.268	.4913	2.035	1.114	.8975	1.1141	50′
20′	.4596	.4436	2.254	.4950	2.020	1.116	.8962	1.1112	40′
30′	.4625	.4462	2.241	.4986	2.006	1.117	.8949	1.1083	30′
40′	.4654	.4488	2.228	.5022	1.991	1.119	.8936	1.1054	20′
50′	.4683	.4514	2.215	.5059	1.977	1.121	.8923	1.1025	10′
27° 00′	.4712	.4540	2.203	.5095	1.963	1.122	.8910	1.0996	63° 00′
		cos α	sec α	cot α	tan α	csc α	sin α	Radians	Degrees
									m(α)

Table 6 Values of Trigonometric Functions for Angles in Degrees

m(α) Degrees	m(α) Radians	sin α	csc α	tan α	cot α	sec α	cos α		
27° 00′	.4712	.4540	2.203	.5095	1.963	1.122	.8910	1.0996	63° 00′
10′	.4741	.4566	2.190	.5132	1.949	1.124	.8897	1.0966	50′
20′	.4771	.4592	2.178	.5169	1.935	1.126	.8884	1.0937	40′
30′	.4800	.4617	2.166	.5206	1.921	1.127	.8870	1.0908	30′
40′	.4829	.4643	2.154	.5243	1.907	1.129	.8857	1.0879	20′
50′	.4858	.4669	2.142	.5280	1.894	1.131	.8843	1.0850	10′
28° 00′	.4887	.4695	2.130	.5317	1.881	1.133	.8829	1.0821	62° 00′
10′	.4916	.4720	2.118	.5354	1.868	1.134	.8816	1.0792	50′
20′	.4945	.4746	2.107	.5392	1.855	1.136	.8802	1.0763	40′
30′	.4974	.4772	2.096	.5430	1.842	1.138	.8788	1.0734	30′
40′	.5003	.4797	2.085	.5467	1.829	1.140	.8774	1.0705	20′
50′	.5032	.4823	2.074	.5505	1.816	1.142	.8760	1.0676	10′
29° 00′	.5061	.4848	2.063	.5543	1.804	1.143	.8746	1.0647	61° 00′
10′	.5091	.4874	2.052	.5581	1.792	1.145	.8732	1.0617	50′
20′	.5120	.4899	2.041	.5619	1.780	1.147	.8718	1.0588	40′
30′	.5149	.4924	2.031	.5658	1.767	1.149	.8704	1.0559	30′
40′	.5178	.4950	2.020	.5696	1.756	1.151	.8689	1.0530	20′
50′	.5207	.4975	2.010	.5735	1.744	1.153	.8675	1.0501	10′
30° 00′	.5236	.5000	2.000	.5774	1.732	1.155	.8660	1.0472	60° 00′
10′	.5265	.5025	1.990	.5812	1.720	1.157	.8646	1.0443	50′
20′	.5294	.5050	1.980	.5851	1.709	1.159	.8631	1.0414	40′
30′	.5323	.5075	1.970	.5890	1.698	1.161	.8616	1.0385	30′
40′	.5352	.5100	1.961	.5930	1.686	1.163	.8601	1.0356	20′
50′	.5381	.5125	1.951	.5969	1.675	1.165	.8587	1.0327	10′
31° 00′	.5411	.5150	1.942	.6009	1.664	1.167	.8572	1.0297	59° 00′
10′	.5440	.5175	1.932	.6048	1.653	1.169	.8557	1.0268	50′
20′	.5469	.5200	1.923	.6088	1.643	1.171	.8542	1.0239	40′
30′	.5498	.5225	1.914	.6128	1.632	1.173	.8526	1.0210	30′
40′	.5527	.5250	1.905	.6168	1.621	1.175	.8511	1.0181	20′
50′	.5556	.5275	1.896	.6208	1.611	1.177	.8496	1.0152	10′
32° 00′	.5585	.5299	1.887	.6249	1.600	1.179	.8480	1.0123	58° 00′
10′	.5614	.5324	1.878	.6289	1.590	1.181	.8465	1.0094	50′
20′	.5643	.5348	1.870	.6330	1.580	1.184	.8450	1.0065	40′
30′	.5672	.5373	1.861	.6371	1.570	1.186	.8434	1.0036	30′
40′	.5701	.5398	1.853	.6412	1.560	1.188	.8418	1.0007	20′
50′	.5730	.5422	1.844	.6453	1.550	1.190	.8403	.9977	10′
33° 00′	.5760	.5446	1.836	.6494	1.540	1.192	.8387	.9948	57° 00′
10′	.5789	.5471	1.828	.6536	1.530	1.195	.8371	.9919	50′
20′	.5818	.5495	1.820	.6577	1.520	1.197	.8355	.9890	40′
30′	.5847	.5519	1.812	.6619	1.511	1.199	.8339	.9861	30′
40′	.5876	.5544	1.804	.6661	1.501	1.202	.8323	.9832	20′
50′	.5905	.5568	1.796	.6703	1.492	1.204	.8307	.9803	10′
34° 00′	.5934	.5592	1.788	.6745	1.483	1.206	.8290	.9774	56° 00′
10′	.5963	.5616	1.781	.6787	1.473	1.209	.8274	.9745	50′
20′	.5992	.5640	1.773	.6830	1.464	1.211	.8258	.9716	40′
30′	.6021	.5664	1.766	.6873	1.455	1.213	.8241	.9687	30′
40′	.6050	.5688	1.758	.6916	1.446	1.216	.8225	.9657	20′
50′	.6080	.5712	1.751	.6959	1.437	1.218	.8208	.9628	10′
35° 00′	.6109	.5736	1.743	.7002	1.428	1.221	.8192	.9599	55° 00′
10′	.6138	.5760	1.736	.7046	1.419	1.223	.8175	.9570	50′
20′	.6167	.5783	1.729	.7089	1.411	1.226	.8158	.9541	40′
30′	.6196	.5807	1.722	.7133	1.402	1.228	.8141	.9512	30′
40′	.6225	.5831	1.715	.7177	1.393	1.231	.8124	.9483	20′
50′	.6254	.5854	1.708	.7221	1.385	1.233	.8107	.9454	10′
36° 00′	.6283	.5878	1.701	.7265	1.376	1.236	.8090	.9425	54° 00′
		cos α	sec α	cot α	tan α	csc α	sin α	Radians	Degrees
								m(α)	

Table 6   Values of Trigonometric Functions for Angles in Degrees

m(α) Degrees	Radians	sin α	csc α	tan α	cot α	sec α	cos α		
36° 00'	.6283	.5878	1.701	.7265	1.376	1.236	.8090	.9425	54° 00'
10'	.6312	.5901	1.695	.7310	1.368	1.239	.8073	.9396	50'
20'	.6341	.5925	1.688	.7355	1.360	1.241	.8056	.9367	40'
30'	.6370	.5948	1.681	.7400	1.351	1.244	.8039	.9338	30'
40'	.6400	.5972	1.675	.7445	1.343	1.247	.8021	.9308	20'
50'	.6429	.5995	1.668	.7490	1.335	1.249	.8004	.9279	10'
37° 00'	.6458	.6018	1.662	.7536	1.327	1.252	.7986	.9250	53° 00'
10'	.6487	.6041	1.655	.7581	1.319	1.255	.7969	.9221	50'
20'	.6516	.6065	1.649	.7627	1.311	1.258	.7951	.9192	40'
30'	.6545	.6088	1.643	.7673	1.303	1.260	.7934	.9163	30'
40'	.6574	.6111	1.636	.7720	1.295	1.263	.7916	.9134	20'
50'	.6603	.6134	1.630	.7766	1.288	1.266	.7898	.9105	10'
38° 00'	.6632	.6157	1.624	.7813	1.280	1.269	.7880	.9076	52° 00'
10'	.6661	.6180	1.618	.7860	1.272	1.272	.7862	.9047	50'
20'	.6690	.6202	1.612	.7907	1.265	1.275	.7844	.9018	40'
30'	.6720	.6225	1.606	.7954	1.257	1.278	.7826	.8988	30'
40'	.6749	.6248	1.601	.8002	1.250	1.281	.7808	.8959	20'
50'	.6778	.6271	1.595	.8050	1.242	1.284	.7790	.8930	10'
39° 00'	.6807	.6293	1.589	.8098	1.235	1.287	.7771	.8901	51° 00'
10'	.6836	.6316	1.583	.8146	1.228	1.290	.7753	.8872	50'
20'	.6865	.6338	1.578	.8195	1.220	1.293	.7735	.8843	40'
30'	.6894	.6361	1.572	.8243	1.213	1.296	.7716	.8814	30'
40'	.6923	.6383	1.567	.8292	1.206	1.299	.7698	.8785	20'
50'	.6952	.6406	1.561	.8342	1.199	1.302	.7679	.8756	10'
40° 00'	.6981	.6428	1.556	.8391	1.192	1.305	.7660	.8727	50° 00'
10'	.7010	.6450	1.550	.8441	1.185	1.309	.7642	.8698	50'
20'	.7039	.6472	1.545	.8491	1.178	1.312	.7623	.8668	40'
30'	.7069	.6494	1.540	.8541	1.171	1.315	.7604	.8639	30'
40'	.7098	.6517	1.535	.8591	1.164	1.318	.7585	.8610	20'
50'	.7127	.6539	1.529	.8642	1.157	1.322	.7566	.8581	10'
41° 00'	.7156	.6561	1.524	.8693	1.150	1.325	.7547	.8552	49° 00'
10'	.7185	.6583	1.519	.8744	1.144	1.328	.7528	.8523	50'
20'	.7214	.6604	1.514	.8796	1.137	1.332	.7509	.8494	40'
30'	.7243	.6626	1.509	.8847	1.130	1.335	.7490	.8465	30'
40'	.7272	.6648	1.504	.8899	1.124	1.339	.7470	.8436	20'
50'	.7301	.6670	1.499	.8952	1.117	1.342	.7451	.8407	10'
42° 00'	.7330	.6691	1.494	.9004	1.111	1.346	.7431	.8378	48° 00'
10'	.7359	.6713	1.490	.9057	1.104	1.349	.7412	.8348	50'
20'	.7389	.6734	1.485	.9110	1.098	1.353	.7392	.8319	40'
30'	.7418	.6756	1.480	.9163	1.091	1.356	.7373	.8290	30'
40'	.7447	.6777	1.476	.9217	1.085	1.360	.7353	.8261	20'
50'	.7476	.6799	1.471	.9271	1.079	1.364	.7333	.8232	10'
43° 00'	.7505	.6820	1.466	.9325	1.072	1.367	.7314	.8203	47° 00'
10'	.7534	.6841	1.462	.9380	1.066	1.371	.7294	.8174	50'
20'	.7563	.6862	1.457	.9435	1.060	1.375	.7274	.8145	40'
30'	.7592	.6884	1.453	.9490	1.054	1.379	.7254	.8116	30'
40'	.7621	.6905	1.448	.9545	1.048	1.382	.7234	.8087	20'
50'	.7650	.6926	1.444	.9601	1.042	1.386	.7214	.8058	10'
44° 00'	.7679	.6947	1.440	.9657	1.036	1.390	.7193	.8029	46° 00'
10'	.7709	.6967	1.435	.9713	1.030	1.394	.7173	.7999	50'
20'	.7738	.6988	1.431	.9770	1.024	1.398	.7153	.7970	40'
30'	.7767	.7009	1.427	.9827	1.018	1.402	.7133	.7941	30'
40'	.7796	.7030	1.423	.9884	1.012	1.406	.7112	.7912	20'
50'	.7825	.7050	1.418	.9942	1.006	1.410	.7092	.7883	10'
45° 00'	.7854	.7071	1.414	1.000	1.000	1.414	.7071	.7854	45° 00'
		cos α	sec α	cot α	tan α	csc α	sin α	Radians	Degrees
								m(α)	

Table 7　Values of Circular Functions and Trigonometric Functions for Angles in Radians

Real Number x or $m^R(\alpha)$	$m(\alpha)$	sin x or sin α	csc x or csc α	tan x or tan α	cot x or cot α	sec x or sec α	cos x or cos α
0	0°	0	Undefined	0	Undefined	1	1
0.01	0° 34′	0.0100	100.0	0.0100	100.0	1.000	1.000
.02	1° 09′	.0200	50.00	.0200	49.99	1.000	0.9998
.03	1° 43′	.0300	33.34	.0300	33.32	1.000	0.9996
.04	2° 18′	.0400	25.01	.0400	24.99	1.001	0.9992
0.05	2° 52′	0.0500	20.01	0.0500	19.98	1.001	0.9988
.06	3° 26′	.0600	16.68	.0601	16.65	1.002	.9982
.07	4° 01′	.0699	14.30	.0701	14.26	1.002	.9976
.08	4° 35′	.0799	12.51	.0802	12.47	1.003	.9968
.09	5° 09′	.0899	11.13	.0902	11.08	1.004	.9960
0.10	5° 44′	0.0998	10.02	0.1003	9.967	1.005	0.9950
.11	6° 18′	.1098	9.109	.1104	9.054	1.006	.9940
.12	6° 53′	.1197	8.353	.1206	8.293	1.007	.9928
.13	7° 27′	.1296	7.714	.1307	7.649	1.009	.9916
.14	8° 01′	.1395	7.166	.1409	7.096	1.010	.9902
0.15	8° 36′	0.1494	6.692	0.1511	6.617	1.011	0.9888
.16	9° 10′	.1593	6.277	.1614	6.197	1.013	.9872
.17	9° 44′	.1692	5.911	.1717	5.826	1.015	.9856
.18	10° 19′	.1790	5.586	.1820	5.495	1.016	.9838
.19	10° 53′	.1889	5.295	.1923	5.200	1.018	.9820
0.20	11° 28′	0.1987	5.033	0.2027	4.933	1.020	0.9801
.21	12° 02′	.2085	4.797	.2131	4.692	1.022	.9780
.22	12° 36′	.2182	4.582	.2236	4.472	1.025	.9759
.23	13° 11′	.2280	4.386	.2341	4.271	1.027	.9737
.24	13° 45′	.2377	4.207	.2447	4.086	1.030	.9713
0.25	14° 19′	0.2474	4.042	0.2553	3.916	1.032	0.9689
.26	14° 54′	.2571	3.890	.2660	3.759	1.035	.9664
.27	15° 28′	.2667	3.749	.2768	3.613	1.038	.9638
.28	16° 03′	.2764	3.619	.2876	3.478	1.041	.9611
.29	16° 37′	.2860	3.497	.2984	3.351	1.044	.9582
0.30	17° 11′	0.2955	3.384	0.3093	3.233	1.047	0.9553
.31	17° 46′	.3051	3.278	.3203	3.122	1.050	.9523
.32	18° 20′	.3146	3.179	.3314	3.018	1.053	.9492
.33	18° 55′	.3240	3.086	.3425	2.920	1.057	.9460
.34	19° 29′	.3335	2.999	.3537	2.827	1.061	.9428
0.35	20° 03′	0.3429	2.916	0.3650	2.740	1.065	0.9394
.36	20° 38′	.3523	2.839	.3764	2.657	1.068	.9359
.37	21° 12′	.3616	2.765	.3879	2.578	1.073	.9323
.38	21° 46′	.3709	2.696	.3994	2.504	1.077	.9287
.39	22° 21′	.3802	2.630	.4111	2.433	1.081	.9249
0.40	22° 55′	0.3894	2.568	0.4228	2.365	1.086	0.9211
.41	23° 30′	.3986	2.509	.4346	2.301	1.090	.9171
.42	24° 04′	.4078	2.452	.4466	2.239	1.095	.9131
.43	24° 38′	.4169	2.399	.4586	2.180	1.100	.9090
.44	25° 13′	.4259	2.348	.4708	2.124	1.105	.9048
0.45	25° 47′	0.4350	2.299	0.4831	2.070	1.111	0.9004
.46	26° 21′	.4439	2.253	.4954	2.018	1.116	.8961
.47	26° 56′	.4529	2.208	.5080	1.969	1.122	.8916
.48	27° 30′	.4618	2.166	.5206	1.921	1.127	.8870
.49	28° 05′	.4706	2.125	.5334	1.875	1.133	.8823

Table 7   Values of Circular Functions and Trigonometric Functions for Angles in Radians

Real Number x or $m^R(\alpha)$	$m(\alpha)$	sin x or sin α	csc x or csc α	tan x or tan α	cot x or cot α	sec x or sec α	cos x or cos α
0.50	28° 39′	0.4794	2.086	0.5463	1.830	1.139	0.8776
.51	29° 13′	.4882	2.048	.5594	1.788	1.146	.8727
.52	29° 48′	.4969	2.013	.5726	1.747	1.152	.8678
.53	30° 22′	.5055	1.978	.5859	1.707	1.159	.8628
.54	30° 56′	.5141	1.945	.5994	1.668	1.166	.8577
0.55	31° 31′	0.5227	1.913	0.6131	1.631	1.173	0.8525
.56	32° 05′	.5312	1.883	.6269	1.595	1.180	.8473
.57	32° 40′	.5396	1.853	.6410	1.560	1.188	.8419
.58	33° 14′	.5480	1.825	.6552	1.526	1.196	.8365
.59	33° 48′	.5564	1.797	.6696	1.494	1.203	.8309
0.60	34° 23′	0.5646	1.771	0.6841	1.462	1.212	0.8253
.61	34° 57′	.5729	1.746	.6989	1.431	1.220	.8196
.62	35° 31′	.5810	1.721	.7139	1.401	1.229	.8139
.63	36° 06′	.5891	1.697	.7291	1.372	1.238	.8080
.64	36° 40′	.5972	1.674	.7445	1.343	1.247	.8021
0.65	37° 15′	0.6052	1.652	0.7602	1.315	1.256	0.7961
.66	37° 49′	.6131	1.631	.7761	1.288	1.266	.7900
.67	38° 23′	.6210	1.610	.7923	1.262	1.276	.7838
.68	38° 58′	.6288	1.590	.8087	1.237	1.286	.7776
.69	39° 32′	.6365	1.571	.8253	1.212	1.297	.7712
0.70	40° 06′	0.6442	1.552	0.8423	1.187	1.307	0.7648
.71	40° 41′	.6518	1.534	.8595	1.163	1.319	.7584
.72	41° 15′	.6594	1.517	.8771	1.140	1.330	.7518
.73	41° 50′	.6669	1.500	.8949	1.117	1.342	.7452
.74	42° 24′	.6743	1.483	.9131	1.095	1.354	.7385
0.75	42° 58′	0.6816	1.467	0.9316	1.073	1.367	0.7317
.76	43° 33′	.6889	1.452	.9505	1.052	1.380	.7248
.77	44° 07′	.6961	1.437	.9697	1.031	1.393	.7179
.78	44° 41′	.7033	1.422	.9893	1.011	1.407	.7109
.79	45° 16′	.7104	1.408	1.009	.9908	1.421	.7038
0.80	45° 50′	0.7174	1.394	1.030	0.9712	1.435	0.6967
.81	46° 25′	.7243	1.381	1.050	.9520	1.450	.6895
.82	46° 59′	.7311	1.368	1.072	.9331	1.466	.6822
.83	47° 33′	.7379	1.355	1.093	.9146	1.482	.6749
.84	48° 08′	.7446	1.343	1.116	.8964	1.498	.6675
0.85	48° 42′	0.7513	1.331	1.138	0.8785	1.515	0.6600
.86	49° 17′	.7578	1.320	1.162	.8609	1.533	.6524
.87	49° 51′	.7643	1.308	1.185	.8437	1.551	.6448
.88	50° 25′	.7707	1.297	1.210	.8267	1.569	.6372
.89	51° 00′	.7771	1.287	1.235	.8100	1.589	.6294
0.90	51° 34′	0.7833	1.277	1.260	0.7936	1.609	0.6216
.91	52° 08′	.7895	1.267	1.286	.7774	1.629	.6137
.92	52° 43′	.7956	1.257	1.313	.7615	1.651	.6058
.93	53° 17′	.8016	1.247	1.341	.7458	1.673	.5978
.94	53° 52′	.8076	1.238	1.369	.7303	1.696	.5898
0.95	54° 26′	0.8134	1.229	1.398	0.7151	1.719	0.5817
.96	55° 00′	.8192	1.221	1.428	.7001	1.744	.5735
.97	55° 35′	.8249	1.212	1.459	.6853	1.769	.5653
.98	56° 09′	.8305	1.204	1.491	.6707	1.795	.5570
.99	56° 43′	.8360	1.196	1.524	.6563	1.823	.5487

Table 7 Values of Circular Functions and Trigonometric Functions for Angles in Radians

Real Number x or $m^R(\alpha)$	$m(\alpha)$	sin x or sin α	csc x or csc α	tan x or tan α	cot x or cot α	sec x or sec α	cos x or cos α
1.00	57° 18′	0.8415	1.188	1.557	0.6421	1.851	0.5403
1.01	57° 52′	.8468	1.181	1.592	.6281	1.880	.5319
1.02	58° 27′	.8521	1.174	1.628	.6142	1.911	.5234
1.03	59° 01′	.8573	1.166	1.665	.6005	1.942	.5148
1.04	59° 35′	.8624	1.160	1.704	.5870	1.975	.5062
1.05	60° 10′	0.8674	1.153	1.743	0.5736	2.010	0.4976
1.06	60° 44′	.8724	1.146	1.784	.5604	2.046	.4889
1.07	61° 18′	.8772	1.140	1.827	.5473	2.083	.4801
1.08	61° 53′	.8820	1.134	1.871	.5344	2.122	.4713
1.09	62° 27′	.8866	1.128	1.917	.5216	2.162	.4625
1.10	63° 02′	0.8912	1.122	1.965	0.5090	2.205	0.4536
1.11	63° 36′	.8957	1.116	2.014	.4964	2.249	.4447
1.12	64° 10′	.9001	1.111	2.066	.4840	2.295	.4357
1.13	64° 45′	.9044	1.106	2.120	.4718	2.344	.4267
1.14	65° 19′	.9086	1.101	2.176	.4596	2.395	.4176
1.15	65° 53′	0.9128	1.096	2.234	0.4475	2.448	0.4085
1.16	66° 28′	.9168	1.091	2.296	.4356	2.504	.3993
1.17	67° 02′	.9208	1.086	2.360	.4237	2.563	.3902
1.18	67° 37′	.9246	1.082	2.428	.4120	2.625	.3809
1.19	68° 11′	.9284	1.077	2.498	.4003	2.691	.3717
1.20	68° 45′	0.9320	1.073	2.572	0.3888	2.760	0.3624
1.21	69° 20′	.9356	1.069	2.650	.3773	2.833	.3530
1.22	69° 54′	.9391	1.065	2.733	.3659	2.910	.3436
1.23	70° 28′	.9425	1.061	2.820	.3546	2.992	.3342
1.24	71° 03′	.9458	1.057	2.912	.3434	3.079	.3248
1.25	71° 37′	0.9490	1.054	3.010	0.3323	3.171	0.3153
1.26	72° 12′	.9521	1.050	3.113	.3212	3.270	.3058
1.27	72° 46′	.9551	1.047	3.224	.3102	3.375	.2963
1.28	73° 20′	.9580	1.044	3.341	.2993	3.488	.2867
1.29	73° 55′	.9608	1.041	3.467	.2884	3.609	.2771
1.30	74° 29′	0.9636	1.038	3.602	0.2776	3.738	0.2675
1.31	75° 03′	.9662	1.035	3.747	.2669	3.878	.2579
1.32	75° 38′	.9687	1.032	3.903	.2562	4.029	.2482
1.33	76° 12′	.9711	1.030	4.072	.2456	4.193	.2385
1.34	76° 47′	.9735	1.027	4.256	.2350	4.372	.2288
1.35	77° 21′	0.9757	1.025	4.455	0.2245	4.566	0.2190
1.36	77° 55′	.9779	1.023	4.673	.2140	4.779	.2092
1.37	78° 30′	.9799	1.021	4.913	.2035	5.014	.1994
1.38	79° 04′	.9819	1.018	5.177	.1931	5.273	.1896
1.39	79° 39′	.9837	1.017	5.471	.1828	5.561	.1798
1.40	80° 13′	0.9854	1.015	5.798	0.1725	5.883	0.1700
1.41	80° 47′	.9871	1.013	6.165	.1622	6.246	.1601
1.42	81° 22′	.9887	1.011	6.581	.1519	6.657	.1502
1.43	81° 56′	.9901	1.010	7.055	.1417	7.126	.1403
1.44	82° 30′	.9915	1.009	7.602	.1315	7.667	.1304
1.45	83° 05′	0.9927	1.007	8.238	0.1214	8.299	0.1205
1.46	83° 39′	.9939	1.006	8.989	.1113	9.044	.1106
1.47	84° 14′	.9949	1.005	9.887	.1011	9.938	.1006
1.48	84° 48′	.9959	1.004	10.98	.0911	11.03	.0907
1.49	85° 22′	.9967	1.003	12.35	.0810	12.39	.0807

Table 7 Values of Circular Functions and Trigonometric Functions for Angles in Radians

Real Number x or $m^R(\alpha)$	$m(\alpha)$	$\sin x$ or $\sin \alpha$	$\csc x$ or $\csc \alpha$	$\tan x$ or $\tan \alpha$	$\cot x$ or $\cot \alpha$	$\sec x$ or $\sec \alpha$	$\cos x$ or $\cos \alpha$
1.50	85° 57′	0.9975	1.003	14.10	0.0709	14.14	0.0707
1.51	86° 31′	.9982	1.002	16.43	.0609	16.46	.0608
1.52	87° 05′	.9987	1.001	19.67	.0508	19.70	.0508
1.53	87° 40′	.9992	1.001	24.50	.0408	24.52	.0408
1.54	88° 14′	.9995	1.000	32.46	.0308	32.48	.0308
1.55	88° 49′	0.9998	1.000	48.08	0.0208	48.09	0.0208
1.56	89° 23′	.9999	1.000	92.62	.0108	92.63	.0108
1.57	89° 57′	1.000	1.000	1256	.0008	1256	.0008
$\frac{\pi}{2}$	90°	1	1	Undefined	0	Undefined	0

answers to self-tests

CHAPTER 1, SELF-TEST 1, PAGE 10
1. $6 \notin \{1, 2, 3\}$ 2. $\{3\}$ 3. $\emptyset$
4.

(number line from -1 to 2)

5.

(number line from -3 to 1)

6. Closure Axiom for Multiplication
7. Axiom of Multiplicative Inverses
8. Commutative Axiom for Addition
9. Distributive Axiom 10. $\{-\frac{1}{7}\}$

CHAPTER 1, SELF-TEST 2, PAGE 26
1. -12 2. -20 3. -9 4. -3 5. -9

6.

Statements	Reasons
1. $b \cdot \left(\frac{1}{ab}\right) = b \cdot \left(\frac{1}{a} \cdot \frac{1}{b}\right)$	Property of the Reciprocal of a Product
2. $b \cdot \left(\frac{1}{a} \cdot \frac{1}{b}\right) = b \cdot \left(\frac{1}{b} \cdot \frac{1}{a}\right)$	Commutative Axiom for Multiplication
3. $b \cdot \left(\frac{1}{b} \cdot \frac{1}{a}\right) = \left(b \cdot \frac{1}{b}\right) \cdot \frac{1}{a}$	Associative Axiom for Multiplication
4. $\left(b \cdot \frac{1}{b}\right) \cdot \frac{1}{a} = 1 \cdot \frac{1}{a}$	Axiom of Multiplicative Inverses
5. $1 \cdot \frac{1}{a} = \frac{1}{a}$	Axiom of 1

CHAPTER 2, SELF-TEST 1, PAGE 48
1. $4t + s$ 2. $r - 18$ 3. $7x^2 - 7x$
4. $y^2 - y - 1$ 5. $z = 1$ 6. $r = -1$
7. $x = -\dfrac{b + c}{a}$ 8. 8, 11 9. $43°, 47°$
10. 6 km/h

CHAPTER 2, SELF-TEST 2, PAGE 64
1. $\{x: x < 10\}$

(number line from -5 to 10)

2. $\{r: r < 1\}$

(number line from -1 to 1)

3. $\{z: z \leq 6\}$

(number line from -3 to 6)

4. $\{k: -2 \leq k < 2\}$

(number line from -2 to 2)

5. 18

6. Assume $2n + 1 = 7$.

$$2n + 1 + (-1) = 7 + (-1)$$ — Additive Property of Equality

$$2n = 6$$ — Axioms of Addition

$$\tfrac{1}{2} \cdot 2n = \tfrac{1}{2} \cdot 6$$ — Multiplicative Property of Equality

$$n = 3$$ — Rules for Multiplication

But $n = 3$ contradicts the hypothesis that $n \neq 3$.

7. $\{x: -5 \leq x \leq 11\}$

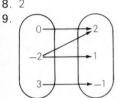

8. $\{t: t \leq -4\} \cup \{t: t \geq 3\}$

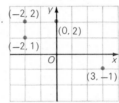

CHAPTER 3, SELF-TEST 1, PAGE 75

1–4. See pages 69, 72, 73. **5.** -1 **6.** 4 **7.** 4
8. 2

9.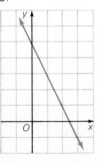

10.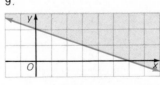

CHAPTER 3, SELF-TEST 2, PAGE 81

1–5. See pages 76, 77, 79.

6.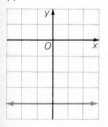

7.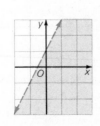

8.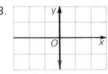

9.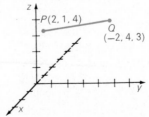

10.

CHAPTER 3, SELF-TEST 3, PAGE 90

1–5. See pages 82, 87. **6.** 4
7. $4x - 3y + 12 = 0$ **8.** $3x + y - 11 = 0$
9. $2x + y + 10 = 0$ **10.** $3x - y - 4 = 0$

CHAPTER 3, SELF-TEST 4, PAGE 96

1–6. See pages 90, 91. **7.** $6\tfrac{3}{4}$ **8.** $12.25

CHAPTER 4, SELF-TEST 1, PAGE 128

1–4. See pages 112, 116, 121.
5. See graph at right; consistent
6. a. 1   b. no solution
   c. infinite set of solutions
7. $(6, 2)$ **8.** $(1, 3)$ **9.** $(-5, 2)$
10. $12.50, $2.50

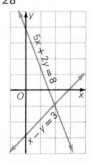

CHAPTER 4, SELF-TEST 2, PAGE 137

1–4. See pages 133, 134.

5.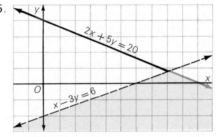

6.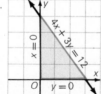

7.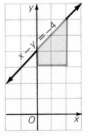

8. 14, 5 **9.** 15, 7
10. $4,000

CHAPTER 5, SELF-TEST 1, PAGE 155

1–5. See pages 142, 147.

6.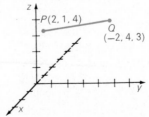

7. $(3, 0, 0), (0, -2, 0), (0, 0, 1)$ **10.** $(3, 1, -4)$

8. 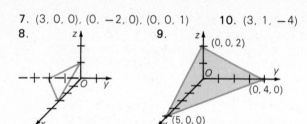 **9.**

CHAPTER 7, SELF-TEST 3, PAGE 254

1–10. See pages 245, 246, 247, 250.

11. $6\frac{7}{8}, \frac{1}{8}, \frac{2}{n^2}$ **12.** $\frac{3}{4}, \frac{1}{4}, \frac{1}{n}$

13. $\frac{3}{10}$ **14.** -6

CHAPTER 8, SELF-TEST 1, PAGE 273

1–10. See pages 259, 260, 263, 265, 266, 269.

11. $y = 28$ **12. a.** $\frac{2}{3}$ **b.** $-\frac{3}{2}$ **13.** $\{-2, -3, \frac{1}{2}\}$

14. $0.\overline{5}$ **15.** $\frac{172}{999}$ **16. a.** 23.1125

b. $23.112111211112\dots$

CHAPTER 5, SELF-TEST 2, PAGE 168

1–3. See pages 157, 163. **4.** $(-2, -3, 2)$

5. Myron, $10; Nelson, $6.50; Pete, $5.50

6. -12

CHAPTER 6, SELF-TEST 1, PAGE 190

1–6. See pages 177, 178, 185. **7.** $\dfrac{-20}{x^3}$

8. $\dfrac{5x^5z^8}{4}$ **9.** 3.751×10^3 **10.** 1.25×10^{-4}

11. $7,000,000$

12. $8x^6 - 8x^5 + 2x^4 + 10x^3 - 5x^2$

13. $(x - 5)(x + 2)$ **14.** $(x - 2y)(x^2 + 2xy + 4y^2)$

CHAPTER 6, SELF-TEST 2, PAGE 195

1. $\{6, -9\}$ **2.** $\{\frac{5}{4}, -\frac{3}{5}\}$ **3.** $8, 10, 12$

4. $\{x: x > 1\} \cup \{x: x < -5\}$

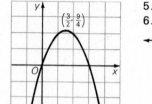

CHAPTER 6, SELF-TEST 3, PAGE 212

1–4. See pages 196, 208. **5.** $y - 2$

6. $x^2 + 2x + 11 + \dfrac{24x + 26}{x^2 - 2x - 3}$

7. $\dfrac{x + 1}{6}$ **8.** $\dfrac{x + 2}{x + 3}$ **9.** 3 days **10.** 4

CHAPTER 7, SELF-TEST 1, PAGE 229

1–5. See pages 217, 218, 221, 224.

6. $-11, -5, 1, 7, 13$ **7.** -61 **8.** 423

9. 19.5 kilograms **10.** 168

CHAPTER 7, SELF-TEST 2, PAGE 243

1–4. See pages 230, 231, 235, 239.

5. $\frac{5}{2}, \frac{5}{3}, \frac{10}{9}, \frac{20}{27}$ **6.** $-32,768$ **7.** $8, 4, 2, 1, \frac{1}{2}$ or $8, -4, 2, -1, \frac{1}{2}$ **8.** $312\frac{3}{5}$ **9.** 665,500 units

10. 1 milligram

CHAPTER 8, SELF-TEST 2, PAGE 288

1–2. See pages 276, 284. **3.** $-\dfrac{2}{x^2}\sqrt[3]{2x^2}$

4. $10\sqrt{3}$ **5.** $49\sqrt[3]{25} - 4$ **6.** $\dfrac{\sqrt{4a^2 + 1}}{4a^2 + 1}$

7. $\{-2\sqrt{3}, 2\sqrt{3}\}$ **8.** $\left\{\dfrac{\sqrt{2}}{12}, -\dfrac{\sqrt{2}}{12}\right\}$

9. $\left\{\dfrac{7}{2}, -\dfrac{1}{2}\right\}$ **10.** $\left\{\dfrac{5 + \sqrt{73}}{6}, \dfrac{5 - \sqrt{73}}{6}\right\}$

CHAPTER 9, SELF-TEST 1, PAGE 306

1–6. See pages 292, 295, 296, 301. **7.** $-i$

8. a. $4 - 2i$ **b.** $-2 + 6i$ **c.** $11 + 2i$

d. $\dfrac{-1 + 2i}{5}$ **9. a.** real, rational

b. real, rational **10. a.** (a) $\frac{3}{4}$ (b) $-\frac{1}{2}$

b. $b = -3, c = -4$

CHAPTER 9, SELF-TEST 2, PAGE 314

1–2. See pages 307, 308.

3. $x = -2, (-2, 10)$, maximum

4. 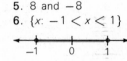 **5.** 8 and -8

6. $\{x: -1 < x < 1\}$

CHAPTER 9, SELF-TEST 3, PAGE 328

1–5. See pages 315, 316, 318, 319, 320, 326.

6. a. -6 **b.** $8i$ **7.** $Q(x) = x^2 + 3x + 20$; $R = 124$ **8.** $\{-\frac{1}{3}, i\sqrt{2}, -i\sqrt{2}\}$

9. $\{(1 - i), (1 + i), -2\}$ **10.** $\{1.53\}$

CHAPTER 10, SELF-TEST 1, PAGE 339

–2. See pages 333, 334. **3.** $4\sqrt{5}$
. $3x - 2y + 12 = 0$

CHAPTER 10, SELF-TEST 2, PAGE 356

1–6. See pages 341, 344, 347, 352.
7.

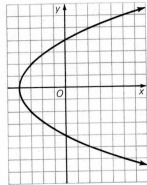

8.

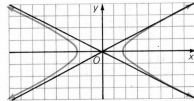

9. $x^2 + y^2 + 4x - 8y + 11 = 0$
10. $y = -\frac{1}{18}x^2 + \frac{1}{3}x - 1$ **11.** $y = 9\frac{3}{5}$ **12.** $\frac{40}{4}$

CHAPTER 10, SELF-TEST 3, PAGE 364

1–2. See pages 358, 362.
3.

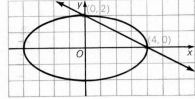

4. $\{(-4, -\frac{3}{2}), (3, 2)\}$
5. $\{(1, -3), (-1, -3), (\frac{3}{2}, 2), (-\frac{3}{2}, 2)\}$

CHAPTER 11, SELF-TEST 1, PAGE 373

1. $4\sqrt[15]{4}$ **2.** 9 **3.** 64 **4.** 1296 **5.** $\{6\}$ **6.** $\{2\}$
7. $\{-2\}$ **8.** $\{-2\}$

CHAPTER 11, SELF-TEST 2, PAGE 378

1–4. See pages 373, 374, 375, 376.
5. $\{(x, y): x = 2y - 5\}$ **6.** $\{(x, y): x = \sqrt{y}\}$ is a
function. (See page 374.) **7.** $\log_{12} 144 = 2$
8. $(\frac{1}{2})^{-3} = 8$ **9.** $\{0\}$ **10.** $\{2\}$

CHAPTER 11, SELF-TEST 3, PAGE 403

1–7. See pages 380, 382, 383, 385, 387.
8. 1.5072 **9.** 0.02076 **10.** 0.1 m **11.** 0.05 m
12. 0.64% **13.** 31.61 **14.** 53.4 **15.** $\{1.61\}$
16. $\{242\}$

CHAPTER 12, SELF-TEST 1, PAGE 415

1–3. See pages 408, 410. **4.** 27 **5.** 120
6. 336 **7.** 27,600 **8.** 302,400

CHAPTER 12, SELF-TEST 2, PAGE 420

1. See page 416. **2.** 55 **3.** 1001 **4.** 300
5. 35,562,240

CHAPTER 12, SELF-TEST 3, PAGE 424

1–2. See pages 420, 423.
2. $t^4 - 20t^3 + 150t^2 - 500t + 625$

4. $\dfrac{t^5}{32} - \dfrac{5t^4}{16} + \dfrac{5t^3}{4} - \dfrac{5t^2}{2} + \dfrac{5t}{2} - 1$ **5.** $-1792x^5$

CHAPTER 12, SELF-TEST 4, PAGE 436

1–6. See pages 428, 429, 431, 434.
7. $\{J, U, P, I, T, E, R\}, \{U, I, E\}$ **8.** $\frac{3}{8}$ **9.** $\frac{5}{8}$
10. no; $(P(A) \cdot P(B) = \frac{11}{324}; P(A \cap B) = \frac{1}{18})$

CHAPTER 13, SELF-TEST 1, PAGE 457

1–4. See pages 439, 441, 446. **5.** $\begin{bmatrix} 2 & 3 & 2 \\ 1 & 0 & 2 \end{bmatrix}$

6. $\begin{bmatrix} 3 & 5 \\ 1 & -2 \\ 1 & -7 \end{bmatrix}$ **7.** $\begin{bmatrix} -11 & -4 \\ 8 & 0 \end{bmatrix}$

8. $X = \begin{bmatrix} 1 & 1 \\ 1 & -11 \end{bmatrix}$ **9.** $X = \begin{bmatrix} \frac{11}{3} & 1 \\ 5 & 11 \end{bmatrix}$

10. $\begin{bmatrix} 2x + 4y \\ -x - 5y \end{bmatrix}$

CHAPTER 13, SELF-TEST 2, PAGE 462

1–3. See pages 459, 460. **4.** $\begin{bmatrix} -\frac{7}{3} & \frac{5}{3} \\ -3 & 2 \end{bmatrix}$

5. $X = \begin{bmatrix} -1 & 0 \\ 3 & 5 \end{bmatrix}$ **6.** $\begin{bmatrix} 4 & 3 \\ 2 & -1 \end{bmatrix}\begin{bmatrix} x \\ y \end{bmatrix} = \begin{bmatrix} 7 \\ 10 \end{bmatrix}$

7. $\{(-4, -5)\}$

CHAPTER 13, SELF-TEST 3, PAGE 473

1–5. See pages 465, 470. **6.** $\begin{bmatrix} x' \\ y' \end{bmatrix} = \begin{bmatrix} x \\ y \end{bmatrix} + \begin{bmatrix} 3 \\ -4 \end{bmatrix}$

7. $P'(-\frac{7}{2}, \frac{5}{2})$ **8.** $P(-2, 1)$ **9.** $P'(-6, 8)$
10. $P(-28, 22)$

CHAPTER 14, SELF-TEST 1, PAGE 486

1–5. See pages 480, 481, 482, 484.
6. 1055.04 cm **7.** $\frac{13\pi^R}{6}$ **8.** $-480°$

CHAPTER 14, SELF-TEST 2, PAGE 506

1–8. See pages 487, 488, 489, 493, 499, 502.

9. $\cos \alpha = \dfrac{2}{\sqrt{29}}$, $\sin \alpha = -\dfrac{5}{\sqrt{29}}$

10. $\sin \alpha = -\frac{12}{13}$ **11. a.** $\dfrac{\sqrt{3}}{2}$ **b.** $\dfrac{\sqrt{3}}{2}$ **12.** 0.4496

13. 0.2696 **14.** 0.7790 **15.** -0.6525
16.

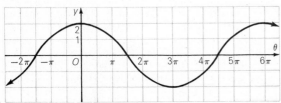

CHAPTER 14, SELF-TEST 3, PAGE 516

1–6. See pages 506, 507, 513.

7. $\sin \alpha = \dfrac{-5}{\sqrt{34}}$, $\cos \alpha = \dfrac{3}{\sqrt{34}}$,

$\tan \alpha = -\dfrac{5}{3}$, $\cot \alpha = -\dfrac{3}{5}$,

$\sec \alpha = \dfrac{\sqrt{34}}{3}$, $\csc \alpha = -\dfrac{\sqrt{34}}{5}$

8. $m(B) = 54°50'$, $m(C) = 90°$, $a = 8.455$, $c = 14.68$

CHAPTER 15, SELF-TEST 1, PAGE 524

1. $\sin x \sec x = \sin x \cdot \dfrac{1}{\cos x} = \dfrac{\sin x}{\cos x} = $

$\tan x$ $(\cos x \neq 0)$

2. $\cos x(\sec x - \cos x) = \cos x \left(\dfrac{1}{\cos x} - \cos x \right) = $

$\dfrac{\cos x}{\cos x} - \cos^2 x = 1 - \cos^2 x = \sin^2 x$ $(\cos x \neq 0)$

3. $\sec x - \cos x = \dfrac{1}{\cos x} - \cos x = \dfrac{1}{\cos x} - $

$\dfrac{\cos^2 x}{\cos x} = \dfrac{1 - \cos^2 x}{\cos x} = \dfrac{\sin^2 x}{\cos x} = \dfrac{\sin x \sin x}{\cos x} = $

$\sin x \cdot \dfrac{\sin x}{\cos x} = \sin x \tan x$ $(\cos x \neq 0)$

4. $\dfrac{\cos x}{1 - \sin x} = \dfrac{\cos x}{1 - \sin x} \cdot \dfrac{1 + \sin x}{1 + \sin x} = $

$\dfrac{\cos x + \sin x \cos x}{1 - \sin^2 x} = \dfrac{\cos x + \sin x \cos x}{\cos^2 x} = \dfrac{\cos x}{\cos^2 x} + $

$\dfrac{\sin x \cos x}{\cos^2 x} = \dfrac{1}{\cos x} + \dfrac{\sin x}{\cos x} = \sec x + \tan x$

$(\cos x \neq 0, \sin x \neq 1)$

CHAPTER 15, SELF-TEST 2, PAGE 543

1–5. See pages 526, 529, 538, 539.
6. $-\cos 30°$

7. $\sin \dfrac{\pi}{3}$ **8.** $\dfrac{\sqrt{3}}{2}$ **9.** $\frac{24}{25}$

10. $\csc 2\alpha = \dfrac{1}{\sin 2\alpha} = \dfrac{1}{2 \sin \alpha \cos \alpha} = $

$\dfrac{1}{\sin \alpha} \cdot \dfrac{1}{2 \cos \alpha} = \dfrac{\csc \alpha}{2 \cos \alpha}$ $(\sin \alpha \neq 0, \cos \alpha \neq 0)$

CHAPTER 15, SELF-TEST 3, PAGE 550

1–2. See pages 544, 547. **3.** $c \doteq 10.3$
4. $a \doteq 23.2$ **5.** 126.2 **6.** 14.7 nautical miles
7. 145.9 cm

CHAPTER 16, SELF-TEST 1, PAGE 560

1–3. See pages 553, 555. **4.** $\left\{ y: y = \dfrac{\pi}{6} + k\pi \right\}$

5. $30°$ **6.** $\left\{ x: x = \dfrac{\pi}{4} + k\dfrac{\pi}{2} \right\}$

7. $\{30°, 90°, 150°, 270°\}$

CHAPTER 16, SELF-TEST 2, PAGE 575

1–7. See pages 561, 566, 572, 573.
8. $(\sqrt{13}, 146°19')$, $(-\sqrt{13}, 326°19')$
9. $r = 8 \tan \theta \sec \theta$
10. $z_1 = \sqrt{2}(\cos 135° + i \sin 135°)$,
$z_2 = 3\sqrt{2}(\cos 225° + i \sin 225°)$, $z_1 z_2 = 6$,
$\dfrac{z_1}{z_2} = -\dfrac{1}{3}i$, $z_1^3 = 2 + 2i$, $z_2^3 = 54 - 54i$
11. $\sqrt{2} + \sqrt{2}i$, $2(\cos 165° + i \sin 165°)$,
$2(\cos 285° + i \sin 285°)$
12. $\|u + v\| = 24.6$, $m(\theta) = 22°$

glossary

abscissa (p. 73). The x-coordinate of a point.

absolute value (p. 60). The nonnegative (0 or positive) one of the pair a and $-a$, where $a \in \mathfrak{R}$.

accuracy of a measurement (p. 387). The relative error of a measurement; that is, the ratio of the maximum possible error in the measurement to the measurement itself.

additive inverse (p. 8). For each $a \in \mathfrak{R}$, there exists an additive inverse $-a \in \mathfrak{R}$ such that $a + (-a) = 0$ and $(-a) + a = 0$.

amplitude of a periodic function (p. 502). When a periodic function attains a maximum value M and a minimum value m, you say the function has an amplitude of $\frac{M - m}{2}$.

angle (p. 480). The union of two noncollinear rays that have the same endpoint. *See also* directed angle.

angle of depression (p. 514). The angle between the line of sight to an object (below the observer) and a horizontal ray through the observer.

angle of elevation (p. 514). The angle between the horizontal ray through the observer and the line of sight to an object (above the observer).

antilogarithm (p. 383). If $\log x = a$, then x is called the antilogarithm of a.

arithmetic mean (or **average**) (p. 222). A single arithmetic mean inserted between two numbers is the average or *the* arithmetic mean of the two numbers.

arithmetic means (p. 221). The terms between two given terms of an arithmetic sequence.

arithmetic progression (p. 218). *See* arithmetic sequence.

arithmetic sequence (p. 218). Any sequence in which each term after the first is obtained by adding a fixed number, called the common difference, to the preceding term. Also called *arithmetic progression*.

arithmetic series (p. 225). A series whose terms are in arithmetic progression.

bounded sequence (p. 246). A sequence for which there exists a number which equals or exceeds the absolute value of every term of the sequence.

Cartesian coordinate system (p. 72). A rectangular system which establishes a one-to-one correspondence between the set of points in the plane and the set of ordered pairs of real numbers. Also called *plane rectangular coordinate system*.

Cartesian product (p. 408). If a finite set A contains r elements and a finite set B contains s elements, then the set of ordered pairs (a, b) with $a \in A$ and $b \in B$ is called the Cartesian product of A and B (denoted by $A \times B$) and contains rs elements.

characteristic (p. 382). The integral part of a logarithm to base 10 when the fractional part (the part between 0 and 1) is nonnegative.

circle (p. 339). In a plane, a circle is the set of all points at a given distance, called the radius, from a given point, called the center of the circle.

circular functions (p. 489). The trigonometric functions with domain pictured as lengths of arcs on the unit circle, rather than as the set of angles.

circular permutation (p. 412). An arrangement of objects in a circular pattern.

coefficient of a monomial (p. 34). *See under* monomial.

column matrix (or **column vector**) (p. 440). Matrix with only one column.

combination (p. 416). An r-element subset of a set with n elements is called a combination of n elements taken r at a time.

combined variation (p. 354). A variation defined by an equation where a given variable varies directly with a second variable and inversely with a third variable.

common logarithm (p. 380). Logarithm to the base 10.

complement of A (p. 429). If an event A is in the sample space S, the complement of A is the set of elements of S that are not members of A.

complete factorization (p. 186). The factorization of a polynomial is complete when it has been expressed as the product of a constant and one or more prime polynomials or powers of prime polynomials.

completing the square (p. 284). Transforming a quadratic expression into a square of a binomial.

complex conjugate (p. 296). For any real numbers a and b, the complex conjugate of $a + bi$ is $a - bi$; conversely, the complex conjugate of $a - bi$ is $a + bi$.

complex number (p. 295). Any number of the form $a + bi$ where $a \in \mathfrak{R}$ and bi is a pure imaginary number. If $b \neq 0$, $a + bi$ is also called an imaginary number.

conditional probability (p. 434). The probability of an event occurring given that another event has occurred.

conic sections (p. 350). The curves (circle, ellipse, parabola, hyperbola) which are formed by the intersection of a plane with a conical surface of two nappes.

conjunction (p. 53). A compound sentence formed by joining two sentences by the word *and*.

consistent system of equations (p. 112). A system of equations that has at least one solution.

constant function (p. 91). A linear function where $m = 0$ and, therefore, $y = b$ for all $x \in \mathfrak{R}$.

constant of proportionality (pp. 91, 352). *See* constant of variation.

constant of variation (pp. 91, 352). In a direct variation $y = mk$ or in an inverse variation $xy = k(k \neq 0)$, k is the constant of variation. Also called *constant of proportionality*.

convergent sequence (p. 245). An infinite sequence which has a limit.

converse (p. 49). Any two "If-then" statements are converses of each other if each can be obtained from the other by interchanging hypothesis and conclusion.

coordinate(s) of a point (pp. 5, 72, 142). The number or ordered pair (ordered triple) of numbers associated with a point.

cosecant function (p. 506). A trigonometric function such that cosecant: $\alpha \rightarrow \dfrac{1}{\sin \alpha}$, $\sin \alpha \neq 0$.

cosine function (p. 487). If α is an angle in standard position, with $P(u, v)$ any point other than the origin on the terminal side of α, and if $\sqrt{u^2 + v^2} = r$, then cosine: $\alpha \rightarrow \dfrac{u}{r}$.

cotangent function (p. 506). A trigonometric function such that cotangent: $\alpha \rightarrow \dfrac{\cos \alpha}{\sin \alpha}$, $\sin \alpha \neq 0$.

coterminal angles (p. 480). Angles that have the same initial side and the same terminal side.

degree (of rotation) (p. 482). Each of the 360 equal parts into which a complete revolution is divided, in one system of measuring angles.

degree of a monomial (p. 34). In the monomial ax^n, $a \neq 0$, the number denoted by n.

degree of a polynomial (p. 35). The degree of the nonzero term of highest degree of a polynomial.

dependent events (p. 434). Events for which the probability of one depends on the occurrence of the other.

depressed equation (p. 320). Whenever r is a root of the polynomial equation $P(x) = 0$, $P(x) \div (x - r) = 0$ is called the depressed equation.

determinant (pp. 121, 157, 439). A square array of numerals, set off with vertical bars, which names a real number. The numerals in the array are called the entries (or elements) of the determinant. The order of the determinant is the number of rows (or columns).

direct variation (p. 91). A linear function of the form $y = mx$, $m \neq 0$.

directed angle (p. 480). An ordered pair of rays with a common endpoint, one ray called the initial side of the angle and the other called the terminal side of the angle, together with a rotation from the initial to the terminal side.

discriminant (p. 301). The number $b^2 - 4ac$, which is named under the radical sign in the quadratic formula, is called the discriminant of the quadratic equation $ax^2 + bx + c = 0$.

disjunction (p. 53). A compound sentence formed by joining two sentences by the word *or*.

divergent sequence (p. 247). An infinite sequence that does not have a limit.

domain of a function (p. 69). *See* function.

domain of a variable (p. 3). The set whose members may be used as a replacement for the variable. Also called *replacement set*.

ellipse (p. 344). In the plane, the set of points for each of which the sum of the distances from two fixed points, called foci, is a given constant.

equivalent equations (p. 37). Equations that have the same solution set over a given set.

equivalent expressions (p. 36). Two expressions are equivalent if, when they are joined by the = symbol, the resulting equation is a true statement for every numerical replacement of the variable.

equivalent inequalities (p. 51). Inequalities with the same solution set over a given set.

equivalent systems (p. 115). Systems with the same solution set.

equivalent vectors (p. 572). Vectors with the same norm and same direction.

even function (pp. 260, 526). A function such that whenever it contains (a, b), it also contains $(-a, b)$.

event (p. 426). Any subset of a sample space.

exponential form (p. 368). Form of a radical expression when it is written as a power (or product of powers) with rational exponents.

extremes of a proportion (p. 91). In the proportion $\dfrac{y_1}{x_1} = \dfrac{y_2}{x_2}$, y_1 and x_2 are called the extremes.

factor of a polynomial (p. 185). If a given polynomial is the product of polynomials, each of the latter polynomials is called a factor of the given polynomial.

factor set (p. 185). A designated set to which the factors of a polynomial belong.

finite sequence (p. 217). A sequence which has a last term.

fractional equation (p. 209). An equation involving one or more rational expressions in which a variable appears in the denominator.

function (p. 69). A set of ordered pairs in which each first component is paired with exactly one second component according to a given rule. The set of first components is called the domain, and the set of second components the range, of the function.

fundamental period (p. 493). If there is a least positive period p for a periodic function, p is called the fundamental period of the function.

geometric mean (p. 236). A single geometric mean inserted between two numbers. Also called *geometric proportional*.

geometric means (p. 235). The terms between two given terms of a geometric sequence are called geometric means between the given terms.

geometric progression (p. 230). *See* geometric sequence.

geometric proportional (p. 236). *See* geometric mean.

geometric sequence (p. 230). Any sequence in which each term after the first is the product of the preceding term and a fixed number, called the common ratio. Also called *geometric progression*.

geometric series (p. 239). A series whose terms are in geometric sequence.

hyperbola (p. 347). The two-branched curve formed by the set of points in the plane such that for each point, the absolute value of the difference of its distances, called focal radii, from two fixed points, called foci, is a constant.

identity (p. 489). An equation which is true for all real values of the variable.

imaginary number (p. 295). *See under* complex number.

imaginary unit (p. 292). The number i which is a square root of -1; thus, $i = \sqrt{-1}$.

inconsistent system of equations (p. 112). System of equations whose solution set is the empty set $\emptyset$.

independent events (p. 434). Events such that the probability of one does not depend on the occurrence of the other.

indirect proof (p. 57). A method of proof which begins by assuming that the conclusion of a theorem is false and reasons from this to a contradiction of the hypothesis, an axiom, or a previously proved theorem.

infinite sequence (p. 217). A sequence which has no last term.

inverse function (p. 374). The inverse of a function, which is also a function.

inverse relation (p. 373). The relation (set of ordered pairs) which results when we interchange the components of each of the ordered pairs in a relation.

inverse variation (p. 352). In general, any function defined by an equation of the form $xy = k$ where k (called the constant of variation) is a nonzero constant.

irrational numbers (p. 266). Real numbers that are not rational.

irreducible polynomial (p. 185). A polynomial that cannot be expressed as a product of polynomials of lower positive degree.

joint variation (p. 354). A variation defined by an equation of the form $y = kxz$, where y varies directly with x and also directly with z. We say y varies jointly as x and z.

limit of a sequence (p. 245). A number such that the absolute value of the difference of a_n (the nth term of a sequence) and this number can be made less than any given positive number, however small, by choosing n large enough.

linear combination (p. 116). When both members of an equation are multiplied by the same nonzero constant and the resulting expressions are added to the corresponding members of another equation, a linear combination of the two equations is obtained.

linear equation in two variables (p. 76). An equation which can be transformed into the form $Ax + By = C$ where $A, B, C \in \Re$ and A and B are not both zero. The graph of such an equation is a straight line.

linear function (p. 90). A function f for which the rule for pairing is given by a linear equation of the form $y = mx + b$, $(m, b \in \Re)$.

linear inequality in two variables (p. 70). An inequality which has the linear equation in two variables $Ax + By = C$ as its associated linear equation.

linear interpolation (p. 325). The process of approximating a value of a polynomial function by using a line segment.

linear programming (p. 132). A means of finding maximum and minimum values of a linear expression over a region (feasibility region) which satisfies a system of inequalities (constraints).

logarithm (p. 375). In the exponential function with base b, $x = b^y$ $(b > 0, b \neq 1)$, the exponent y is called the logarithm of x to the base b.

mantissa (p. 382). The fractional part (the nonnegative part between 0 and 1) of the logarithm of a number.

matrix (plural, **matrices**) (p. 439). In general, a rectangular array of numerals. Each numeral in the array is called an entry of the matrix. The number of rows and columns of entries in the matrix are its dimensions.

maximum possible error (p. 387). The maximum possible error of a measurement is half the precision (unit) of the measurement.

means of a proportion (p. 91). In the proportion $\dfrac{y_1}{x_1} = \dfrac{y_2}{x_2}$, x_1 and y_2 are called the means.

minor of an element in a determinant (p. 163). The determinant obtained by deleting the row and column containing the element.

monomial (p. 34). A monomial in the variable x is an expression of the form ax^n where $a \in \Re$ and n denotes a positive integer. The number denoted by a is called the coefficient (or numerical coefficient) of the monomial.

multiplicative inverse (p. 8). For each nonzero $a \in \Re$, there exists a multiplicative inverse $\dfrac{1}{a} \in \Re$ such that $\dfrac{1}{a} \cdot a = 1$ and $a \cdot \dfrac{1}{a} = 1$. Also called *reciprocal*.

mutually exclusive events (p. 431). Events that have no outcome in common.

nonsingular (or **invertible**) **matrix** (p. 460). A matrix A such that det $A \neq 0$.

norm of a vector (p. 572). The length of a vector.

nth root (p. 263). Each solution of the equation $x^n = b$, n a positive integer, is called an nth root of b.

numerical coefficient (p. 34). *See* coefficient of a monomial.

octant (p. 142). Each of the eight regions into which space is separated by the three coordinate planes, the xy-plane, the yz-plane, and the xz-plane.

odd function (pp. 260, 526). A function with the property that whenever it contains (a, b), it also contains $(-a, -b)$.

odds (p. 429). The odds that the event A in sample space S will occur are given by $\dfrac{P(A)}{P(\bar{A})}$.

one-to-one function (p. 374). A function such that not only is each element in the domain paired with exactly one element in the range, but also each element in the range is paired with exactly one element in the domain.

ordinate (p. 73). The y-coordinate of a point.

parabola (p. 341). A curve consisting of the set of all points P whose distance from a fixed point, called the focus, is equal to the perpendicular distance from P to a line, called the directrix, that does not contain the focus.

partial sum (p. 250). In general, for any infinite series $a_1 + a_2 + \cdots + a_n + \cdots$, $S_n = \sum_{i=1}^{n} a_i$ is called a partial sum.

periodic decimal (p. 269). See repeating decimal.

periodic function (p. 493). A function f is periodic if there is some nonzero constant p such that $f(x + p) = f(x)$ for all x in the domain of f. p is called a period of the function.

permutation (p. 410). An arrangement of the elements of a set in a definite order.

perpendicular lines (p. 336). Two lines intersecting at right angles.

plane rectangular coordinate system (p. 72). See Cartesian coordinate system.

point-slope form (p. 87). An equation of a line of the form $y - y_1 = m(x - x_1)$, where m is the slope and point $P(x_1, y_1)$ is a point on the line.

polar axis (p. 561). The nonnegative x-axis in the polar coordinate system.

polar coordinates (p. 561). The components of the ordered pair $(r, m(\theta))$, usually written (r, θ), which specifies the location of point P in the plane in terms of r, the distance from the origin to P, and θ, an angle having the nonnegative x-axis as its initial side and the ray $\overrightarrow{OP}$ as its terminal side.

polar form (p. 566). The expression $r(\cos \theta + i \sin \theta)$ is called the polar form for denoting the complex number $x + yi$, where (r, θ) are the polar coordinates of the point (x, y).

pole (p. 561). The origin in the polar coordinate system.

polynomial (p. 34). An expression which consists of a string of monomials connected by plus signs.

polynomial functions (p. 315). Functions whose values are given by polynomials.

power function (p. 259). A function f defined by an equation of the form $f(x) = x^n$.

precision of a measurement (p. 387). The smallest unit on the scale of the measuring device used in making the measurement.

prime polynomial (p. 185). An irreducible polynomial with integral coefficients whose greatest monomial factor is 1.

principal-value inverse function (p. 554). An inverse function defined by restricting (according to custom) the range of the inverse of a circular or trigonometric function.

probability (p. 428). Let S be a sample space of an experiment in which there are n possible outcomes, each equally likely. If an event A is a subset of S such that A contains h elements, then the probability of the event A is given by $\dfrac{h}{n}$.

proportion (p. 91). An equality of ratios.

quadrantal angle (p. 481). An angle in standard position whose terminal side coincides with a coordinate axis.

quadratic function (p. 307). A function f with domain $\mathfrak{R}$ and values given by a quadratic polynomial, that is, $f = \{(x, y): y = ax^2 + bx + c, a, b, c, \text{ and } x \in \mathfrak{R}, a \neq 0\}$, is called a quadratic function, or a polynomial function of degree two, over $\mathfrak{R}$.

quadratic polynomial (p. 35). A polynomial of degree 2 that contains a single variable.

radian (p. 484). Unit which can be used to measure any angle in standard position. If the length of an arc on the unit circle measured from point $(1, 0)$ is a units, then the measure of the angle in standard position intercepting that arc is said to be a radians.

radical (p. 263). The symbol $\sqrt[n]{b}$ is called a radical; b is the radicand and n the index.

radicand (p. 263). See under radical.

range of a function (p. 69). See under function.

rational algebraic expression (p. 196). The quotient of two polynomials (divisor not 0).

rational number (p. 196). Any number which is the quotient of two integers (divisor not 0).

rationalizing the denominator (p. 276). The process of transforming an expression with a radical (or radicals) in its denominator into an equivalent expression with the denominator free of radicals.

real numbers (p. 5). The set of all the positive numbers, the negative numbers, and zero.

reciprocal (p. 8). See multiplicative inverse.

reducible polynomial (p. 185). A polynomial that can be expressed as a product of two or more polynomials of lower positive degree.

reduction formula (p. 529). A formula which can be used to ''reduce'' a given circular or trigonometric function value in any quadrant to a function value in Quadrant I.

relation (p. 72). Any pairing of the elements of one set, the domain, with those of another, the range, in accordance with some rule.

repeating decimal (p. 269). A decimal numeral for a rational number which consists of an endlessly repeating block of digits (the repetend). Also called *periodic decimal*.

replacement set (p. 3). *See* domain of a variable.

right angle (p. 480). An angle having a rotation of $\frac{1}{4}$ of a revolution.

round-off error (p. 178). The difference between a number and its approximation.

row matrix (or **row vector**) (p. 440). A matrix with only one row.

sample space (p. 426). A set S of elements that correspond one-to-one with the outcomes of an experiment. Also called *universe*.

scalars (p. 446). In dealing with matrices, we often refer to real numbers as scalars.

scientific notation (p. 177). Another name for standard notation when used in the expression of measurements.

secant function (p. 506). A trigonometric function such that secant: $\alpha \rightarrow \dfrac{1}{\cos \alpha}$, $\cos \alpha \neq 0$.

sequence (p. 217). A set of numbers (some of which can be repeated) in a particular order.

series (p. 224). In general, given any sequence a_1, $a_2, \ldots$ with n or more terms, the associated series of n terms, S_n, is $S_n = a_1 + a_2 + \cdots + a_n$.

significant digit (p. 177). In a numeral, each digit reporting the number of units of measure contained in a measurement.

similar, or **like, monomials** (p. 34). Monomials which are exactly the same or which differ only in numerical coefficients.

simple form of a polynomial (p. 35). A form of a polynomial in which no two terms are like (or similar) monomials.

simplifying a polynomial (p. 36). Replacing one polynomial by an equivalent polynomial in simple form.

sine function (p. 487). If α is an angle in standard position, with $P(u, v)$ any point other than the origin on the terminal side of α, and if $\sqrt{u^2 + v^2} = r$, then sine: $\alpha \rightarrow \dfrac{v}{r}$.

singular matrix (p. 460). A square matrix A such that det $A = 0$.

slope-intercept form (p. 87). An equation of a line of the form $y = mx + b$, where m is the slope and b is the y-intercept.

slope of a line (p. 82). Ratio of rise to run. Let (x_1, y_1) and (x_2, y_2) be the coordinates of any two different points of a nonvertical line. Then the slope m of the line is given by $m = \dfrac{y_2 - y_1}{x_2 - x_1}$.

solution set (p. 3). The set that consists of the values of the variable for which an open sentence is true. Also called *truth set*.

square matrix (p. 440). A matrix with the same number of rows as columns.

standard notation (p. 177). An expression of a number as a product, $a \times 10^n$, where $1 \leq |a| < 10$ and n is an integer. *See also* scientific notation.

standard position (p. 480). Position of an angle placed on a rectangular coordinate system with the vertex of the angle at the origin and the initial side of the angle as the positive part of the horizontal axis.

straight angle (p. 481). An angle having a rotation of $\frac{1}{2}$ of a revolution.

sum of infinite series (p. 250). If the sequence $S_1, S_2, \ldots, S_n, \ldots$ of partial sums converges to S, then the sum of the infinite series is defined to be S.

tangent function (p. 506). A trigonometric function such that tangent: $\alpha \rightarrow \dfrac{\sin \alpha}{\cos \alpha}$, $\cos \alpha \neq 0$.

terminating decimal (p. 269). A decimal numeral containing only a finite number of digits; that is, having 0 as repetend.

terms of a polynomial (p. 34). The monomials in the expression for the polynomial.

trace of a plane (p. 147). The line in which a plane intersects a coordinate plane is called the trace of the given plane in that coordinate plane.

transformations on a system (p. 115). Operations performed on a system of equations to produce an equivalent system.

translation (p. 465). A transformation, or mapping, of the plane in which each point P of the plane is mapped onto a corresponding point P' of the plane. P' is said to be the image of P, and P to be the preimage of P' under the mapping.

trigonometric form (p. 566). *See* polar form.

trigonometric functions (p. 488). The set of functions (sine, cosine, tangent, cotangent, secant, cosecant) with domain of each function the set of all angles.

truth set (p. 3). *See* solution set.

variable (p. 3). A symbol which may represent any one of the members of a specified set.

variation. *See* combined variation, direct variation, inverse variation, joint variation.

vector (p. 572). A directed line segment in the plane or in space, from one endpoint, called the initial point, to the other endpoint, called the terminal point.

Venn diagram (p. 431). A diagram used to picture set relationships.

x-intercept (p. 87). The abscissa of the point where a graph intersects the x-axis.

y-intercept (p. 87). The ordinate of the point where a graph intersects the y-axis.

zero matrix (p. 441). A matrix each of whose entries is zero.

zero of a function (p. 302). Any value of x in the domain of a function f which satisfies the equation $f(x) = 0$.

index

Triangle(s), area of, 44
  equilateral, 44
  isosceles, 44
  Pascal's, 422–423
  right, 44
  solving, 512–514, 544, 547
Trigonometric functions, 487–559
  identities involving, 519–541
  inverses of, 554–556
  using tables, 494–496
Trigonometry, 479–559
Truth set, 3

Union of sets, 54
Unique, 8
Unit circle, 483
Using Computing Devices, 390

Value, of a series, 225
  of a variable, 3
Variable, 3
Variation, 90–91, 260, 352–354
  combined, 354
  constant of, 91, 260, 352
  direct, 90–91
  inverse, 352–353
  joint, 354
Vector(s), 14, 572–574
  column, 440
  components of, 573
  equivalent, 572
  norm of, 572
  resultant of, 572
  row, 440

Venn diagram(s), 431 *n*.
Vertex, 308, 342
VON MISES, HILDA G., 543

Whole numbers, 5
WIENER, NORBERT, 75
Wind speed, 124

x-axis, 72, 141
x-coordinate, 73, 142
x-intercept, 87, 146
xy-plane, 142
xz-plane, 142

y-axis, 72, 141
y-coordinate, 73, 142
y-intercept, 87, 146
yz-plane, 142

z-axis, 141
z-coordinate, 142
z-intercept, 146
Zero, axiom of, 8
  of a function, 302
  matrix, 441
  multiplication property of, 17
  polynomial, 34

CREDITS

answers to selected exercises

Chapter 1 Review of Essentials

Exercises, page 3

1. $\notin$ 3. $\subset$ or $\neq$ 5. $\notin$ 7. $\neq$ 9. $\not\subset$ or $\neq$

Exercises, page 4

1. $\emptyset$ 3. $\{3\}$ 5. $\{4\}$ 7. $\emptyset$ 9. $\{2\}$

Exercises, pages 5–6

1.
3.
5.
7.
9.
11.
13.
15.

Exercises, page 10

1. Closure axiom for addition   3. Associative axiom for addition   5. Axiom of additive inverses   7. Substitution principle   9. Substitution principle   11. Distributive axiom
13. 80   15. 17   17. $\{-2\}$ 19. $\{-18\}$
21. $\{6\}$ 23. $\{3\}$ 25. $\{-3\}$

Exercises, pages 14–16

1. 5   3. 14   5. 5   7. 0   9. -9 11. 75
13. 13.1   15. -6 17. 3   19. -13 21. 15
23. -2.6 25. 1. Hypothesis   2. Axiom of additive inverses   3. Property of the negative of a sum
4. Axiom of additive inverses   .5. Substitution principle

27. 1. $c + a = c + b$ — Hyp.
2. $c + a = a + c$, $c + b = b + c$ — Comm. ax. for add.
3. $a + c = b + c$ — Subs. prin.
4. $a = b$ — Theorem, p. 12

29. 1. $a + b = 0$ — Hyp.
2. $(b + a) + (-a) = b$ — Theorem, p. 11
3. $(a + b) + (-a) = b$ — Comm. ax. for add.
4. $0 + (-a) = b$ — Subs. prin.
5. $-a = b$ — Ax. of 0
6. $b = -a$ — Symm. prop. of $=$

31. 1. $a = b$ and $c = d$ — Hyp.
2. $a + c = a + c$ — Refl. prop. of $=$
3. $a + c = b + c$ — Subs. prin.
4. $a + c = b + d$ — Subs. prin.

33. 1. $x + 3 = 8$ — Hyp.
2. $x + 3 = 5 + 3$ — Subs. prin.
3. $x = 5$ — Canc. prop. of add.

35. 1. $x + 7 = -5$ — Hyp.
2. $= -5 + 0$ — Ax. of 0
3. $= -5 + [(-7) + 7]$ — Ax. of add. inv.
4. $= [-5 + (-7)] + 7$ — Assoc. ax. for add.
5. $= [-(5 + 7)] + 7$ — Prop. of neg. of sum
6. $= -12 + 7$ — Subs. prin.
7. $x = -12$ — Canc. prop. of add.

37. 1. $x = a + (-b)$ — Hyp.
2. $x + 0 = a + (-b)$ — Ax. of 0
3. $x + [b + (-b)] = a + (-b)$ — Ax. of ad. inv.
4. $(x + b) + (-b) = a + (-b)$ — Assoc. ax. for add.
5. $x + b = a$ — Canc. prop. of add.

Exercises, page 19

1. 120   **3.** -9 **5.** -27 **7.** -7 **9.** $\frac{3}{2}$
11. 100   **13.** -18 **15.** -12 **17.** positive
19. negative   **21.** 0

23. 1. b, c are real numbers, $c \neq 0$ Hyp.

   2. $bc\left(\dfrac{1}{c}\right) = b\left[(c)\left(\dfrac{1}{c}\right)\right]$ Assoc. ax. for mult.

   3. $= b \times 1$ Ax. of mult. inv.
   4. $= b$ Ax. of 1

   5. $bc\left(\dfrac{1}{c}\right) = b$ Trans. prop. of $=$

25. 1. $ca = cb$ Hyp.
   2. $ac = bc$ Comm. ax. for mult.
   3. $a = b$ Ex. 24

27. 1. $ab = a, a \neq 0$ Hyp.
   2. $ba = a$ Comm. ax. for mult.

   3. $ba\left(\dfrac{1}{a}\right) = a\left(\dfrac{1}{a}\right)$ Subs. prin.

   4. $b = a\left(\dfrac{1}{a}\right)$ Theorem, p. 16

   5. $b = 1$ Ax. of mult. inv.

29. 1. a is a real number, $a \neq 0$ Hyp.

   2. $\dfrac{1}{a} \cdot a = 1$ Ax. of mult. inv.

   3. Therefore $a = \dfrac{1}{\frac{1}{a}}$ Ex. 28 (Uniqueness)

   4. and $\dfrac{1}{\frac{1}{a}} = a$ Symm. prop. of $=$

31. 1. a, b real numbers   Hyp.
   2. $a(-b) = a[(b)(-1)]$ Mult. prop. of -1
   3. $= (ab)(-1)$ Assoc. ax. for mult.
   4. $= -ab$ Mult. prop. of -1
   5. $a(-b) = -ab$ Trans. prop. of $=$

33. 1. $a = b$ Hyp.

   2. $a\left(\dfrac{1}{a}\right) = 1, b\left(\dfrac{1}{b}\right) = 1$ Ax. of mult. inv.

   3. $a\left(\dfrac{1}{a}\right) = b\left(\dfrac{1}{b}\right)$ Trans. prop. of $=$

   4. $a\left(\dfrac{1}{a}\right) = a\left(\dfrac{1}{b}\right)$ Subs. prin.

   5. $\dfrac{1}{a} = \dfrac{1}{b}$ Canc. prop. of mult.

35. 1. $xb = a, b \neq 0$ Hyp.
   2. $xb = a \cdot 1$ Ax. of 1

   3. $= a\left(\dfrac{1}{b} \cdot b\right)$ Ax. of mult. inv.

   4. $= \left(a \cdot \dfrac{1}{b}\right)b$ Assoc. ax. for mult.

   5. $xb = \left(a \cdot \dfrac{1}{b}\right)b$ Trans. prop. of $=$

   6. $x = a \cdot \dfrac{1}{b}$ Canc. prop. of mult.

Exercises, pages 21–22

1. -9 **3.** -93 **5.** -235 **7.** 12   **9.** 56
11. -20 **13.** -55
15. $(5 - 3)(5 + 5) = 2 \cdot 10 = 20$;
$2 \cdot 5 + 10 = 10 + 10 = 20$
17. $[3 - (-4)](-4 - 2) = (7)(-6) = -42$;
$-(-4 + 1)(-4 - 2) + 6(-4) = -(-3)(-6) + (-24) = -18 - 24 = -42$ **19.** 1. Hypothesis
2. Axiom of additive inverses   **3.** Commutative axiom for addition   **4.** Relationship between addition and subtraction   **5.** Transitive property of equality
21. 1. a, b real numbers   Hyp.
   2. $(a - b) + b = [a + (-b)] + b$ Rel. bet. add. and subtr.
   3. $= a + [(-b) + b]$ Assoc. ax. for add.
   4. $= a + 0$ Ax. of add. inv.
   5. $= a$ Ax. of 0
   6. $(a - b) + b = a$ Trans. prop. of $=$
23. 1. a, b, c real numbers   Hyp.
   2. $-a(b - c) = (-a)b - (-a)c$ Theorem I, p. 20
   3. $= -ab - (-ac)$ Prop. of neg. in products
   4. $= -ab + ac$ Theorem II, p. 20
   5. $= ac - ab$ Ex. 19, above
   6. $-a(b - c) = ac - ab$ Trans. prop. of $=$
25. 1. $c - a = c - b$ Hyp.
   2. $-a + c = -b + c$ Ex. 19, above
   3. $-a = -b$ Canc. prop. of add.
   4. $-(-a) = -(-b)$ Ex. 26, p. 15
   5. $a = b$ Ex. 30, p. 15
27. 1. $a = b$ Hyp.
   2. $c - a = c - a$ Refl. prop. of $=$
   3. $c - a = c - b$ Subs. prin.
29. 1. $x - b = a$ Hyp.
   2. $x - b = a + 0$ Ax. of 0
   3. $= a + [b + (-b)]$ Ax. of add. inv.
   4. $= (a + b) + (-b)$ Assoc. ax. for add.
   5. $x - b = (a + b) + (-b)$ Trans. prop. of $=$
   6. $x + (-b) = (a + b) + (-b)$ Rel. bet. add. and subtr.
   7. $x = a + b$ Canc. prop. of add.

1. -2 3. 5 5. $87\frac{1}{2}$ 7. 378 9. 11 11. 1

13. -50 15. $\frac{8-3}{5} + 2 = \frac{5}{5} + 2 = 1 + 2 = 3;$

$8 + \frac{8+2}{-2} = 8 + \frac{10}{-2} = 8 + (-5) = 3$

17. $2(2)(2 - 3) + \frac{2}{2-3} = 4(-1) + \frac{2}{-1} =$

$-4 + (-2) = -6; \; -3(2) = -6$

19. 1. $ax = b, a \neq 0$ — Hyp.
   2. $ax = 1 \cdot b$ — Ax. of 1
   3. $= \left(a \cdot \frac{1}{a}\right) b$ — Ax. of mult. inv.
   4. $= a\left(\frac{1}{a} \cdot b\right)$ — Assoc. ax. for mult.
   5. $= a\left(b \cdot \frac{1}{a}\right)$ — Comm. ax. for mult.
   6. $= a\left(\frac{b}{a}\right)$ — Rel. bet. mult. and div.
   7. $ax = a\left(\frac{b}{a}\right)$ — Trans. prop. of $=$
   8. $x = \frac{b}{a}$ — Canc. prop. of mult.

21. 1. a, b, c real numbers, $c \neq 0$ — Hyp.
   2. $\frac{a-b}{c} = \frac{a+(-b)}{c}$ — Rel. bet. add. and subtr.
   3. $= \frac{a}{c} + \frac{(-b)}{c}$ — Theorem I, p. 23
   4. $= \frac{a}{c} + \left(-\frac{b}{c}\right)$ — Theorem II, p. 23
   5. $= \frac{a}{c} - \frac{b}{c}$ — Rel. bet. add. and subtr.
   6. $\frac{a-b}{c} = \frac{a}{c} - \frac{b}{c}$ — Trans. prop. of $=$

23. 1. a is a real number — Hyp.
   2. $\frac{-a}{a} = -\frac{a}{a}$ — Theorem II, p. 23
   3. $= -1$ — Ex. 22, above
   4. $\frac{-a}{a} = -1$ — Trans. prop. of $=$

25. 1. a is a real number, $a \neq 0$ — Hyp.
   2. $1 + \frac{a}{-a} = 1 + a\left(\frac{1}{-a}\right)$ — Rel. bet. mult. and div.
   3. $= (-a)\left(\frac{1}{-a}\right) + a\left(\frac{1}{-a}\right)$ — Ax. of mult. inv.
   4. $= (-a + a)\left(\frac{1}{-a}\right)$ — Dist. ax.
   5. $= 0\left(\frac{1}{-a}\right)$ — Ax. of add. inv.
   6. $= 0$ — Ax. of 0
   7. $1 + \frac{a}{-a} = 0$ — Trans. prop. of $=$
   8. $\frac{a}{-a} = -1$ — Uniqueness of add. inv. (See Ex. 29, p. 15)

Chapter 2   Review of Essentials

1. $3z^3 - 2z^2 + 8$ 3. $7n^5 - 2n^3 - 3n^2 + 2n + 1$
5. $3p^2q - 4pq^2 + 3pq$ 7. $z^3 - 4z^2 + 4z + 2$
9. $3n^5 - 4n^3 + 3n^2 + 2n - 3$
11. $5p^2q - 2pq^2 + 5pq - 10$ 13. $4y - 3$
15. 0 17. $4n^2 + 6n - 3$ 19. $-5n^2 + 7n - 2$
21. $-z^3 - 6z^2 + z + 4$ 23. $x^2 + 3xy + 5y^2$
25. $3x^2 + x + 2$ 27. $-t^2 - t - 4$
29. $12s - 9$ 31. $-4z^5 + 3z^2 - 2z$

1. Subtraction property; Division property   3. Additive property; Multiplicative property   5. Distributive axiom; Substitution principle   7. Subtraction property; Additive property   9. $\{12\}$ 11. $\{1\}$ 13. $\{-6\}$ 15. $\left\{\frac{3}{2}\right\}$
17. $\{12\}$ 19. $\{-10\}$ 21. $\{-2\}$ 23. $\{5\}$
25. $\{-1\}$

27. $r = \frac{b+c}{3a}$ 29. $n = 2$ 31. $t = \frac{v-k}{g}$

33. $I = \frac{E}{R}$ 35. $d = \frac{S}{3\pi} - \frac{5}{3}D$ 37. $b = \frac{ad}{c}$

39. $x = \frac{3z}{y} + 2z = 42$ 41. $t = \frac{6q+p}{3p-q} = \frac{8}{5}$

43. 1. $a = b$; a, b, c real numbers   Hyp.
    2. $a + c = a + c$ Refl. prop. of $=$
    3. $a + c = b + c$ Subs. prin.
45. 1. $a = b$; a, b, c real numbers   Hyp.
    2. $ac = ac$ Refl. prop. of $=$
    3. $ac = bc$ Subs. prin.
47. 1. $ax + b = c$; a, b, c real nos.   Hyp.
      $a \neq 0$
    2. $ax = c - b$ Subtr. prop.
    3. $x = \dfrac{c - b}{a}$ Div. prop.

Problems, pages 46–48

1. 43, 67   3. $88\,l$, $104\,l$ 5. 50, 51, 52   7. 12, 14
9. $40°$, $40°$, $100°$ 11. length, 14 m; width, 3 m
13. 5 min   15. 30 min   17. 25 yr   19. Carlos:
17 yr; father: 37 yr

Exercises, page 52

1. Additive property of order; Multiplicative property of
order   3. Additive property of order; Additive property of
order   5. Additive property of order; Multiplicative property
of order   7. Distributive axiom; Additive property of order
9. $\{z\colon z < 15\}$
11. $\{x\colon x < 3\}$
13. $\{x\colon x < -12\}$
15. $\{d\colon d < -8\}$
17. $\{z\colon z > 6\}$
19. $\{z\colon z < -14\}$
21. $\{t\colon t < 4\}$
23. $\{a\colon a > \frac{9}{2}\}$

25. 1. $a > 0$, $a \in \mathcal{R}$ Hyp.
    2. $a + (-a) > 0 + (-a)$ Add. prop. of order
    3. $0 > 0 + (-a)$ Ax. of add. inv.
    4. $0 > (-a)$ Ax. of 0
    5. $-a < 0$ Rewriting inequality
27. 1. $a < b$, $c > 0$; $a, b, c \in \mathcal{R}$ Hyp.
    2. There exists $d \in \mathcal{R}_+$ Def. of $<$
      such that $a + d = b$
    3. $(a + d)c = bc$ Mult. prop. of $=$
    4. $ac + dc = bc$ Dist. ax.
    5. dc is a positive real no.   Closure ax. for $\mathcal{R}_+$
    6. $ac < bc$ Def. of $<$

29. Restatement: For all real numbers a and b,
(1) if $a < b$, then $a - b < 0$ and (2) if $a - b < 0$, $a < b$
(1) 1. $a < b$; $a, b \in \mathcal{R}$ Hyp.
    2. $a + (-b) < b + (-b)$ Add. prop. of order
    3. $a + (-b) < 0$ Ax. of add. inv.
    4. $a - b < 0$ Rel. between add.
                       and subtr.
(2) 1. $a - b < 0$; $a, b \in \mathcal{R}$ Hyp.
    2. $a + (-b) < 0$ Rel. between add.
                       and subtr.
    3. $a + (-b) + b < 0 + b$ Add. prop. of order
    4. $a + 0 < 0 + b$ Ax. of add. inv.
    5. $a < b$ Ax. of 0
31. 1. $a > b$, $c > d$; $a, b, c, d \in \mathcal{R}$ Hyp.
    2. $a + c > b + c$,   Add. prop. of order
      $b + c > b + d$
    3. $a + c > b + d$ Trans. prop. of order

Exercises, page 55

1. $\{z\colon z \le 12\}$
3. $\{x\colon 7 < x < 10\}$
5. $\{t\colon 1 \le t \le 4\}$
7. $\{t\colon t \ge 7\}$
9. $\{z\colon z \ge 40\}$
11. $\{k\colon -2 < k \le \frac{1}{3}\}$
13. $\{r\colon r \ge \frac{21}{4}\}$
15. $\{z\colon z \ge -4\}$
17. $\{x\colon x \ge \frac{2}{3}\}$
19. $\{z\colon 0 > z > -\frac{2}{3}\}$
21. $\{b\colon b \ge \frac{3}{2}\}$

Problems, pages 55–56

1. 6, 17   3. Fahrenheit temperature between $-4°$ and
$50°$ 5. $2\frac{1}{2}$ h after take-off   7. 75 km/h
9. $14\frac{1}{2}$ min

4 ANSWERS TO SELECTED EXERCISES

1. Assume that $x = 1$.   **3.** Assume that $\frac{1}{a} = \frac{1}{b}$.

5. Assume that $-a = -b$.   **7.** Assume that $a = b$.
9. Assume that $x = 1$. Then $2x = 2$ by the multiplicative property of equality, and $2x - 1 = 1$. By hypothesis $2x - 1 = 3$. Therefore the assumption $x = 1$ is false and $x \neq 1$.

11. Assume that $\frac{1}{a} = \frac{1}{b}$. Then $\frac{b}{a} = 1$ and $b = a$. By hypothesis $a \neq b$. Therefore the assumption $\frac{1}{a} = \frac{1}{b}$ is false and $\frac{1}{a} \neq \frac{1}{b}$.   **13.** Assume $-a = -b$. Then $-(-a) = -(-b)$ by Ex. 26 on page 15. But $-(-a) = a$ and $-(-b) = b$ (Ex. 30, page 15), so $a = b$ by the substitution principle. But by hypothesis, $a \neq b$. Therefore the assumption $-a = -b$ is false and $-a \neq -b$.

15. Assume $a = b$. Then, using Ex. 33 on page 19, $\frac{1}{a} = \frac{1}{b}$. By hypothesis, $\frac{1}{a} \neq \frac{1}{b}$.   **17.** Assume $2a - 4 = 0$. Then $2a = 4$ and $a = 2$. But by hypothesis, $a \neq 2$. Therefore the assumption $2a - 4 = 0$ is false and $2a - 4 \neq 0$.   **19.** Assume $\frac{1}{a} \not< 0$. We must show two cases: **(1)** $\frac{1}{a} = 0$ and **(2)** $\frac{1}{a} > 0$.

Case 1: Assume $\frac{1}{a} = 0$.

1. $\frac{1}{a} = 0$ Hyp.

2. $\frac{1}{a} \cdot a = 0 \cdot a$ Mult. prop. of $=$

3. $1 = 0 \cdot a$ Ax. of mult. inv.

4. $1 = 0$ Ax. of 0

Case 2: Assume $\frac{1}{a} > 0$.

1. $\frac{1}{a} > 0$, $a < 0$ Hyp.

2. $\frac{1}{a} \cdot a < 0 \cdot a$ Mult. prop. of order.

3. $1 < 0 \cdot a$ Ax. of mult. inv.
4. $1 < 0$ Ax. of 0
In each case, the last step contradicts the true statement $1 > 0$. Therefore the assumption $\frac{1}{a} \not< 0$ is false and $\frac{1}{a} < 0$.

21.
1. $\frac{1}{a} < 1$, $a > 0$, $a \in \mathfrak{R}$	Hyp.
2. $\frac{1}{a} \cdot a < 1 \cdot a$	Mult. prop. of order
3. $1 < 1 \cdot a$	Ax. of mult. inv.
4. $1 < a$	Ax. of 1
5. $a > 1$	Rewriting inequality

23.
1. $\frac{1}{a} < \frac{1}{b}$, $a > 0$, $b > 0$, $a, b \in \mathfrak{R}$	Hyp.
2. $ab > 0$	Closure ax. for $\mathfrak{R}_+$
3. $\frac{1}{a}(ab) < \frac{1}{b}(ab)$	Mult. prop. of order
4. $\frac{1}{a}(ab) < \frac{1}{b}(ba)$	Comm. ax. for mult.
5. $\left(\frac{1}{a} \cdot a\right)b < \left(\frac{1}{b} \cdot b\right)a$	Assoc. ax. for mult.
6. $1 \cdot b < 1 \cdot a$	Ax. of mult. inv.
7. $b < a$	Ax. of 1
8. $a > b$	Rewriting inequality

25.
1. $a > b$, $a > 0$, $b > 0$; $a, b \in \mathfrak{R}$	Hyp.
2. $a^2 > ab$, $ab > b^2$	Mult. prop. of order
3. $a^2 > b^2$	Trans. prop. of order

1. 5   **3.** -6 **5.** 0   **7.** 1   **9.** $\frac{13}{3}$ **11.** 2
13. $-1\frac{5}{13}$
15. $\{2, -2\}$

17. $\{7, -5\}$

19. $\{1, 7\}$

21. $\{x: x \leq -2\} \cup \{x: x \geq 6\}$

23. $\{x: -\frac{13}{2} < x < \frac{11}{2}\}$

25. $\{a: a < -8\} \cup \{a: a > 12\}$

27. $\{x: -5 < x < -1\} \cup \{x: 1 < x < 5\}$

29. $\{x: -4 < x \leq -3\} \cup \{x: 5 \leq x < 6\}$

Chapter 3   Linear Functions and Relations

Written Exercises, page 71

1. -2 3. -10 5. -35 7. $\frac{21}{16}$ 9. $y = 3x$

11. $y = \frac{x}{2}$ 13. $y = 2x + 1$ 15. $y = x^3$

17. $y = x^2 - 1$ 19. 17   21. $\frac{173}{4}$ 23. $3a^2 + 1$

27. $h^2 + 6h$

Written Exercises, pages 74–75

1. $\{(1, 1), (1, 2), (2, 2), (3, 1)\}$; No.

3. $\{(-5, 4), (0, 6), (5, 2), (10, 6)\}$; Yes.

5. Yes   7. No   9. Yes

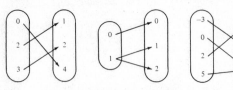

11. 13. 15.

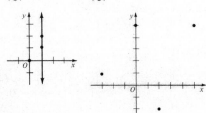

17. function.   19. not a function.   21. function.

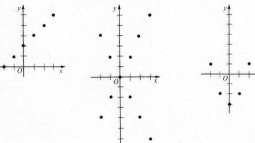

23. not a function.

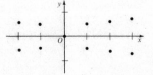

25.   27. 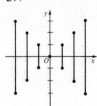   29.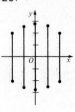

Written Exercises, pages 78–79

1. 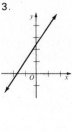   3. 5.

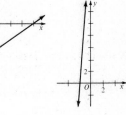

7. 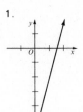   9. 11.

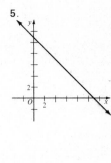

13. 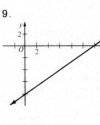   15.

17. $k = -3$ 19. $k = 0$

21. 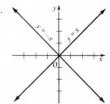   23.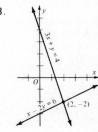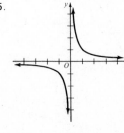

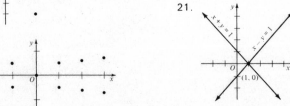

6 *ANSWERS TO SELECTED EXERCISES*

Written Exercises, page 81

1.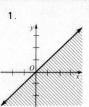

3.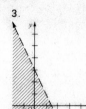

5.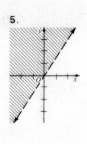

7.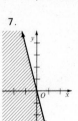

9.

11.

13.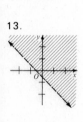

15.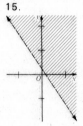

17.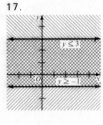

Answers for Q may vary in Ex. 15–20

15. $Q(2, 2)$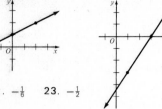

17. $Q(3, 0)$

19. $Q(-2, 3)$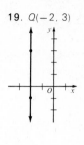

21. $-\frac{1}{6}$ 23. $-\frac{1}{2}$

Written Exercises, pages 88–89

1. $2x - y = -1$ 3. $4x - 5y = -40$
5. $6x - y = 0$ 7. $y = \frac{2}{3}$ 9. $x = 2$
11. $x + 3y = 6$ 13. $5x - 2y = 0$
15. $2x - y = 10$ 17. $16x - 40y = 19$
19. $3x - y = 2$ 21. $2x + y = 0$ 23. $y = 3$
25. $5x + y = 37$ 27. $2x - y = 14$
29. $2x - 3y = -13$ 31. $2x - y = -7$
33. $2x - y = 2$ 35. $2x - y = 6$
37. $3x - 2y = 6$ 39. $a = 1$

Written Exercises, page 93

1. $f: x \rightarrow -x + 3$ 3. $f: x \rightarrow -2x + 3$ 5. $f: x \rightarrow 2$
7. $f: x \rightarrow x + 1$ 9. Yes; $m = 2$ 11. No
13. No 15. No ($m = 0$) 17. $a = \frac{3}{2}$
19. $a = 6$ 21. $a = \frac{18}{5}$ 23. $a = \frac{45}{4}$
25. $x = 7.5$ 27. $C = 8\pi$ 29. $x = -\frac{13}{4}$ 31. Yes;
$f(x) = -\frac{1}{2}x$

Problems, page 94

1. $72\frac{2}{9}$ 3. 12 g hydrogen; 192 g oxygen 5. $640
7. $1180 9. $1466\frac{2}{3}$ m

Chapter 4 Solving Systems of Linear Equations or Inequalities

Written Exercises, page 85

1. $m = 2$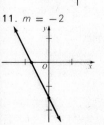

3. $m = 0$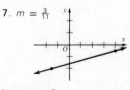

5. $m = \frac{4}{3}$

7. $m = \frac{3}{11}$

9. $m = \frac{1}{2}$

11. $m = -2$

13. $m = -5$

Written Exercises, pages 114–115

1. $\{(1, 1)\}$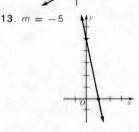

3. $\{(1, 2)\}$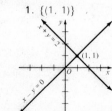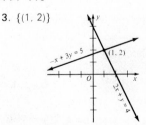

5. $\{(4, 1)\}$

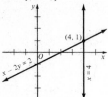

7. $\{(x, y): 4x - 5y = 2\}$

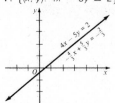

1.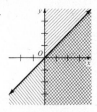

3.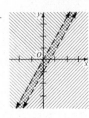

9. $\emptyset$

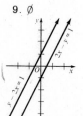

11. $\{(-1, 2)\}$

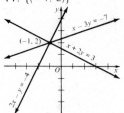

5.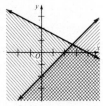

7.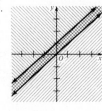

13. $\emptyset$

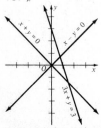

15. $\{(x, y): -x - 2y = 4\}$

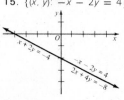

9.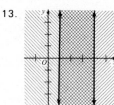

11.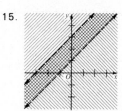

13.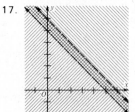

15.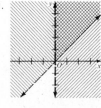

Written Exercises, pages 118-120

1. $\{(1, -2)\}$ 3. $\{(\frac{5}{6}, -\frac{1}{3})\}$ 5. $\{(-\frac{3}{2}, -\frac{7}{4})\}$
7. $\{(\frac{1}{3}, \frac{1}{3})\}$ 9. $\{(2, -3)\}$ 11. $\{(-5, -\frac{11}{3})\}$
13. $\{(1, -2)\}$ 15. $\{(\frac{5}{6}, -\frac{1}{3})\}$ 17. $\{(-\frac{3}{2}, -\frac{7}{4})\}$
19. $\{(\frac{1}{3}, \frac{1}{3})\}$ 21. $\{(2, -3)\}$ 23. $\{(-5, -\frac{11}{3})\}$
25. $\{(3, 0)\}$ 27. $\emptyset$ 29. $\{(1, -\frac{1}{2})\}$ 31. $\{(\frac{1}{5}, \frac{1}{4})\}$
33. $2x + 3y = 7$ 35. $3x - y = 11$

17.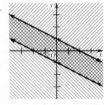

19.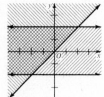

Written Exercises, page 123

1. $\{(2, 3)\}$ 3. $\{(-3, 4)\}$ 5. $\{(\frac{3}{2}, 0)\}$ 7. -2
9. -18 11. $\{2\}$ 13. $\{-2\}$ 15. $\{-1, 1\}$
17. $\{(-\frac{18}{19}, -\frac{22}{19})\}$ 19. $\{(\frac{2}{5}, -\frac{1}{5})\}$ 21. $\{(\frac{2}{5}, \frac{7}{5})\}$

21.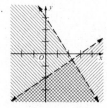

23.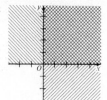

Problems, pages 126-128

1. Arnie had $3; Bernie had $5.   3. 28, 35
5. $-\frac{5}{4}, -\frac{45}{8}$ 7. $40°, 50°$ 9. 15 dimes, 14 quarters
11. 945 kg, 1455 kg   13. 560 km/h
15. $\frac{1}{2}x + \frac{3}{8}y = 6$ 17. $y = 3x + 4$ 19. $R = 4C + 5$
21. 35   23. 37   25. 4 km/h
27. 10 km/h (west), 2 km/h (east)

25.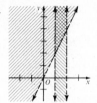

27.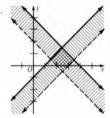

29.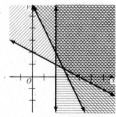

31.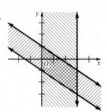

33.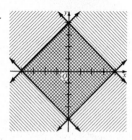

Chapter 5 Graphs in Space; Determinants

Written Exercises, page 144

1.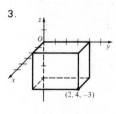

3.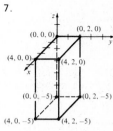

5.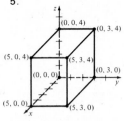

7.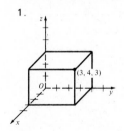

9.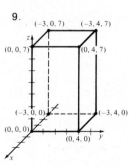

11.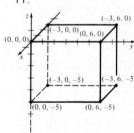

13.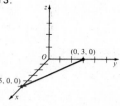

15.

17.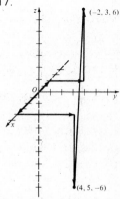

Written Exercises, pages 134–135

1. a.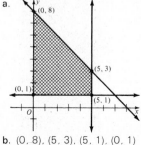

b. (0, 8), (5, 3), (5, 1), (0, 1)
c. −1 **d.** maximum: 9 at (5, 1); minimum: −8 at (0, 8)

3. a.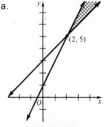

b. (2, 5) **c.** 26
d. no maximum; minimum: 26 at (2, 5)

5. a.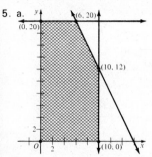

b. (0, 0), (0, 20), (6, 20), (10, 12), (10, 0) **c.** 30
d. maximum: 42 at (10, 12); minimum: 0 at (0, 0)

9. $1100

19.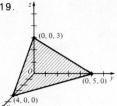

(0, 0, 3)

O

(0, 5, 0) y

(4, 0, 0)

21.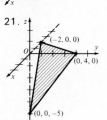

O

(−2, 0, 0)

(0, 4, 0) y

x

(0, 0, −5)

23.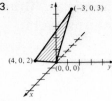

(−3, 0, 3)

(4, 0, 2)

(0, 0, 0) y

x

25.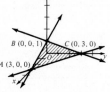

z

B

C

O

E y

A

x

D

$V = \frac{256}{3}$ cubic units

7. a. $z = 0$
$2x + y = -5$

$y = 0$
$2x - 5z = -5$

$x = 0$
$y - 5z = -5$

b.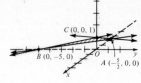

C (0, 0, 1)

B (0, −5, 0)

O

A $(-\frac{5}{2}, 0, 0)$

x

9.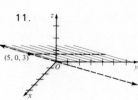

z

O y

$(\frac{5}{4}, 0, 0)$

x

11.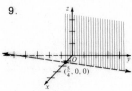

z

(5, 0, 3)

O y

x

13.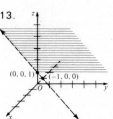

z

(0, 0, 1) (−1, 0, 0)

O

x

15.

z

$(0, 0, \frac{3}{2})$

O y

x

Written Exercises, page 150

1. a. $z = 0$
$x + y = 3$

$y = 0$
$x + 3z = 3$

$x = 0$
$y + 3z = 3$

b.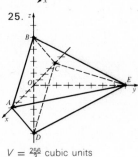

z

B (0, 0, 1)   C (0, 3, 0)

A (3, 0, 0)   O   y

x

3. a. $z = 0$
$3x + 4y = 12$

$y = 0$
$3x - 6z = 12$

$x = 0$
$4y - 6z = 12$

3. b.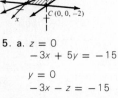

z

O

B (0, 3, 0)

A (4, 0, 0)

C (0, 0, −2)

x

5. a. $z = 0$
$-3x + 5y = -15$

$y = 0$
$-3x - z = -15$

$x = 0$
$5y - z = -15$

5. b.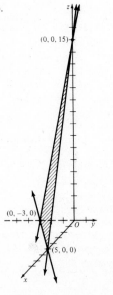

z

(0, 0, 15)

(0, −3, 0)

O y

(5, 0, 0)

x

17.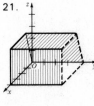

z

O y

x

19.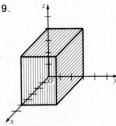

z

O y

x

21.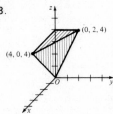

z

O y

x

23.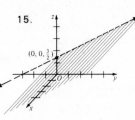

z

(0, 2, 4)

(4, 0, 4)

O y

x

25.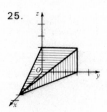

z

O y

x

27. $A = 2, B = -3$

29. $A = -2, B = 3$

Written Exercises, pages 154–155

1. $\{(1, 2, -6)\}$ 3. $\{(1, -1, 2)\}$ 5. $\{(3, 4, -5)\}$
7. $\{(-1, 2, 1)\}$ 9. $\{(1, 3, 3)\}$ 11. $\{(4, -1, 6)\}$
13. $\{(1, 3, -2)\}$ 15. $\{(4, -2, 2)\}$
17. $\{(-16, \frac{1}{4}, 14)\}$ 19. $\emptyset$ 21. Infinite solution set
23. $A = 3, B = -1, C = 2$ 25. $A = 5, B = 3, C = 4$

Written Exercises, pages 159–160

1. 6 3. 0 5. -1 7. $\{(1, 1, 2)\}$ 9. $\{(2, 1, 3)\}$
11. $\{(-\frac{10}{3}, \frac{26}{3}, -\frac{17}{3})\}$ 13. $0 = 0$; infinite solution set
15. $D = 0$; inconsistent 17. $A = 3, B = -1, C = 2$
19. $A = 5, B = 3, C = 4$

Problems, pages 161–162

1. 5, 2, -3 3. 4, 2, 1 5. 20 cm, 19 cm, 5 cm
7. 6 one-dollar bills, 15 five-dollar bills, 9 ten-dollar bills
9. 282 11. Mr. Leland: 40 yr; Mrs. Leland: 30 yr

Written Exercises, page 167

1. -67 3. -22 5. 45 7. $\{(1, 3, 0, -2)\}$

Cumulative Review, pages 170–171

1. 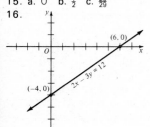 2. Axiom of additive inverses
3. -38 4. 10 5. 5 6. $-\frac{31}{3}$ 7. $4t^2 - t$
8. $2n^2 + 2n - 1$ 9. $\{12\}$ 10. $\{45\}$
11. $\{z: z \geq -11\}$ 12. $41°, 41°, 98°$
13. 7 14. $\{x: -\frac{8}{3} \leq x \leq 4\}$
15. a. 0 b. $\frac{1}{2}$ c. $\frac{20}{29}$

16. 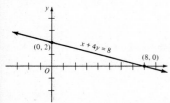   18.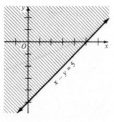

17. 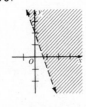   19.

20. 2 21. $y = 2x + 5$ 22. $2x + 3y = -3$
23. $y = 2$ 25. $\{(1, -1)\}$ 26. $\{(2, -2)\}$
27. $\{(-2, 3)\}$ 28. 18

24.

29.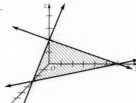

30. $\{(\frac{3}{5}, -1, \frac{12}{5})\}$
31. 1, 1, 0

Chapter 6   Polynomials and Rational Algebraic Expressions

Written Exercises, pages 176–177

1. $-6x^5$ 3. $\dfrac{-14x^3}{y}$ 5. $-15r^3t^4$ 7. $-12p^4q^3$

9. $-500a^8b^7c^{15}$ 11. $2x^2y$ 13. $-14r^2t$ 15. $\dfrac{-a^4}{2b^3}$

17. $\dfrac{y^6}{x^5}$ 19. $\dfrac{y^7}{x^5z^7}$ 21. $172a^4b^3$ 23. $22c^2 - 188c^4$

Written Exercises, page 179

1. 3.15×10^2 3. 7.8×10^0 5. 3.6×10^{-2}
7. 2.7315×10^4 9. 2.1×10^{-4}
11. 3.002×10^3 13. 610 15. 103,000
17. 0.00592 19. 0.2163 21. 30,200,000
23. 0.00003214 25. 40,000 27. 0.004
29. 7,000,000

Written Exercises, pages 181–182

1. $a^2 - 2a - 3$ 3. $p^2 + 6pq + 9q^2$ 5. $b^6 + 6b^3 + 9$
7. $x^{6a} - 10x^{3a} + 25$ 9. $8a^3 - 12a^2b + 6ab^2 - b^3$
11. $6x^3 + x^2 + 11x + 6$ 13. $s^4 + 2s^3t - 2st^3 - t^4$
15. $a^4b + 3a^3b^2 + 3a^2b^3 + ab^4$
17. $x^4 - 12x^3y + 54x^2y^2 - 108xy^3 + 81y^4$
19. $2t^4 - \frac{3}{2}t^2 + t - 4$ 21. $9a^{-4} + 6a^{-2} + 1$
23. $49 - 14x^{-3} + x^{-6}$ 25. $a = 3$ 27. $a = 4$
29. $a = -2$

Written Exercises, page 188

1. $2a(a - 3)$ 3. $6rs^2t(rs + 3)$ 5. $17n^2q(q^4 - 2n)$
7. $(x - 4)(x + 4)$ 9. $(6 - m)(6 + m)$
11. $(2y - 3)(2y + 3)$ 13. $(s^2 + 5)(s^2 - 5)$
15. $(x^2 + 8)^2$ 17. $(pq - 3)^2$ 19. $(3 + c)(2 - c)$
21. $(9x - 1)(2x - 9)$
23. $(p + 2)(p - 2)(p^4 + 4p^2 + 16)$
25. $(2 - 3y^2)(4 + 6y^2 + 9y^4)$ 27. $(z + t)(a - b)$
29. $(4r^2 + 3q^2)^2$ 31. $(c - 3)(c + d)$
33. $(y - 3)(y + 3)(y + 4)$ 35. $(2y^a - 5)(y^a + 3)$
37. $(a - 2b)^3(1 - a + 2b)(1 + a - 2b)$
39. $(3x^2 - y^2 - xy)(3x^2 - y^2 + xy)$

Written Exercises, pages 192–193

1. $\{3, -3\}$ 3. $\{-3\}$ 5. $\{-3, -1\}$
7. $\{5, -3\}$ 9. $\{4, -4\}$ 11. $\{-\frac{2}{3}, -\frac{1}{2}\}$
13. $\{4, -4\}$ 15. $\{2, 6\}$ 17. $\{2, 3\}$
19. $\{8a, -7a\}$ 21. $\{-2, 0, 3\}$
23. $\{3, -3, 4, -4\}$

25. $\{x: x \in \mathcal{R}, a = b\} \cup \left\{x: x = \dfrac{1}{a + b}, a \neq -b\right\}$

27. $\{x: x \in \mathcal{R}, a = b\} \cup \{x: x = 2 + a + b\}$

Problems, pages 193–194

1. 8   3. 4, 5, 6, and 7   5. 5 meters
7. 400 seconds   9. $m(\overline{AB}) = 4$
11. Truck: 15 km/h; sedan: 36 km/h

Written Exercises, page 195

1. $\{x: 0 < x < 9\}$
3. $\{y: y \leq -3 \text{ or } y \geq 4\}$
5. $\{x: -7 \leq x \leq 3\}$
7. $\{c: -6 \leq c \leq 6\}$
9. $\{y: 0 < y < 4 \text{ or } y < -4\}$
11. $\{r: r \geq 0\}$
13. $\emptyset$
15. $\{y: y \leq -3 \text{ or } y \geq 3\}$

Written Exercises, pages 197–198

1. $\dfrac{9}{25}$ 3. $\dfrac{b^2}{-5as}$ 5. $\dfrac{3x^{-6}}{2}$ 7. $\dfrac{x}{2x + 6}$
9. $\dfrac{-1}{(a - 3)^2}$ 11. $\dfrac{1}{(x - 5)^2}$ 13. $\dfrac{3b^2c}{b + 2c}$
15. $\dfrac{a - 2}{a + 1}$ 17. $\dfrac{1}{y - 1}$ 19. $\dfrac{x^2 + x + 1}{2(x + 2)}$ 21. 1
23. $\dfrac{1 - 2x}{x^2 - 2}$ 25. $\dfrac{a(3a - 1)^2(9a^2 - 12a + 13)}{(a^2 + 1)^3}$

Written Exercises, page 200

1. $7x^3 + 9xy - 4y$ 3. $-a + ab - 3$ 5. $y + 12$
7. $3n - 2$ 9. $4x^2 + 2x - 1$ 11. $y - 3 + \dfrac{3}{y + 3}$
13. $x + a + \dfrac{a^2 - a}{x - a}$ 15. $2x^2 + 2x + \dfrac{3}{1 - x}$
17. $3x^2 + 2x + 7 + \dfrac{20x - 8}{x^2 - 2x - 1}$ 19. $2x + 2y$
21. yes   23. $k = 7$ 25. $a = -1; b = 4$

Written Exercises, page 202

1. $\dfrac{972}{x}$ 3. k 6. $6(s - 2)$ 7. $\dfrac{xy}{4}$ 9. $\dfrac{m + 1}{m - 1}$
11. $4(x - 3)$ 13. $\dfrac{b - 5}{3b^3}$ 15. $\dfrac{2x - 1}{4}$

Written Exercises, page 205

1. 1   3. $\dfrac{1 - 9a}{2a^2}$ 5. $\dfrac{14}{9}$ 7. $\dfrac{5y - 13}{6}$
9. $\dfrac{17b^2 - 2b + 6}{12b^2}$ 11. $\dfrac{2x + 1}{x + 3}$ 13. $\dfrac{m(m + 1)}{m + 5}$
15. $\dfrac{y^2}{x^2 - y^2}$ 17. $\dfrac{-1}{p - q}$ 19. $\dfrac{x^4 - 2x^2 + 2x + 4}{x^2 - 1}$
21. $\dfrac{t + 1}{2t + 1}$ 23. 1   25. $\dfrac{y^2 + 1}{y^3 + 2y}$

Problems, pages 207–208

1. 20 and 50   3. 12 minutes   5. $8\frac{4}{7}$ hours
7. 4910 meters   9. $4\frac{2}{7}$ weeks   11. $\frac{20}{7}$ liters

Written Exercises, pages 210–211

1. $\{\frac{1}{10}\}$ 3. $\{\frac{13}{8}\}$ 5. $\emptyset$ 7. $\{2\}$ 9. $\{2\}$
11. $\{-\frac{1}{4}, 5\}$ 13. $\{(6, -1)\}$ 15. $\{(2, -1)\}$
17. $\{(4, 2)\}$ 23.
19. $y > -23$

-28 -26 -24 -22 -20 -18

21. $\{x: x > \frac{1}{2}$ or $x < -2\}$

  -3   -2   -1   0   1

25. $\{(-\frac{3}{2}, -\frac{1}{4})\}$ 27. $\{3, -1\}$

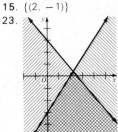

Problems, pages 211–212

1. 3 km/h   3. 21 and 56   5. 16   7. 20 km/h
9. $5\frac{1}{4}$ hours   11. 5 km

Chapter 7   Sequences and Series

Written Exercises, pages 219–220

1. 7, 9, 11, 13   3. 9, 5, 1, -3
5. -3, -1.5, 0, 1.5   7. $a_1 = -2, a_2 = 2$
9. $a_1 = 9, a_2 = 7$ 11. $a_1 = -3.8, a_2 = -3.5$
13. $a_{n+1} = a_n + 3$; yes   15. $a_{n+1} = a_n + (n+1)$; no
17. $a_{n+1} = (n+1)a_n$; no
19. 1, 1, 2, 3, 5, 8, 13, 21   21. a. -20, -5, 10, 25
b. Yes, the common difference is 15.
23. a. 16, 1, 4, 25   b. No, $1 - 16 \neq 4 - 1$
25. a. $-4k, -k, 2k, 5k$ b. Yes, the common difference
is $3k$.   27. -5

Written Exercises, pages 222–223

1. 61   3. -32   5. 476   7. 50   9. -21
11. 201   13. 1248.5   15. 4, -1, -6
17. -6, -4, -2, 0, 2   19. -8.25, -8.5, -8.75
21. 3, 9, 15, 21, 27   23. 47, 40, 33, 26, 19
25. 14, 7, 0, -7, -14   27. 22nd   29. $x = -1$
31. $s = 5$

Problems, pages 223–224

1. $11,250   3. $32   5. 5, 9, 13, 17 and 25 grams
7. $465   9. 29 credits   11. 13 meters/second

Written Exercises, pages 227–228

1. 78   3. -99   5. 172   7. -187   9. -6
11. -6   13. 30   15. 63   17. 0
19. $\sum_{n=1}^{4} (5n - 2)$ 21. $\sum_{n=1}^{5} (3n - 8)$ 23. 4   25. 10

Problems, pages 228–229

1. 456 seats   3. 78 times   5. $1350
7. $3850 profit   9. 1683   11. $1500

Written Exercises, page 233

1. 1, 4, 16, 64   3. $\frac{1}{2}, -\frac{3}{2}, \frac{9}{2}, -\frac{27}{2}$ 5. $\frac{27}{4}, \frac{9}{2}, 3, 2$
7. 48   9. $-\frac{2}{59,049}$ 11. -8   13. 0.0000002
15. 20

Problems, page 234

1. $1,048,576   3. 16,807 measures   5. 128 letters
7. 3 cm   11. $1221.02

Written Exercises, pages 237–239

1. $r = 2$ 3. $r = -\frac{1}{3}$ 5. $r = 7$ or $r = -7$
7. $r = 1$ or $r = -1$ 9. 3, 6, 12, 24, 48
11. 108, -36, 12, -4, $\frac{4}{3}$ 13. $\frac{3}{7}$, 3, 21, 147, 1029 or
$-\frac{3}{7}$, 3, -21, 147, -1029
15. -2, -2, -2, -2, -2 or -2, 2, -2, 2, -2
17. 1, 5, 25, 125   19. $-\frac{1}{2}, \frac{1}{4}, -\frac{1}{8}, \frac{1}{16}$
21. $-\frac{2}{9}, -\frac{2}{3}, -2, -6, -18$ or $-\frac{2}{9}, \frac{2}{3}, -2, 6, -18$
23. $\frac{2}{9}, \frac{1}{6}, \frac{1}{8}, \frac{3}{32}, \frac{9}{128}$ or $\frac{2}{9}, -\frac{1}{6}, \frac{1}{8}, -\frac{3}{32}, \frac{9}{128}$
25. 7th   27. $n = 7$ 29. 16   31. $\frac{3}{25}$ 33. 10%

Written Exercises, page 241

1. 242   3. -7812   5. -819   7. $121\frac{13}{27}$ 9. 93
11. $-2\frac{341}{512}$ 13. $6\frac{7}{9}$ 15. $a_5 = 648, S_5 = 488$
17. $a_1 = \frac{9}{25}, S_5 = 281\frac{4}{25}$ 19. $a_1 = 25, a_4 = \frac{8}{5}$
21. $n = 4, a_4 = -15$ 23. $r = -2, n = 5$
25. $r = \frac{1}{2}$ or $r = -\frac{3}{2}, a_3 = -\frac{1}{2}$ or $a_3 = -\frac{9}{2}$

Problems, pages 242–243

1. $1\frac{143}{625}$ meters   3. $59,062.50   5. $236\frac{1}{4}$ cm
7. $\frac{125}{128}$ grams   11. 1,048,575; 1,048,576

Written Exercises, page 248

1. $n = 1: 6, 1$. $n = 2: 5\frac{1}{4}, \frac{1}{4}$. $n = 3: 5\frac{1}{9}, \frac{1}{9}$.

$n = 4: 5\frac{1}{16}, \frac{1}{16}$. $|L - a_n| = \dfrac{1}{n^2}$ 3. $n = 1: 1.7, 0.3$.

$n = 2: 1.91, 0.09$. $n = 3: 1.973, 0.027$
$n = 4: 1.9919, 0.0081$. $|L - a_n| = (0.3)^n$
5. $n = 1: 3, 1$. $n = 2: 2\frac{1}{2}, \frac{1}{2}$. $n = 3: 2\frac{1}{3}, \frac{1}{3}$. $n = 4: 2\frac{1}{4}, \frac{1}{4}$.

$|L - a_n| = \dfrac{1}{n}$ 7. $n = 1: 3\frac{2}{3}, \frac{1}{3}$. $n = 2: 3\frac{8}{9}, \frac{1}{9}$.

$n = 3: 3\frac{26}{27}, \frac{1}{27}$. $n = 4: 3\frac{80}{81}, \frac{1}{81}$. $|L - a_n| = (\frac{1}{3})^n$
9. $n = 1: 0.36, 0.06$. $n = 2: 0.312, 0.012$.
$n = 3: 0.3024, 0.0024$. $n = 4: 0.30048, 0.00048$.
$|L - a_n| = (0.3)(0.2)^n$ 11. 4   13. 2   15. 11
17. 3   19. 1

Written Exercises, pages 252–253

1. 200   3. Not convergent   5. Not convergent
7. $33\frac{1}{3}$ 9. $2\frac{2}{999}$ 11. -3 13. 15   15. 35
17. $7\frac{1}{2}$ 19. -2 21. $\frac{1}{2}$ 23. $\frac{4}{11}$ 25. $\frac{4}{9}$ 27. $\frac{1}{33}$
29. $\frac{427}{999}$ 31. $3\frac{2}{9}$ 33. $1\frac{7}{18}$ 37. $-\frac{1}{3} < x < \frac{1}{3}$;

$\dfrac{5}{1 - 3x}$

Problems, pages 253–254

1. 250 meters   3. 4 meters   5. 72 cm

7. $\dfrac{1}{(1 - x)^2}$ 9. $\dfrac{2\sqrt{3}}{5}$ square units

Chapter 8   Radicals and Irrational Numbers

Written Exercises, page 261

1.   3.   5.

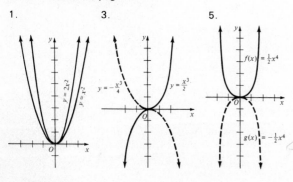

7. $a = 1$ 9. $a = \frac{7}{4}$ 11. $a = \frac{9}{4}$ 13. $y = 24$
15. $s = 5832$ 17. s is multiplied by $\frac{1}{16}$.

19. $a = \dfrac{1}{\sqrt{2}}$ or $a = -\dfrac{1}{\sqrt{2}}$

Problems, page 262

1. $4500   3. 28.8 meters   5. 500 watts
7. 108   9. 64 joules

Written Exercises, pages 264–265

1. 2.2   3. 1.1   5. 3.0   7. 1.6   9. $\{\frac{5}{6}, -\frac{5}{6}\}$
11. $\{\frac{7}{3}\}$ 13. $\{\frac{10}{11}, -\frac{10}{11}\}$ 15. $x = 1$
17. $x \geq -1$ 19. All real numbers   21. $x \geq 5$
23. All real numbers   25. $\{-5\}$ 27. $x - y = -7$

Written Exercises, pages 267–268

15. $\{-1, 2, -2\}$ 17. $\{0, \frac{15}{2}\}$

Written Exercises, page 270

1. $0.17\overline{5}$ 3. $1.\overline{6}$ 5. $0.38\overline{3}$ 7. $0.01\overline{142857}$

9. $\dfrac{1077}{500}$ 11. $\dfrac{39}{1000}$ 13. $\dfrac{10,251}{50,000}$ 15. $\dfrac{7}{9}$

17. $\dfrac{601}{495}$ 19. $-\dfrac{1237}{333}$ 21. $\dfrac{6,121,997}{99,900}$ 25. $\dfrac{5}{11}$

Written Exercises, pages 272–273

1. 1.73   3. 1.26   5. a. 0.65   b. $\dfrac{\sqrt{6}}{4} \doteq 0.6124$

7. a. 1.65   b. 1.6161161116 . . .   9. a. 0.263
b. 0.263030030003 . . .   11. a. 2.2364
b. 2.236464464446 . . .   13. a. -3.145
b. -3.14515515551 . . .

Written Exercises, pages 277–278

1. 25.45   3. 10.39   5. 5.20   7. -3.78
9. $\frac{2}{5}\sqrt[3]{2}$ 11. $\frac{1}{4}\sqrt{6}$ 13. $\frac{2}{7}\sqrt[3]{2}$

15. $\dfrac{|a|}{b}\sqrt[4]{b}, b > 0$ 17. $\dfrac{\sqrt{a^2 + b^2}}{a^2 + b^2}, a^2 + b^2 \neq 0$

19. $\dfrac{\sqrt[5]{20(x + h)^4}}{x + h}, x + h \neq 0$ 21. $\dfrac{y^2\sqrt[6]{32x^4}}{x^2}, x \neq 0$

23. $\dfrac{2x}{\sqrt{10x}}$ 25. $\dfrac{2(x + 1)^3}{\sqrt[3]{4(x + 1)^2}}$ 27. $\dfrac{7(t^2 + 3)}{\sqrt[4]{343(t^2 + 3)^3}}$

Problems, pages 278–279

1. $\frac{88}{49}\sqrt{5}$ s, 4 s   3. $\frac{1}{11}\sqrt{2982}$ cm, 5 cm
5. $140\sqrt{3}$ m/s, 242 m/s   7. $4\sqrt{77}$ cm, 35 cm
9. $\frac{1}{21}\sqrt{231}$, $\frac{5}{7}$

Written Exercises, pages 280–281

1. $9\sqrt{2} \doteq 12.73$ 3. $-19\sqrt{3} \doteq -32.91$
5. $15 + \frac{1}{6}\sqrt[3]{180} \doteq 15.94$ 7. $-18x\sqrt{x}$
9. $(-2x^2 + 3)\sqrt[4]{3}$ 11. $-42\sqrt{2}$ 13. $10 + 2\sqrt{21}$
15. $122 + 7\sqrt{11}$ 17. $-2(\sqrt{7} - 3)$
19. $-\frac{8}{5}(\sqrt{14} + 3)$ 21. -2 23. $x + y$
25. $\frac{1}{9}(\sqrt[3]{49} - \sqrt[3]{14} + \sqrt[3]{4})$ 27. $\dfrac{4\sqrt{x + 3} + 8}{x - 1}$
33. $(x + \sqrt{2})^2$
35. $(x + 3\sqrt[3]{3})(x^2 - 3\sqrt[3]{3}x + 9\sqrt[3]{9})$
37. $(x + 2y + \sqrt{3})(x + 2y - \sqrt{3})$

Written Exercises, pages 282–283

1. $\{36\}$ 3. $\{25\}$ 5. $\{\frac{48}{5}\}$ 7. $\{162\}$
9. $\{-\frac{1}{27}\}$ 11. $\{9\}$ 13. $\{8, -9\}$ 15. $\{3\}$
17. $\{-\frac{17}{4}\}$ 19. $\{-32\}$ 21. $\emptyset$ 23. $\{16\}$
25. $\{\frac{1}{4}\}$ 27. $d = \dfrac{3w}{4\pi r^3}$ 29. $a = \sqrt{c^2 - b^2}$,
$a = -\sqrt{c^2 - b^2}$ 31. $d = \dfrac{T}{4v^2 - 1}$

Written Exercises, page 286

1. $\{3 + \sqrt{14}, 3 - \sqrt{14}\}$ or $\{6.7, -0.7\}$
3. $\{4 + \sqrt{19}, 4 - \sqrt{19}\}$ or $\{8.4, -0.4\}$
5. $\{-\frac{5}{2} + \frac{1}{2}\sqrt{5}, -\frac{5}{2} - \frac{1}{2}\sqrt{5}\}$ or $\{-1.4, -3.6\}$
7. $\{-\frac{11}{12} + \frac{1}{12}\sqrt{409}, -\frac{11}{12} - \frac{1}{12}\sqrt{409}\}$ or $\{0.8, -2.6\}$
9. $\{3 + \sqrt{14}, 3 - \sqrt{14}\}$ or $\{6.7, -0.7\}$
11. $\{4 + \sqrt{19}, 4 - \sqrt{19}\}$ or $\{8.4, -0.4\}$
13. $\{-\frac{5}{2} + \frac{1}{2}\sqrt{5}, -\frac{5}{2} - \frac{1}{2}\sqrt{5}\}$ or $\{-1.4, -3.6\}$
15. $\{-\frac{11}{12} + \frac{1}{12}\sqrt{409}, -\frac{11}{12} - \frac{1}{12}\sqrt{409}\}$ or $\{0.8, -2.6\}$
17. $\{0.6, -\frac{2}{3}\}$ 19. $\{\frac{3}{8} + \frac{1}{8}\sqrt{89}, \frac{3}{8} - \frac{1}{8}\sqrt{89}\}$ 21. $\emptyset$
23. $\{4 + \sqrt{14}, 4 - \sqrt{14}\}$
25. $\{-1 + \sqrt{1 + \sqrt{3}}, -1 - \sqrt{1 + \sqrt{3}}\}$
27. $\{\sqrt{-2 + \sqrt{6}}, -\sqrt{-2 + \sqrt{6}}\}$ 29. $\{\sqrt[3]{2}, \sqrt[3]{-2}\}$

Problems, pages 286–287

1. $7\frac{1}{2}$ cm, $12\frac{1}{2}$ cm   3. 11.5 cm wide, 18.5 cm long
5. $-\frac{5}{2} + \frac{3}{2}\sqrt{5}$ meters   7. 4 hours   9. $n = 4$

Chapter 9   Complex Numbers and Polynomial Functions

Written Exercises, pages 294–295

1. -1 3. $-i$ 5. -17 7. $i\sqrt{7}$ 9. $6i\sqrt{5}$
11. $\frac{1}{3}\sqrt{6}i$ 13. -6 15. 3 17. $\frac{4}{3}$
19. $-i\sqrt{3}$ 21. $23i\sqrt{3}$ 23. $19i\sqrt{2}$
25. $-\frac{1}{6}\sqrt{6}i$ 27. 0 29. 0 31. $(x\sqrt{x} + \sqrt{x} + x)i$

Written Exercises, pages 297–298

1. a. $5 + 10i$ b. $5 + 6i$
3. a. $2 - 5i$ b. $-2 - 7i$
5. a. $6 + 13i$ b. $-4 + i$ 7. a. $5 - i$ b. $1 - 7i$
9. a. 10 b. $-6i$ 11. a. -2 b. $-2i$
13. a. 10 b. $-10i$ 15. $\{(-3, 8)\}$
17. $\{(1, -2)\}$ 19. $\{(1, 2)\}$

Written Exercises, pages 299–300

1. 17 3. 13 5. 1 7. $-\frac{1}{2} + \frac{1}{2}\sqrt{3}i$
9. $\frac{7}{5} - \frac{6}{5}i$ 11. $\frac{1}{25} - \frac{18}{25}i$ 13. $-\frac{1}{2} - \frac{1}{2}\sqrt{3}i$
15. $-4 + 3i$ 17. $\frac{19}{17} - \frac{9}{17}i$ 19. $\{-\frac{9}{20} + \frac{3}{20}i\}$
21. $\{5i\}$

Written Exercises, pages 302–303

1. Two unequal rational roots   3. Two complex conjugate
roots   5. Two unequal irrational roots   7. Two unequal
irrational roots   9. One, irrational   11. None
13. $\{5, 4\}$ 15. $\{-\frac{1}{2} + \frac{1}{2}\sqrt{15}i, -\frac{1}{2} - \frac{1}{2}\sqrt{15}i\}$
17. $2\sqrt{3}, -2\sqrt{3}$ 19. $k < -9$ 21. $\{i, -3i\}$

Written Exercises, pages 305–306

1. $x^2 + 3x + 2 = 0$ 3. $x^2 - 6x + 8 = 0$
5. $x^2 - 2x - 1 = 0$ 7. $x^2 - 4\sqrt{2}x = 0$
9. $x^2 - 2x + 2 = 0$ 11. $x^2 - 2ix = 0$
13. $\{-\frac{5}{3}\}, -\frac{5}{3}$ 15. $\{-15 - \sqrt{7}\}, -164 - 40\sqrt{7}$
17. $\{\frac{5}{2}\}, \frac{25}{4}$ 19. $\frac{5}{4}$

Written Exercises, page 309

1. $(-4, 3)$ 3. $(-4, -1)$ 5. $(m - p, q)$
7. 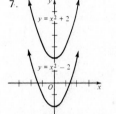   9.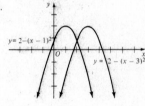

11.

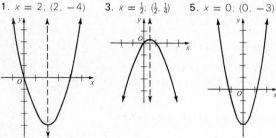

$F(x) = \frac{1}{2} + \frac{1}{2}(x + \frac{3}{2})^2$

$G(x) = \frac{1}{2} - \frac{1}{2}(x + \frac{3}{2})^2$

13. 1   15. −9
17. 3, −3   19. 0, 4
21. $a = 1, k = -5$
23. $a = -\frac{1}{2}, k = -1$
25. No

Written Exercises, page 312

1. $x = 2; (2, -4)$ 3. $x = \frac{1}{2}; (\frac{1}{2}, \frac{1}{4})$ 5. $x = 0; (0, -3)$

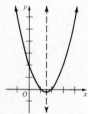  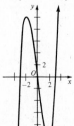

7. $x = \frac{3}{2}; (\frac{3}{2}, -\frac{1}{4})$ 9. $x = -1; (-1, -2)$

11. $x = -1; (-1, 6)$

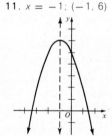

13. $y = -x^2 + 1$
15. $y = x^2 + 2x - 5$

Problems, pages 312–313

1. 8, 8   3. 5, 5   5. 40.625 meters
7. At the midpoint   9. a. $y = 330 - (15 - x)(11 - x)$
b. $\overline{RA}$: 4; $\overline{AS}$: 0

Written Exercises, page 314

1. $\{x: x < -2 \text{ or } x > 2\}$ 3. $\{x: x \leq 0 \text{ or } x \geq 2\}$

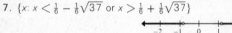

5. $\{x: x \leq -2 \text{ or } x \geq 4\}$

7. $\{x: x < \frac{1}{6} - \frac{1}{6}\sqrt{37} \text{ or } x > \frac{1}{6} + \frac{1}{6}\sqrt{37}\}$

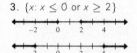

9. $\{x: -1 < x < 3\}$

Written Exercises, page 317

1. 0; 3 is a zero of $P(x)$ 3. 0; −2 is a zero of $P(x)$
5. 3   7. $39 + 4i$ 9. 0; 3 is a zero of $R(x)$
11. 60   13. 0; a is a zero of $S(y)$ 15. −106
17. $4\frac{1}{2}$ 19. $a = 2, b = 1$

Written Exercises, page 320–322

1. $P(x) = (x - 2)(4x^2 + 3x + 8) + 17$
3. $P(x) = (x + 3)(x^2 + x + 2) - 4$

5. $x^2 + 7x - 17 + \dfrac{83}{x + 4}$

7. $2x^3 + (-1 + 6i)x^2 - (18 + 3i)x + (11 - 54i) + \dfrac{166 + 33i}{x - 3i}$

17. $2x^2 - 3x - 16$ 19. $2x^2 - 5x + 16$
21. $\{4, -3, -2\}$ 23. $\{2, 1, \frac{3}{2}, -1\}$ 29. −6
31. −8   33. $\{\frac{1}{2}i + \frac{1}{2}\sqrt{3}, \frac{1}{2}i - \frac{1}{2}\sqrt{3}\}$
35. $\{i\sqrt{2}, -i\sqrt{2}\}$

Written Exercises, page 324

1. $-i\sqrt{3}$ 3. $2 + i; x^3 - 11x^2 + 33x - 35 = 0$
5. $\{2 + i, -4, 3\}$
7. a. $(x^2 + 3)(x + 1)$ b. $(x + \sqrt{3}\,i)(x - \sqrt{3}\,i)(x + 1)$
9. a. $(x + 5)(x - \frac{5}{2} - \frac{1}{2}\sqrt{5})(x - \frac{5}{2} + \frac{1}{2}\sqrt{5})$ b. Same as (a).
11. a. $(x + 4)(x^2 - 4x + 6)$
b. $(x + 4)(x - 2 - i\sqrt{2})(x - 2 + i\sqrt{2})$

Written Exercises, page 326

1. $\{-3, 0, 3\}$ 3. $\{0, 3\}$ 5. $\{0, 2, 3\}$

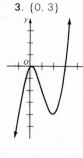 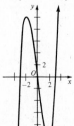 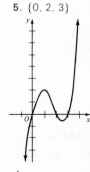

7. $\{-2, -1, 1, 2\}$
(graph at right)

9. 0.20   11. 3

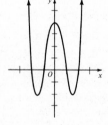

1. -47 2. Commutative axiom for multiplication

3. $5p^2 + 2$ 4. $\{\frac{1}{2}\}$ 5.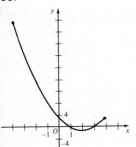

6. 0 7. a. -3 b. 4 c. 0 8. $5x - 9y = -53$

9. $\{(1, 0, 2)\}$ 10. $\dfrac{7bc}{a^2}$ 11. $x^4 - x^2 + 5x - 2$

12. $2(x - 5)(x + 2)$ 13. $3(1 - 3y)(1 + 3y + 9y^2)$
14. $(x - 2)(x + y)$ 15. $(x + 3y)(x - 3y)(x^2 + 9y^2)$

16. $\{1, -4\}$ 17. $4y$ 18. $\dfrac{n - 3}{(n + 1)(n + 3)}$

19. $\dfrac{x + 2z}{z + 2x}$ 20. $\dfrac{-6x - 4}{(x - 4)(x + 4)(x - 1)}$ 21. 58

22. -12 23. $5, 15, 45, 135$ 24. -62
25. $0.56 + 0.56(0.01) + 0.56(0.01)^2 + \cdots; \frac{56}{99}$
26. $\{0.9, -0.9\}$ 27. $28\sqrt{2}$ 28. $\sqrt[3]{x}$
29. $-3\sqrt{3}$ 30. $-15 - 7\sqrt{7}$
31. $\{1 + \sqrt{2}, 1 - \sqrt{2}\}$ 32. 12
33. $12 + i$ 34. $-1 - 4i$ 35. $\frac{7}{34} - \frac{11}{34}i$
36.   37. $7 - 4i$ 38. Root $\doteq -\frac{1}{3}$

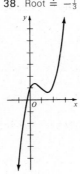

Chapter 10   Quadratic Relations and Systems

1. a. 4 b. $(2, 6)$ 3. a. 2 b. $(\frac{1}{2}, 6)$ 5. a. $\sqrt{13}$
b. $(4, \frac{13}{2})$ 7. a. $\sqrt{5}$ b. $(\frac{3}{2}, -4)$ 9. a. $|m - n|\sqrt{2}$
b. $\left(\dfrac{m + n}{2}, \dfrac{m + n}{2}\right)$ 11. a. $4\sqrt{2} + 2\sqrt{10}$ b. Yes

c. No   13. a. $3\sqrt{10} + 5\sqrt{2}$ b. No   c. Yes
15. a. 48 b. No   c. No

17. $ABCD$ is a parallelogram.   19. $ABCD$ is not a parallelogram.

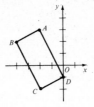 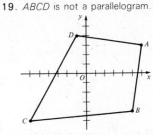

21. $A(3, 5)$ 23. $A(0, 6)$
25. $|a - b|$ 27. $7x - y = 1$
29. 3

1. $y = x$ 3. $y = \frac{2}{3}x + \frac{5}{3}$ 5. $y = -\frac{1}{55}x + 1\frac{54}{55}$
7. $y = -\frac{1}{3}x + \frac{5}{3}$ 9. $x = -1$ 11. $y = -\frac{1}{4}x + 6\frac{5}{8}$

1. $x^2 + y^2 - 2x - 4y + 1 = 0$ 3. $x^2 + y^2 - 36 = 0$

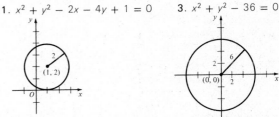

5. $x^2 + y^2 - x - 7y + \frac{23}{2} = 0$
    9. $(x - 0)^2 + (y - 0)^2 = 5^2$

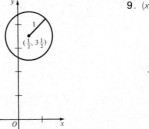 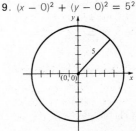

7. $x^2 + y^2 - 2hx - 2ky + h^2 + k^2 - r^2 = 0.$
    11. $(x - (-2))^2 + (y - 0)^2 = 2^2$

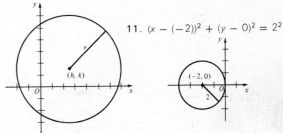

13. $(x - (-3))^2 + (y - 1)^2 = 3^2$

15. $(x - 3)^2 + (y - (-2))^2 = 4^2$

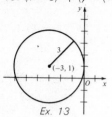

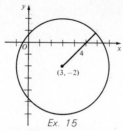

Ex. 13

Ex. 15

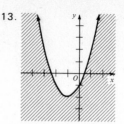

13.

15. $x = \frac{1}{8}y^2$

17. $y = \frac{1}{8}x^2 - \frac{1}{4}x + \frac{1}{8}$

19. $y = \frac{1}{8}x^2 - \frac{1}{2}x + \frac{7}{2}$

17.

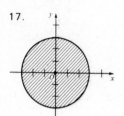

19.

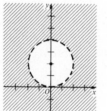

Written Exercises, pages 346–347

1.

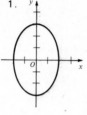

3.

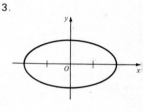

21. $x^2 + y^2 + 4x - 2y - 29 = 0$

23. $x^2 + y^2 - 2hx - 2ky + h^2 + k^2 - 25 = 0$

25. $x^2 + y^2 - 4x - 2y - 40 = 0$ **27.** $y = -\frac{2}{3}x + 4\frac{1}{3}$

5.

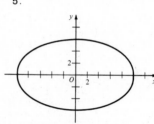

7.

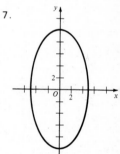

Written Exercises, pages 343–344

1.

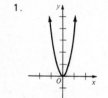

3.

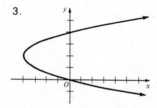

9.

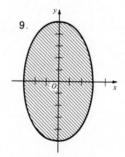

11. $\dfrac{x^2}{9} + \dfrac{y^2}{4} = 1$

13. $\dfrac{x^2}{4} + \dfrac{y^2}{13} = 1$

15. $\dfrac{x^2}{25} + \dfrac{y^2}{16} = 1$

5.

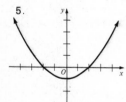

7.

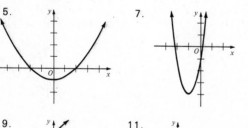

9.

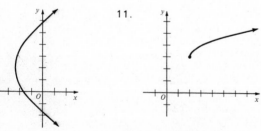

11.

19.

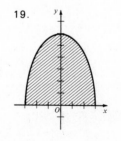

21.

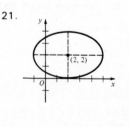

Written Exercises, pages 351–352

1.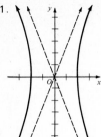

3.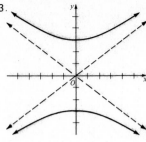

5.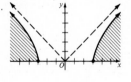

7.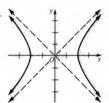

9.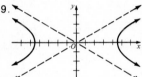

11. $\dfrac{y^2}{16} - \dfrac{x^2}{9} = 1$

13. $\dfrac{y^2}{9} - \dfrac{x^2}{7} = 1$

15. $\dfrac{4x^2}{49} - \dfrac{4y^2}{51} = 1$

19.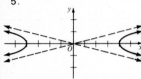

21.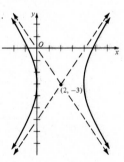

Written Exercises, pages 354–355

1. $\frac{1}{2}$ **3.** -1 **5.** $\frac{1}{45}$ **7.** 4 or -4 **9.** $\frac{1}{3}$ **11.** $\frac{3}{4}$
13. 48 **15.** $\frac{512}{243}$ **17.** 6 **19.** y is halved.
21. $xy = 2$

Problems, pages 355–356

1. 32 cubic meters **3.** 21,377 plants **5.** $4\frac{1}{6}$ cm
7. 2.5 tonnes

Written Exercises, pages 357–358

1. $\{(-1, -4), (5, 20)\}$

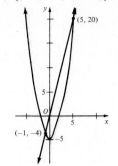

3. $\{(-1, 4), (2, 1)\}$

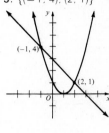

5. $\{(1, 3), (-1, 3), (-1, -3), (1, -3)\}$

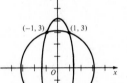

9. $\{(2, 2), (-2, -2)\}$

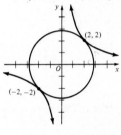

7. $\{(2, 2), (-2, 2), (-2, -2), (2, -2)\}$

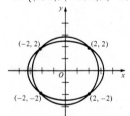

11. $\{(\frac{1}{2}, -8), (4, -1)\}$

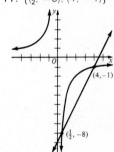

13.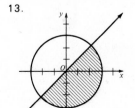

15.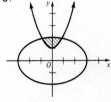

Written Exercises, pages 360–361

1. $\{(5, 20), (-1, -4)\}$ 3. $\{(2, 3), (3, 2)\}$
5. $\{(2, 4), (4, 2)\}$
7. $\{(\frac{16}{9} + \frac{2}{9}\sqrt{19}, -\frac{4}{9} + \frac{4}{9}\sqrt{19}), (\frac{16}{9} - \frac{2}{9}\sqrt{19}, -\frac{4}{9} - \frac{4}{9}\sqrt{19})\}$
9. $\{(i\sqrt{7}, 4), (-i\sqrt{7}, 4)\}$
11. $\{(4, -3), (-3, 4)\}$ 13. $\{(2, 0), (3, 1)\}$
15. $\{(-1, -3)\}$ 17. $\{(3, 12)\}$

19. $\left\{(1, 1), \left(\dfrac{a}{b}, \dfrac{b}{a}\right)\right\}$

Problems, page 361

1. 2, 3   3. 1 m by 12 m   5. 6, 8   7. 6, 9

Written Exercises, page 363

1. $\{(4, 3), (4, -3), (-4, 3), (-4, -3)\}$
3. $\{(3, \sqrt{2}), (-3, \sqrt{2}), (3, -\sqrt{2}), (-3, -\sqrt{2})\}$
5. $\{(0, 2), (0, -2)\}$
7. $\{(\sqrt{3}, 4), (\sqrt{3}, -4), (-\sqrt{3}, 4), (-\sqrt{3}, -4)\}$,
9. $\{(3, 6), (3, -6), (-3, 6), (-3, -6)\}$
11. $\{(\frac{12}{5}i\sqrt{10}, \frac{3}{5}\sqrt{385}), (\frac{12}{5}i\sqrt{10}, -\frac{3}{5}\sqrt{385}),$
$(-\frac{12}{5}i\sqrt{10}, \frac{3}{5}\sqrt{385}), (-\frac{12}{5}i\sqrt{10}, -\frac{3}{5}\sqrt{385})\}$
13. $\{(2, 1), (-2, -1), (i, -2i), (-i, 2i)\}$
15. $\{(4, 3), (-3, -4)\}$
17. $\{(a, a - b), (a, b - a), (-a, a - b), (-a, b - a)\}$

Problems, page 364

1. 4, 5   3. 8 m by 14 m   5. 9 drills

7. $\dfrac{16x^2}{729 + 27\sqrt{697}} + \dfrac{y^2}{6(27 - \sqrt{697})} = 1$

or $\dfrac{16x^2}{729 - 27\sqrt{697}} + \dfrac{y^2}{6(27 + \sqrt{697})} = 1$

Chapter 11   Exponents and Logarithms

Written Exercises, pages 369–370

1. $23^{\frac{1}{2}}$ 3. $11^{\frac{1}{3}}$ 5. $x^{-\frac{1}{5}}$ 7. $a^{\frac{3}{4}}b^{\frac{1}{4}}$ 9. $\dfrac{3^{\frac{1}{3}}}{t^{\frac{1}{3}}}$

11. $(a + b^2)^{\frac{1}{3}}$ 13. $\sqrt[5]{3^2}$ 15. $\sqrt[3]{(3t)^2}$ 17. $\sqrt[3]{r^2 t}$
19. $\sqrt[7]{x^4}$ 21. $\sqrt[11]{m^4 n^{10}}$ 23. $\sqrt[5]{(y^2 + 4)^3}$ 25. 3
27. $\frac{1}{5}$ 29. 128   31. 0.3   33. 3   35. $3\sqrt[6]{3^5}$
37. $\frac{1}{4}\sqrt[3]{2}$ 39. $\frac{1}{4}\sqrt{2}$ 41. 2   43. $y\sqrt[6]{32}$ 45. n^2
47. $\sqrt{n} - 1$ 49. $t - 1$ 51. $c^5 - d^3$ 53. $\{\frac{81}{16}\}$
55. $\{62\}$ 57. $\{1\}$

Written Exercises, page 372

1. 81   3. $2^{4\sqrt{2}+1}$ 5. 125   7. $\frac{1}{8}$ 9. $\{2\}$
11. $\{12\}$ 13. $\{\frac{3}{5}\}$ 15. $\{-\frac{1}{4}\}$ 17. $n = 2$
19. $n = 7$
21.   23.   25. $\{(1, 2), (2, 4)\}$

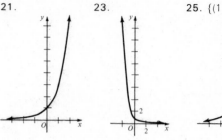

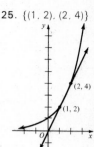

Written Exercises, page 375

1. $F^{-1} = \{(x, y): y = x + 3\}$; F and F^{-1} are functions.
3. $F^{-1} = \{(x, y): y = \pm\sqrt{x}\}$; F is a function, F^{-1} is not.
5. $F^{-1} = \{(x, y): x = 3\}$; F is a function; F^{-1} is not.
7. $F^{-1} = \{(x, y): y = -x\} = F$; F and F^{-1} are functions.
9. $F^{-1} = \{(x, y): y = \pm x, x \geq 0\}$; F is a function; F^{-1} is not.

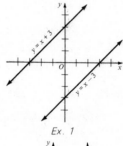

Ex. 1

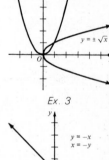

Ex. 3

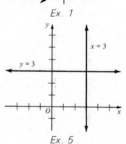

Ex. 5

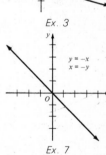

Ex. 7

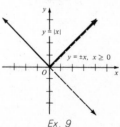

Ex. 9

11. $F^{-1} = \{(x, y): y = \pm\sqrt{4 - x^2}, x \geq 0\}$
F is a function, F^{-1} is not.

13. $F^{-1} = \{(x, y): x = 3^y\}$; F and F^{-1} are functions.

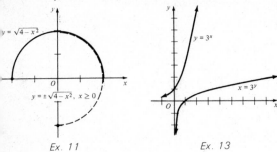

Ex. 11   Ex. 13

Written Exercises, pages 377–378

1. 3   3. 6   5. 3   7. 0   9. 4   11. 1
13. {1}   15. {32}   17. {64}   19. {100}
21. {0}   23. {27}   25. {500}   27. {−5, 2}
29. {401}

Written Exercises, page 381

1. $\{12\frac{1}{2}\}$ 3. {5, −5}   5. {4}   7. {4}   9. ∅
11. {3}

Written Exercises, page 384

1. 1.7076   3. 0.8751   5. 7.8976 − 10
7. 2.0128   9. 5.5682 − 10   11. 5.9031
13. 16.8   15. 0.803   17. 3.39   19. 0.91
21. 0.0229   23. 5.5   25. 27.3   27. 39,000
29. 0.106   31. $\{x: x > 2$ or $0 < x < 1\}$

Written Exercises, page 386

1. 3.1824   3. 9.9383 − 10   5. 2.3083
7. 8.0994 − 10   9. 8.1617 − 10   11. 0.0132
13. 32.25   15. 64.37   17. 0.5076
19. 0.004634   21. 6694   23. 11.91

Written Exercises, page 390

1. 12.9   3. −2.53   5. 17.3   7. −0.247
9. 0.480   11. 10.6   13. −1.34   15. 7.57
17. 3.49   19. 1877   21. $3 \log_a b$

Written Exercises, pages 395–396

1. 375   3. 2.65   5. 7.88   7. 0.923
9. 0.570   11. 1.8   13. 2.44   15. 0.0246
17. −6300   19. 3.57   21. 17.7   23. 0.335
25. {7.03}   27. {5.7}   29. {1.07}   31. $\{\frac{1}{3}\}$
33. $\{\frac{4}{13}\sqrt{195}\}$

Problems, pages 396–397

1. $10,800   3. At sea level, $P = 760$ mm; at 4 km,
$P = 462$ mm   5. 223 m³

Written Exercises, pages 400–401

1. {1.39}   3. {2.93}   5. {62.9}   7. {18.0}
9. 1.89   11. −0.108   13. 2.71   15. 5.13
17. −1.94   19. 0.969   21. {6.25}
23. {1.05}   25. {0.28}

Problems, page 401

1. About 8 years   3. 5.57 km   5. 2.09 cm

Chapter 12   Permutations, Combinations, and Probability

Written Exercises, pages 409–410

1. 25   3. 210   5. 6   7. 17,576,000   9. 60
11. 128   13. 84

Written Exercises, page 413

1. 40,320   3. 39,916,800   5. 120
7. 20,160   9. 1440   11. 720   13. 12
15. 120   23. {3}   25. {7}

Written Exercises, pages 414–415

1. 360   3. 151,200   5. 840   7. 360
9. 420   11. 453,600   13. 60   15. 12

Written Exercises, pages 417–418

1. 495   3. 1,999,000   5. 21   7. 20   9. 70
11. 20   13. {100}

Written Exercises, page 419

1. 11,760   3. 22,308   5. 5040   7. 1320
9. 1440   11. 2880   13. 7200   15. 1320; 60

Written Exercises, page 422

1. $x^4 + 8x^3 + 24x^2 + 32x + 16$
3. $y^6 - 18y^5 + 135y^4 - 540y^3 +$
$$1215y^2 - 1458y + 729$$
5. $16x^4 - 16x^3 + 6x^2 - x + \frac{1}{16}$
7. $1024 + 640z + 160z^2 + 20z^3 + \frac{5}{4}z^4 + \frac{1}{32}z^5$
9. $n^8 - 8n^6 + 24n^4 - 32n^2 + 16$
11. $p^{12} - 6p^{10}q^2 + 15p^8q^4 - 20p^6q^6 +$
$$15p^4q^8 - 6p^2q^{10} + q^{12}$$
13. $495a^8b^4$ 15. $5005n^{18}$ 17. $120t^{14}$
19. 1.0721 21. 1.218

Written Exercises, page 424

1. $r^7 + 7r^6 + 21r^5 + 35r^4 + 35r^3 + 21r^2 + 7r + 1$
3. $16t^4 + 96t^3 + 216t^2 + 216t + 81$ 5. 1.61051
7. $\frac{1}{64}x^6 - \frac{3}{16}x^5 + \frac{15}{16}x^4 - \frac{5}{2}x^3 + \frac{15}{4}x^2 - 3x + 1$
9. $5376x^3$ 11. $280r^3$ 13. $\frac{105}{2048}y^{13}$

Written Exercises, page 427

1. a. {1, 3, 5, 6, 7, 8}   b. {1, 3, 5, 7}
3. a. {K, I, L, O, G, R, A, M}   b. {I, O, A}
5. a. {(red, red), (red, white), (red, blue), (white, red),
(white, white), (white, blue), (blue, red), (blue, white),
(blue, blue)}   b. {(red, white), (red, blue), (white, red),
(white, blue), (blue, red), (blue, white)}   7. a. {($5, $1),
($5, $10), ($10, $1), ($10, $10)}   b. {($5, $10),
($10, $1), ($10, $10)}   9. a. {(-2, -2), (-2, -1),
(-2, 0), (-2, 1), (-2, 2), (-1, -2), (-1, -1), (-1, 0),
(-1, 1), (-1, 2), (0, -2), (0, -1), (0, 0), (0, 1), (0, 2),
(1, -2), (1, -1), (1, 0), (1, 1), (1, 2), (2, -2), (2, -1),
(2, 0), (2, 1), (2, 2)}   b. {(-2, 2), (-1, 1), (0, 0),
(1, -1), (2, -2)}

Written Exercises, pages 429–431

1. a. $\frac{1}{4}$ b. $\frac{1}{13}$ c. $\frac{1}{2}$ d. $\frac{3}{13}$ e. $\frac{10}{13}$ f. $\frac{1}{52}$ 3. a. $\frac{4}{15}$ b. $\frac{1}{35}$
c. $\frac{11}{21}$ d. $\frac{32}{105}$ e. $\frac{22}{35}$ f. $\frac{2}{35}$ 5. a. 1 to 1   b. 1 to 1
c. 1 to 4   d. 1 to 4   e. 2 to 3   f. 3 to 7   7. a. $\frac{1}{7}$
b. $\frac{1}{14}$ c. $\frac{3}{7}$ d. $\frac{3}{28}$ 9. a. $\frac{25}{676}$ b. $\frac{441}{676}$
11. $3,628,800$; $\frac{1}{945}$ 13. $\frac{3}{10}$ 15. $\frac{1}{2}$

Written Exercises, pages 432–433

1. a. $\frac{31}{105}$ b. $\frac{74}{105}$ c. $\frac{10}{21}$ d. $\frac{23}{35}$ 3. $\frac{5}{36}$ 5. a. $\frac{5}{36}$ b. $\frac{7}{36}$
c. $\frac{7}{18}$ d. $\frac{1}{9}$ 7. $\frac{22}{35}$ 9. Put 1 green gumdrop in one bag
and 9 green gumdrops and 10 yellow gumdrops in the other.

Written Exercises, pages 435–436

1. a. $\frac{5}{26}$ b. $\frac{3}{13}$ c. $\frac{6}{13}$ d. $\frac{1}{2}$ 3. a. $\frac{5}{36}$ b. $\frac{11}{36}$ c. $\frac{2}{11}$
d. $\frac{2}{5}$ 5. a. $\frac{1}{289}$ b. $\frac{121}{48841}$ c. $\frac{11}{3757}$ d. $\frac{100}{289}$ 7. a. $\frac{71}{72}$
b. $\frac{5}{9}$ c. $\frac{5}{36}$ d. $\frac{61}{72}$ 9. $\frac{11}{14}$ 11. a. $\frac{7}{12}$ b. $\frac{1}{3}$ c. No

Chapter 13   Matrices

Written Exercises, pages 442–443

1. $x = 3$ and $y = -4$ 3. $x = 1$; $y = 0$; $z = -2$
5. $x = -5$; $y = 5$; $z = 0$ 7. $\begin{bmatrix} 4 \\ 6 \end{bmatrix}$ 9. $\begin{bmatrix} -1 & 1 \\ -2 & -6 \end{bmatrix}$
11. $\begin{bmatrix} 7 & -1 & 2 \\ 26 & 0 & 15 \end{bmatrix}$ 13. $\begin{bmatrix} -10 \\ 2 \end{bmatrix}$ 15. $\begin{bmatrix} 5 & 1 \\ 2 & -4 \end{bmatrix}$
17. $\begin{bmatrix} -13 & -7 & 2 \\ -2 & -12 & 1 \end{bmatrix}$ 19. $x = -2$; $y = 2$
21. $x = 2$; $y = 1$; $z = 4$; $u = -4$

Written Exercises, pages 445–446

1. $\begin{bmatrix} 5 & 1 \\ 6 & 8 \end{bmatrix}$ 3. $\begin{bmatrix} 0 & -2 \\ 9 & 5 \end{bmatrix}$ 5. $\begin{bmatrix} -3 & -2 & -3 \\ -4 & 0 & 4 \end{bmatrix}$
7. $\begin{bmatrix} 6 & -1 & -8 \\ 0 & -3 & -4 \\ 1 & 4 & -2 \end{bmatrix}$

Written Exercises, pages 448–449

1. $\begin{bmatrix} 12 & -8 & 0 \\ 8 & 12 & 4 \end{bmatrix}$ 3. $\begin{bmatrix} -5 & 0 & 10 \\ 15 & -20 & -30 \end{bmatrix}$
5. $\begin{bmatrix} 10 & -6 & -2 \\ 3 & 13 & 9 \end{bmatrix}$ 7. $\begin{bmatrix} 15 & -8 & -6 \\ -1 & 24 & 22 \end{bmatrix}$
9. $\begin{bmatrix} 8 & -6 & 2 \\ 9 & 5 & -3 \end{bmatrix}$ 11. $\begin{bmatrix} -9 & 12 & -18 \\ -39 & 18 & 48 \end{bmatrix}$
13. $\begin{bmatrix} 1 & -9 \\ 4 & -6 \end{bmatrix}$ 15. $\begin{bmatrix} 1 & 1 \\ \frac{2}{3} & -\frac{8}{3} \end{bmatrix}$ 17. $\begin{bmatrix} -2 & 0 \\ -2 & 6 \end{bmatrix}$

Written Exercises, pages 453–454

1. $\begin{bmatrix} -2 & -5 \\ 4 & -5 \end{bmatrix}$ 3. $\begin{bmatrix} 11 & 6 \\ 3 & 8 \end{bmatrix}$ 5. $\begin{bmatrix} 4 & -1 \\ 5 & 4 \end{bmatrix}$
7. $\begin{bmatrix} 10 & -15 \\ 10 & -5 \end{bmatrix}$ 9. $\begin{bmatrix} 15 & 5 \\ 8 & 12 \end{bmatrix}$ 11. $\begin{bmatrix} 5 & -25 \\ 20 & -20 \end{bmatrix}$
13. No   15. No   17. No   19. $\begin{bmatrix} 4 & 2 \\ -6 & 12 \end{bmatrix}$
21. $\begin{bmatrix} 3 & 6 & 12 \\ 2 & 4 & 8 \\ 1 & 2 & 4 \end{bmatrix}$ 23. $\begin{bmatrix} 890 & 965 & 1040 \\ 120 & 125 & 130 \end{bmatrix}$
(Entries explained below.)

The entries in the top row represent the number of jewels
used in producing both models on Monday, Tuesday and
Wednesday, respectively. The entries in the second row
represent the number of straps used in producing both
models.

Written Exercises, pages 456–457

. True   **3.** False   **5.** False   **7.** False   **9.** True
1. True   **13.** True   **15.** True   **17.** False
9. False

Written Exercises, page 462

. $\begin{bmatrix} 4 & -5 \\ -3 & 4 \end{bmatrix}$ **3.** A is singular   **5.** $\begin{bmatrix} 2 & -\frac{5}{2} \\ -1 & \frac{3}{2} \end{bmatrix}$

. $\begin{bmatrix} 0 & 1 \\ 1 & 0 \end{bmatrix}$ **9.** $\begin{bmatrix} 3 & 2 \\ 0 & 4 \end{bmatrix}$ **11.** $\begin{bmatrix} 5 & 2 \\ 0 & 6 \end{bmatrix}$ **13.** $\{(3, 1)\}$

15. $\{(1, -2)\}$

Written Exercises, pages 467–468

1. $P' = (2, -2)$ **3.** $P' = (-2, -6)$ **5.** $P = (-2, 2)$

7. $P = (0, 0)$ **9.** $\begin{bmatrix} x' \\ y' \end{bmatrix} = \begin{bmatrix} x \\ y \end{bmatrix} + \begin{bmatrix} 2 \\ 4 \end{bmatrix}$

11. $\begin{bmatrix} x' \\ y' \end{bmatrix} = \begin{bmatrix} x \\ y \end{bmatrix} + \begin{bmatrix} 9 \\ 3 \end{bmatrix}$ **13.** $\begin{bmatrix} x' \\ y' \end{bmatrix} = \begin{bmatrix} x \\ y \end{bmatrix} + \begin{bmatrix} -1 \\ 1 \end{bmatrix}$

15. a. $\begin{bmatrix} x' \\ y' \end{bmatrix} = \begin{bmatrix} x \\ y \end{bmatrix} + \begin{bmatrix} -2 \\ 1 \end{bmatrix}$ **b.** $Q' = (-1, 4)$

c. $R = (0, 0)$

Written Exercises, pages 472–473

1. $P' = (0, 6)$ **3.** $P' = (2, -6)$ **5.** $P = (-1, 0)$
7. $P = (\frac{1}{5}, -\frac{3}{5})$ **17.** The image is a parallelogram with
vertices (0, 0), (1, 0), (3, 1), and (2, 1).

Cumulative Review, pages 476–477

1. 1   **2.** $z^2 - 9z - 4$ **3.** $\{\frac{101}{5}\}$ **4.** $\{-3\}$
5. a. 1   **b.** 9   **c.** $3t^2 - 5t + 1$ **6.** $y = -\frac{4}{3}x + 3$
7. $\{(-2, 1)\}$ **8.** $2(2b - 3)(b + 4)$
9. $\{x: -3 \le x \le 8\}$

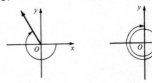

10. $\dfrac{x - 7}{x - 5}$ **11.** $\dfrac{-5(y + 1)}{(2y + 1)(y - 2)}$ **12.** 96   **13.** $\frac{325}{999}$

14. $2ty\sqrt[3]{2t^2}$ **15.** $\dfrac{-8 + 5\sqrt{3}}{11}$

16. $\left\{ \dfrac{3 + i\sqrt{15}}{4}, \dfrac{3 - i\sqrt{15}}{4} \right\}$

17. $19 - 16i$ **18.** 10
19. $(x - 1)^2 + (y - (-3))^2 = 16$;
  $r = 4$ and the center is $(1, -3)$

20. $\dfrac{x^2}{4} + \dfrac{y^2}{64} = 1$ *(graph at right)*

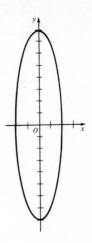

21. 36   **22.** 316

23. $\left\{ (x, y): y = \dfrac{x}{3} + \dfrac{4}{3} \right\}$ **24.** 9

25. 125   **26.** 90   **27.** 100

28. $\frac{1}{12}$ **29.** $\frac{1}{221}$

30. $\begin{bmatrix} 10 & 5 & 0 \\ 0 & 5 & 6 \end{bmatrix}$

31. $\begin{bmatrix} -5 & 19 \\ 1 & 5 \end{bmatrix}$ **32.** $\begin{bmatrix} 1 & -1 \\ 4 & -5 \end{bmatrix}$

33. $\begin{bmatrix} -2 & 10 \\ 4 & -17 \end{bmatrix}$ **34.** $\{(2, 4)\}$

Chapter 14   Trigonometric and Circular Functions

Written Exercises, pages 481–482

1. 220 cm   **3.** 4752 mm   **5.** 177 cm   **7.** 88 m
9. 28 cm   **11.** 7 cm
13.   **15.**   **17.**

19. 1 cm   **21.** 1702.38 km/h   **23.** 291,666,667

Written Exercises, pages 485–486

1. $\dfrac{3\pi}{4}$ **3.** $-\dfrac{3\pi}{2}$ **5.** $-\dfrac{5\pi}{6}$ **7.** $\dfrac{\pi}{2}$ **9.** $-\dfrac{11\pi}{6}$

11. 40°   **13.** −210°   **15.** −270°   **17.** 105°
19. −315°   **21.** 18.84 cm   **23.** 83.73 m
25. 18.84 m   **27.** 133.3 km   **29.** 48°   **31.** 14.4°
33. 360°

Written Exercises, pages 490–491

1. $\sin \alpha = \frac{4}{5}$, $\cos \alpha = \frac{3}{5}$ 3. $\sin \alpha = \frac{5}{13}$, $\cos \alpha = \frac{12}{13}$

5. $\sin \alpha = -\dfrac{\sqrt{2}}{2}$, $\cos \alpha = -\dfrac{\sqrt{2}}{2}$

7. $\sin \alpha = \frac{15}{17}$, $\cos \alpha = -\frac{8}{15}$

9. $\sin \alpha = -1$, $\cos \alpha = 0$ 11. $\sin \alpha = \frac{4}{5}$, $\cos \alpha = -\frac{3}{5}$

Ex. 1   *Ex. 3*   *Ex. 5*

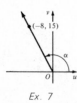
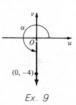
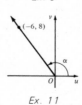

Ex. 7   *Ex. 9*   *Ex. 11*

13. $\sin \alpha = \frac{12}{13}$ and α lies in Quadrant I.
15. $\cos \alpha = \frac{4}{5}$ and α lies in Quadrant IV.

17. $\cos \alpha = -\dfrac{2\sqrt{3}}{13}$ and α lies in Quadrant II.

19. $\sin \alpha = -\dfrac{\sqrt{2}}{2}$ and α lies in Quadrant IV.

21. $\sin \alpha = \dfrac{\sqrt{10}}{10}$, $\cos \alpha = \dfrac{3\sqrt{10}}{10}$

23. $\sin \alpha = \dfrac{\sqrt{17}}{17}$, $\cos \alpha = -\dfrac{4\sqrt{17}}{17}$

25. $\sin \alpha = \dfrac{\sqrt{2}}{2}$, $\cos \alpha = \dfrac{\sqrt{2}}{2}$

Written Exercises, pages 493–494

1. $\dfrac{\sqrt{3}}{2}$ 3. $\dfrac{\sqrt{3}}{2}$ 5. -1 7. $\frac{1}{2}$ 9. $\dfrac{\sqrt{3}}{2}$

11. $\dfrac{\sqrt{2}}{2}$ 13. -1 15. 1 17. $\frac{1}{2}(3\sqrt{2} + 2)$

19. $2\sqrt{3} + 2$ 21. 1

Written Exercises, page 497

1. 0.9090   3. 0.9468   5. 0.9752   7. 0.9394
9. 0.8421   11. 0.7077   13. 18°28'
15. 36°52'   17. 74°16'   19. 82°33'
21. 36°43'   23. 54°02'   25. 0.3333
27. 0.7132   29. 0.9696   31. 0.4375
33. 0.9941   35. 0.0879   37. 1.208ᴿ
39. 0.658   41. 0.590   43. 0.868   45. 0.158
47. 1.426

Written Exercises, pages 500–501

1. $\sin 77°$ 3. $-\cos 77°$ 5. $-\sin 80°$

7. $-\sin 49°30'$ 9. $-\cos 74°10'$ 11. $\sin 0.57^R$

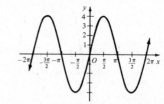

13. 0.9744   15. 0.2250   17. −0.9848
19. −0.7604   21. −0.2728   23. 0.5396
25. −0.3584   27. −0.1219   29. −0.9086
31. −1   33. 0.2764   35. 0.0349
37. 204°10'   39. 161°30'   41. 278°40'
43. 160°20'   45. −2.680

Written Exercises, page 504

1. 4

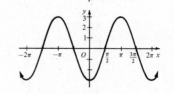

3. $\frac{1}{2}$

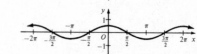

5. 3

7. $\frac{1}{2}$

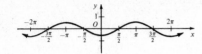

9. $\frac{3}{2}$

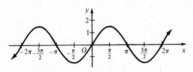

1. $\frac{4}{3}$

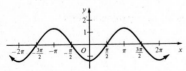

Written Exercises, page 505

1. $|A| = 1$, $P = \dfrac{2\pi}{3}$

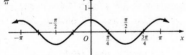

3. $|A| = 1$, $P = 4\pi$

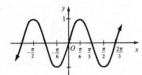

5. $|A| = \frac{1}{2}$, $P = \pi$

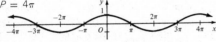

7. $|A| = 2$, $P = \dfrac{2\pi}{3}$

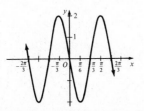

9. $|A| = 2$, $P = \dfrac{2\pi}{3}$

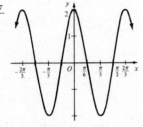

11. $|A| = 1$, $P = 2$

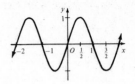

13. $|A| = 1$, $P = 6$

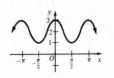

15. $|A| = 1$, $P = \pi$

17. $|A| = 1$, $P = 2\pi$

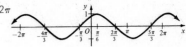

19. $|A| = 1$, $P = \pi$

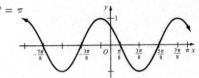

Written Exercises, pages 510–511

1. $\sin x = \frac{4}{5}$, $\cos x = \frac{3}{5}$, $\tan x = \frac{4}{3}$, $\cot x = \frac{3}{4}$,
$\csc x = \frac{5}{4}$, $\sec x = \frac{5}{3}$

3. $\sin x = \dfrac{\sqrt{10}}{10}$, $\cos x = -\dfrac{3\sqrt{10}}{10}$,

$\tan x = -\frac{1}{3}$, $\cot x = -3$, $\csc x = \sqrt{10}$, $\sec x = -\dfrac{\sqrt{10}}{3}$.

5. $\sin x = \dfrac{6\sqrt{37}}{37}$, $\cos x = \dfrac{\sqrt{37}}{37}$, $\tan x = 6$, $\cot x = \frac{1}{6}$,

$\csc x = \dfrac{\sqrt{37}}{6}$, $\sec x = \sqrt{37}$ 7. $\sin x = 1$, $\cos x = 0$,

$\cot x = 0$, $\csc x = 1$, $\tan x$ and $\sec x$ are undefined
since $u = 0$.   9. $\tan 45° = 1$, $\cot 45° = 1$,
$\csc 45° = \sqrt{2}$, $\sec 45° = \sqrt{2}$

11. $\tan 150° = -\dfrac{\sqrt{3}}{3}$, $\cot 150° = -\sqrt{3}$,

$\csc 150° = 2$, $\sec 150° = -\dfrac{2\sqrt{3}}{3}$

13. $\tan \dfrac{\pi^R}{6} = \dfrac{\sqrt{3}}{3}$, $\cot \dfrac{\pi^R}{6} = \sqrt{3}$, $\csc \dfrac{\pi^R}{6} = 2$,

$\sec \dfrac{\pi^R}{6} = \dfrac{2\sqrt{3}}{3}$ 15. $\tan \dfrac{7\pi^R}{6} = \dfrac{\sqrt{3}}{3}$,

$\cot \dfrac{7\pi^R}{6} = \sqrt{3}$, $\csc \dfrac{7\pi^R}{6} = -\dfrac{2\sqrt{3}}{3}$, $\sec \dfrac{7\pi^R}{6} = -\dfrac{2\sqrt{3}}{3}$

17. -7.185 19. -0.3281 21. -1.009

23. -8.293 25. 50.00 27. -0.2770

31. $56°15'$ 33. $63°26'$ 35. $49°03'$
37. 0.559 39. 1.287 41. 1.487
43. $196°20'$ 45. 5.243

47. $P = \pi$ 49. $P = \dfrac{\pi}{2}$

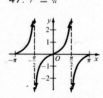
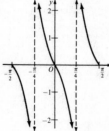

51. $P = 3\pi$

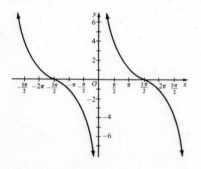

Written Exercises, pages 514–515

1. $m(B) = 36°$, $a \doteq 165.1$, $c \doteq 204.1$

3. $m(A) = 10°$, $a \doteq 1.763$, $c \doteq 10.15$

5. $m(B) = 67°$, $a \doteq 12.50$, $b \doteq 29.46$

7. $m(B) = 52°40'$, $b \doteq 31.46$, $c \doteq 39.58$

9. $m(A) = 80°40'$, $b \doteq 3.244$, $c \doteq 19.74$

11. $b = 8$, $m(A) = 36°52'$, $m(B) = 53°08'$

13. $a = 24$, $m(B) = 22°37'$, $m(A) = 67°23'$

15. $c = 25$, $m(A) = 36°52'$, $m(B) = 53°08'$

17. $c \doteq 11.6$, $m(B) = 38°21'$, $m(A) = 51°39'$

19. $a \doteq 5.36$, $m(A) = 36°22'$, $m(B) = 53°38'$

Problems, page 515

1. 8.66 m; $55°26'$ 3. Approximately 20.5 m   5. $58°$
7. $30°46'$ 9. Approximately 62 m   11. Approximately
7.5 km; approximately 7.7 km

Chapter 15   Trigonometric Identities and Formulas

Written Exercises, pages 521–522

1. $\sec \alpha$, $\cos \alpha \neq 0$, $\sin \alpha \neq 0$ 3. $\tan x$, $\cos x \neq 0$

5. $\dfrac{\cos^2 x}{1 - \cos^2 x}$, $\sin x \neq 0$, $\cos x \neq \pm 1$ 7. $\dfrac{(1 - \cos^2 x)^2}{\cos^2 x}$,

$\cos x \neq 0$, $\sin x \neq \pm 1$ 9. $\dfrac{1}{\sec^2 x}$, $\sec x \neq 0$

11. $\dfrac{1}{\sin^2 x}$, $\sin x \neq 0$, $\cos x \neq 0$ 13. $\tan \alpha$, $\cos \alpha \neq 0$

15. $\tan x$, $\cos x \neq 0$ 17. 1, $\sin x \neq 0$

19. $\dfrac{1}{\sin \alpha}$, $\sin \alpha \neq 0$ 21. $\cos \alpha$, $\cos \alpha \neq 0$, $\sin \alpha \neq 0$

23. 1, $\sin \alpha \neq 0$, $\cos \alpha \neq 0$ 25. a. $\dfrac{-\sin \alpha \sqrt{1 - \sin^2 \alpha}}{1 - \sin^2 \alpha}$

b. $\dfrac{-\sqrt{1 - \sin^2 \alpha}}{\sin \alpha}$ c. $\dfrac{-\sqrt{1 - \sin^2 \alpha}}{1 - \sin^2 \alpha}$ d. $\dfrac{1}{\sin \alpha}$

Written Exercises, pages 530–531

1. $-\dfrac{\sqrt{3}}{2}$ 3. 0   5. $-\dfrac{1}{2}$ 7. 1   9. $-\dfrac{\sqrt{2}}{2}$

11. $\dfrac{1}{2}$ 13. $-\dfrac{\sqrt{2}}{2}$ 15. $\dfrac{\sqrt{3}}{2}$ 17. $-\sin\dfrac{3\pi}{14}$

19. $\sin\dfrac{\pi}{30}$ 21. $-\sin\dfrac{\pi}{10}$ 23. $-\sin\dfrac{\pi}{5}$

25. $-\sin 3°$ 27. $-\sin 39°$ 29. $-\cos 61°10'$

31. $-\cos 75°$ 39. $-\dfrac{1}{2}$ 41. 1   43. $\frac{63}{65}$ 45. $\frac{33}{65}$

Written Exercises, pages 535–537

1. $\cos\dfrac{\pi}{14}$ 3. $\cos\dfrac{\pi}{5}$ 5. $\cos\dfrac{\pi}{9}$ 7. $-\cos\dfrac{\pi}{26}$

9. $-\sin\dfrac{\pi}{8}$ 11. $-\cos\dfrac{\pi}{10}$ 13. $\sin 22°$

15. $-\sin 3°$ 17. $\sin 37°$ 19. $-\sin 37°$

21. $-\cos 36°45'$ 23. $\sin 19°$ 25. $-\dfrac{1}{2}$

27. $-\dfrac{\sqrt{2}}{2}$ 29. -1 31. $\dfrac{\sqrt{3}}{2}$ 33. $\dfrac{1}{2}$

35. $-\dfrac{\sqrt{2}}{2}$ 37. $\dfrac{1}{2}$ 39. $-\dfrac{\sqrt{3}}{2}$ 41. $2-\sqrt{3}$

43. $-2-\sqrt{3}$ 45. $2-\sqrt{3}$ 47. $2+\sqrt{3}$

49. $\sqrt{6}+\sqrt{2}$ 51. $\sqrt{6}+\sqrt{2}$ 53. $\sqrt{6}-\sqrt{2}$

55. $2+\sqrt{3}$ 69. $\dfrac{\sqrt{2}}{2}$ 71. $\dfrac{\sqrt{3}}{2}$ 73. $\sqrt{3}$

Written Exercises, pages 539–540

1. $\frac{1}{2}\sqrt{2-\sqrt{2}}$ 3. $\frac{1}{2}\sqrt{2+\sqrt{2}}$ 5. $-\frac{1}{2}\sqrt{2-\sqrt{3}}$

7. $2-\sqrt{3}$ 9. $\frac{1}{2}\sqrt{2+\sqrt{2}}$ 11. $\frac{1}{2}\sqrt{2-\sqrt{3}}$

13. $\dfrac{\sqrt{2}}{2}$ 15. $\dfrac{\sqrt{3}}{2}$ 17. 1   19. 1

21. $-\dfrac{\sqrt{3}}{3}$ 23. $\frac{24}{25}$ 25. $-\frac{24}{7}$ 27. $-\frac{527}{625}$

29. $\dfrac{2\sqrt{5}}{5}$ 31. 2   33. $\frac{1}{10}\sqrt{50+10\sqrt{5}}$

Written Exercises, page 545

1. 6.8   3. 2.6   5. 9.5   7. 17°50'

9. $b\doteq 13$, $m(A)=80°$, $m(C)=36°$

11. $m(B)=82°$, $m(C)=60°$, $m(A)=38°$

13. $c\doteq 7$, $m(A)=42°$, $m(B)=85°$

Problems, page 546

1. 153.9 km, 26°10'   3. 96.8 m   5. 23°0'
7. 38°10'

Written Exercises, page 549

1. $m(C)=80°$, $b\doteq 10.6$, $c\doteq 21.0$

3. $m(A)=25°40'$, $m(B)=34°20'$, $b\doteq 19.5$

5. $m(B)=58°$, $a\doteq 74.8$, $b\doteq 74.1$

7. $m(A)=23°30'$, $m(C)=126°30'$, $c\doteq 8.0$

9. Two solutions: $m(B)=68°20'$, $m(C)=54°$, and $c\doteq 19.1$ or $m(B)=111°40'$, $m(C)=10°40'$, and $c\doteq 4.4$ 11. 105   13. 126.9   15. 2473.9

Problems, page 550

1. 4.5 km   3. 99.4 cm   5. 3298.9 m²   7. 0.8 h

Chapter 16   Inverses of Periodic Functions; Polar Coordinates and Vectors

Written Exercises, pages 557–558

1. $\{y: y=2k\pi\}$ 3. $\left\{x: x=\dfrac{\pi}{4}+\pi k\right\}$

5. $\{z: z\doteq 0.84+2k\pi\}\cup\{z: z\doteq 5.44+2k\pi\}$

7. $\{\alpha: m(\alpha)=30°+k\cdot 360°\}\cup$
$\{\alpha: m(\alpha)=150°+k\cdot 360°\}$

9. $\{\alpha: m(\alpha)=45°+k\cdot 180°\}$

11. $\{\alpha: m(\alpha)\doteq 22°39'+k\cdot 360°\}\cup$
$\{\alpha: m(\alpha)\doteq 157°21'+k\cdot 360°\}$

13. $\dfrac{\pi}{6}$, 30°   15. 1.1071, 63°26'   17. $\dfrac{\pi}{3}$, 60°

19. 0.8407, 48°8'   21. 0.3200, 18°20'

23. -1.0937, $-62°39'$ 25. $\dfrac{\pi}{4}$, 45°   27. $\dfrac{\pi}{3}$, 60°

29. 0; 0°   31. $\sqrt{3}$ 33. $-\dfrac{1}{\sqrt{2}}$ 35. 2

37. 0.9928   39. 0.1415   41. 0.9600   47. No

Written Exercises, page 560

1. a. $\left\{x: x = \dfrac{\pi}{2} + 2k\pi\right\}$ b. $\{\alpha: m(\alpha) = 90° + k \cdot 360°\}$

3. a. $\left\{x: x = \dfrac{\pi}{4} + 2k\pi\right\} \cup \left\{x: x = \dfrac{3\pi}{4} + 2k\pi\right\}$

b. $\{\alpha: m(\alpha) = 45° + k \cdot 360°\} \cup$
$\qquad\qquad \{\alpha: m(\alpha) = 135° + k \cdot 360°\}$

5. a. $\left\{x: x = \dfrac{\pi}{4} + 2k\pi\right\} \cup \left\{x: x = \dfrac{7\pi}{4} + 2k\pi\right\}$

b. $\{\alpha: m(\alpha) = 45° + k \cdot 360°\} \cup$
$\qquad\qquad \{\alpha: m(\alpha) = 315° + k \cdot 360°\}$

7. a. $\left\{x: x = \dfrac{\pi}{6} + k\pi\right\} \cup \left\{x: x = \dfrac{5\pi}{6} + k\pi\right\}$

b. $\{\alpha: m(\alpha) = 30° + k \cdot 180°\} \cup$

$\{\alpha: m(\alpha) = 150° + k \cdot 180°\}$ 9. $\left\{\dfrac{2\pi}{3}, \pi, \dfrac{4\pi}{3}\right\}$

11. $\left\{0, \dfrac{\pi}{3}, \pi, \dfrac{5\pi}{3}\right\}$ 13. $\left\{\dfrac{\pi}{2}, \dfrac{3\pi}{2}\right\}$ 15. $\left\{0, \dfrac{2\pi}{3}, \dfrac{4\pi}{3}\right\}$

17. $\{0°, 60°, 120°, 180°, 240°, 300°\}$

19. $\left\{\dfrac{\pi}{8}, \dfrac{5\pi}{8}, \dfrac{9\pi}{8}, \dfrac{13\pi}{8}\right\}$ 21. $\left\{\dfrac{\pi}{6}, \dfrac{5\pi}{6}, \dfrac{7\pi}{6}, \dfrac{11\pi}{6}\right\}$

23. $\left\{\dfrac{\pi}{2}, \dfrac{7\pi}{6}\right\}$ 25. $\left\{\dfrac{\pi}{3}, \dfrac{5\pi}{3}\right\}$

27. $\{67\frac{1}{2}°, 157\frac{1}{2}°, 247\frac{1}{2}°, 337\frac{1}{2}°\}$

29. $\left\{x: 0 < x < \dfrac{\pi}{2}\right\} \cup \left\{x: \pi \le x < \dfrac{3\pi}{2}\right\}$

31. $\{2 + \sqrt{3}\}$ 33. $\{x: 0 \le x \le \pi\}$

35. $\left\{0, \dfrac{\pi}{3}, \dfrac{\pi}{2}, \pi, \dfrac{3\pi}{2}, \dfrac{5\pi}{3}\right\}$ 37. $\{0, 4.07\}$

9. $(\frac{5}{2}, \frac{5}{2}\sqrt{3})$ 11. $(0, 4)$ 13. $(-2, 0)$
15. $(2, -2\sqrt{3})$ 17. $r = 4; r = -4$

19. $r(r \sin^2 \theta - 8 \cos \theta) = 0$ 21. $r = \dfrac{5}{2 \cos \theta + \sin \theta}$

23. $r(r - 4 \cos \theta) = 0$
25. $x^2 + y^2 = 25$; circle with center $(0, 0)$ and radius 5
27. $(x - 2)^2 + y^2 = 4$; circle with center $(2, 0)$ and radius
29. $x = \frac{1}{2}y^2 - \frac{1}{2}$, parabola   31. $y = \frac{1}{2}x^2 - \frac{1}{2}$; parabola

33. 35. 37.

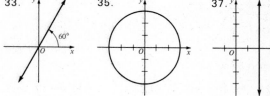

39. 43.

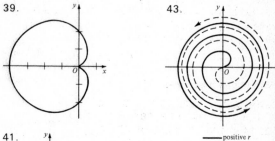

41.

—— positive r
- - - - negative r

Written Exercises, pages 564–566

1. $(3\sqrt{2}, 45°); (-3\sqrt{2}, -135°)$
3. $(1, 150°); (-1, -30°)$
5. $(3, -120°); (-3, 60°)$
7. $(13, -67°20'); (-13, 112°40')$

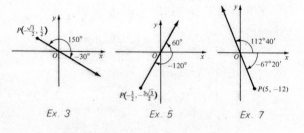

Ex. 1

Ex. 3   Ex. 5   Ex. 7

Written Exercises, pages 570–572

1. $1(\cos 180° + i \sin 180°)$
3. $\sqrt{2}(\cos 315° + i \sin 315°)$
5. $5(\cos 90° + i \sin 90°)$
7. $5(\cos 53°10' + i \sin 53°10')$

9. $1 + \sqrt{3}i$ 11. $-\dfrac{9}{2} + \dfrac{9\sqrt{3}}{2}i$ 13. $-\dfrac{\sqrt{3}}{2} + \dfrac{1}{2}$

15. $2.2059 + 2.0331i$
17. a. $10(\cos 90° + i \sin 90°)$
b. $\frac{2}{5}(\cos 30° + i \sin 30°)$
19. a. $75(\cos 280° + i \sin 280°)$

b. $3(\cos 270° + i \sin 270°)$ 21. $\dfrac{729}{2} + \dfrac{729\sqrt{3}}{2}i$

23. $\dfrac{27}{2} - \dfrac{27\sqrt{3}}{2}i$ 25. $-8 + 0i$ 27. $-8 + 8\sqrt{3}i$

29. $-\dfrac{\sqrt{3}}{64} + \dfrac{1}{64}i$ 31. $\cos 22.5° + i \sin 22.5°$,

$\cos 112.5° + i \sin 112.5°$, $\cos 202.5° + i \sin 202.5°$,

$\cos 292.5° + i \sin 292.5°$

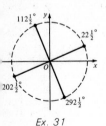 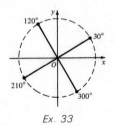

Ex. 31   Ex. 33

33. $2(\cos 30° + i \sin 30°)$, $2(\cos 120° + i \sin 120°)$,
$2(\cos 210° + i \sin 210°)$, $2(\cos 300° + i \sin 300°)$
37. $\{2(\cos 45° + i \sin 45°), 2(\cos 135° + i \sin 135°),$
$2(\cos 225° + i \sin 225°), 2(\cos 315° + i \sin 315°)\}$
39. $\{4\sqrt{2}(\cos 30° + i \sin 30°),$
$\qquad\qquad 4\sqrt{2}(\cos 210° + i \sin 210°)\}$

Written Exercises, page 575

1. 1.5, 2.6   3. 3.5, 6.1   5. 0.2, 0.5
7. 1.7; 11.9   9. 17.8; 38°   11. 19.9; 121°
13. 34.9; 100°   15. 24.8; 4°

Extra Practice

Section 1-6, page 581

1. 6   3. 7   5. −9   7. −46   9. −11
11. −105   13. 1107   15. 6   17. −1
19. 0   21. 65   23. −8   25. −29   27. 8

Section 1-8, page 581

1. −13   3. −2   5. −14   7. −36   9. −8
11. 19   13. 0   15. −163   17. 9   19. 9
21. 81   23. 6   25. 0   27. −1

Section 2-1, page 582

1. $x + 2$ 3. $-3x - 6y$ 5. $n^2 + 4n + 3$
7. $4n^3 + n^2 - 5n + 5$ 9. $-14a + 22$
11. $5a^2 - 5ab - 2b^2$

Section 2-2, page 582

1. $\{2\}$ 3. $\{8\}$ 5. $\{7\}$ 7. $\{-5\}$ 9. $\{3\}$
11. $\{7\}$

Section 2-5, page 582

1. $\{t: t < -2\}$ 3. $\{t: t \geq 10\}$ 5. $\{b: b \geq 1\}$
7. $\{z: 4 < z < 9\}$ 9. $\{t: -8 < t < 2\}$

Section 2-7, page 582

1. 4   3. −2   5. −1   7. −4   9. 1
11. $\{3, -3\}$ 13. $\{2, 8\}$ 15. $\{8, -14\}$
17. $\{-3, -4\}$

Chapter 3, page 583

1. 3   3. 19   5. $3 - 4a + 2a^2$ 23. $-\frac{3}{8}$
25. $\frac{7}{2}$ 27. $3x - y = 7$ 29. $3x - 2y = -11$
31. $x - 2y = -8$ 33. $2x + y = -4$
35. $x - 5y = -10$ 37. $2x - 3y = -12$
39. $f: x \to 3x$ 41. $f: x \to \frac{5}{4}x$ 43. $f: x \to -\frac{1}{2}x$
45. $f: x \to 2x + 1$ 47. $\frac{20}{3}$ 49. 1

Chapter 4, page 584

1. $\{(-2, 3)\}$ 3. $\{(5, 1)\}$ 5. $\{(5, -1)\}$
7. $\{(10, 2)\}$ 9. $\{(3, -2)\}$ 11. $\{(0, -3)\}$
13. $\{(\frac{17}{3}, \frac{2}{3})\}$ 15. $\emptyset$ 17. 37   19. 24
21. 17   23. $\{(2, -3)\}$ 25. $\{(2, 3)\}$ 27. $\emptyset$

Chapter 5, pages 584–585

5. $\{(1, 0, 0)\}$ 7. $\{(-4, -5, -6)\}$
9. $\{(2, -3, \frac{1}{2})\}$ 11. $\{(-\frac{3}{2}, \frac{3}{13}, -\frac{3}{10})\}$ 13. −20
15. 37   17. 8   19. $\{(2, -3, 1)\}$
21. $\{(5, 6, 7)\}$ 23. $\{(6, 1, -5)\}$

Chapter 6, pages 585–586

1. $\dfrac{z}{x^4 y^3}$ 3. $-15x^7$ 5. $\dfrac{9y^6}{16}$ 7. $x^2 + 4x + 3$

9. $\frac{1}{9}r^2 - r - 18$ 11. $4x^4 + 12x^3 + 5x^2 - 12x - 9$
13. $t^6 + 6t^3 + 9$ 15. $n^3 - 4n^2 - 3n + 18$
17. $2r^4 - 24r^3 + 96r^2 - 128r$ 19. $(n - 5)(n + 3)$
21. $(x^2y + 3)(x^2y - 3)$ 23. $(3x + 1)(x + 1)$
25. $(a - b)(2a + 3)$
27. $(x + y - z)(x^2 + 2xy + y^2 + xz + yz + z^2)$
29. $\{3, -3\}$ 31. $\{\frac{1}{2}, 1\}$ 33. $\{\frac{2}{3}, -1\}$
35. $\{x: x > 1\} \cup \{x: x < -2\}$
37. $\{x: x \geq 4\} \cup \{x: x \leq 0\}$
39. $\{r: r > 2\} \cup \{r: r < -5\}$ 41. 0.0719

43. 0.000000801 45. $-\dfrac{b}{8a^3}$ 47. -1

49. $\dfrac{x(3x+1)}{x+3}$ 51. $-x^2+2x-1$ 53. $x+13$

55. $t+4+\dfrac{4}{t-3}$ 57. $6t \neq 1$ 59. $\dfrac{x}{z}$

61. $\dfrac{1}{8a}$ 63. $\dfrac{3x(2x+3)}{(x-1)(1-2x)}$ 65. $\dfrac{2x-1}{2y}$

67. $\dfrac{-5a-7}{6a}$ 69. $-\dfrac{1}{(a+2)(a+3)}$ 71. x

73. $\dfrac{z^3-3}{z^2-1}$ 75. $\{4\}$ 77. $\{\tfrac{16}{3}\}$ 79. $\{6\}$

Chapter 7, page 587

1. $6, 9, 12, 15$ 3. $6.3, 2.5, -1.3, -5.1$

5. -39 7. $\displaystyle\sum_{n=1}^{5}(3n+4)$ 9. $\displaystyle\sum_{n=1}^{50}2n$

11. $\tfrac{1}{3}, \tfrac{1}{9}, \tfrac{1}{27}, \tfrac{1}{81}$ 13. 1 15. -243 17. $\tfrac{1}{5}$
19. $4, 16, 64$ or $4, -16, 64$ 21. $4, 1, \tfrac{1}{4}, \tfrac{1}{16}$
23. 96 25. 3575 27. 300 29. $-3\tfrac{239}{243}$
31. $3\tfrac{1}{3}$ 33. 40 35. -10 37. $\tfrac{71}{99}$ 39. $\tfrac{7}{999}$

Chapter 8, page 588

1. -36 3. 8 5. 2.074 7. 3.448

9. 1.4 11. $0.8\overline{3}$ 13. $0.2\overline{142857}$

15. a. 0.3 b. $0.303303330\ldots$ 17. a. 0.95

b. $0.909909990\ldots$ 19. $6\sqrt{3}$ 21. $3\sqrt[3]{3}$

23. $\dfrac{\sqrt{15}}{5}$ 25. $\dfrac{2xy\sqrt[5]{2xy^2z}}{z}$ 27. $\dfrac{\sqrt{3x^2+1}}{3x^2+1}$

29. $|2x-3y|$ 31. $3\sqrt{2}$ 33. $5\sqrt[3]{2}$

35. $-\sqrt[4]{2}$ 37. 22 39. $21+8\sqrt{5}$

41. $2x+5-2\sqrt{x^2+5x}$ 43. $\tfrac{9}{4}-\tfrac{3}{4}\sqrt{5}$

45. $1-\tfrac{1}{2}\sqrt{2}$ 47. $\{9\}$ 49. $\{-6\}$ 51. $\{5, -5\}$

53. $\{9\}$ 55. $\{-\tfrac{3}{2}+\tfrac{1}{2}\sqrt{5}, -\tfrac{3}{2}-\tfrac{1}{2}\sqrt{5}\}$ 57. $\{1, -\tfrac{4}{3}\}$

59. $\{\tfrac{1}{10}+\tfrac{1}{10}\sqrt{21}, \tfrac{1}{10}-\tfrac{1}{10}\sqrt{21}\}$ 61. $\{1, -\tfrac{1}{6}\}$

63. $\{-\tfrac{4}{3}+\tfrac{1}{3}\sqrt{10}, -\tfrac{4}{3}-\tfrac{1}{3}\sqrt{10}\}$

Chapter 9, page 589

1. $6i\sqrt{2}$ 3. $10i\sqrt{2}$ 5. i 7. -3 9. -4
11. $\tfrac{1}{2}\sqrt{10}$ 13. $-\tfrac{2}{3}i$ 15. $7i\sqrt{2}$ 17. $10/i\sqrt{3}$
19. $5+4i$ 21. $2+5i$ 23. $-3-3i\sqrt{3}$
25. $-8-10i$ 27. $17-7i$ 29. $\tfrac{6}{5}-\tfrac{3}{5}i$
31. $\tfrac{3}{13}+\tfrac{2}{13}i$ 33. $\{\tfrac{1}{2}+\tfrac{1}{2}i\sqrt{3}, \tfrac{1}{2}-\tfrac{1}{2}i\sqrt{3}\}$
35. $\{\tfrac{3}{2}+\tfrac{1}{2}i\sqrt{11}, \tfrac{3}{2}-\tfrac{1}{2}i\sqrt{11}\}$

37. $\{\tfrac{3}{4}+\tfrac{1}{4}i\sqrt{31}, \tfrac{3}{4}-\tfrac{1}{4}i\sqrt{31}\}$ 39. $x^2+x-12=0$
41. $x^2-4x+2=0$ 43. $x^2-2x+5=0$
51. $\{x: -3 \leq x \leq 3\}$ 53. $\{x: x > 2\} \cup \{x: x < 0\}$
55. $\{x: x \geq 4\} \cup \{x: x \leq -3\}$
57. a. $(x+1)(x+3)(x-2)$ b. Same as a.
59. a. $(x+1)(x-3)(x-2)$ b. Same as a.
61. 1.5 63. 2.1

Chapter 10, page 590

1. $2x+y=7$ 3. $2x+5y=0$ 5. $x+8y=-18$
7. $y=1$ 9. $x^2+y^2-6x+4y+9=0$
11. $x^2+y^2+4x+4y+4=0$ 27. $x=\tfrac{1}{12}y^2+1$

29. $y=\tfrac{1}{12}x^2+1$ 31. $\dfrac{x^2}{16}+\dfrac{y^2}{25}=1$

33. $\dfrac{x^2}{7}-\dfrac{y^2}{9}=1$ 35. $\{(0,0)\}$ 37. $\{(4,0),(0,2)\}$

39. $\{(3+i\sqrt{6}, 3-i\sqrt{6}), (3-i\sqrt{6}, 3+i\sqrt{6})\}$
41. $\{(2,5),(1,0)\}$

Chapter 11, page 591

1. $\sqrt[4]{7}$ 3. $7\sqrt[5]{y}$ 5. $\sqrt[4]{m^2n^3}$ 7. 64
9. 27 11. $\{-3\}$ 13. $\{-\tfrac{1}{3}\}$
15. $\{(x,y): y=\tfrac{1}{3}x+\tfrac{2}{3}\}$; F and F^{-1} are functions.
17. $\{(x,y): y=-1\pm\sqrt{x}\}$; F is a function; F^{-1} is not.
19. 0.786 21. 9.55 23. 4390 25. 14.0
27. 9.19 29. 8.18 31. $\{3\}$
33. $\{2\sqrt{2}, -2\sqrt{2}\}$ 35. $\{5\}$ 37. $\{4\}$ 39. $\{2\}$
41. $\{-3\}$ 43. $\{\tfrac{1}{36}\}$ 45. $\{\tfrac{3}{4}\}$ 47. 20
49. $40{,}000$ 51. $\{2.11\}$ 53. $\{-0.793\}$

Chapter 12, page 592

1. 60 3. 32 5. $60{,}480$ 7. 78 9. 420 11. 10
13. $81x^4+540x^3y+1350x^2y^2+1500xy^3+625y^4$
15. $n^{10}-5n^8+10n^6-10n^4+5n^2-1$
17. $-\tfrac{7}{4}t^3$ 19. $\tfrac{25}{102}$ 21. $\tfrac{11}{221}$ 23. $\tfrac{1}{6}$ 25. $\tfrac{4}{9}$
27. $\tfrac{4}{11}$ 29. $\tfrac{54}{55}$

Chapter 13, page 593

1. $\begin{bmatrix} 8 & 3 \\ 4 & -4 \end{bmatrix}$ 3. $\begin{bmatrix} 2 & 3 & 6 \\ 1 & -4 & -1 \\ 0 & 0 & -6 \end{bmatrix}$ 5. $\begin{bmatrix} 9 & -4 \\ 8 & 9 \end{bmatrix}$

7. $\begin{bmatrix} \tfrac{7}{3} & \tfrac{13}{3} \\ \tfrac{5}{3} & 4 \end{bmatrix}$

9. $\begin{bmatrix} -4 & 9 \\ 0 & 2 \end{bmatrix}$ 11. $\begin{bmatrix} -1 & -4 \\ 6 & -2 \end{bmatrix}$ 13. $\begin{bmatrix} 5 & -4 & 1 \\ 2 & -1 & 1 \\ 2 & -1 & 1 \end{bmatrix}$

5. $\begin{bmatrix} 1 & 1 \\ -2 & -3 \end{bmatrix}$ 17. $\{(2, -1)\}$ 19. $\{(1, 3)\}$

21. $P'(1, 1)$ 23. $P'(5, 8)$ 25. $\begin{bmatrix} x' \\ y' \end{bmatrix} = \begin{bmatrix} x \\ y \end{bmatrix} + \begin{bmatrix} 5 \\ -9 \end{bmatrix}$

27. $\begin{bmatrix} x' \\ y' \end{bmatrix} = \begin{bmatrix} x \\ y \end{bmatrix} + \begin{bmatrix} -14 \\ -6 \end{bmatrix}$ 29. $P'(-2, 8)$

Chapter 14, page 594

1. $\dfrac{4\pi^R}{3}$ 3. $480°$ 5. $-945°$ 7. $-3\pi^R$

9. 15π m or approx. 47.1 m 11. $\frac{28}{3}\pi$ m or approx. 29.3 m
13. $75°$ 15. $26\frac{1}{4}°$ 17. $392\frac{8}{11}°$

19. $\sin \alpha = -\frac{4}{5}$; Q IV 21. $\sin \alpha = \dfrac{\sqrt{11}}{\sqrt{12}} = \dfrac{\sqrt{33}}{6}$; Q I

23. 1 25. $\dfrac{\sqrt{3}}{2}$ 27. $\frac{1}{2}$ 29. $\frac{1}{2}$

31. -0.7153 33. 0.1395 39. $|A| = 1$; $P = \dfrac{2\pi}{3}$

41. $|A| = 2$; $P = 3\pi$ 43. $\sin \alpha = \dfrac{5\sqrt{26}}{26}$;
$\cos \alpha = -\dfrac{\sqrt{26}}{26}$; $\tan \alpha = -5$; $\csc \alpha = \dfrac{\sqrt{26}}{5}$;
$\sec \alpha = -\sqrt{26}$; $\cot \alpha = -\frac{1}{5}$ 45. $\sin \alpha = -\dfrac{\sqrt{65}}{65}$;
$\cos \alpha = \dfrac{8\sqrt{65}}{65}$; $\tan \alpha = -\frac{1}{8}$; $\csc \alpha = -\sqrt{65}$;
$\sec \alpha = \dfrac{\sqrt{65}}{8}$; $\cot \alpha = -8$

47. $\sin \alpha = 1$; $\cos \alpha = 0$; $\csc \alpha = 1$; $\cot \alpha = 0$;
$\tan \alpha$ and $\sec \alpha$ are undefined 49. $\sin \alpha = 0$; $\cos \alpha = -1$;
$\tan \alpha = 0$; $\sec \alpha = -1$; $\csc \alpha$ and $\cot \alpha$ are undefined
51. $m(B) = 62°$; $a \doteq 21.27$; $c \doteq 45.32$ 53. $m(A) = 13°$, $b \doteq 108.3$. $c \doteq 111.1$ 55. $m(A) \doteq 26°34'$;
$m(B) \doteq 63°26'$; $c \doteq 6.708$ 57. $a = 3$;
$m(A) \doteq 36°52'$; $m(B) \doteq 53°8'$

Chapter 15, page 595

11. $-\sin 45° = -\dfrac{\sqrt{2}}{2}$ 13. $-\cos 60° = -\frac{1}{2}$

15. $\cos \dfrac{\pi}{2} = 0$ 17. $\cos 15°$ 19. $-\cos 33°$

21. $\sin \dfrac{\pi^R}{26}$ 23. $\frac{119}{169}$ 25. $\frac{120}{119}$ 27. $\frac{1}{5}$ 33. 56.0
35. 14.5 37. $c \doteq 13.9$; $m(B) \doteq 112°30'$; $m(A) \doteq 27°30'$
39. $c \doteq 19.5$; $m(B) \doteq 25°40'$; $m(C) \doteq 34°20'$

Chapter 16, page 596

1. $\dfrac{\sqrt{2}}{2}$ 3. $\dfrac{\pi}{6}$ 5. $60°$

7. $\{\alpha: m(\alpha) = k \cdot 360°\}$; $\{0°\}$ 9. $\{\alpha: m(\alpha) = 60° + k \cdot 180°\} \cup \{\alpha: m(\alpha) = 120° + k \cdot 180°\}$; $\{60°, 120°, 240°, 300°\}$ 11. $\left\{x: x = \dfrac{\pi}{6} + 2k\pi\right\} \cup \left\{x: x = \dfrac{11\pi}{6} + 2k\pi\right\}$; $\left\{\dfrac{\pi}{6}, \dfrac{11\pi}{6}\right\}$ 13. $\{\alpha: m(\alpha) = 90° + k \cdot 360°\} \cup \{\alpha: m(\alpha) = 210° + k \cdot 360°\} \cup \{\alpha: m(\alpha) = 330° + k \cdot 360°\}$; $\{90°, 210°, 330°\}$ 15. $\{\alpha: m(\alpha) = 0° + k \cdot 90°\} \cup \{\alpha: m(\alpha) = 67\frac{1}{2}° + k \cdot 90°\}$; $\{0°, 67\frac{1}{2}°, 90°, 157\frac{1}{2}°, 180°, 247\frac{1}{2}°, 270°, 337\frac{1}{2}°\}$ 17. $\left\{x: x = \dfrac{\pi}{12} + k\dfrac{\pi}{3}\right\}$; $\left\{\dfrac{\pi}{12}, \dfrac{5\pi}{12}, \dfrac{3\pi}{4}, \dfrac{13\pi}{12}, \dfrac{17\pi}{12}, \dfrac{21\pi}{12}\right\}$ 19. $(6, 30°)$, $(-6, -150°)$ 21. $(3, -30°)$, $(-3, -150°)$ 23. $(5, -53°10')$, $(-5, 126°50')$ 25. $x^2 + y^2 = 64$; circle with center $(0, 0)$ and radius 8

27. $\dfrac{(x + \frac{16}{3})^2}{(\frac{8}{3})^2} - \dfrac{y^2}{\left(\dfrac{8}{\sqrt{3}}\right)^2} = 1$; hyperbola 29. $1(\cos 270° + i \sin 270°)$ 31. $2(\cos 330° + i \sin 330°)$

33. $\dfrac{3\sqrt{2}}{2} + \dfrac{3i\sqrt{2}}{2}$ 35. $-\dfrac{3}{2} + \dfrac{3i\sqrt{3}}{2}$ 37. $-32i$

39. $2 - 2i$ 41. $-\frac{2}{125} - \frac{2}{125}i$ 43. $\|u_x\| \doteq 8.7$; $\|u_y\| = 5$ 45. $\|u_x\| \doteq 17.3$; $\|u_y\| = 10$ 47. 11.3; $-8°$